PHYSICAL CHEMISTRY

An Advanced Treatise

Volume VIB / Kinetics of Gas Reactions

PHYSICAL CHEMISTRY

An Advanced Treatise

Edited by

HENRY EYRING
Departments of Chemistry
and Metallurgy
University of Utah
Salt Lake City, Utah

DOUGLAS HENDERSON
IBM Research Laboratories
San Jose, California

WILHELM JOST
Institut für Physikalische
Chemie der Universität
Göttingen
Göttingen, Germany

PHYSICAL CHEMISTRY
An Advanced Treatise

Volume VIB/Kinetics of Gas Reactions

Edited by

WILHELM JOST
*Institut für Physikalische
Chemie der Universität
Göttingen
Göttingen, Germany*

 1975

ACADEMIC PRESS   NEW YORK / SAN FRANCISCO / LONDON
A Subsidiary of Harcourt Brace Jovanovich, Publishers

ACADEMIC PRESS, INC.
111 Fifth Avenue, New York, New York 10003

United Kingdom Edition published by
ACADEMIC PRESS, INC. (LONDON) LTD.
24/28 Oval Road, London NW1

Library of Congress Cataloging in Publication Data

Main entry under title:

Physical chemistry, an advanced treatise.

Includes bibliographies.
CONTENTS.–v. 1.   Thermodynamics, edited by W. Jost.–
v. 2.   Statistical mechanics, edited by H. Eyring. [etc.]
    1.   Chemistry, Physical and theoretical–Collected
works.   I.   Eyring, Henry, (date) ed.   II.   Henderson,
Douglas.
QD453.P55   541'.3   67-4203
ISBN 0–12–245656–4 (v. 6B)

Contents

Chapter 7 / Elastic and Reactive Scattering of Ions on Molecules
A. Henglein

Chapter 8 / Collision Processes, Theory of Elastic Scattering
H. Pauly

Chapter 9 / Atom Reactions
Juergen Wolfrum

Chapter 10 / Relaxation Methods in Gases

A. B. Callear

Chapter 11 / Unimolecular Reactions: Experiments and Theories

Jürgen Troe

Chapter 12 / Interactions of Chemical Reactions, Transport Processes, and Flow

K. H. Hoyermann

Contents

List of Contributors

Numbers in parentheses indicate the pages on which the authors' contributions begin.

A. B. Callear, Physical Chemistry Laboratory, University of Cambridge, Cambridge, England (719)

A. Henglein, Hahn-Meitner-Institut für Kernforschung, Berlin, Germany (509)

K. H. Hoyermann, Institut für Physikalische Chemie der Universität Göttingen, Göttingen, Germany (931)

H. Pauly, Max-Planck-Institut für Strömungsforschung, Göttingen, Germany (553)

Jürgen Troe, Institut de Chimie-Physique, Ecole Polytechnique Fédérale de Lausanne, Lausanne, Switzerland (835)

Juergen Wolfrum, Max-Planck-Institut für Strömungsforschung, Göttingen, Germany (629)

Foreword

In recent years there has been a tremendous expansion in the development of the techniques and principles of physical chemistry. As a result most physical chemists find it difficult to maintain an understanding of the entire field.

The purpose of this treatise is to present a comprehensive treatment of physical chemistry for advanced students and investigators in a reasonably small number of volumes. We have attempted to include all important topics in physical chemistry together with borderline subjects which are of particular interest and importance. The treatment is at an advanced level. However, elementary theory and facts have not been excluded but are presented in a concise form with emphasis on laws which have general importance. No attempt has been made to be encyclopedic. However, the reader should be able to find helpful references to uncommon facts or theories in the index and bibliographies.

Since no single physical chemist could write authoritatively in all the areas of physical chemistry, distinguished investigators have been invited to contribute chapters in the field of their special competence.

If these volumes are even partially successful in meeting these goals we will feel rewarded for our efforts.

We would like to thank the authors for their contributions and to thank the staff of Academic Press for their assistance.

HENRY EYRING
DOUGLAS HENDERSON
WILHELM JOST

Preface

The aim of Volume VI as a whole has been discussed in the preface to Part A. Those first six chapters gave for the most part a survey of the general background, while Chapters 7 to 12 in Part B are primarily devoted to some special topics. A perfectly clear-cut separation could not be realized. The editor is much indebted to the contributors of both parts of Volume VI for their cooperation and patience.

A. Henglein, in Chapter 7, deals with elastic and inelastic scattering of ions on molecules, including such topics as rainbow scattering, reactive scattering, and experimental procedures and results of high-resolution measurements. In Chapter 8, H. Pauly presents a very thorough discussion of collision processes and the theory of elastic scattering. Juergen Wolfrum treats, in Chapter 9, atom reaction with a discussion of experimental techniques (static, flow, and pulse methods), among the selected examples being the reactions of H, O, C, and N atoms with alkanes, alkenes, acetylene, sulfur, and nitrogen compounds.

In Chapter 10 A. B. Callear gives a critical survey of experimental methods and results obtained by the several techniques of relaxation methods in gases. The main topics discussed are blackbody flash photolysis, excitation with pulsed lasers, flash photolysis with the resonance radiation of atoms, microwave techniques for rotational relaxation, fluorescence and the lifetimes of electronically excited molecules, relaxation studies of reaction rates following electrical discharge in a static gas, and relaxation following chemical production of excited species. Of the wide field of unimolecular reactions, Jürgen Troe, in Chapter 11, concentrates on thermal unimolecular reactions, including theories of high- and low-pressure limits and dissociation at ultrahigh pressures; photochemical unimolecular reactions (covering distribution of products and distribution of energy in products); unimolecular dissociation of molecular ions; secondary unimolecular reactions; and unimolecular reactions with chemical activation. In practical investigations of gas reactions it is often not possible to avoid interference by flow and transport processes. In addition, there are many instances where this coupling is of primary importance, as in flames, combustion, and detonations (i.e., shock waves with coupled exothermal reactions). On the other hand, these processes provide new methods for experimental investigations of reaction rates; e.g., endothermal reactions are accessible to a study under very extreme conditions of temperature and pressure. This is the field discussed in Chapter 12 by K. H. Hoyermann.

WILHELM JOST

Contents of Previous and Future Volumes

Chapter 7

Elastic and Reactive Scattering of Ions on Molecules

A. HENGLEIN

I. Introduction

Studies of scattering phenomena and chemical reactions between ions and molecules have yielded useful information for the understanding of various fields of chemistry in which gaseous ions are involved, such as radiation chemistry, electric discharges, flames, and the chemistry of the upper atmosphere and space. A number of review articles on ion–molecule

509

reactions have recently appeared in which experimental procedures, cross sections, isotope effects, comparisons with thermodynamic data, and theoretical considerations, mainly based on the polarization theory, are described (Stevenson and Schissler, 1961; Lampe *et al.*, 1961; Gould, 1966; Friedman, 1968; Futrell and Tiernan, 1969; Fite, 1969; Ferguson, 1967, 1970; Franklin 1972).

In physical chemistry, the more recent kinematic investigations, i.e., measurements of the velocity and angular distributions of elastically scattered ions or of the products of reactive collisions, are most interesting. A great part of our present knowledge of the kinematics of chemical reations has been gleaned from such ion–molecule interaction studies. The results complement those obtained from angular and velocity distribution measurements of reaction products formed in crossed molecular beams (Herschbach, 1966; see also Chapter 5).

Kinematic studies allow immediate calculation of some interesting reaction parameters, such as available energy fractions (center-of-mass energy plus heat of reaction), which appear as translational or internal energy of the products. Simple models for reactive collisions that are similar to those used in nuclear physics have been developed to which the experimental results of angular and velocity distribution measurements can be compared. Kinematic studies of ion–molecule reactions have been reviewed in some articles (Mahan, 1968; Wolfgang, 1969; Henglein, 1970; Herman and Wolfgang, 1972).

The kinematics of a reaction, of course, is determined by its dynamics, i.e., the acting forces. The reactants and the products move in a potential field which depends on the distances and angles between the various atoms. Our present knowledge of potential hypersurfaces of polyatomic systems is very limited. It is hoped that kinematic studies will shed some light on this problem. A number of trajectory studies have been carried out by assuming plausible potential functions for the ion–molecule interaction. Accurate ab initio calculations have recently become possible for some di- or triatomic ions, such as HeH^+, NeH^+, ArH^+, He_2^+, and H_3^+. It was possible to confirm the results of these calculations by high-resolution elastic scattering experiments in which wave-mechanical effects such as the rainbow structure and superimposed fine structure were observed. In Sections II and III, the more fundamental effects in ion–molecule interactions, such as potential functions, trajectory calculations, and elastic scattering phenomena, are treated, and then the kinematic studies of reactive collisions are described in Section IV.

II. Polarization Theory; Trajectories at Low Energies

A. THE LANGEVIN CROSS SECTION FOR CAPTURE COLLISIONS

In Langevin's treatment (1905; see also McDaniel, 1964), the ion was regarded as a point charge and the molecule as a sphere with the polarizability α. A dipole moment is induced in the molecule by the ionic electric field and an attractive force thus arises between the ion and the induced dipole, the potential being

$$V_{\mathrm{p}}(r) = -\tfrac{1}{2}\alpha e^2/r^4 , \tag{2.1}$$

where r is the distance and e the elementary charge. At short distances, the potential V_{p} of Eq. (2.1) cannot be correct since the interaction of the electron shells of the two particles, dependent on their chemical nature, becomes important. This interaction will always be strongly repulsive at small distances. Figure 1(a) shows the simplest potential function that has

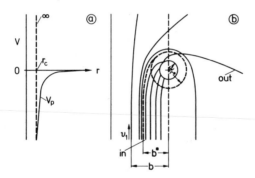

FIG. 1. (a) Simplest potential function for the ion–molecule interaction. ($V = \infty$ for $r < r_c$; $V = V_{\mathrm{p}}$ according to Eq. (2.1) for $r > r_c$.) (b) Trajectories of the ion about the molecule.

been used. At distances larger than r_c, the polarization potential derived from Eq. (2.1) is assumed to be valid. At smaller distances, the two particles are assumed to act like hard spheres, i.e., the potential is infinitely high.

The phenomenon of the capture cross section can best be understood by consideration of the "effective potential" of a collision V_{eff}. Let us regard the case of Fig. 1(b), in which the trajectories of ions with initial velocity v_1 and various collision parameters b around a molecule are shown (for the sake of simplicity, the mass of the molecule M_2 is assumed to be much larger than the mass of the ion M_1, i.e., the molecule is practically motionless). During the approach, the ion is acted upon by a centrifugal force, the corresponding potential being $L^2/2\mu r^2$, where

$$L = \mu v_r b, \qquad (2.2)$$

with L the translational angular momentum, μ the reduced mass, and v_r the relative velocity. The effective potential is

$$V_{eff}(r) = \frac{L^2}{2\mu r^2} - \frac{1}{2}\frac{\alpha e^2}{r^4} . \qquad (2.3)$$

The center-of-mass collision energy at infinite separation is

$$E_c = \tfrac{1}{2}\mu v_r^2 . \qquad (2.4a)$$

If E_1 is the translational energy of the ion at infinite separation in the laboratory system and if the molecule is at rest before the collision,

$$E_c = E_1 M_2/(M_1 + M_2) ; \qquad (2.4b)$$

substitution of (2.2) and (2.4a) into (2.3) gives

$$V_{eff}(r) = E_c \left(\frac{b}{r}\right)^2 - \frac{1}{2}\frac{\alpha e^2}{r^4} . \qquad (2.5)$$

$V_{eff}(r)$ has a single maximum at $r = r^*$:

$$r^* = \left(\frac{\alpha e^2}{E_c}\right)^{1/2} \frac{1}{b} . \qquad (2.6)$$

The height of the maximum (centrifugal barrier) is

$$V_{eff}^* = \tfrac{1}{2}E_c \frac{b^2}{r^2} = \tfrac{1}{2}E_c^2 \frac{b^4}{\alpha e^2} . \qquad (2.7)$$

The classical trajectories can now easily be described. If E_c is less than the maximum potential energy given by Eq. (2.7), the distance of closest approach is greater than r^*. The condition for $E_c < V_{eff}^*$ is $b > \sqrt{2}\,r^*$ according to Eq. (2.7). Four trajectories with $b > b^*$, where $b^* = \sqrt{2}\,r^*$, are shown in Fig. 1(b). If $E_c = V^*_{eff}$ or $b = b^*$, the ion is captured into a circular orbit of radius r^* around the molecule. Collisions with $E_c > V^*_{eff}$ or $b < b^*$ lead to a close approach until reflection at the distance r_c occurs. Several trajectories for $b < b^*$ are included in Fig. 1(b); the outgoing trajectory after reflection is shown for only one example.

For the case of $V^*_{eff} = E_c$, b^* is calculated from Eq. (2.7) giving,

$$b^* = (2\alpha e^2/E_c)^{1/4} . \tag{2.8}$$

The cross section for capture σ_L is therefore given by

$$\sigma_L(E_c) = \pi b^{*2} = \pi(2\alpha e^2/E_c)^{1/2} . \tag{2.9}$$

This Langevin cross section has frequently been used as a cross section for chemical reaction between ions and molecules, the assumption being made that reaction always occurs at distances between r^* and r_c. In fact, Eq. (2.9) leads one to understand why certain ion–molecule reactions have cross sections of several 100 Å² at thermal energies. In a few cases, such as for the reaction

$$Ar^+ + D_2 \longrightarrow ArD^+ + D \tag{2.10}$$

the calculated cross sections agree very well with the observed cross sections in the energy range from about 1 to 5 eV of incident ion energy E_1 (Stevenson and Schissler, 1958; Hyatt and Lacmann, 1968). In principle, Eq. (2.9) can only yield cross sections for reactions at low ion energies (generally for $E_c < 1$ eV). At higher energies the calculated σ_L values are of the order of only a few Å², i.e., of the order of gas-kinetic cross sections. Under these circumstances, the original assumptions of the polarization theory [i.e., point charge of the ion and the concept of static polarizability in Eq. (2.1)], which seem to be reasonably correct for large values of r, no longer hold. Most of the ion–molecule reactions observed to date have smaller cross sections even at low energies than those given by Eq. (2.9).

B. MODIFIED THEORY; MOLECULES WITH ALIGNED PERMANENT DIPOLE MOMENT

If the molecule has a permanent dipole moment γ, the potential energy at large values of r is given by the expression

$$V_d(r) = -\frac{e\gamma \cos\theta}{r^2} - \frac{e^2\alpha}{2r^4} . \tag{2.11}$$

The second term takes care of the electronic polarization [Eq. (2.1)]. θ is the angle between the dipolar axis and the radius vector r. If the collision occurs slowly enough to allow the dipole to align in the electric field of the incident ion, $\cos \theta$ will be equal to unity. In this "adiabatic" case of a collision, the angular momentum of the system is purely a function of translation and not of internal rotation of the partners and depends only on the impact parameter b at a given energy of the incident ion. Under these conditions, the trajectories correspond to scattering or capture dependent on whether b is greater or smaller than b^* as in the case of the potential of Eq. (2.1). The cross section was calculated according to the procedure outlined in Section II,A with the effective potential

$$V_{eff} = E_c \frac{b^2}{r^2} - \frac{\gamma e}{r^2} - \frac{\alpha e^2}{2r^4}.$$ (2.12)

The cross section obtained for $\theta = 0$ represents a maximum cross section for capture of an ion by a polar molecule, i.e.,

$$\sigma^* = \pi e \left[\left(\frac{2\alpha}{E_c} \right)^{1/2} + \frac{\gamma}{E_c} \right]$$ (2.13)

(Theard and Hamill, 1962; Moran and Hamill, 1963). Figure 2 allows one to compare the maximum cross section calculated from Eq. (2.13) with

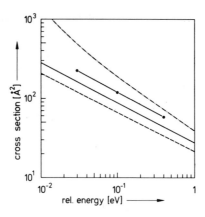

FIG. 2. Comparison of various theoretical ion capture cross sections by the HCl molecule as a function of the relative kinetic energy according to Dugan and Magee (1971). (—) Langevin, Eq. (2.1). (—·—) Maximum, Eq. (2.13). (— —) Rotating dipole, Eq. (2.15). (—●—) Numerical, Eq. (2.17). The last two curves were averaged for $E_{rot} = 0.043$ eV.

the Langevin cross section of Eq. (2.9) for capture collisions of ions with the HCl molecule. The Langevin case is, of course, for a molecule with the same polarizability as HCl but no dipole moment. It can be seen that the maximum cross section for collision with an aligned dipole is much larger than with an induced dipole (Dugan and Magee, 1971). In fact, reaction cross sections larger than those calculated from Eq. (2.9) have been observed in a few cases, where the molecule had a high permanent dipole moment (Moran and Hamill 1963; Pritchard et al., 1968). Generally, the effect of the dipole moment has to be considered only at relative energies below about 1 eV.

C. COLLISION WITH ROTATING DIPOLAR MOLECULE

Let us now consider the more general situation of a rotating dipolar molecule. At distances r where the ion–dipole potential $e\gamma/r^2$ is much smaller than the rotational energy of the molecule, the rotation will not be hindered. The attraction between the ion and the molecule will now be smaller than in the case of an aligned dipole, since the average value of $\cos\theta$ in Eq. (2.11) during the collision is smaller than unity.

The effective potential method can again be used to calculate a cross section if one adds to the effective potential the rotational energy changes that the molecule experiences in the ionic electric field. Such energy changes result from the torques exerted by the electric field on the molecular dipole moment. The change in energy ΔW due to the field is different for symmetric-top and linear molecules ("first"- and "second"-order rotational Stark effect). In the first case, the energy change ΔW_1 is proportional to the field strength: $\Delta W_1 = Ar^{-2}$. In the second case, ΔW_2 is proportional to the square of the field strength: $\Delta W_2 = Br^{-4}$ (Townes and Schawlow, 1955). The effective potential has now the form

$$V_{\text{eff}} = E_{\text{c}}\frac{b^2}{r^2} + \Delta W_1 - \frac{\alpha e^2}{2r^4} + \Delta W_2. \qquad (2.14)$$

If one uses this effective potential in the previously described procedure, the following capture cross section is obtained:

$$\sigma = \pi e \left(\frac{2\alpha'}{E_{\text{c}}}\right)^{1/2} - \frac{\pi A}{E_{\text{c}}}, \qquad (2.15)$$

where

$$\alpha' = \alpha - (2B/e^2) \qquad (2.16)$$

represents an "effective" polarizability.

The cross section calculated for the capture of an ion by a rotating HCl dipole is also shown in Fig. 2 for various energies. It can be seen that the cross section for collision with the rotating dipolar molecule is slightly smaller than the Langevin cross section.

Su and Bowers (1973) derived an expression for the cross section of ion–dipolar molecule reactions by introducing a suitable average value of θ into Eq. (2.11). The probability of finding the dipole at an orientation θ is proportional to $(\sin \theta)/\dot{\theta}$, where the factor $\sin \theta$ describes the number of ways of arranging the dipole in space such that it makes an angle θ with the radius vector r. Here $\dot{\theta}$ is the angular velocity of the rotating dipole in the plane of collision and is proportional to $E_{\mathrm{rot}}^{1/2} - V_{\mathrm{d}}(r)$. The average value of θ was calculated by weighting over the rotational energies in the Boltzmann distribution of the molecule.

D. Results of Numerical Trajectory and Cross Section Calculations

Numerical calculations of trajectories were recently carried out by Dugan and Magee (1971). They were based on the classical model of a structureless ion, using the potential of Eq. (2.11) for $r > r_{\mathrm{c}}$. For the short-range interaction the extreme approximation of a hard inner core, i.e., $V = \infty$ for $r < r_{\mathrm{c}}$, was applied. Trajectories were calculated for many impact parameters by using the Lagrange equations of motion. For each impact parameter and fixed rotational energy of the molecule, about 50 trajectories were calculated for random initial orientations of the rotating molecule. These calculations yielded two important results: (1) The capture cross section for the interaction of an ion with a dipolar molecule cannot be defined simply as in the effective potential method described in Sections II,B and II,C; and (2) multiple reflections of the ion on the molecule may occur.

In the case of Langevin collisions described in Section II,A, the probability of capture C_{R} is unity for $b < b^*$ and zero for $b > b^*$. $C_{\mathrm{R}}(b)$ is a simple step function (b_{L}^2 in Fig. 3). In the case of a rotating dipolar molecule there is no straightforward answer to the question of capture. For any

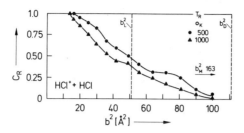

FIG. 3.   Variation of capture ratio C_R with square of impact parameter for HCl target rotators at temperatures $T_R = 500$ and $1000°K$. Initial HCl$^+$ velocity, 5.5×10^4 cm/sec (Dugan and Magee, 1971).

initial ion energy and impact parameter there is a probability that the system will arrive at an ion–molecule separation $r < r^*$ corresponding to capture. The fraction of collisions resulting in capture is called the capture ratio C_R. In Fig. 3, C_R is plotted vs. the square of the impact parameter for collisions of HCl$^+$ on HCl at two rotational temperatures. C_R is also plotted for three other cases: the Langevin interaction [Eq. (2.1)], $b_L{}^2$ plot; the permanent dipole interaction $V = e\gamma/r^2$, $b_D{}^2$ plot; and finally the sum [Eq. (2.11)], $b_M{}^2$ plot. With increasing b, the capture ratio decreases. A reasonable definition of the "capture collision" cross section is

$$\sigma = \pi \int_0^{b_0{}^2} C_R(b)\, d(b^2), \qquad (2.17)$$

where b_0 is the impact parameter at which C_R becomes zero. The calculated cross section for the HCl$^+$–HCl system as function of the energy is also shown in Fig. 2.

The trajectories of a Langevin collision [Eq. (2.1), Fig. 1(b)] are simple: One specular reflection occurs at the hard core and the outward trajectory is symmetric with respect to the inward trajectory. The situation is different for a collision involving a molecule with a dipole moment. The rotating dipole alters the potential for the outward trajectory, and the impinging ion may be recaptured and rereflected several times in succession. This can increase the collision time significantly. It should be noted that multiple reflections are also expected for ion–molecule collisions involving polyatomic molecules without dipole moment since actual short-range potentials probably have sufficient angular dependence to produce the same effect. The total time available for chemical reaction or vibrational excitation of the molecule is increased in this way. Figure 4 gives results of a calculation

A. Henglein

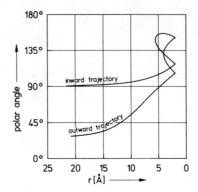

FIG. 4.   Variations of polar angle for Ar^+ relative to CO during capture collision with multiple reflections (Dugan and Magee, 1971).

for a nonreactive collision between Ar^+ and CO. The trajectories do not lie in a plane. This can be recognized from Fig. 4 by the change in polar angle (angle between **r** and a given axis through the center of mass of the molecule). Three reflections at the hard core of radius $r_c = 2$ Å occur in the collision shown.

The phenomena described so far are typical for the interaction of slow ions with molecules. They are mainly determined by the attractive potential at large distances, the exact form of the potential at smaller distances being of minor importance. However, it is the potential at distances around the equilibrium value that furnishes the chemical driving force. Experimental information on this part of the potential can be obtained from scattering experiments (Section III).

III. Rainbow Scattering of Ions and Other Wave-Mechanical Effects

A. CLASSICAL RAINBOW SCATTERING

In a typical scattering experiment, a narrow beam of ions is directed at gas molecules either in a small collision chamber or in a molecular beam at right angles to the ion beam. The intensity of scattered ions is measured as a function of the scattering angle. The intensity often does not decrease monotonically with increasing angle but exhibits distinct maxima. The "rainbow" oscillations are caused by wave-mechanical interferences if scattering occurs at both the attractive and repulsive parts of the inter-action potential (Ford and Wheeler, 1959). This effect was first observed in scattering experiments with crossed molecular beams of neutral particles at about thermal energies (see Chapters 4 and 6 of this volume).

The rainbow effect can as a rule be expected if the interaction potential has the general form shown by the upper part of Fig. 5(a). If the depth of the potential well and the corresponding distance are designated by $\mathscr{E}$ and r_m, the potential can be written in reduced units $U(\rho)$, where $U = V/\mathscr{E}$ is the reduced potential and $\rho = r/r_m$ the reduced distance. Similarly, the impact parameter can be written as a reduced entity $\beta = b/r_m$.

The classical scattering angle in the center-of-mass system of an incident particle is given by the following relation:

$$\vartheta = \pi + 2\beta \int_{\rho_0}^{\infty} \frac{d\rho}{\rho^2[1 - (U\mathscr{E}/E_c) - (\beta^2/\rho^2)]^{1/1}}, \qquad (3.1)$$

where U is the reduced interaction potential and E_c the translational energy in the center-of-mass system. ρ_0 is the reduced distance of closest approach and corresponds to the largest value of ρ for which the square root term is zero. Equation (3.1) relates an angle of deflection to every impact parameter. The curve shown by the lower part of Fig. 5(a) repre-sents the deflection function calculated for the potential shown in the upper part of the figure. The numbered points on both curves permit extraction of the distance of closest approach and the potential at closest approach for various collision parameters at a given energy E_c. In general, there are three impact parameters, β_1, β_2, and β_3, that lead to the same angle of deflection. In calculating the differential cross section, it is neces-sary to sum the contributions from all impact parameters leading to the same scattering angle:

$$I(\vartheta) = \frac{r_m^2}{\sin \vartheta} \sum_i \beta_i \left| \frac{d\beta_i}{d\vartheta} \right|. \qquad (3.2)$$

A singularity arises here at $\beta = \beta_r$ since $d\vartheta/d\beta = 0$ (Fig. 5a, lower part). A maximum in the differential cross section of scattering can therefore be observed at the corresponding angle ϑ_r (classical rainbow angle). Classical calculations with Eqs. (3.1) and (3.2) have been used to evaluate the rain-bow angle ϑ_r as a function of the ratio $E_c/\mathscr{E}$ (Mason and Vanderslice, 1959;

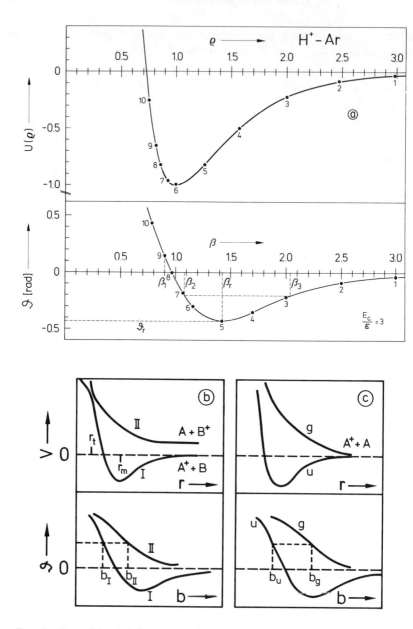

Fig. 5. Potential and deflection functions for (a) rainbow scattering, (b) Stueckelberg scattering, and (c) g–u scattering. The upper part always shows potential functions [in reduced units in (a), the reduced Morse potential with $G_1 = 2.5$ and $G_2 = 0.86$], the lower part the corresponding deflection functions.

Ioup and Thomas, 1969). The potential used in these calculations had the following form:

$$U(\rho) = \tfrac{1}{2}[(1 + \gamma)\rho^{-12} - 4\gamma\rho^{-6} - 3(1 - \gamma)\rho^{-4}]. \tag{3.3}$$

The term in ρ^{-12} describes most of the strongly repulsive part of the potential at small distances. The term in ρ^{-4} describes the attraction at long distances, which arises by the ion–induced dipole potential of Eq. (2.1). The term in ρ^{-6} was introduced in order to account for dispersion forces at short distances. γ is a weighting factor (<1) for the ρ^{-6} contribution. Figure 6 shows a plot of ϑ_r versus the ratio $E_c/\mathscr{E}$. Curves (a) and (b) repre-

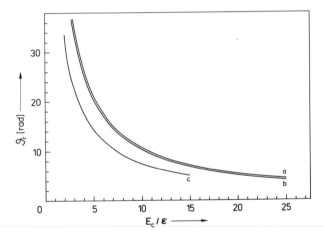

FIG. 6. Dependence of the classical rainbow angle on the ratio $E_c/\mathscr{E}$ (a, b) for the potential of Eq. (3.3) with $\gamma = 0.4$ and $\gamma = 0.2$, respectively, and (c) for the modified Morse potential of Eq. (3.4) with $G_1 = 2.5$ and $G_2 = 0.86$.

sent the results of Ioup and Thomas (1969) for two values of γ. It can be seen that the classical rainbow angle increases with decreasing collision energy E_c and with increasing depth of the potential well.

The classical rainbow was observed in a number of early experiments in which the angular resolution was relatively low. For example, the scattering of Cs$^+$ ions on Ar, Kr, and N$_2$ and of H$^+$ ions on Ar was noted (Menendez and Datz, 1965; Herrero *et al.*, 1969). Curve (a) or (b) in Fig. 6 was used in order to calculate the potential depth for the observed rainbow angle ϑ_r at a given energy E_c. However, the accuracy of such an evaluation of the experimental data is rather poor. The reliability of curves (a) and (b) in

Fig. 6 depends on how close the form of the assumed potential according to Eq. (3.3) agrees with the true potential. In order to demonstrate the effect of the potential form, calculations of $\vartheta_r(E_c/\mathscr{E})$ were also carried out by using the following modified Morse potential (Mittmann *et al.*, 1971a):

$$U = \exp[2G_1G_2(1 - \rho)] - 2\exp[G_1G_2(1 - \rho)], \qquad \begin{array}{ll} G_2 = 1 & \text{for} \quad \rho < 1 \\ G_2 \neq 1 & \text{for} \quad \rho \geqslant 1 \end{array}$$

$$(3.4)$$

in which G_1 and G_2 are parameters that determine the width of the potential well. [This potential function has the advantage of varying the attractive part ($\rho > 1$) of the potential without changing the repulsive part and vice versa. For example, if the product $G_1 G_2$ is kept constant, the attractive part remains constant, while the repulsive part can be varied by using different values of the parameter G_1. With increasing G_1 and G_2 the potential well becomes narrower]. Curve (c) in Fig. 6 was calculated by using $G_1 = 2.50$ and $G_2 = 0.86$, i.e., the parameters of the potential given in the upper part of Fig. 5. The potential well is much broader under these conditions than that given by Eq. (3.3). The angle ϑ_r is now observed at nearly half the ratio $E_c/\mathscr{E}$ as in the case of Eq. (3.3). The measurement of a single maximum in the differential cross section of scattering is not sufficient to obtain information on both the depth and the width of the potential function. As will be discussed below, the secondary rainbow structure and superimposed fine structure must also be observed.

B. Wave-Mechanical Rainbow Scattering

The semiclassical treatment of scattering predicted that the differential cross section should not only possess a maximum at the angle $\bar{\vartheta}_r$ (primary rainbow) but also show oscillations (secondary rainbows) between $\vartheta = 0$ and $\vartheta = \bar{\vartheta}_r$. With decreasing collision energy E_c, $\bar{\vartheta}_r$ becomes larger and more and more maxima appear between $\vartheta = 0$ and $\vartheta = \bar{\vartheta}_r$ (Ford and Wheeler, 1959). Further the classical rainbow angle ϑ_r lies at the point where the intensity of the observed primary rainbow maximum at $\bar{\vartheta}_r$ has dropped to 43.88% at larger angles (Hundhausen and Pauly, 1965). The secondary rainbows result from the interference of partial waves belonging to the collision parameters β_2 and β_3 in the lower part of Fig. 5. The angular distance between two rainbows is approximately

$$\Delta\vartheta_s = \frac{2\pi}{r_m k|\beta_3 - \beta_2|}, \qquad (3.5)$$

where k is the wave number of the incident ion in the center-of-mass system. At a given value of r_m, the difference $\beta_3 - \beta_2$ increases with increasing width of the potential well and $\Delta\vartheta_s$ decreases.

The contribution to the scattering amplitude resulting from the collision parameter β_1 in Fig. 5 causes additional oscillations with smaller angular distances. This effect was first observed by Hundhausen and Pauly (1965) in scattering experiments with neutral particles. The angular distance of the fine oscillation in the neighborhood of the primary rainbow is given by

$$\Delta\vartheta_f = \frac{2\pi}{r_m k |\beta_1 + \beta_r|}. \tag{3.6}$$

Further, since $\beta_1 + \beta_r \sim 2$,

$$\Delta\vartheta_f \sim \pi/k r_m. \tag{3.7}$$

This equation allows one to obtain an approximate value of r_m from the measured angular distance $\Delta\vartheta_f$.

The approximations of Eqs. (3.5)–(3.7), however, do not hold well enough to permit evaluation of scattering experiments at high angular resolution. The partial wave method using WKB scattering phases was successfully applied in studies of the scattering of neutral atoms as well as ions. According to this method, the differential cross section is equal to

$$I(\vartheta) = |f(\vartheta)|^2, \tag{3.8}$$

where $f(\vartheta)$ is the scattering amplitude:

$$f(\vartheta) = \frac{1}{2ik} \sum_{l=0}^{\infty} (2l+1)[\exp(2i\eta_l) - 1] P_l(\cos\vartheta); \tag{3.9}$$

η_l is the scattering phase and the P_l are the Legendre functions. The WKB method gives for η_l

$$\eta_l = k r_m \left\{ \int_{\rho_0}^{\infty} \left(1 - \frac{U(\rho)\mathscr{E}}{E_c} - \frac{\beta_l}{\rho^2} \right)^{1/2} d\rho - \int_{\beta_1}^{\infty} \left(1 - \frac{\beta_l^2}{\rho^2} \right)^{1/2} d\rho \right\}. \tag{3.10}$$

The maximum of the angular momentum l_{max}, which must be taken into consideration when forming the sum of Eq. (3.9), can easily be estimated $l_{max} = k r_m \beta_{max}$, where β_{max} is the maximum value of the reduced impact parameter that can produce a resolvable contribution to the scattering intensity at low angles. In practice, the scattering angles for $\beta > 2.5$ become comparable to the angular width of the incident ion beam. Since ρ_0 is approximately equal to β for large values of β, β_{max} is about equal to 2.5. With r_m equal to a few angstroms and for typical values of k corresponding to energies between 1 and 30 eV, l_{max} becomes approximately equal to 1000. Computer calculations are necessary to obtain $I(\vartheta)$ from Eqs. (3.8)–(3.10).

C. Stueckelberg Oscillations and g–u Oscillations in the Differential Cross Section

Undulations of the differential cross section can also be observed if interference of partial waves that result from scattering at different potential curves of the colliding particles occurs. Figure 5(b) shows the case where the respective potential curves I and II of the systems $A^+ + B$ and $B^+ + A$ come close together at the small distance r_t. A certain probability exists that the incident ion A^+ transfers its charge to B at the distance r_t. The two particles then approach each other along the potential curve II until a distance of closest approach r_0 is reached. Upon separation, B^+ may transfer the change back to A at the distance r_t. The scattered ions A^+ will therefore contain particles that were scattered simply along the potential curve I and particles that experienced the potential II at small distances. A given angle of scattering can therefore be realized in the deflection function by two collision parameters b_I and b_{II}. The wave-mechanical treatment shows that the angular distance in the undulations (Stueckelberg oscillations) that are caused this way is

$$\Delta\vartheta_{St} = 2/k(b_{II} - b_I). \tag{3.11}$$

In the case of Fig. 5(b), the scattering curve would contain the rainbows at small angles and the Stueckelberg oscillations at larger angles. If r_t is not significantly smaller than r_m, the rainbow and Stueckelberg oscillations overlap. Stueckelberg oscillations may always be expected if the ionization potential of A is higher than that of B.

If A^+ ions are scattered on A atoms, oscillations may be produced by scattering at the gerade and ungerade potential curves. This situation is shown by Fig. 5(c). A given angle of scattering can be realized by the two collision parameters b_g and b_u and the angular distance of the g–u oscillations is

$$\Delta\vartheta_{g-u} = 2/k(b_g - b_u). \tag{3.12}$$

Stueckelberg and g–u oscillations give information about the difference of the two potential functions involved. If one of them is known, the other one can be obtained by appropriate evaluation of the experimental observations.

D. RESULTS OF HIGH-RESOLUTION MEASUREMENTS

Most of the investigations have been concerned with the scattering of protons and He$^+$ ions on noble gases and of protons on polyatomic molecules. In the case of the noble gases, the potential field is of spherical symmetry and inelastically scattered ions can be readily separated from the elastically scattered ones since they suffer significant energy losses. In the case of molecules, the potential field depends on the configuration of the atoms in the molecule with respect to the direction of the incident ion beam and small energy losses due to excitation of the molecule may accompany the scattering process. Resolution of both the secondary rainbow and the superimposed fine structure is therefore only possible for atomic targets, although secondary rainbows may sometimes be seen for molecules.

The apparatus has been described elsewhere (Mittmann *et al.*, 1971a). Protons or He$^+$ ions are produced in a plasma discharge, accelerated and mass-analyzed by a Wien filter (combination of magnetic and electric fields), focused by a system of electrostatic lenses, decelerated to the desired energy, and directed through a molecular beam of the neutral target. The scattered ions pass through a small slit into the analyzer which can turn about the scattering center. The analyzer has a system of fine metal grids to one of which was applied a retarding potential in order to prevent inelastically scattered protons or He$^+$ ions from reaching the secondary-electron multiplier. Each ion is counted and the signal stored in a multi-channel analyzer, the channels of which are correlated to the position of the analyzer, i.e., to the scattering angle. Work with high intensity proton beams of low angular divergence (0.5–1°) in the energy range of 1–30 eV is a rather delicate matter, since small deflections of the beam can easily be caused by traces of impurities on the metal slits or the lenses that confine and focus the beam.

Figure 7 shows the measured differential cross section for the scattering of 20 eV protons and deuterons on argon as function of the scattering angle in the laboratory frame. The arrows pointing downward designate the rainbows. The distance between two rainbows is $\sqrt{2}$ times smaller for D$^+$ than for H$^+$. The arrows pointing upward show the minima of

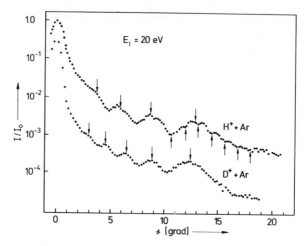

Fig. 7. Differential cross section for the scattering of protons and deuterons on argon as function of the scattering angle (Mittmann et al., 1971a).

the superimposed fine structure, which can be better localized than the maxima. The fine structure is best resolved in the surroundings of the primary rainbow.

Approximate values of r_m can be obtained from the angular distance of the fine structure [Eq. (3.7)] and for $\mathscr{E}$ from the angle of the primary rainbow (Fig. 6). Using these values and the potential of Eq. (3.4), the parameters G_1 and G_2 were varied until the partial wave calculation described in Section III,B yielded approximate agreement between the observed and calculated secondary rainbow angles. It was then necessary to adjust slightly both r_m and $\mathscr{E}$ and recalculate G_1 and G_2. The procedure was repeated several times until agreement with experiment was reached within the error of measurement. The fitting procedure has been described in detail (Mittmann et al., 1971a).

Figure 8 shows comparison of the experimental curve (a) for the system H^+–Ar with the calculated curve (b) using the potential of Eq. (3.4) with the following parameters: $\mathscr{E} = 4.04$ eV, $r_m = 1.31$ Å, $G_1 = 2.50$, and $G_2 = 0.86$. The agreement is very satisfactory. The same parameters give the best fit at other energies of the incident proton. Comparison of various potentials for the system H^+–Ar is made in Fig. 9: Curve (a) represents the best potential of Fig. 8. Curve (b) is the potential from an ab initio calculation of Roach and Kuntz (1970). Curve (c) shows the polarization potential of Eq. (2.1). It clearly does not describe the interaction at $\rho < 2.5$.

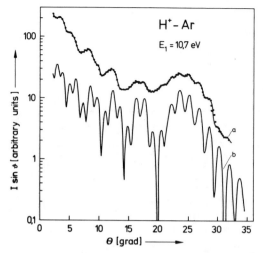

FIG. 8.   (a) Measured and (b) calculated differential cross section for the scattering of protons on argon (Mittmann *et al.*, 1971a).

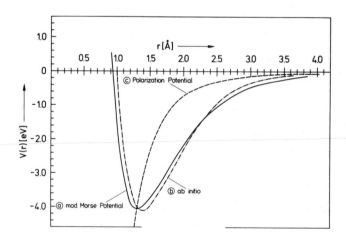

FIG. 9.   (a) Best potential for H^+–Ar according to Eq. (3.4) (modified Morse potential) (Mittmann *et al.*, 1971a), (b) Potential of ab initio calculations by Roach and Kuntz (1970), and (c) polarization potential of Eq. (2.1).

(It should be noted that rainbow scattering experiments do not yield reliable information about the potential at $\rho > 2.5$.)

The potential of Eq. (3.4) was also found to be useful for describing the scattering of protons on other noble gases and of He^+ ions on He (Weise *et al.*, 1971). Table I shows the values for r_m and $\mathscr{E}$ obtained. The results

TABLE I

Properties of Some Ionic Molecules from Scattering
Experiments, ab initio Calculations, and Other Data

System	Scattering experiments[a]				Ab initio calculations		Van der Waals radii (Å)	Isoelectronic molecules	
	$\mathscr{E}$ (eV)	r_m (Å)	G_1	G_2	$\mathscr{E}$ (eV)	r_m (Å)		System	r_m (Å)
H^+–He	2.00	0.77	2.20	0.85	1.94[b]	0.77	He: 1.1	H–H	0.74
H^+–Ne	2.28	0.99	2.68	0.85	2.21[b]	0.97	Ne: 1.5	H–F	0.92
H^+–Ar	4.04	1.31	2.50	0.86	4.10[c]	1.38	Ar: 1.9	H–Cl	1.27
H^+–Kr	4.45	1.47	2.50	0.80	—	—	Kr: 2.0	H–Br	1.41
H^+–Xe	6.75[e]	1.74	3.80	1.08	—	—	Xe: 2.2	H–I	1.60
He^+–He	2.55	1.05	2.35	0.90	2.32[d]	1.09	—	—	—

[a] Mittmann et al. (1971a); Weise et al. (1971).
[b] Peyerimhoff (1965).
[c] Roach and Kuntz (1970).
[d] Gupta and Matsen (1967).
[e] Upper limit; complications arose here because of the crossing of the potential curves for H^+–Xe and H–Xe$^+$.

of ab initio calculations as well as the van der Waals radii of the noble gases and the r_m values of the isoelectronic neutral hydrides are also shown. The results of scattering experiments and ab initio calculations are in good agreement. The r_m values of the protonated noble gases are always slightly higher than those of the isoelectronic neutral molecules. The following relation between the r_m value of the protonated noble gases and the van der Waals radius r_W is true within 10%:

$$r_m = 0.72 r_W. \tag{3.13}$$

This indicates that the proton penetrates rather deeply into the electron shells of the noble gases upon formation of the protonated species.

The $\mathscr{E}$ value of the system Xe–H$^+$ given in Table I is an upper limit. Here $\mathscr{E}$ varied with the energy of the incident protons. This effect was attributed to the crossing of the potential curve of the system Xe–H$^+$ with that of Xe$^+$ + H. A more recent interpretation of the scattering results led to the supposition that the observed oscillations might mainly be caused by the Stueckelberg effect described in Section III,C and that $\mathscr{E}$ is equal to 5.4 eV (Kubach et al., 1974).

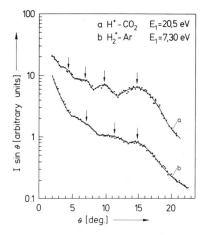

FIG. 10.   Differential cross section as function of angle for the scattering of (a) protons on CO_2 and (b) of H_2^+ on Ar (Mittmann *et al.*, 1971b).

Figure 10 shows rainbow phenomena in the scattering of H^+ on CO_2 and of H_2^+ on Ar. At the collision energies used, the time of collision is of the order of 10^{-14} sec, i.e., much shorter than the period required for one rotation of the molecules involved. The anisotropy in the potential that is expected from the different molecular orientations during the collision is evidently not too pronounced, however, since otherwise the secondary rainbow structure would not be observable. The superimposed fine structure, on the other hand, is washed out by the anisotropy and by the occurrence of inelastic processes. If a realistic estimate is made for r_m, a Morse potential can be used to obtain agreement between calculated and experimental rainbow structures. For the system $CO_2 + H^+$, r_m was obtained as 1.21 Å and $\mathscr{E}$ as 5.1 eV. The value of $\mathscr{E}$ for the system H_2^+–Ar can be determined from the angular position of the primary rainbow in Fig. 10 and using the curves of Fig. 6. A value of 1.3 ± 0.2 eV was obtained for $\mathscr{E}(ArH_2^+)$ (Mittmann *et al.*, 1971b). It must be pointed out, however, that these $\mathscr{E}$ values are averages over all molecular orientations and are therefore smaller than the maximum $\mathscr{E}$ value of the configuration of lowest energy.

Figure 11 shows two examples for g–u undulations in the differential cross section. The scattering curves for the system $^4He^+$–^4He and $^4He^+$–^3He were obtained at the rather high collision energy of 300 eV. The rainbow phenomenon cannot be observed, since it occurs at very small angles for

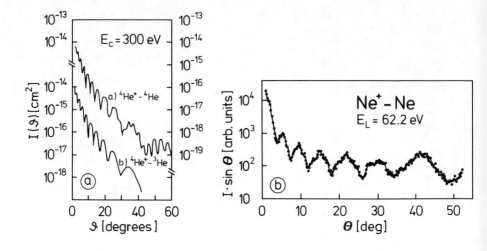

FIG. 11.   Differential cross section as a function of the angle for the scattering of ^{4}He$^+$ on ^{4}He, ^{4}He$^+$ on ^{3}He, and Ne$^+$ on Ne (Aberth *et al.*, 1965; Mittmann and Weise, 1974).

this high energy. The undulations are the same for both systems at angles below 40°. They are attributed to the g–u oscillations described in Section III,C. The ^{4}He$^+$–^{4}He system exhibits an additional set of oscillations at larger angles which is not present in the ^{4}He^3–^{3}He system. It was attributed to the fact that the two ^{4}He nuclei are not identical in the quantum statistical sense (Aberth *et al.*, 1965). The undulations in the scattering of Ne$^+$ on Ne show a long-wavelength structure with superimposed rapid oscillations. The system Ne$^+$–Ne can exist in a $^2\Pi$ or $^2\Sigma$ state and both these states split into gerade or ungerade branches. As consequence, both $^2\Sigma_g$–$^2\Sigma_u$ and $^2\Pi_g$–$^2\Pi_u$ undulations can occur. The long-wavelength structure in Fig. 11(b) was attributed to the $^2\Sigma_{g,u}$ interference (Mittmann and Weise, 1974).

IV. Reactive Scattering

A. Experimental Procedure

An apparatus for measuring the velocity and angular distribution of the product ions from an ion–molecule reaction generally consists of the following principal components: (1) The primary ion source, (2) the collision chamber containing the target gas or a molecular beam of the gas,

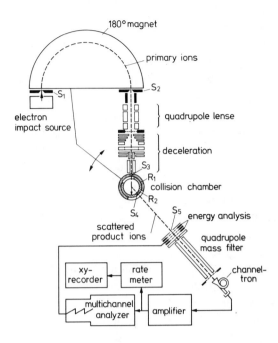

FIG. 12.   Schematic presentation of an apparatus for measuring velocity and angular distributions of reactively scattered ions (Bosse *et al.*, 1971a).

and (3) the analyzer. Either the analyzer or the ion source can rotate about the scattering center.

Figure 12 shows schematically the apparatus used by Bosse *et al.* (1971a). The primary ions are produced by electron impact in a commercial ion source, accelerated to about 200 eV, and mass-analyzed in a 180° magnet of 4 cm radius. After passage through the exit slit S_2, they are focused and decelerated by a system of electrostatic lenses and enter the collision chamber through slit S_3. The collision chamber consists of two concentric tubes R_1 and R_2 each with a small hole S_3 and S_4 and a wide, horizontal slit on the opposite side. R_1 is mechanically connected to the primary ion producer. While the analyzer and R_2 are in a fixed position, the ion source together with R_1 can rotate around R_2. The scattered ions enter through slit S_5 into the analyzer. Energy analysis is carried out according to the retarding potential method, mass analysis by a quadrupole mass filter, and detection by a Channeltron-type secondary-emission multiplier. At high ion intensities, the amplified signals are integrated with a rate meter. At low intensities, the signals are fed into a multichannel analyzer. In order to obtain the integrated energy distribution at a given scattering angle, the potential of the stopping grid of the energy analyzer is periodically modulated with a voltage that is proportional to that of the channel address. Similar apparatus have been described by other authors (Champion *et al.*, 1966; Gentry *et al.*, 1967; Herman *et al.*, 1969a). In these machines, operational since about 1965, the analyzer has a small angular acceptance and thus allows one to measure angular distributions of product ions. In the earlier work, either discrimination or wide acceptance angle methods were used to measure the velocity distribution only (Henglein and Muccini, 1962, 1963; Henglein and Lacmann, 1966; Ding *et al.*, 1968a). These simple methods gave information about some of the basic collision mechanisms, such as stripping and the complex model. The conclusions drawn from these simple kinematic experiments were confirmed and investigated in more detail using the later, more sophisticated machines.

Most of the experiments were carried out at incident ion energies above 5 eV. It is difficult to produce intense ion beams at energies as low as a few eV or even tens of eV since beams in this energy range tend to diverge through Coulombic repulsion. In addition, surface potentials at the collimating slits through which the beam must pass often change the nominal potentials (given by the voltage applied to the electrodes) to an unknown extent. These surface potentials usually depend on gas pressure and the nature of the rest gas in the apparatus.

When H_2 or D_2 was used as target molecule the incident ions were naturally much heavier; under these conditions, the translational energy E_c in the center-of-mass system is much smaller than the energy E_1 of the ion in the laboratory system. In other words, even when E_1 amounted to a few eV, the relative translational energy is only of the order of thermal energies at a few hundred degrees K [Eq. (2.4b)].

B. Newton Diagrams and Intensity Contour Diagrams

The scattering center is designated by SC in Fig. 13. The primary ion of mass M_1 moves from left to right with velocity $\mathbf{v}_1$, the molecule of mass M_2 moves at right angles to it with velocity $\mathbf{v}_2$, and $\mathbf{v}_r$ is the relative velocity of the reactants. The center of mass CM lies on $\mathbf{v}_r$; $\mathbf{u}_1$ and $\mathbf{u}_2$ are the velocities of the two particles as they would appear to an observer at the center of mass. Since the total momentum is zero in the center-of-mass system, $M_1 u_1 = M_2 u_2$. From this relation, the position of the point CM on $\mathbf{v}_r$ can easily be determined. The center of mass moves with the velocity

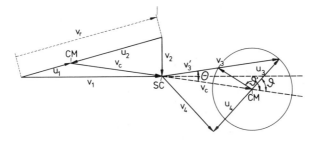

FIG. 13. Newton diagram of velocity vectors for a chemical reaction. v and u are the velocities in the laboratory and center-of-mass systems, respectively, v_c is the velocity of the center of mass, and v_r is the relative velocity.

$\mathbf{v}_c$ (forward direction). After the collision, the center-of-mass velocity remains unchanged (dashed arrow $\mathbf{v}_c$). $\mathbf{v}_3$ and $\mathbf{v}_4$ are the velocities of the charged and neutral products of the reaction in the center-of-mass system. The relation $M_3 u_3 = M_4 u_4$ allows one to calculate u_4 if only u_3 is known, M_3 and M_4 being the masses of the ionic and neutral products, respectively. $\mathbf{v}_3$ is the velocity of the product ion in the laboratory system as measured by an analyzer that sees particles emerging from the SC point at the angle θ. ϑ is the corresponding angle in the center-of-mass system. However, there is not an unambiguous relation between θ and ϑ. A product ion may emerge from the center of mass at different angles ϑ. The tip of the vector $\mathbf{u}_3$ lies on a circle for all ions having the same center-of-mass velocity $\mathbf{u}_3$ but different scattering angles. The analyzer at the laboratory angle θ also sees ions scattered at ϑ' in the center-of-mass system although the velocity $\mathbf{v}_3'$ of these ions is smaller than that of ions scattered at angle ϑ. Generally the product ion has a range of u_3 values, i.e., circles with various radii about the center of mass must be taken into consideration.

In most of the cases studied, the incident ion is much faster than the neutral target, and the direction of $\mathbf{v}_c$ is almost coincident with that of $\mathbf{v}_1$, the absolute value of $\mathbf{v}_c$ being

$$v_c = \frac{M_1}{M_1 + M_2} v_1. \tag{4.1}$$

Both the ion and the target molecule have a range of initial velocities, which must be kept to a minimum to ensure a well-defined center-of-mass velocity. Figure 14 shows how an intensity diagram is obtained. Experimentally, velocity distributions are measured as a function of analyzer angle in the laboratory system. Three typical curves are shown in Fig. 14(b),

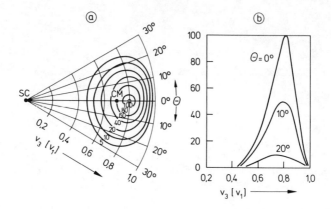

FIG. 14. (a) Intensity contour diagram in polar coordinates (laboratory system) obtained from (b) velocity distributions at various angles. v_3 is expressed in units of v_1, the velocity of the incident ion.

the maximum observed intensity being set equal to 100 and the velocity v_3 of the product ion being expressed in units of v_1, the velocity of the incident ion. The case shown in Fig. 14 corresponds to a target at rest and to $v_c = 0.7v_1$. In Fig. 14(a), a polar coordinate system around the scattering center SC is shown. v_c is the distance between points SC and CM. The coordinates of points of equal intensity can be read from the curves in Fig. 14(b). The intensity contours shown in Fig. 14(a) are thus obtained. As can be seen, the isointensity lines are not concentric with respect to the center of mass in this example and it may be concluded that the reaction occurs by a collision mechanism that makes the product ion move preferentially in the forward direction.

It must be recognized, however, that these intensities are still relative to the laboratory origin. The measured intensity represents the number of ions per unit time that are scattered into a solid angle with a range of velocities in the laboratory system. In order to discuss the contours of a reaction with respect to a collision model, it is required to transform the intensities from the laboratory into the center-of-mass system. There are two possible approaches:

1. One can transform to a polar coordinate system with its origin at the center of mass. This represents intensities as they would be seen by a detector traveling in the center-of-mass system. It can be shown that such a transformation can be accomplished by multiplying measured intensities by the ratio $u_3{}^2/v_3{}^2$. The disadvantage of this transformation consists in

the artificial "hole" that appears at velocities u_3 close to zero in the intensity distribution.

2. One can transform to Cartesian coordinates in the center-of-mass system in which all volume elements have the same size. Such a transfer can be achieved by multiplying measured intensities by the corresponding value of $1/v_3{}^2$.

C. SPECTATOR STRIPPING AND HARD-SPHERE SCATTERING

Reactions of rather simple ions and molecules, such as the following D-atom transfer processes, have been studied in most of the kinetic investigations:

$$Ar^+ + D_2 \longrightarrow ArD^+ + D \tag{4.2}$$

$$N_2{}^+ + D_2 \longrightarrow N_2D^+ + D \tag{4.3}$$

$$CO^+ + D_2 \longrightarrow COD^+ + D. \tag{4.4}$$

The mechanism of these reactions was first recognized in experiments where the velocity distribution of the product ion in the forward direction was measured using the wide angle of acceptance method. Figure 15 shows the velocity distributions of both the incident Ar^+ ion and product ArD^+ at a center-of-mass energy E_c of 2.3 eV. The peak of the ArD^+ intensity

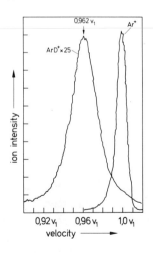

FIG. 15. Velocity spectrum of the reaction $Ar^+ + D_2 \rightarrow ArD^+ + D$ at $E_c = 2.3$ eV (Ding, Lacmann, and Henglein, 1967).

is observed at 0.962 times the velocity v_1 of the Ar$^+$ ion. This velocity is much higher than the velocity $v_c = 0.909v_1$ of the center of mass according to Eq. (4.1). Apparently, the product ion is strongly scattered in the forward direction rather than isotropically in the center-of-mass system. If the possible intermediate XD$_2$$^+$ (X = Ar, N$_2$, CO) of these reactions would move with the velocity v_c before it breaks up into the final products, the XD$^+$ product should have a velocity distribution around v_c. The observed forward scattering indicates an "impulsive" reaction, in which the transfer of the D atom occurs faster than the formation of the intermediate XD$_2$$^+$ with velocity v_c.

The spectator stripping model discussed in earlier work (Henglein and Muccini, 1962, 1963) was used to explain the velocity distribution of Fig. 15. It is assumed here that the incident Ar$^+$ ion interacts only with one D atom, no momentum being transferred to the other D atom (spectator). The collision can thus be viewed as the pickup of a quasi-free D atom by the Ar$^+$ ion. Since conservation of momentum requires

$$M_1 v_1 = M_3 v_3 \qquad (4.5)$$

(the D$_2$ molecule being regarded at rest), the velocity v_3 of the product ion is equal to v_s where

$$v_s = \frac{M_1}{M_1 + m} v_1 = 0.953 v_1, \qquad (4.6)$$

m being the mass of the transferred D atom. The velocity v_s is only slightly smaller than the velocity at which the intensity maximum in Fig. 15 appears. The collision model was cross-checked by measurement of the velocity spectra of the two product ions from the reactions of Ar$^+$ with HD:

$$\text{Ar}^+ + \text{HD} \begin{cases} \rightarrow \text{ArH}^+ + \text{D} & (4.7) \\ \rightarrow \text{ArD}^+ + \text{H} & (4.8) \end{cases}$$

If symmetric scattering around the center of mass were to occur, both ArH$^+$ and ArD$^+$ would be expected to have velocity distributions centered at v_c. For stripping, however, ArH$^+$ should appear at a higher velocity than ArD$^+$ since v_s is dependent only on the mass of the transferred atom and not on the mass of the spectator [Eq. (4.6)]. In fact this effect was observed (Henglein et al., 1965).

Having discussed the reaction with respect to an idealized collision model, it is now necessary to consider deviations from the ideal model. According to the stripping model, the product ion should move exactly in the forward direction with velocity v_s and the velocity distribution should therefore be as narrow for ArD^+ as for the incident Ar^+ ion. However, inspection of Fig. 15 shows that the product ion band is broader than that of Ar^+. Apparently, the spectator receives some recoil momentum which is almost isotropically directed around the velocity v_s. This has been attributed to a repulsion between the D atoms during the reaction, the recoil momentum being practically independent of the direction of the axis of the D_2 molecule with respect to the direction of the primary ion beam ("recoil stripping," Henglein, 1970). A similar assumption is made in the DIPR model ("direct interaction with product repulsion") that is described in Chapter 6 (Kuntz *et al.*, 1969; Kuntz, 1970).

Further deviations can be recognized from the intensity contour diagram shown in Fig. 16. The intensity band in the velocity spectrum of Fig. 15 now appears as a peak at a slightly higher velocity than v_s [point S in Fig. 16, calculated from Eq. (4.6)]. The low-intensity lines of the diagram, however, are concentric around the center of mass CM, indicating that there is a second type of reactive collision in which the ArD^+ is isotropically scattered with appreciable amounts of translational energy in the center-of-mass system. This isotropic contribution reminds one of the elastic scattering of hard spheres. Chiang *et al.* (1970) have shown that

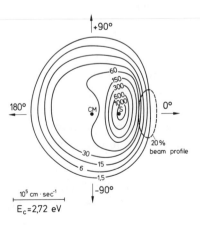

FIG. 16. Contour map of the intensity of ArD^+ in the center-of-mass coordinate system. CM: center-of-mass velocity. S: Ideal stripping velocity of Eq. (4.L6). $E_c = 2.72$ eV (Chiang *et al.*, 1970).

538

A. Henglein

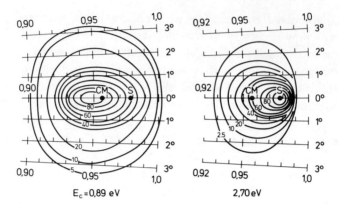

FIG. 17. Intensity contour maps of KrD$^+$ at $E_c = 0.89$ and 2.70 eV (Bosse *et al.*, 1971b).

the "stripping" fraction and "hard-sphere" fraction of the reactive collisions between Ar$^+$ and D$_2$ are about equal.

Intensity contour diagrams are shown in Fig. 17 for the product of the reaction

$$\text{Kr}^+ + \text{D}_2 \longrightarrow \text{KrD}^+ + \text{D} \qquad (4.9)$$

at two energies. At $E_c = 0.89$ eV in Fig. 17, the intensity is isotropically distributed around the center-of-mass point; at 2.7 eV, the intensity is peaking at the point S predicted from the stripping model; an appreciable amount of intensity, however, is still distributed isotropically around the center of mass. It has to be concluded that in this reaction the stripping fraction is much smaller than the hard-sphere fraction.

Scattering of the incident ion on the spectator atom during the reaction is expected to occur in head-on collisions. In a glancing collision, however, little interaction with the spectator atom should occur and stripping should take place. If $p(b)$ is the reaction probability in a collision with collision parameter b, the total cross section can be written as

$$\sigma = 2\pi \int_{b=0}^{\infty} bp(b)\, db. \qquad (4.10)$$

The stripping fraction would dominate if $p(b)$ is still significant at large values of b (a few angstroms). Otherwise, it is the hard-sphere fraction which is mainly expected to determine the angular distribution of reactively scattered ions. Further, processes that show stripping behavior should have large cross sections.

Most ion–molecule reactions in which an H atom or another atom is transferred show the typical stripping behavior at higher collision energies (generally above 2 eV). The spectator stripping model has become a standard model against which the experimental data are often compared. In reactions (4.2)–(4.4), the products were found to be strongly forward scattered even at center-of-mass collision energies at room temperature (Herman *et al.*, 1967; Ding *et al.*, 1968c). This showed that a common prejudice was unjustified, according to which all chemical reactions where there is strong attraction between the reactants should proceed through a complex if only the incident energy is low enough. However, most reactions show a change in the collision mechanism at low energies which is often indicated by a concentric distribution of intensity of the scattered products around the center of mass. Such a distribution has to be explained either by reactive hard-sphere scattering as mentioned above or by complex formation (see Section IV,E). In order to distinguish between these two possibilities, additional experiments or theoretical considerations have to be applied. For example, if the reacting system has no hollow in its potential hypersurface that is accessible to the reactants and in which they can be kept together for some time, a concentric distribution cannot be explained by complex formation.

D. Rebound versus Stripping Reactions

The Ar^+ and Kr^+ ions also abstract a hydrogen atom from methane to form ArH^+ and KrH^+, respectively. The intensity distributions peak near the velocity v_s of Eq. (4.6) (Ding *et al.*, 1968c; Gislason *et al.*, 1969a; Hierl, 1975). The Kr^+ ion can also react according to

$$Kr^+ + CH_4 \longrightarrow KCH_2^+ + H_2 \qquad (4.11)$$

with about five times smaller cross section. In addition, small intensities of $KrCH_3^+$ were observed. Figure 18 shows intensity contour maps for both products KrH^+ and $KrCH_2^+$. While KrH^+ has a distribution of intensity around the stripping point, most of the intensity of $KrCH_2^+$ is found in the rear hemisphere of the center-of-mass system (the asymmetry of $KrCH_2^+$ intensity appears to have been caused by strong fields penetrating the collision region). Reactions in which the product is preferentially scattered into the rear hemisphere are called "rebound."

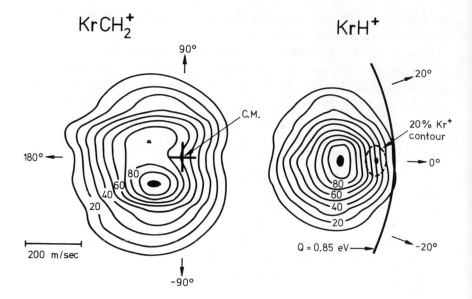

FIG. 18. Intensity contour maps of KrH$^+$ and KrCH$_2^+$ from the reactions of Kr$^+$ with CH$_4$; $E_c = 1.38$ eV (Hierl, 1975).

The explanation given for the effects in Fig. 18 follows the line expressed by Eq. (4.10). Large-impact-parameter collision leads to abstraction and forward scattering, while small-impact-parameter collision leads to displacement and rebound scattering (Hierl, 1975).

The more complicated reaction

$$CH_3^+ + CH_4 \longrightarrow C_2H_5^+ + H_2, \tag{4.12}$$

in which two bonds are broken and two new bonds formed, also occurs impulsively. The product ion is preferentially scattered in the forward direction at center-of-mass collision energies in the range of 0.6–0.5 eV (Ding *et al.*, 1968b; Herman *et al.*, 1969b). More indirect investigations of the collision mechanism in which product abundances were measured led to the result that a relatively long-lived complex C$_2$H$_7^+$ exists at thermal energies (Futrell *et al.*, 1970; Fluegge and Landman, 1971). C$_2$H$_7^+$ is known as a stable product of the ion–molecule reaction C$_2$H$_6^+$ + C$_2$H$_6 \rightarrow$ C$_2$H$_7^+$ + C$_2$H$_5$ (Henglein and Muccini, 1962).

E. COMPLEX FORMATION

The spectator stripping model discussed above represents an extreme case of an impulsive mechanism. At the other extreme is the formation of a complex by the collision partners with a life long enough to ensure a statistical distribution of its excess energy among its internal degrees of freedom. Obviously, a complex can only be formed if the system has a potential well capable of holding the particles together long enough. Once the system reaches this well, the decay of the complex into the products may be described by the theory of unimolecular decay. Kassel's theory (1932) provides us with the following rough estimate of the lifetime of a complex having s internal degrees of vibrational freedom:

$$\tau \approx \nu^{-1}\left(\frac{U_t - D - E_A}{U_t}\right)^{1-s}, \qquad (4.13)$$

where ν is a factor of the order of vibrational frequencies and U_t is the total internal energy of the complex, with

$$U_t = E_c + D_0 + U^*, \qquad (4.14)$$

D_0 being the depth of the potential well and U^* the excitation energy of the reactants. $D + E_A$ is the energy required for dissociation into the products, E_A being the activation energy for dissociation. Figure 19 shows the interrelationships of these quantities.

In the earlier work on ion–molecule reactions occurring in the ion source of a conventional mass spectrometer, a few collision complexes having

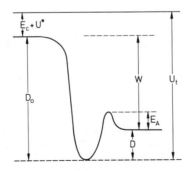

FIG. 19.   Cross section across a potential energy surface with potential well for complex formation.

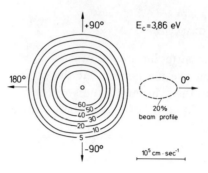

FIG. 20. Intensity contour map for the reaction $O_2^+(^2\Pi_g) + D_2 \rightarrow O_2D^+ + D$ (Gislason et al., 1969b).

lifetimes longer than 10^{-6} sec, i.e., the time of flight through the spectrometer, were observed (Pottie and Hamill, 1959; Henglein, 1962; Henglein et al., 1963). Most complexes, however, decay much faster, i.e., practically instantaneously. If the lifetime of a complex is longer than the time required for about one rotation, its dissociation products are scattered with equal frequency into both the front and rear hemispheres of the center-of-mass system. The formation of an intermediate complex can therefore be recognized by the symmetry about a plane passing through the center of the mass point and normal to the forward direction in the intensity contour diagram of a reaction product.

Figures 20 and 21 show intensity contour maps of the products from the reactions

$$O_2^+ + D_2 \quad \longrightarrow \quad O_2D^+ + D \tag{4.15}$$

$$C_2H_4^+ + C_2H_4 \quad \longrightarrow \quad C_3H_5^+ + CH_3. \tag{4.16}$$

In both cases, symmetric distributions were observed and interpreted as complex formation. The distribution of intensity is isotropic in Fig. 20, while symmetric forward–backward peaking can be seen in Fig. 21. The degree of forward–backward peaking is an indication of the angular momentum of the complex. A complex formed in a more or less head-on collision possesses almost no angular momentum and contains its excess energy mainly as vibrational energy. The products of its dissociation will be scattered practically isotropically into space. In a glancing collision, however, where some rotational angular momentum is imparted to the complex, the products will fly apart with an equally large angular momentum, provided their

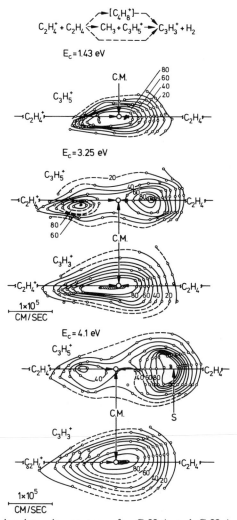

FIG. 21. Cartesian intensity contours for $C_3H_5^+$ and $C_3H_3^+$ resulting from the reaction (4.16) at various center-of-mass collision energies (Herman *et al.*, 1969c).

internal spin momentum can be neglected. If **L** denotes the angular momentum of the system and $\mathbf{v}_r$ the relative velocity, the products move in the same plane as the reactants, i.e., a plane perpendicular to **L** as shown by Fig. 22. The probability of the product ion scattering into the angular range between ϑ and $\vartheta + d\vartheta$ is independent of ϑ. The **L** vector, is uniformly distributed in space with all values of the azimuthal angle equally probable due to uniform distribution of the collision parameter. The distribution

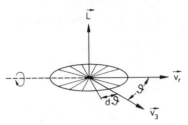

FIG. 22. Relationship between angular momentum, relative velocity, and product velocity for complex formation without rotation of either reactant or product.

of **L** therefore has cylindrical symmetry around $\mathbf{v}_r$, as indicated in Fig. 22. All product ions that are scattered into ϑ and $\vartheta + d\vartheta$ move into the solid angle $2\pi \sin \vartheta \, d\vartheta$. A detector of solid angle acceptance $d\Omega$ in the center-of-mass system can detect the fraction $d\Omega/(2\pi \sin \vartheta \, d\vartheta)$, i.e., the intensity is proportional to $1/\sin \vartheta$ and peaking occurs at $\vartheta = 0$ and 180° in the center-of-mass system. The more complicated case in which the products carry part of the angular momentum of the complex as internal spin has been treated by Miller *et al.* (1967) in their studies on complex formation in alkali atom–halide reactions.

The reaction (4.15) can be initiated by $O_2{}^+$ in its ground state $^2\Pi_g$ or the first excited state $^4\Pi_u$, which is relatively long lived. The reaction is endothermic by 1.8 eV in the former case and exothermic by 2.0 eV in the latter. The reaction of $O_2{}^+({}^2\Pi_g)$ has an energy threshold of about 17 eV (laboratory system), while that of $O_2{}^+({}^4\Pi_u)$ can occur at very low energies. Since the quantities shown in Fig. 19 can be derived from thermodynamic and ionization measurements (assuming that the intermediate $O_2D_2{}^+$ is identical with ionized hydrogen peroxide), the lifetime of the complex can be estimated from Eq. (4.13). D_0 is 2.6 eV, $W = 1.8$ eV, and $D = 4.4$ eV. Assuming $E_A = 0$ and $v = 5 \times 10^{13}$ sec^{-1}, τ is calculated at $E_c = 3.1$ eV ($E_1 = 28$ eV) as 2×10^{-10} sec. This lifetime is essentially longer than the time required for one rotation, which makes the isotropic distribution of the product ion in Fig. 20 understandable. In the case of $O_2{}^+({}^4\Pi_u)$ reaction, U_t is larger by the excess energy of the ion of 3.8 eV. The calculated lifetime is now shorter than the time of one rotation, i.e., a symmetric distribution of the product ion would not be expected. Similarly, $O_2{}^+({}^2\Pi_g)$ is expected to react impulsively at higher collision energies; τ, for example, is calculated to be as small as 8×10^{-13} sec at $E_c = 7$ eV.

The contour map of Fig. 23 shows what has been observed at high energies. The primary ion beam contained $O_2{}^+({}^2\Pi_g)$ as well as $O_2{}^+({}^4\Pi_u)$

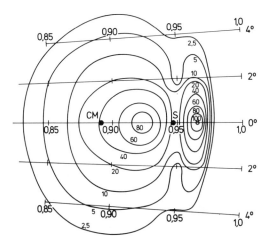

FIG. 23. Intensity contour map for the reaction $O_2^+ + D_2 \rightarrow O_2D^+ + D$ at $E_c = 4.14$ eV. The O_2^+ beam contained both $O_2^+(^2\Pi_g)$ and $O_2^+(^4\Pi_u)$ ions (Bosse et al., 1971a).

ions since both states are formed from oxygen under electron impact. The narrow peak at the velocity $0.963v_1$ in the forward direction is attributed to O_2D^+ resulting from the reaction of $O_2^+(^4\Pi_u)$. The forward scattering is even stronger than expected from the spectator stripping model (point S). The broader peak at $0.927v_1$ is attributed to O_2D^+ from the reaction of $O_2^+(^2\Pi_g)$. A comparison with Fig. 20 shows that this peak has shifted from the center-of-mass point to a higher velocity. At even higher energies, the peak finally reaches the position S, i.e., a transition from complex formation to a stripping process takes place with increasing energy (Ding and Henglein, 1969; Bosse et al., 1971a).

Changes in the collision mechanism were also observed for the reaction (4.16) (see Fig. 27). With increasing collision energy the distributions of $C_3H_5^+$ become less symmetric and shift toward those characteristic of a direct reaction of the stripping type. At high collision energies, $C_3H_3^+$ appears as second product of the reaction $C_2H_4^+ + C_2H_4$ with increasing abundance. Its symmetric distribution shows that it is still formed via a complex. The formation of $C_3H_3^+$ is explained by the decomposition of an intermediate, highly excited $C_3H_5^+$ ion:

$$C_3H_5^+ \longrightarrow C_3H_3^+ + H_2. \tag{4.17}$$

It thus appears probable that $C_3H_5^+$ may be formed at all energies via a complex and at higher energies also via direct reaction. The intermediate $C_4H_8{}^+$ complex contains so much excess energy at higher collision energy that the product $C_3H_5{}^+$ is also internally excited and decays according to Eq. (4.17). If $C_3H_5{}^+$ is formed in a stripping process, it contains less energy and does not undergo further decomposition (Herman and Wolfgang, 1972).

Since intermediate complex formation can generally be expected only at low incident ion energies, where the experimental difficulties mentioned in Sections II,C and IV,A arise, other methods of reaching the low-energy range have been developed. Such methods are the merging beam techniques (Rol and Entemann, 1968) and special mass spectrometric methods, such as the double chamber-deflection techniques (Durup and Durup, 1968) and the double pulse techniques (Matus et al., 1967). These methods are particularly useful for the low-energy range of 0.1–1.0 eV. They have recently been reviewed by Herman and Wolfgang (1972).

F. ENERGY CONSIDERATIONS

An interesting problem in chemical kinematics is the conversion of translational and internal energy of the reactants into internal or translational energy, respectively, of the products. If E_c' is the average translational energy of the reactants in the center-of-mass system. $\Delta H°$ the enthalpy of reaction, and U the internal energy of the products, then the conservation of energy requires

$$E_c - \Delta H° = \bar{E}_c' + U, \qquad (4.18)$$

assuming that the reactants are not internally excited. The difference between the translational energies of the products and reactants is called the translational exoergicity of the reaction

$$\bar{E}_c' - E_c = Q = -(\Delta H + U). \qquad (4.19)$$

$\bar{E}_c'$ can be obtained by appropriate integration of the scattering intensity in the contour map over all velocities. A description of this procedure has recently been given by Eisele et al. (1974). The maximum value of E_c' is equal to $(E_c - \Delta H°)$. It corresponds to a collision in which all the "available energy" $(E_c - \Delta H°)$ appears as translational energy of the products, i.e., $U = 0$. The minimum value of E_c' is generally zero, corresponding to a collision in which $U = (E_c - \Delta H°)$. However, at large collision energies

E_c, the product ion may carry more internal energy than corresponds to its dissociation energy if too little translational energy is given to the products. Under these conditions, a minimum value of E_c' exists which is equal to $E_c - (\Delta H° + D)$. The velocity of a product ion must therefore lie between a maximum value u_{3max} and a minimum value u_{3min} in the center-of-mass system. An "allowed" zone of product ion intensity is thus defined by the area between two circles of radii u_{3max} and u_{3min} in an intensity contour diagram. Figure 24 shows these circles in the contour diagram of the reaction

$$CH_2^+ + H_2 \longrightarrow CH_3^+ + H \tag{4.20}$$

at three collision energies. The circles were calculated using $\Delta H° = -0.92$ eV. At $E_c = 0.54$ and 4.53 eV, $u_{3max} = 0$ and therefore also $E_{c,min} = 0$. At 7.54 eV, u_{3min} is already rather large. That low intensities are still observed within the "forbidden" zone is due to the finite angular and energy resolution of the apparatus. The concentric symmetry of the intensity around the center of mass at low collision energies has been explained by CH_4^+ complex formation since the enthalpy of formation of CH_4^+ is 2.6 eV lower than that of $CH_2^+ + H_2$. The transition to a stripping process becomes noticeable at the higher collision energies. The peak of intensity lies at velocities even greater than v_s at collision energies exceeding those given in Fig. 24. This is understood in terms of the fact that the radius u_{3min} of the forbidden zone increases with E_c. Only those ions that are even more strongly forward-scattered than in a spectator stripping process have internal energies less than D and can be detected.

Energy considerations of this kind also allow one to understand certain changes in the abundance ratio of competing reactions paths, which was already recognized in the earlier experiments of Henglein *et al.* (1965). Let us regard the two product ions SiH_2D^+ and SiD_3^+ formed in the reactions

$$SiH_2^+ + SiD_4 \begin{cases} \longrightarrow SiH_2D^+ + SiD_3 & (4.21) \\ \longrightarrow SiH_2D + SiD_3^+ & (4.22) \end{cases}$$

by D-atom or D^--ion transfer, respectively (Mayer and Lampe, 1974). Both processes occur impulsively even at collision energies at about 1 eV: SiH_2D^+ has a peak in its velocity distribution close to the velocity v_s of Eq. (4.6) and SiD_3^+ has about thermal velocities at all collision energies.

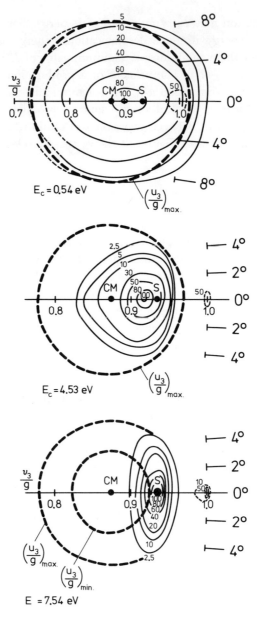

Fig. 24. Intensity contour diagrams for the product of reaction (4.20) at three collision energies (all velocities in units of g, the relative velocity of the reactants) (Eisele *et al.*, 1974).

In the latter case, the positive charge remains at the "spectator" of the reaction, which moves with thermal velocity before (and after) the reaction. At higher collision energies, above 3 eV, the relative abundance of SiH_2D^+ decreases and that of SiD_3^+ increases. This is understood in terms of the increasing fraction of the SiH_2D^+ ions that contain too much internal energy and decompose before they can be detected. The product ion of the D^- transfer process, however, contains very little internal energy and can thus be detected even at high collision energies.

REFERENCES

ABERTH, W., LORENTS, D. C., MARCHI, R. P., and SMITH, F. T. (1965). *Phys. Rev. Lett.* **14**, 776.

BOSSE, G., DING, A., and HENGLEIN, A. (1971a). *Ber. Bunsenges. Phys. Chem.* **75**, 413.

BOSSE, G., DING, A., and HENGLEIN, A. (1971b). *Z. Naturforsch.* **26a**, 932.

CHAMPION, R. L., DOVERSPIKE, L. D., and BAILEY, T. L. (1966). *J. Chem. Phys.* **45**, 4377.

CHAMPION, R. L., DOVERSPIKE, L. D., RICH, W. G., and BOBBIO, S. M. (1970). *Phys. Rev.* **A2**, 2327

CHIANG, M., GISLASON, E. A., MAHAN, B. H., TSAO, C.-W., and WERNER, A. S. (1970). *J. Chem. Phys.* **52**, 2698

DING, A., LACMANN, K., and HENGLEIN, A. (1967). *Ber. Bunsenges Phys. Chem.* **71**, 596.

DING, A., and HENGLEIN, A. (1969). *Ber. Bunsenges. Phys. Chem.* **73**, 562.

DING, A., HENGLEIN, A., and LACMANN, K. (1968a). *Z. Naturforsch.* **23a**, 779.

DING, A., HENGLEIN, A., and LACMANN, K. (1968b). *Z. Naturforsch.* **23a**, 780.

DING, A., HENGLEIN, A., HYATT, D., and LACMANN, K. (1968c). *Z. Naturforsch.* **23a**, 2084.

DUGAN, J. V. JR., and MAGEE, J. L. (1971) *In* "Chemical Dynamics" (O. Hirschfelder, ed., p. 207), New York. References of earlier work of these authors can be found here.

DUGAN, J. V. JR., RICE, J. H., and MAGEE, J. L. (1969). *Chem. Phys. Lett.* **3**, 323.

DURUP, M., and DURUP, J. (1968). *Advan. Mass Spectromet.* **4**, 677.

EISELE, G., HENGLEIN, A., and BOSSE, G. (1974), *Ber. Bunsenges. Phys. Chem.* **78**, 140.

FERGUSON, E. E. (1967). *Rev. Geophys.* **5**, 305.

FERGUSON, E. E. (1970). *Accounts Chem. Res.* **3**, 402.

FITE, W. L. (1969). *Can. J. Chem.* **47**, 1797.

FLUEGGE, R. A., and LANDMAN, D. A. (1971). *J. Chem. Phys.* **54**, 1576.

FORD, K. W., and WHEELER, J. A. (1959). *Ann. Phys.* **7**, 259.

FRANKLIN, J. L. (ed.) (1972). "Ion-Molecule Reactions," Vols. 1 and 2. Butterworths, London and New York.

FRIEDMAN, L. (1968). *Ann. Rev. Phys. Chem.* **19**, 273.

FUTRELL, J. H. and TIERNAN, T. O. (1969). *In* "Fundamental Processes in Radiation Chemistry" (P. Ausloos, ed.). Wiley (Interscience), New York.

FUTRELL, J. H., ABRAMSON, F. P., BHATTACHARYA, A. K., and TIERNAN, T. O. (1970). *J. Chem. Phys.* **52**. 3655.

GELB, A., and SUPLINSKAS, R. J. (1970). *J. Chem. Phys.* **53**, 2249.

GENTRY, W. R., GISLASON, E. A., LEE, Y. T., MAHAN, B. H., and TSAO, C.-W. (1967). *Discus. Faraday Soc.* **44**, 137.

GENTRY, W. R., GISLASON, E. A., MAHAN, B. H., and TSAO, C.-W. (1968). *J. Chem. Phys.* **49**, 3058.

GIOUMOUSIS, G., and STEVENSON, D. P. (1958). *J. Chem. Phys.* **29**, 294.

GISLASON, E. A., MAHAN, B. H., TSAO, C.-W. and WERNER, A. S. (1969a). *J. Chem. Phys.* **50**, 142.

GISLASON, E. A., MAHAN, B. H., TSAO, C.-W., and WERNER, A. S. (1969b). *J. Chem. Phys.* **50**, 5418.

GOULD, R. F. (ed.) (1966). *Advan. Chem. Ser.* **58**.

GUPTA, B. K., and MATSEN, F. A. (1967). *J. Chem. Phys.* **47**, 4860.

HENGLEIN, A. (1962). *Z. Naturforsch.* **17a**, 44.

HENGLEIN, A. (1970). In *Proc. School Phys. Enrico Fermi, Course 44* (Ch. Schlier, ed.) p. 139.

HENGLEIN, A., and LACMANN, K. (1966). *Advan. Mass Spectromet.* **3**, 331.

HENGLEIN, A., and MUCCINI, G. (1963). *Z. Naturforsch.* **18a**, 753.

HENGLEIN, A., and MUCCINI, G. (1962). *Z. Naturforsch.* **17a**, 98.

HENGLEIN, A., JACOBS, G., and MUCCINI, G. (1963). *Z. Naturforsch.* **18a**, 98.

HENGLEIN, A., LACMANN, K., and KNOLL, B. (1965). *J. Chem. Phys.* **43**, 1048.

HERMAN, Z., and WOLFGANG, R. (1972). *In* "Ion-Molecule Reactions" (J. L. Franklin, ed.), Vol. 2, p. 553. Butterworths, London and New York.

HERMAN, Z., KERSTETTER, J., ROSE, T., and WOLFGANG, R. (1967). *Discuss. Faraday Soc.* **44**, 123.

HERMAN, Z., KERSTETTER, J. D., ROSE, T. L., and WOLFGANG, R. (1969a). *Rev. Sci. Instrum.* **40**, 538.

HERMAN, Z., HIERL, P., LEE, A., and WOLFGANG, R. (1969b). *J. Chem. Phys.* **51**, 454.

HERMAN, Z., LEE, A., and WOLFGANG, R. (1969c). *J. Chem. Phys.* **51**, 452.

HERRERO, F. A., NEMETH, E. M., and BAILEY, T. L. (1969). *J. Chem. Phys.* **50**, 4591.

HERSCHBACH, D. R. (1966). *Advan. Chem. Phys.* **10**, 319.

HIERL, P. (1975). *J. Phys. Chem.* (in press).

HUNDHAUSEN, E., and PAULY, H. (1965). *Z. Phy.* **187**, 305.

HYATT, D., and LACMANN, K. (1968). *Z. Naturforsch.* **23a**, 2080.

IOUP, G. E., and THOMAS, B. S. (1969). *J. Chem. Phys.* **50**, 5009.

KUBACH, C., SIDIS, V., and DURUP, J. (1974). In press.

KUNTZ, P. J. (1969). *Chem. Phys. Lett.* **4**, 129.

KUNTZ, P. J. (1970). *Trans. Faraday Soc.* **66**, 2980.

KUNTZ, P. J., MOK, M. H., and POLANYI, J. C. (1969). *J. Chem. Phys.* **50**, 4623.

LACMANN, K., and HENGLEIN, A. (1965). *Ber. Bunsenges. phys. Chem.* **69**, 286.

LAMPE, F. W., FRANKLIN, J. L., and FIELD, F. H. (1961). *Progr. Reaction Kinet.*, Vol. **1**, 69.

LANGEVIN, P. (1905). Ann. Chem. Phys. **5**, 245.

MAHAN, B. H. (1968). *Accounts Chem. Res.* **1**, 217.

MASON, E. A., and VANDERSLICE, J. T. (1959). *J. Chem. Phys.* **31**, 594.

MATUS, L., OPAUSZKY, I., HYATT, D., MASSON, A. J., BIRKINSHAW, K., and HENCHMAN, M. J. (1967). *Discuss. Faraday Soc.* **44**, 146.

MAYER, T., and LAMPE, F. W. (1974), J. Phys. Chem., **78**, 2795

McDANIEL, E. W. (1964). "Collision Phenomena in Ionized Gases," p.67, Appendix II. Wiley, New York.

MENENDEZ, M. G., and DATZ, S. (1965). *Int. Conf. Phys. Electr. At. Collisions*, Quebec 1965.

MILLER, W. B., SAFRON, S. A., and HERSCHBACH, D. R. (1967). *Discuss. Faraday Soc.* **44**, 108.

MITTMANN, H.-U., and WEISE, H.-P. (1974). *Z. Naturforsch.* **29a**, T400.

MITTMANN, H.-U., WEISE, H.-P., DING, A., and HENGLEIN, A. (1971a). *Z. Naturforsch.* **26a**, 1112.
MITTMANN, H.-U., WEISE, H.-P., DING, A., and HENGLEIN, A. (1971b). *Z. Naturforsch* **26a**, 1282.
MORAN, T. F., and HAMILL, W. H. (1963). *J. Chem. Phys.* **39**, 1413.
PEYERIMHOFF, S. (1965). *J. Chem. Phys.* **43**, 998.
POTTIE, R. F., and HAMILL, W. H. (1959). *J. Phys. Chem.* **63**, 877.
PRITCHARD, H., THYNNE, J. C. V., and HARRISON, A. G. (1968). *Can. J. Chem.* **46**, 2141.
ROACH, A. C., and KUNTZ, P. J. (1970). *Chem. Commun.* 1336.
ROL, P. K. and ENTEMANN, E. A. (1968). *J. Chem. Phys.* **49**, 1430.
STEVENSON, D. P., and SCHISSLER, D. O. (1958). *J. Chem. Phys.* **29**, 282.
STEVENSON, D. P., and SCHISSLER, D. O. (1961). *In* "Actions chimiques et biologiques des radiations" (M. Haissinsky, ed.), Vol. 5, p.167. Masson, Paris.
SU, T., and BOWERS, M. T. (1973). *J. Chem. Phys.* **58**, 3027.
THEARD, L. P., and HAMILL, W. H. (1962). *J. Amer. Chem. Soc.* **84**, 1134.
TOWNES, C. H., and SCHAWLOW, A. L. (1955). "Microwave Spectroscopy," chapters 5 and 10. McGraw-Hill, New York.
WEISE, H-.P., MITTMANN, H.-U., DING, A., and HENGLEIN, A. (1970). *Z. Naturforsch.* **25a**, 1154.
WEISE, H.-P., MITTMANN, H.-U., DING, A., and HENGLEIN, A. (1971). *Z. Naturforsch.* **26a**, 1122.
WOLFGANG, R. (1969), *Accounts Chem. Res.* **2**, 248.

Chapter 8

Collision Processes, Theory of Elastic Scattering

H. PAULY

I. Introduction

From the analysis of transport properties in gases it is well known that the elastic scattering of atoms and molecules may be described, to a large extent, by classical mechanics alone [see, for example, Hirschfelder (1954)]. Molecular beam investigations, however, show that a number of important features of the scattering behavior require a quantum mechanical treatment (Pauly and Toennies, 1965, 1968; Bernstein, 1966; Bernstein and Muckermann, 1967; Beck, 1970; Massey et al., 1971).

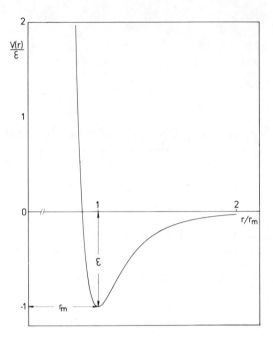

F<small>IG</small>. 1. The intermolecular potential between two atoms.

We therefore divide the discussion of the elastic scattering into three main sections: the classical, the quantum mechanical, and the semiclassical treatments. The last not only shows clearly the limits of the classical description and the modifications of the classical results introduced by quantum effects, but also allows a simple interpretation of the abstract expressions for the scattering cross sections and their relation to the interatomic potential.

For most discussions we assume a realistic, spherically symmetric interaction potential $V(r)$, consisting of a long-range attractive and a short-range repulsive part, as is shown schematically in Fig. 1. The potential energy curve is characterized by the potential well depth ε, the equilibrium distance r_m, and by its shape, which may be described by further parameters if the potential is expressed in an analytic form.* This has usually been

---

*For different model potentials frequently used in the interpretation of experimental data see, for example, Pauly and Toennies (1965), and Toennies, Volume VIA, Chapter 5. For 5–7-parameter potential models used to evaluate recent high-resolution scattering data see, for example, Buck and Pauly (1968), and Düren and Schlier (1967). Some simple analytic functions are also included in Table I.

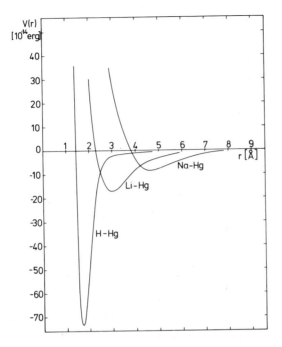

FIG. 2. Potential energy curves for the H–Hg, Li–Hg, and Na–Hg interaction, determined from spectroscopic data [H–Hg, (Stwalley, 1972)] and molecular beam scattering data [Li–Hg (Buck *et al.*, 1974); Na–Hg (Buck and Pauly 1971)].

done in connection with the interpretation of experimental data, but is by no means necessary. Ab initio calculations of intermolecular potentials as well as inversion procedures of scattering data yield numerical values $V_i(r_i)$ at discrete values of r_i.

The potential shape as well as ε and r_m depend on the collision partners. Especially the potential well depth ε may vary over several orders of magnitude. Figure 2 shows some examples of potential curves which have recently been determined experimentally (Buck and Pauly, 1968, 1971; Buck *et al.*, 1974).

Let us consider the interaction of two atoms or molecules for which chemical bonding is not possible (e.g., two rare gas atoms). For large distances only an extremely weak attractive potential is observed, due to the dispersion forces, the potential of which can be expanded in powers of the inverse distance r:

$$V_{\text{attr}}(r) = - [C_6/r^6 + C_8/r^8 + C_{10}/r^{10} + \cdots]. \tag{1.1}$$

At short distances, where the electron clouds overlap, repulsive forces arise due to electron exchange and Coulomb repulsion. In the medium range the potential energy curve $V(r)$ has a rather small minimum (10^{-3}–10^{-1} eV) in the region of 3–6 Å.

If the two neutral particles can form a stable molecule, the valence forces due to the electron exchange are partly attractive, so that the potential energy curve is characterized by a large well depth ε (several eV) and an equilibrium distance r_m (1–2 Å) which is small compared with the 3–6 Å of a van der Waals molecule.

Similar considerations are valid for the interaction between an ion and a neutral particle. The expansion of the long-range attractive potential, however, starts with an r^{-4} term, due to the interaction of the ion charge with the dipole moment induced in the neutral particle [see, for example, Henglein, this volume, Chapter 7].

In some applications the behavior of an observed quantity is well described by considering only the attractive part or only the repulsive part of the potential. In order to obtain approximate results in closed form, we then represent the attractive part of the potential by the main contribution to the inverse power expansion, Eq. (1.1):

$$V_{\text{attr}}(r) = -C_s/r^s = -C_{0s}\,\varepsilon r_m^{\,s}/r^s \tag{1.2}$$

TABLE I

REDUCED NOTATION

$\rho = r/r_m$	Distance
$\beta = b/r_m$	Impact parameter
$K = E/\varepsilon$	Energy
$A = kr_m$	Wave number
$l^* = l/(2\mu\varepsilon r_m^2)^{1/2} = \beta\sqrt{K}$	Angular momentum
$B = 2\mu\varepsilon r_m/\hbar^2$	Quantum parameter[a]
$v_c = 2\varepsilon r_m/\hbar = (B/A)v$	Characteristic velocity
$f(\rho) = V(\rho)/\varepsilon$	Potential
$f(\rho) = [s/(n-s)][\rho^{-n} - (n/s)\rho^{-s}]$	Lennard-Jones (n, s) potential
$f(\rho) = [\alpha/(\alpha - s)][(s/\alpha)e^{\alpha(1-\rho)} - \rho^{-s}]$	Buckingham (α, s) potential
$f(\rho) = e^{-2\gamma(\rho-1)} - 2e^{-\gamma(\rho-1)}$	Morse potential

[a] B is refered to as "potential well capacity" since the number of bound vibrational states with zero angular momentum is proportional to $\sqrt{B}$. The connection between B and the quantum parameter Λ^* frequently used in the quantum theory of transport phenomena is $B = 8\pi^2/\Lambda^{*2}$.

(with $s = 6$ or $s = 4$ for neutral–neutral or ion–neutral interaction, respectively), and the repulsive part by

$$V_{rep}(r) = c/r^n = c_0\, \varepsilon r_m{}^n/r^n. \tag{1.3}$$

It is often convenient to measure all lengths in units of r_m and all energies in units of ε, in order to have to deal only with dimensionless quantities. Table I gives a survey of the reduced notation used in the following sections.

II. Particle Scattering in Classical Mechanics*

A. Basic Formulas for Spherically Symmetric Potentials

The two-particle collision problem is formally reduced to a one-particle problem by a transformation to the center-of-mass system. If $\mathbf{r}_i$ and $\mathbf{p}_i$ are the position and momentum of particle i ($i = 1, 2$) before the collision and $\mathbf{r}_i{}'$ and $\mathbf{p}_i{}'$ are the position and momentum after the collision, we introduce the position and momentum of the center of mass $(\mathbf{r}_0, \mathbf{p}_0)$ and the position of one particle with respect to the other and the momentum of the relative motion $(\mathbf{r}, \mathbf{p})$ as

$$\mathbf{r}_0 = (m_1\mathbf{r}_1 + m_2\mathbf{r}_2)/M, \qquad \mathbf{p}_0 = \mathbf{p}_1 + \mathbf{p}_2$$
$$\mathbf{r} = \mathbf{r}_1 - \mathbf{r}_2, \qquad\qquad \mathbf{p} = (m_2/M)\mathbf{p}_1 - (m_1/M)\mathbf{p}_2 \tag{2.1}$$

where M is the total mass $m_1 + m_2$. Thus we find

$$\mathbf{p}_2 = (m_2/M)\mathbf{p}_0 - \mathbf{p}, \qquad \mathbf{p}_1 = (m_1/M)\mathbf{p}_0 + \mathbf{p} \tag{2.2}$$

and similar equations for the momenta after the collision

$$\mathbf{p}_2{}' = (m_2/M)\mathbf{p}_0{}' - \mathbf{p}', \qquad \mathbf{p}_1{}' = (m_1/M)\mathbf{p}_0{}' + \mathbf{p}'. \tag{2.3}$$

The conservation of momentum yields

$$\mathbf{p}_0 = \mathbf{p}_0{}' \tag{2.4}$$

*For a formal classical scattering theory based on the scattering solutions of the Liouville equation, which clearly shows the correspondence between the classical approach with that of time-dependent scattering theory in quantum mechanics, see, for example, Miles and Dahler (1970).

and from the conservation of energy we obtain for an elastic collision

$$|\mathbf{p}| = |\mathbf{p}'|. \qquad (2.5)$$

With these equations, which, for practical applications, may be expressed in spherical coordinates (Herschbach, 1960; Russek, 1960; Datz et al., 1961; Morse and Bernstein, 1962; Helbing, 1963, 1968), it is possible to perform the transformation from the laboratory system to the center-of-mass system and vice versa. The transformation from the center-of-mass system is always unique, whereas the reverse transformation is not, since one laboratory angle may correspond to two center-of-mass system angles. Our considerations will always refer to the center-of-mass system. In the elastic case the transformation of experimental data into this system can always be done, even if this may require in some cases the velocity analysis of the scattered particles. For details, including the inelastic case, see Pauly and Toennies (1965).

In the center-of-mass system the problem reduces to the scattering of a particle (of reduced mass $\mu = m_1 m_2/M$) which is moving with the relative momentum $\mathbf{p}$ with respect to an infinitely heavy stationary particle. The angle of deflection ϑ as a function of the reduced impact parameter β is obtained directly from the conservation of energy and angular momentum:

$$\vartheta = \pi - 2\beta \int_{\rho_0}^{\infty} \frac{d\rho}{\rho^2 \{1 - [f(\rho)/K] - (\beta/\rho^2)\}^{1/2}}. \qquad (2.6)$$

ρ_0 is the reduced distance of closest approach, which is given by the largest positive root of

$$1 - [f(\rho_0)/K] - (\beta^2/\rho_0{}^2) = 0. \qquad (2.7)$$

For a fixed energy K, Eq. (2.6) relates an angle of deflection ϑ to every impact parameter b (classical deflection function), which, when inverted, provides the functional relationship $b = b(\vartheta, K)$. All incident particles with impact parameters between b and $b + db$ will be scattered into the angular range between ϑ and $\vartheta + d\vartheta$ [because of the spherical symmetry of $V(r)$ we have no dependence on the azimuthal angle φ]. The differential cross section for elastic scattering $d\sigma/d\omega$ is defined by

$$d\sigma(\vartheta) = 2\pi (d\sigma/d\omega) \sin \vartheta \, d\vartheta$$

$$= \frac{\text{number of particles scattered into solid angle } d\omega \text{ per unit time}}{\text{incident flux density}}. \qquad (2.8)$$

If j_0 is the incident flux density, the number of particles per unit time incident upon the ring of width db at a distance b from the scattering center is $j_0 2\pi b \, db$. This is equal to the number of particles scattered into the solid angle element $d\omega$. Thus we obtain

$$d\sigma/d\omega = (b/\sin \vartheta)|\, db/d\vartheta| \, . \tag{2.9}$$

B. APPLICATION TO REALISTIC INTERATOMIC POTENTIALS

1. *The Classical Deflection Function*

For realistic intermolecular potentials, b is, in a certain angular range which depends on the reduced energy K, a three-valued function of ϑ. Figure 3 shows classical trajectories as a function of the reduced impact parameter β; the lower half of the figure shows the corresponding deflection function $\vartheta(\beta)$. Collisions with positive scattering angle can be attributed largely to the repulsive portion of the potential at small impact parameters. The scattering angle decreases with increasing impact parameter, until the average repulsive and attractive forces just cancel and no deflection is observed (reduced impact parameter β_0). For still larger impact parameters the long-range attractive forces lead to a change in the direction of deflection to negative angles. After going to a maximum at β_r the deflection function converges to zero as r tends to infinity. Figure 4 shows the classical deflection function $\vartheta(\beta)$ for different reduced energies K. For small values of the reduced energy K (the exact value depends on the shape of the potential) the maximum negative angle of deflection corresponding to the impact parameter β_r goes to infinity (orbiting collisions).

When observing the particles that are scattered into a certain angle of deflection, the individual trajectories leading to this angle cannot be resolved. This means that for the differential cross section in Eq. (2.9) one has to sum over all possible impact parameters b_i $(i = 1, 2, 3)$ which lead to the same angle of deflection. Hence for a realistic potential the differential cross section will be

$$\frac{d\sigma}{d\omega} = \sum_{i=1}^{3} \frac{b_i}{\sin \vartheta} \left|\frac{db_i}{d\vartheta}\right| = \frac{r_m^{\,2}}{\sin \vartheta} \sum_{i=1}^{3} \beta_i \left|\frac{d\beta_i}{d\vartheta}\right| . \tag{2.10}$$

2. *Small-Angle Scattering*

For small angles the main contribution to the differential scattering cross section arises from the asymptotic branch of the deflection function at large impact parameters. Compared with the contributions at larger

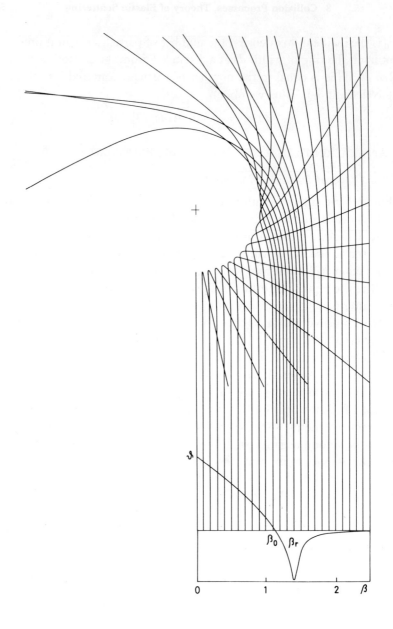

FIG. 3. Classical trajectories for various reduced impact parameters β for a realistic interatomic potential [Lennard-Jones (12, 6) with $K = 1.25$] and the corresponding deflection function $\vartheta(\beta)$.

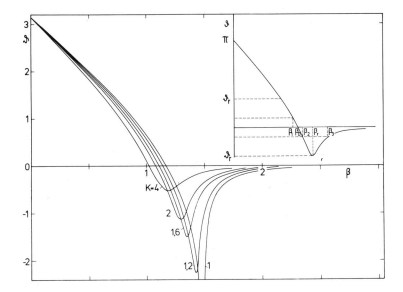

FIG. 4. Classical deflection function $\vartheta(\beta)$ at different reduced energies K for a Lennard-Jones (12, 6) potential. With decreasing energy the maximum negative angle ϑ_r (rainbow angle) increases until it goes to infinity for $K \leq 0.8$ (orbiting collisions). The diagram in the upper right-hand corner gives the definition of various reduced impact parameters.

angles, both factors in the sum, β and $d\beta/d\vartheta$, become large. Considering only these impact parameters, we can expand the integral in Eq. (2.6) retaining from the potential only the attractive term (Miykao, 1942; Mott-Smith, 1960; Lehmann and Leibfried, 1962; Smith et al., 1966). Assuming an inverse power law for the attractive potential, we obtain

$$\vartheta(b) = -(C/E) \sum_{n=0}^{\infty} (C/E)^n b^{-s(n+1)} f_n(s) \qquad (2.11)$$

with

$$f_n(s) = \sqrt{\pi}\, \Gamma(\tfrac{1}{2}(n+1)s + \tfrac{1}{2})/\Gamma(n+2)\Gamma(\tfrac{1}{2}(n+1)s - n).$$

Taking only the first term of this sum yields

$$\vartheta(b) = -f_0(s)(C/E)b^{-s} \qquad (2.12)$$

562 H. Pauly

and the differential scattering cross section at small angles becomes[†]

$$\frac{d\sigma}{d\omega}(\vartheta) = \frac{1}{s}\left[\frac{f_0(s)C}{E}\right]^{2/s}\vartheta^{-(2s+s)/s}. \tag{2.13}$$

3. Glory Scattering

Superimposed on the singularity at $\vartheta = 0$ resulting from the long-range attractive forces according to Eq. (2.13) there is a second singularity coming from collisions with an impact parameter b_0. This singularity as well as all others that are entirely the result of $\sin\vartheta = 0$ are designated the "glory effect" in analogy to the situation in optics (Ford and Wheeler, 1959). Additional glory singularities may occur, if the deflection function passes through $\pm\pi$, $\pm 2\pi$, etc., at impact parameter $b \neq 0$ (for example, in the case of orbiting, see Section II,A,4). The condition $\vartheta = -2n\pi$ (with $n = 0$, 1, 2, ...) yields glory singularities in forward direction, $\vartheta = -(2n+1)\pi$ ($n = 0$, 1, 2, ...) yields glory singularities in backward direction. We consider here only the forward glory at $\vartheta = 0$ for $b = b_0$. In the vicinity of the impact parameter b_0 the deflection function can be approximated by

$$\vartheta = \gamma_0(\beta - \beta_0). \tag{2.14}$$

The glory contribution to the differential cross section in the forward direction is the sum of two equal contributions from $\vartheta > 0$ and $\vartheta < 0$ and is given by

$$(d\sigma/d\omega)_\mathrm{g} = 2\beta_0 r_m{}^2/|\gamma_0|\,\vartheta. \tag{2.15}$$

Values of β_0 and γ_0 as a function of the reduced energy K are tabulated for a Kihara potential by Düren and Pauly (1963).

4. Orbiting Collisions

Another effect which influences the differential scattering cross section is due to orbiting collisions. To discuss this effect we consider Fig. 5, which shows the reduced effective potential $f_\mathrm{eff}(\rho) = f(\rho) + \beta^2 K/\rho^2$ as a function of ρ; the different curves belong to different reduced angular momenta $l^* = \sqrt{K}\,\beta$. For realistic potentials $f(\rho)$, f_eff as a function of ρ exhibits a minimum (due to the minimum in the potential) at $\rho = \rho_1$ and

---

[†]Equation (2.13) is usually written in terms of a function $f(s) = \frac{1}{2}\sqrt{\pi}\,\Gamma((\frac{1}{2}s - 1))/\Gamma(\frac{1}{2}s)$. The relation between $f(s)$ and $f_0(s)$ is $f_0(s) = (s-1)f(s)$.

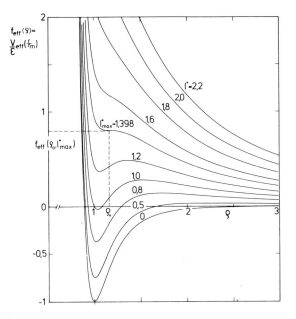

FIG. 5. Reduced effective potential $f_{\text{eff}}(\rho,\ l^*) = f(\rho) + l^{*2}/\rho^2$ as a function of the reduced separation ρ for various values of the reduced angular momentum $l^* = \sqrt{K}\beta$, calculated for the Lennard-Jones (12, 6) potential. For $l^* > 1.389$ the effective potential is monotonic. For $l^* = 1.398$ the point of inflection is characterized by a reduced energy $K = 0.8$. For smaller values of the reduced energy orbiting occurs.

a maximum (due to the centrifugal barrier) at $\rho = \rho_2$ if the reduced angular momentum l^* is sufficiently small but not equal to zero. With increasing l^* these two extrema approach each other until they coincide at $l^* = l^*_{\max}$ and $\rho_1 = \rho_2 = \rho_0$. For still larger angular momenta f_{eff} becomes a monotonic function of ρ. Orbiting occurs if

$$K \leq f_{\text{eff}}(\rho_0, l^*_{\max})$$

since then a value l^* always exists at which $K = f_{\text{eff}}(\rho_2)$, so that the radial motion comes to rest at the top of the centrifugal barrier. For energies in the orbiting region we can assume, in a first approximation, that the height and the position of the centrifugal barrier are determined by the attractive part of the potential alone, and by the centrifugal barrier $l^2/2\mu r^2$. If the attractive part of the potential is represented by an inverse power law, we have

$$V_{\text{eff}}(r,\ l) = (l^2/2\mu r^2) - (C_s/r^s). \tag{2.16}$$

The position r_2 of the maximum follows from

$$dV_{\text{eff}}/dr = 0 \qquad (2.17)$$

with the result

$$r_2(l) = (sC\mu/l^2)^{1/(s-2)}. \qquad (2.18)$$

The equation

$$E = (l^2/2\mu r_2^2) - (C_s/r_2^s), \qquad (2.19)$$

together with Eq. (2.18), yields the angular momentum l for which orbiting occurs:

$$l_{\text{orb}} = (s\mu C)^{1/s}\left(\frac{2s}{s-2}\,\mu E\right)^{(s-2)/2s}. \qquad (2.20)$$

From Eq. (2.20) we obtain the orbiting impact parameter b_{orb}

$$b_{\text{orb}} = \frac{l}{2\mu E} = \left(\frac{s}{s-2}\right)^{(s-2)/2s}\left(\frac{sC}{2E}\right)^{1/s}. \qquad (2.21)$$

This approximation has been frequently used to calculate capture cross sections in ion–molecule reactions (Henglein, this volume, Chapter 7; Langevin, 1905). In this case we have $s = 4$, and it is assumed that all collisions with impact parameter $b \leq b_{\text{orb}}$ lead to a reaction, whereas all collisions with impact parameter $b > b_{\text{orb}}$ lead to elastic scattering. Thus the reaction cross section becomes

$$\sigma_{\text{r}}(E) = \pi b_{\text{orb}}^2 = \pi(4C/E)^{1/2}. \qquad (2.22)$$

5. Rainbow Scattering

The classical differential scattering cross section contains the factor $(d\vartheta/d\beta)^{-1}$ and will have a singularity where $d\vartheta/d\beta$ vanishes (see Fig. 4). Since the optical analog of this phenomenon is responsible for rainbows, the scattering in the neighborhood of the angle ϑ_{r} is called rainbow scattering. Near the rainbow angle ϑ_{r} the deflection function may be expanded in the form

$$\vartheta = \vartheta_{\text{r}} + \tilde{q}(\beta - \beta_{\text{r}})^2 \qquad (2.23)$$

with

$$\tilde{q} = \frac{1}{2}\left(\frac{d^2\vartheta}{d\beta^2}\right)_{\vartheta = \vartheta_r}. \qquad (2.24)$$

From this expansion the rainbow part of the cross section (i.e., the contributions from β_3 and β_2; see Fig. 4) can be easily derived. On the bright side of the rainbow ($\vartheta < \vartheta_r$) the rainbow cross section will be

$$d\sigma/d\omega = r_m{}^2\beta_r/(\sin \vartheta_r)\,|\tilde{q}(\vartheta - \vartheta_r)|^{1/2}, \tag{2.25}$$

whereas for the dark side ($\vartheta > \vartheta_r$) the rainbow cross section will be zero. Numerical values of the quantities needed to describe the classical rainbow scattering, ϑ_r, β_r, and $\tilde{q}$, are tabulated by Schlier (1963) and Mason et al. (1966).

6. Large-Angle Scattering

The additional branch of the deflection function which describes the scattering at small impact parameters ($\beta_1 \, d\beta_1/d\vartheta$) is mainly determined by the repulsive part of the potential. If this repulsive part of the potential is approximated by an inverse power law, the deflection function may be expanded (Miykao, 1942; Lehmann and Leibfried, 1962; Smith et al., 1966; Mott-Smith, 1960) in the form

$$\vartheta(\beta) = \pi - 2(K/c_0)^{1/n}g(n)\beta - + \cdots \tag{2.26}$$

with

$$g(n) = \sqrt{\pi}\,\Gamma\left(\frac{n+1}{n}\right)\Big/\Gamma\left(\frac{n+2}{2n}\right). \tag{2.27}$$

This yields for the differential scattering cross section at large angles

$$\frac{d\sigma}{d\omega} = \frac{r_m{}^2 c_0^{2/n}(\pi - \vartheta)}{4K^{2/n}g^2(n)\sin(\pi - \vartheta)} \approx \frac{r_m{}^2 c_0^{2/n}}{4g^2(n)K^{2/n}}. \tag{2.28}$$

The differential cross section at large angles is nearly angle independent and it depends only weakly on the reduced energy K, since in general n is a larger number.

7. Summary of the Classical Results for the Differential Scattering Cross Section

Figure 6 shows the characteristic behavior of the classically calculated differential scattering cross section, weighted with $\sin \vartheta$, as a function of the angle with the reduced energy K as parameter. [The calculations have

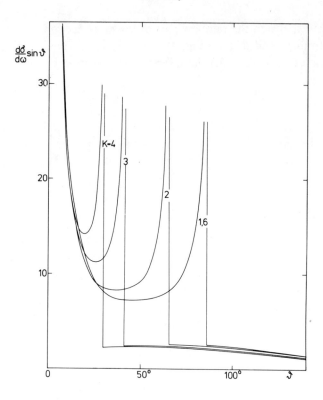

FIG. 6.   Differential scattering cross section (weighted with sin ϑ) as a function of the angle of deflection in the center-of-mass system for different reduced energies K, calculated classically for a Lennard-Jones (12, 6) potential.

been performed for a Lennard-Jones (12, 6) potential.] This figure confirms the approximate considerations of the preceding sections: We observe a monotonic decrease at small angles $d\sigma/d\omega \sim \vartheta^{-7/3}$, which is followed by the rainbow singularity. The angular position of this singularity depends on the reduced energy K. On the dark side of the rainbow the differential scattering cross section shows a sharp drop to a nearly angle-independent value (the angle dependence of this part in Fig. 6 is due to the weight factor $\sin \vartheta$). The validity of the approximate formulas (2.13), (2.25), and (2.28) may be estimated from Fig. 7, which shows a comparison between exact and approximate calculations of $(d\sigma/d\omega) \sin \vartheta$ as a function of ϑ for a Lennard-Jones (12, 6) potential at a reduced energy $K = 1.6$. Tables of classically calculated differential scattering cross sections for a Buckingham potential are given by Mason (1957).

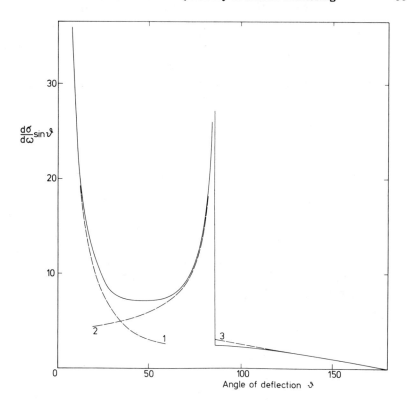

FIG. 7. Classically calculated differential scattering cross section (weighted with sin ϑ) as a function of the angle of deflection ϑ in the center-of-mass system [Lennard-Jones (12, 6) potential, $K = 1.6$]. The dashed curves are calculated using the various approximations discussed in Sections II,B,2, II,B,5, and II,B,6. Curve 1, small-angle approximation, Eq. (2.13); curve 2, rainbow scattering approximation, Eq. (2.25); curve 3; large-angle approximation, Eq. (2.28).

8. *Total Elastic Cross Sections*

The total elastic scattering cross section is the integral of the differential cross section over all scattering angles

$$\sigma(v) = 2\pi \int_0^\pi (d\sigma/d\omega)(\vartheta, v) \sin \vartheta \, d\vartheta. \tag{2.29}$$

If the scattering field extends to infinity, as is the case for realistic potentials, the total scattering cross section diverges in the classical approach.

This arises from the infinitesimal scattering angles corresponding to infinitely large impact parameters. These infinitesimal scatterings will not contribute to the transport properties such as viscosity, heat conduction, and diffusion, where the relevant quantity is a transport cross section

$$\sigma^n(v) = 2\pi \int_0^\pi G_n(\vartheta)(d\sigma/d\omega)(\vartheta,\, v) \sin \vartheta \; d\vartheta \qquad (2.30)$$

in which the differential cross section is weighted with

$$G_n(\vartheta) = 1 - \cos^n\vartheta. \qquad (2.31)$$

$n = 1$ yields the diffusion cross section and $n = 2$ determines the cross section for viscosity and heat conduction. These cross sections are finite for $\vartheta \to 0$ (in contrast to the differential cross section itself) since the weight function $G_n(\vartheta)$ with $\vartheta \to 0$ will cancel the singularity of $d\sigma/d\omega$. With the relationship

$$S(\alpha) = 2\pi \int_\alpha^\pi (d\sigma/d\omega)(\vartheta,\, v) \sin \vartheta \; d\vartheta = 2\pi r_m{}^2 \int_0^{\beta(\alpha)} \beta \; d\beta \qquad (2.32)$$

we define an "incomplete" total scattering cross section that accounts for all scattering with angles larger than a certain angle α. If β_1, β_2, and β_3 are impact parameters corresponding to α (see Fig. 4), then

$$S(\alpha)/\pi r_m{}^2 = \beta_3{}^2 + \beta_1{}^2 - \beta_2{}^2 \approx \beta_3{}^2 + 2\beta_0\,\Delta\beta \qquad (2.33)$$

$$= S_a + \Delta S. \qquad (2.33a)$$

Thus, the incomplete cross section consists of a contribution S_a, which is almost entirely determined by the attractive part of the potential, and a glory contribution ΔS, which tends to zero for $\alpha \to 0$. Consequently, for small angles the classical cross section has the limit

$$S(\alpha)/\pi r_m{}^2 \to \beta_3{}^2. \qquad (2.34)$$

The integration of Eq. (2.13) leads to

$$S(\alpha) = \pi[(s-1)f(s)C/E]^{2/s}\alpha^{-2/s}. \qquad (2.35a)$$

Once more the divergence of the total cross section for $\alpha \to 0$ becomes apparent. From the uncertainty principle it follows that the uncertainty in the scattering angle will be largest for grazing collisions with large impact parameters. Since the magnitude of the scattering angle for such collisions is also small, the uncertainty in the angle will become larger than the scattering angle, and it is no longer possible to use classical mechanics in this angular region (Pauly, 1961).

The foregoing discussion only holds if the reduced energy K is not too large. With increasing energy the influence of the attractive part of the potential decreases ($\vartheta_r \to 0$). In the high-energy limit, therefore, we only need to consider the repulsive part of the potential in order to calculate differential and incomplete total scattering cross sections. With an inverse power law for the repulsive potential, $V(r) = c/r^n$, the differential scattering cross section at small angles is again given by Eq. (2.13), but with the replacement $s = n$.

Consequently, the incomplete total scattering cross section at high energies becomes

$$S(\alpha) = \pi[(n-1)f(n)c/E]^{2/n}\alpha^{-2/n}. \qquad (2.35b)$$

This formula has been frequently used in the interpretation of incomplete total scattering cross-section measurements in the energy range from several hundred eV to several thousand eV (Amdur and Jordan, 1966).

C. Classical Scattering of Identical Particles

If the two colliding particles are indistinguishable, then the flux in a given direction, which consists both of missiles and of recoil particles associated with missiles flying off in the opposite direction (in the center-of-mass system), has to be measured as a whole. Consequently, the center-of-mass scattering cross section is the sum of the cross sections for the two opposed directions,

$$\frac{d\sigma}{d\omega}(\vartheta) = \frac{d\sigma_1}{d\omega}(\vartheta) + \frac{d\sigma_2}{d\omega}(\pi - \vartheta). \qquad (2.36)$$

Thus the differential cross section for identical particles is symmetric about $\pi/2$ (for spherically symmetric potentials).

D. THE INVERSE PROBLEM

In the formulation of the scattering problem the potential is assumed given, and the scattering cross section is calculated from it. In the inverse scattering problem one assumes that the cross section is determined by experiment and the potential is to be found.

The inversion can be solved in two steps:

(1) The determination of the classical deflection function $\vartheta(b)$ from the experimental data.

(2) The determination of the potential from $\vartheta(b)$.

The solution of the second step is straightforward (Keller *et al.*, 1956; Firsov, 1953; Lane and Everhart, 1960). Into Eq. (2.6) we introduce the substitution

$$s(\rho) = \rho\{1 - [f(\rho)/K]\}^{1/2} \tag{2.37}$$

and we obtain

$$\vartheta(\beta) = \pi - 2\beta \int_{\rho_0}^{\infty} \frac{d\rho}{\rho^2[s^2(\rho) - \beta^2]^{1/2}}. \tag{2.38}$$

It can be shown that $s'(\rho) > 0$ if the reduced energy K is greater than that at which orbiting can occur. With this restriction, therefore, $\rho(s)$ exists. Now we introduce

$$I(s) = \log[\rho(s)/s] \tag{2.39}$$

and the expression for the classical deflection function reduces to

$$\vartheta(\beta) = -2\beta \int_{\beta}^{\infty} \frac{I(s)\, ds}{(s^2 - \beta^2)^{1/2}}. \tag{2.40}$$

This is an Abel integral equation, which can be inverted to yield

$$I(s) = \frac{1}{\pi} \int_{s}^{\infty} \frac{\vartheta(\beta)}{(\beta^2 - s^2)^{1/2}}. \tag{2.41}$$

From Eqs. (2.39) and (2.37) we obtain finally

$$f(\rho) = K(1 - e^{-2I(s)}) \tag{2.42}$$

with

$$\rho(s) = se^{I(s)}.$$

The first step, the determination of the classical deflection function from the differential scattering cross section $(d\sigma/d\omega)(\vartheta)$, is complicated by the fact that both attractive and repulsive forces contribute to the scattering. As has been shown, for angles smaller than the rainbow angle there is no one-to-one connection between angle and impact parameter. From Eq. (2.10) we obtain

$$\Sigma(\vartheta) = 2\pi \int_{\vartheta}^{\pi} \frac{d\sigma}{d\omega}\,(\theta)\,\sin\theta\;d\theta$$

$$= \pi r_m{}^2\{\beta_1{}^2(\vartheta) + h(\vartheta - \vartheta_r)[\beta_3{}^2(\vartheta) - \beta_2{}^2(\vartheta)]\} \qquad (2.43)$$

where $h(\vartheta - \vartheta_r)$ is a step function:

$$h(\vartheta - \vartheta_r) = 1 \qquad \text{for} \quad \vartheta \leq \vartheta_r$$
$$h(\vartheta - \vartheta_r) = 0 \qquad \text{for} \quad \vartheta > \vartheta_r.$$

Thus the construction of the first branch $\beta_1(\vartheta)$ of the deflection function, which corresponds to angles ϑ with $\pi \geq \vartheta > \vartheta_r$, is simple. From Eq. (2.43) we find

$$\beta_1(\vartheta) = (1/\sqrt{\pi}\,r_m)[\Sigma(\vartheta)]^{1/2} \qquad (2.44)$$

where $\beta(\vartheta)$ is the inverse function of $\vartheta(\beta)$.

For impact parameters corresponding to angles smaller than ϑ_r an exact determination of the deflection function from the differential cross section is impossible. Approximate solutions can be obtained by parameterizing the deflection function (Miller, 1969a,b) and determining the parameters from Eq. (2.43). Other approximations result from the semiclassical description of the scattering (see Section IV,E,2).

E. CLASSICAL SCATTERING BY NONSPHERICAL POTENTIALS

As has been shown in Section A, the scattering by spherically symmetric potentials is completely specified by the energy E of the relative motion, the orbital angular momentum l of the incident particle, and the reduced mass μ of the two-particle system. For angle-dependent potentials additional dynamical variables must be specified and the scattering problem becomes more complicated.

If we consider, for example, the scattering of an atom by a molecule, which we assume to be a rigid rotator, then these additional variables are: the rotational angular momentum $\mathbf{j}$, described by its absolute magnitude j and two angles θ_j, ϕ_j ; an azimuthal angle φ describing the orientation of the molecular axis in a plane perpendicular to $\mathbf{j}$; and the moment of inertia I of the molecule.

By introducing adequate coordinates, the equations of motion reduce to seven simultaneous differential equations, which must be solved numerically.

Calculations of this type have been performed by Cross and Herschbach (1965) for a simple anisotropic potential model of the form

$$f(\rho, \gamma) = (\rho^{-12} - 2\rho^{-6})[1 + aP_2(\cos \gamma)].$$

Here the asymmetry of the potential is represented by the Legendre polynomial $P_2(\cos \gamma)$, where γ is the angle between the atom and the axis of the molecule. The parameter a characterizes the strength of the asymmetry. The numerical calculations show that the anisotropy of the potential causes appreciable deviations in the scattering angle which are approximately proportional to the asymmetry parameter a. The largest deviations occur in the vicinity of the rainbow angle, so that the differential scattering cross section is severely distorted in the rainbow scattering region. Furthermore, the elastic scattering is accompanied by an appreciable amount of rotational inelastic scattering with angular momentum transfer over a wide region of impact parameters (LaBudde and Bernstein, 1971).

Approximations for treating the small-angle scattering from anisotropic potentials which correspond to the approximation used in the spherically symmetric case [Eq. (2.12)] have been discussed by Cross (1967).

III. Quantum Treatment

A. General Formulation of the Problem

In quantum mechanics it is not possible to describe the trajectory of a single particle, since the uncertainty principle does not allow an exact specification of the position $\mathbf{r}(t)$ and the momentum $\mathbf{p}(t)$ at a given time t. Instead of having the initial conditions $\mathbf{r}(t_i)$ and $\mathbf{p}(t_i)$, we have a wave packet described by a wave function $\psi_i(\mathbf{r}, t_i)$ which yields the probability with which the particle may be found at a certain position $\mathbf{r}(t_i)$ at the initial time t_i. This wave packet must be constructed in such a way that it represents the initial expectation values

$$\langle \mathbf{r} \rangle_i = \langle \psi_i | \mathbf{r} | \psi_i \rangle \quad \text{and} \quad \langle \mathbf{p} \rangle_i = \langle \psi_i | \mathbf{p} | \psi_i \rangle .$$

The equation of motion is the time-dependent Schrödinger equation

$$H | \psi(\mathbf{r}, t) \rangle = i\hbar (\partial/\partial t) | \psi(\mathbf{r}, t) \rangle \tag{3.1}$$

with

$$H = (\hbar^2/2\mu) \, \nabla^2 + V(\mathbf{r}) .$$

In a field-free region the most general solution of this equation can be constructed from plane waves

$$\psi(\mathbf{r}, t) = \int d\mathbf{p}' \, a_{\mathbf{p}'} \, \exp\{(i/\hbar)[(\mathbf{p}'\mathbf{r}) - E't]\} \tag{3.2}$$

with

$$E' = p'^2/2\mu .$$

From Eq. (3.2) any initial wave packet may be constructed by choosing appropriate amplitudes $a_{\mathbf{p}'}$. Then its evolution with time due to the dispersion of the de Broglie waves in the scattering field can be calculated by solving the time-dependent Schrödinger equation (3.1). The result is the final state $\psi_f(\mathbf{r}, t_f)$ at the time t_f after the collision.

B. STATIONARY SCATTERING THEORY

The foregoing procedure is considerably simplified if we discuss the scattering of a monoenergetic beam of particles. In this case the initial wave packet degenerates to a simple plane wave, since the requirement of being monoenergetic is incompatible with the localization in space which is required to study the motion of the wave packet in time. The monoenergetic limit of the wave packet is obtained from Eq. (3.2) if the amplitude $a_{\mathbf{p}'}$ is replaced by a δ-function:

$$a_{\mathbf{p}'} = \delta(\mathbf{p}' - \mathbf{p}) .$$

This yields for the wave function in the field-free space

$$\psi(\mathbf{r}, t) = \exp\{(i/\hbar)[(\mathbf{pr}) - Et]\}. \tag{3.3}$$

In the presence of a scattering field the plane wave is no longer a solution. If the scattering field is time independent, however, a separation of time and space is possible:

$$\psi(\mathbf{r}, t) = \psi_k(\mathbf{r})e^{-(iE/\hbar)t}. \tag{3.4}$$

Substituting Eq. (3.4) into Eq. (3.1) yields a time-independent Schrödinger equation

$$[\nabla^2 - U(\mathbf{r}) + k^2]\psi_k(\mathbf{r}) = 0 \tag{3.5}$$

with

$$\mathbf{p} = \mathbf{k}\hbar, \qquad U(\mathbf{r}) = (2\mu/\hbar^2)V(\mathbf{r}), \qquad \text{and} \qquad k^2 = (2\mu/\hbar^2)E.$$

This is the starting point of the so-called stationary scattering theory. It can be visualized with the following picture: The incoming plane wave represents a steady beam of particles. The beam is scattered and at each angle a time-independent scattered beam intensity is observed. This stationary treatment is applicable if two conditions are fulfilled:

(1) The beam must be constant for times τ which are large compared to $\hbar/\Delta E$, where ΔE is the experimental energy spread in the beam.

(2) The beam must be uniform in space over dimensions which are large compared with the extent of the scattering field.

Both conditions are fulfilled in molecular beam experiments.

From the picture connected with the stationary scattering theory it is easy to obtain the asymptotic behavior of the wave function $\psi_k(\mathbf{r})$: Asymptotically ψ_k must consist of an incoming plane wave and an outgoing spherical wave centered about the origin of the scattering field. The amplitude of the scattered wave must depend on two angles ϑ and φ of a polar coordinate system. Thus we obtain

$$\psi_k(\mathbf{r}) \xrightarrow[r \to \infty]{} \exp[i(\mathbf{kr})] + \frac{\exp(ikr)}{r}f(\vartheta, \varphi) = \psi_0 + \psi_s. \tag{3.6}$$

From this asymptotic behavior of the wave function the cross sections can be obtained by considering the particle flux, as in classical mechanics. The particle flux density is

$$\mathbf{j} = (\hbar/2i\mu)(\psi_k{}^* \nabla \psi_k - \psi_k \, \nabla \psi_k{}^*). \tag{3.7}$$

The incident plane wave ψ_0 yields a steady particle flux density

$$\mathbf{j}_0 = \hbar \mathbf{k}/\mu \tag{3.8}$$

whereas the scattered wave ψ_s yields a flux density

$$\mathbf{j}_s = (\hbar \mathbf{k}/\mu) |f(\vartheta, \varphi)|^2/r^2. \tag{3.9}$$

The flux density due to the cross term of incident and scattered waves can be shown to vanish everywhere except in the forward direction.

Following the definition of the differential scattering cross section

$$d\sigma(\vartheta, \varphi) = \frac{\text{particle flux scattered into solid angle } d\omega}{\text{incident particle flux density}} \tag{3.10}$$

we obtain

$$d\sigma/d\omega = |f(\vartheta, \varphi)|^2 \tag{3.11}$$

and

$$\sigma = \int d\omega \, |f(\vartheta, \varphi)|^2. \tag{3.12}$$

C. Scattering by a Spherically Symmetric Potential

1. Partial Wave Analysis

So far we have not assumed a central scattering field. If we restrict ourselves to central fields, the scattering amplitude becomes independent of the azimuthal angle φ. We will now consider this case in detail.

We start with the time-independent Schrödinger equation, in which we can separate the angular motion from the radial motion. The angular motion is described by the Legendre polynomials $P_l(\cos \vartheta)$, so that we can expand the general solution of the time-independent Schrödinger equation in terms of Legendre polynomials:

$$\psi(r) = \sum_l (2l + 1)i^l(\alpha_l/kr)\chi_l(r)P_l(\cos \vartheta). \tag{3.13}$$

The special form of the expansion coefficients $(2l+1)i^l(\alpha_l/kr)\chi_l(r)$ has been chosen for future convenience. The radial wave functions obey the differential equation

$$\frac{d^2\chi_l}{dr^2} + \left[k^2 - U(r) - \frac{l(l+1)}{r^2}\right]\chi_l = 0 \tag{3.14}$$

or, in reduced notation,

$$\frac{d^2\chi_l}{d\rho^2} + \left[A^2 - Bf(\rho) - \frac{l(l+1)}{\rho^2}\right]\chi_l = 0. \tag{3.15}$$

The problem is now to determine the expansion coefficients in such a way that the foregoing solution has the required asymptotic form. This leads to the following equation, only valid asymptotically:

$$e^{ikz} + f(\vartheta)\frac{e^{ikr}}{r} = \sum_{l=0}^{\infty}(2l+1)i^l\alpha_l\left[\lim_{r\to\infty}\frac{1}{kr}\chi_l(r)\right]. \tag{3.16}$$

From the radial wave equation we find the asymptotic form of χ_l

$$\chi_l \to \sin(kr - \tfrac{1}{2}l\pi + \delta_l), \tag{3.17}$$

where the unknown phase has been chosen to be $-\tfrac{1}{2}l\pi + \delta_l$, since the asymptotic behavior of the field-free equation yields

$$\chi_{lf} \to \sin(kr - \tfrac{1}{2}l\pi). \tag{3.18}$$

Using Eq. (3.17), Eq. (3.16) becomes

$$(\exp ikz) + f(\vartheta)\frac{\exp ikr}{r} = \sum_{l=0}^{\infty}(2l+1)i^l\frac{\alpha_l}{kr}P_l(\cos\vartheta)$$

$$\times\frac{\exp i(kr - \tfrac{1}{2}l\pi + \delta_l) - \exp -i(kr - \tfrac{1}{2}l\pi + \delta_l)}{2i}. \tag{3.19}$$

A basic expansion for the plane wave is

$$e^{ikz} = \sum_{l=0}^{\infty} i^l(2l+1)j_l(kr)P_l(\cos\vartheta) \tag{3.20}$$

where $j_l(kr)$ are the spherical Bessel functions. With this expansion, using the asymptotic expression for j_l, Eq. (3.19) becomes

$$f(\vartheta) \frac{\exp ikr}{r} = \sum_{l=0}^{\infty} \frac{2l+1}{2ikr} i^l \left\{ [\alpha_l(\exp i\delta_l) - 1] \exp i\left(kr - \frac{l\pi}{2}\right) \right.$$

$$\left. - [\alpha_l(\exp -i\delta_l) - 1] \exp -i\left(kr - \frac{l\pi}{2}\right) \right\}. \qquad (3.21)$$

On the left side of Eq. (3.21) we have an outgoing spherical wave, whereas on the right side we have both an outgoing and an incoming spherical wave. Thus the amplitude of the incoming wave must vanish:

$$\alpha_l(\exp -i\delta_l) - 1 = 0 \qquad (3.22)$$

and the expansion coefficients α_l become

$$\alpha_l = \exp i\delta_l. \qquad (3.23)$$

The scattering amplitude $f(\vartheta)$ reduces to

$$f(\vartheta) = -(i/k) \sum_{l=0}^{\infty} (2l+1)[(\exp 2i\delta_l) - 1]P_l(\cos \vartheta). \qquad (3.24)$$

The asymptotic behavior of the wave function $\psi(r)$ [see Eq. (3.13)] can be represented as a sum of an incoming and an outgoing wave

$$\psi(r) \xrightarrow[r \to \infty]{} (1/2kr) \sum_{l=0}^{\infty} (2l+1)i^{l+1}[e^{-i(kr - l\pi/2)} - S_l(k)e^{i(kr - l\pi/2)}]P_l(\cos \vartheta).$$

$$(3.25)$$

The ratio of the amplitude of the outgoing wave to the amplitude of the incoming wave is called the scattering, or S, matrix. For scattering in a central field it depends on k only:

$$S_l(k) = \exp 2i\delta_l. \qquad (3.26)$$

Thus the scattering amplitude becomes

$$f(\vartheta) = (i/2k) \sum_{l=0}^{\infty} (2l+1)(1 - S_l)P_l(\cos \vartheta). \qquad (3.27)$$

Making use of the orthogonality property of the Legendre polynomials, we obtain for the total cross section

$$\sigma = \frac{4\pi}{k^2} \sum_{l=0}^{\infty} (2l+1) \sin^2 \delta_l = \frac{\pi}{k^2} \sum_{l=0}^{\infty} (2l+1)|1-S_l|^2. \qquad (3.28)$$

A comparison of Eq. (3.28) and Eq. (3.24) shows the validity of the optical theorem

$$\sigma = (4\pi/k) J_m(f(0)), \qquad (3.29)$$

which was first derived for the scattering of light by spherically symmetric obstacles.

Equations (3.27) and (3.28) can be used to calculate the cross sections for collisions between unlike atoms in which one is in the $^1S_0$ state and the other may be either in a $^1S_0$ or $^2S_{1/2}$ state yielding the single molecular state $^1\Sigma^+$ or $^2\Sigma^+$, respectively, so that only one potential is involved in the scattering process. If the colliding atoms are in other states, more than one molecular state exists and the corresponding potentials will all contribute to the scattering if the beams are not selected with respect to their states. The cross sections become sums of contributions from each state, properly weighted according to the multiplicity of the molecular state.

The numerical calculation of cross sections according to Eqs. (3.27) and (3.28) is straightforward. For each angular momentum l one has to solve the radial Schrödinger equation with the boundary condition $\chi_l(0) = 0$ and to determine the asymptotic behavior of the radial wave function. This asymptotic behavior of χ_l is compared with the asymptotic behavior of the field-free equation. From this comparison one obtains the phase shifts δ_l and after carrying out the summations one gets the cross sections. The necessary computer time for such calculations depends on the number of angular momenta l involved. This number is approximately given by $l_{max} = kr_0$, where r_0 describes the size of the scattering field. For the scattering of heavy particles l_{max} is of the order of magnitude of several hundred to several thousand, depending on the mass and velocity of the particles. To illustrate this situation, we have listed in Table II the number of phase shifts required for cross-section calculations. These numbers are given for some collision partners covering a wide range of the quantum parameter B. The velocity range given by v_{min} and v_{max} (accessible in experiments with thermal beams) leads to reduced wave numbers A_{min}

TABLE II

NUMERICAL VALUES OF THE QUANTUM PARAMETER B, THE REDUCED WAVE NUMBER A, AND THE NUMBER OF PHASE SHIFTS REQUIRED FOR CROSS-SECTION CALCULATIONS FOR VARIOUS COLLISION PARTNERS[a]

Collision partners	B	Velocity range (m sec^{-1})		Reduced wave number corresponding to v_{min} and v_{max}		Number of phase shifts required	
		v_{min}	v_{max}	A_{min}	A_{max}	l_{min}	l_{max}
He–He	7.5	100	4000	0.9	38	6	180
He–Xe	70	100	4000	2.4	97	12	480
Ne–Kr	665	100	2000	9	180	45	900
Li–Hg	3040	1000	4000	32	127	160	640
Xe–Xe	6800	100	1000	47	470	240	2400
Cs–Hg	49700	250	1000	160	640	800	3200

[a]See text for description.

and A_{max}, respectively. Finally, the respective numbers of phase shifts are given by l_{min} and l_{max}. Only approximately one-half of these must be actually calculated, either by numerical solution of the radial Schrödinger equation or by some approximate method, such as numerical integration of the JWKB integral (see Section IV) or more refined expressions (Rosen and Yennie, 1964). The remaining phase shifts are small and can usually be calculated in closed form using an expansion of the JWKB integral valid for large angular momenta l or the Born approximation only considering the attractive part of the potential.

For the interpretation of scattering experiments at higher energies, which are accessible using the seeded beam technique, sputtering sources, or charge exchange sources, more phase shifts are required.

2. Discussion of Numerical Results

As a result of those exact calculations, Fig. 8 shows the phase shifts δ_l as a function of l for different values of the reduced wave number A for a fixed value of the quantum parameter $B = 2000$. The calculations have been performed for a Lennard-Jones $(12, 6)$ potential (Bernstein, 1963). The discontinuities (each of magnitude π) in the curves belonging to A values smaller than 30 ($K < 0.8$) correspond to resonance levels within the barrier (see Section II,B,4). They disappear for $K = A^2/B > 0.8$.

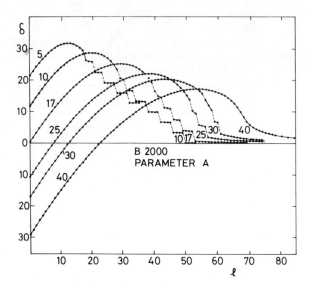

FIG. 8. Dependence of the phase shift δ_l upon the angular momentum quantum number l and the reduced wave number A, calculated for a Lennard-Jones (12, 6) potential (Bernstein, 1963) for a fixed value of the quantum parameter B ($=2000$). For low angular momenta the phase shifts are negative since the repulsive part of the potential determines the scattering, whereas for large l the attractive part of the potential makes the main contribution to the scattering. With decreasing energy the influence of the attractive part of the potential increases and all phase shifts become positive.

Figure 9 shows a plot of the differential scattering cross section $(d\sigma/d\omega)(\vartheta)$, weighted with $\sin \vartheta$, as a function of the angle of deflection ϑ. The calculations have been performed for a Lennard Jones (12, 6) potential for a reduced energy $K = 4$ and three different values of the reduced wave number A ($A = 400$, 300, and 200).

Two angular regions can be distinguished, as for the classical results, which are also given in Fig. 9 for the same parameters. At low angles ($\vartheta < \vartheta_r$), where in the classical case three impact parameters lead to the same angle of deflection, we observe a marked interference structure, whereas at angles larger than the classical rainbow angle the interferences die out and we obtain a monotonic behavior of the cross section, similar to the classical result. The increase of the angular separation of the interference oscillations with decreasing reduced wave number is clearly demonstrated from the three cross-section curves (a), (b), and (c).

The oscillations with large angular separation are called the rainbow effect in analogy to optics. The dependence of their angular position on

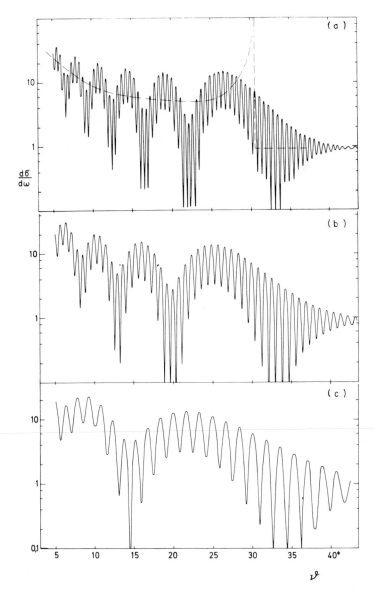

FIG. 9.   Differential scattering cross section, weighted with sin ϑ, as a function of the angle of deflection, calculated quantum mechanically for a Lennard-Jones (12, 6) potential. All three curves (a), (b), and (c) refer to the same reduced energy $K = 4$ but different values of the reduced wave number A: (a) $A = 400$; (b) $A = 300$; (c) $A = 200$. The increase of the angular separation of the interference oscillations with decreasing wave number (velocity) is clearly demonstrated. The classical differential cross section [dashed curve in part (a)] is the same in all three cases.

TABLE III

A

K	∞	400						300						200					
2	65.3	60.2	53.8	50.0	46.5	43.8	41.0	58.5	52.0	46.9	43.0	40.0	37.0	56.0	48.2	42.0	37.6	33.5	30.2
3	41.3	37.6	33.3	30.2	27.3	25.3	23.2	36.6	31.4	27.7	24.5	22.3	20.0	35.0	28.8	23.9	20.5	17.5	15.2
4	30.4	27.2	23.6	21.0	18.5	16.9	15.0	26.3	22.1	18.8	16.0	14.4	12.3	25.0	20.0	15.8	11.9	10.4	8.6
5	24.1	21.2	18.0	15.2	13.5	12.1	10.4	20.3	17.0	13.8	11.7	10.0	8.1	19.2	14.9	11.2	8.8	6.5	5.1
6	19.9	17.3	14.3	12.4	10.4	9.0	7.5	16.5	13.5	10.6	8.8	7.1	5.5	15.4	11.6	8.2	6.2	4.0	2.8
7	17.0	14.6	11.7	9.9	8.2	6.9	5.4	13.8	10.9	8.4	6.7	5.2	3.8	12.7	9.3	6.1	4.5		
8	14.9	12.6	10.0	8.2	6.5	5.2	4.1	11.9	9.2	6.8	5.3	3.8	2.9	10.8	7.7	4.6	3.2		
10	11.8	9.9	7.4	5.8	4.6			9.3	6.6	4.6	3.6			8.2	5.5	2.6			
15	7.9	6.1						5.5	3.5										
20	5.9	4.4																	

K	∞	150						125						100					
2	65.3	54.3	44.8	38.9	33.0	28.0	24.0	53.1	41.9	35.3	29.0	24.3	19.7	51.9	39.5	31.6	25.4	15.8	15.3
3	41.3	33.5	26.6	21.0	17.0	13.5	10.5	32.5	24.6	18.8	14.3	10.3	8.0	31.5	22.6	16.2	10.8	6.1	6.0
4	30.4	23.8	18.1	13.2	9.9	7.7	5.8	23.9	16.5	11.1	8.2	4.6	3.8	21.7	14.8	8.8	5.6		
5	24.1	18.0	13.3	8.8	6.3	4.5	3.5	17.2	11.8	6.9	5.1			16.0	10.4	4.5	3.2		
6	19.9	14.4	10.0	5.9	4.1			13.5	8.6	4.0	3.0			12.4	7.4				
7	17.0	11.7	7.8	4.0	2.7			10.9	6.5					9.7	5.7				
8	14.9	9.9	6.3					9.1	5.2										
10	11.8	7.2	4.5					6.4	3.9										

the reduced energy K and the reduced wave number A can be extracted from Table III, which has been calculated for a Lennard-Jones (12, 6) potential.

Superimposed on this rainbow structure we have oscillations of small angular separation. A discussion of all these oscillations in terms of interfering partial waves is given in Section IV.

If we average over all oscillations, the classical cross section is a good approximation to the scattering, except in the direct vicinity of the classical rainbow singularity (see Fig. 9). This is the reason why transport properties usually can be treated by classical mechanics. An exception are collision partners with a very small attractive well (small value of the quantum parameter B) at low velocities (small values of the reduced wave number A) (for instance, He–He at low temperatures). In these cases the angular separation of the interference extrema become large enough so that quantum effects become observable in spite of the averaging processes which have to be made in the calculation of the transport cross sections.

The velocity dependence of the total elastic scattering cross section is shown in Fig. 10, calculated for a Lennard-Jones (12, 6) potential. The velocity scale is v/v_c, with $v_c = 2\varepsilon r_m/\hbar$. Here we can distinguish between two velocity regions. At low velocities $v/v_c < 1$ we observe an oscillatory structure, since both the attractive and repulsive portions of the potential contribute to the scattering, giving rise to inference oscillations (referred

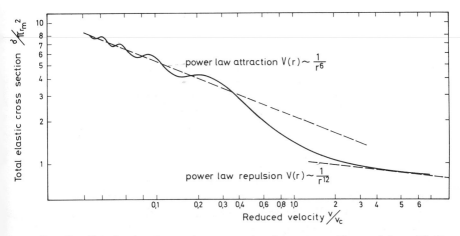

FIG. 10. Calculated total scattering cross section, for an assumed Lennard-Jones (12, 6) potential, as a function of the reduced relative velocity $v\hbar/2\varepsilon r_m$. The dashed lines result from the semiclassical approximation, assuming only a power law attraction [σ_{LL} from Eqs. (4.55) and (4.57)] or a power law repulsion [Eq. (4.62)].

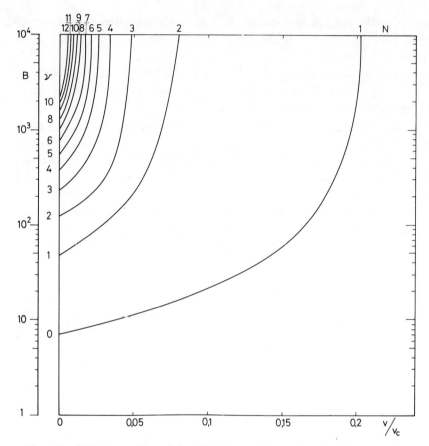

FIG. 11. Velocity position of the Nth glory maximum (in units of the characteristic velocity v_c) as a function of the quantum parameter B, calculated for a Lennard-Jones (12, 6) potential. With $v/v_c \to 0$ the B value corresponding to the Nth maximum tends to the critical value B_c, for which the potential just contains N vibrational states. The vibrational quantum numbers ν are given at the ordinate scale, the number N at the abscissa scale.

to as glory undulations in analogy to optics), which are closely related to the rainbow structure in the differential scattering cross section (Buck and Pauly, 1968). See also Chapter 5, Fig. 13.

The maxima usually are numbered with $N = 1, 2, \ldots$, etc., starting from the maximum at the highest velocity.

There is also a close relationship between the total number m of glory maxima and the number n_0 of bound vibrational states of the collision pair (Bernstein, 1962, 1963). This is illustrated in Fig. 11, where the velocities of the Nth maxima (in units of the characteristic velocity v_c) are shown as a function of B for a Lennard-Jones (12, 6) potential. With increasing values of B the total number of glory maxima increases approximately proportional to $\sqrt{B}$. For large values of B and low values of N the position of the extrema becomes independent of v/v_c, thus making the construction of a reduced total cross-section curve $\sigma(v/v_c)$ possible (see Fig. 10). With $v/v_c \to 0$, the B value corresponding to the Nth maximum tends to the critical value B_c, for which the potential just contains N vibrational states. Thus the observation of n maxima in the velocity dependence of the total cross section implies the existence of at least n vibrational states of the collision pair.

For velocities $v > v_c$, σ becomes a monotonic function of the velocity, since the collision is governed mainly by the repulsive part of the potential. For a more detailed discussion of the cross section and an explanation of the different interference effects see Section IV.

Numerical results from quantum mechanical calculations of phase shifts and cross sections as well as a discussion of the computational procedure are reported by Bernstein (1960, 1961). An efficient numerical method for solving the radial Schrödinger equation is discussed by Gordon (1969). Another rapid numerical solution is discussed by Newman and Thorson (1972). Computer programs for calculating elastic differential and total scattering cross sections for any arbitrary potential belong to the standard equipment of all molecular beam groups investigating atomic collision processes.

3. Resonance Scattering

Let us consider an interaction potential with a repulsive barrier which extends to infinity, as is shown in Fig. 12a. If the potential barrier is high enough, there may be a number of bound states of given angular momentum lying above the zero-energy asymptote. When the repulsive barrier is finite, as in Fig. 12b, the bound states no longer exist as stationary states but decay in time, due to tunneling through the barrier. They are called quasibound, resonating, or decaying states and their energy eigenvalues E_r are more or less shifted and broadened, depending on the thickness of the barrier, as compared with those of the bound states. Since in the stationary scattering theory the time dependence of the total wave function is

$$\psi(\mathbf{r}, t) = \psi(\mathbf{r})e^{-i(E/\hbar)t},$$

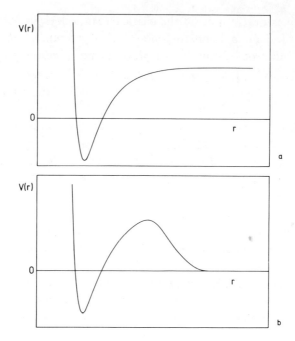

FIG. 12.   (a) Potential $V(r)$ with a repulsive barrier which extends to infinity. (b) Potential $V(r)$ with a repulsive barrier of finite extent.

the probability $\psi^*\psi$ to find a particle at a certain position is independent of time, as long as only real values of the energy are considered. Thus decaying states require a full time-dependent description or, in the stationary theory, complex energies. Assuming that the spacings of the decaying levels are large compared with the width of the levels, we put at the resonance

$$E = E_{\mathrm{r}} - \tfrac{1}{2} i \Gamma \tag{3.30}$$

with E_{r} and Γ real and $\Gamma > 0$. Now the probability $\psi^*\psi$ to find a particle at a certain position becomes time dependent:

$$\psi^*\psi \; d\mathbf{r} = \psi^*\psi \; d\mathbf{r} \; e^{-(\Gamma/\hbar)t} . \tag{3.31}$$

The probability of decay per unit time is $w = \Gamma/\hbar$. The width of the level, according to the uncertainty principle, is Γ. We now investigate the consequences of complex energies for the radial wave functions. The asymptotic behavior of $\chi_l(r)$ [see Eq. (3.17)] may be written

$$\chi_l(r) \xrightarrow[r=\infty]{} A_l(E) e^{-ikr} + A_l^*(E) e^{ikr} \tag{3.32}$$

where $A_l(E)$ are complex functions of the complex energy

$$A_l(E) = \exp -i(\delta_l - \tfrac{1}{2}l\pi) \qquad (3.33)$$

such that $A_l(E_r - \tfrac{1}{2}i\Gamma) = 0$ and only the outgoing wave e^{ikr} remains, describing the particles leaving the potential well through the barrier which are responsible for the decay. In the vicinity of $E_r - \tfrac{1}{2}i\Gamma$ we expand A_l, obtaining

$$A_l(E) = A_l(E_r - \tfrac{1}{2}i\Gamma) + a_l[E - (E_r - \tfrac{1}{2}i\Gamma)] + \cdots \qquad (3.34)$$

with

$$a_l = \left(\frac{dA_l}{dE}\right)_{E = E_r - (i/2)\Gamma}$$

Since the total probability current $(\hbar k/\mu)|i\Gamma a_l^*|^2$ is equal to the decay probability per unit time $\Gamma/\hbar$, we get

$$|a_l|^2 = 1/\hbar v\Gamma,$$

where v is the relative velocity $\hbar k/\mu$. With Eq. (3.34) we obtain for the S matrix

$$S_l(E) = e^{il\pi} \frac{a_l^*}{a_l} \frac{E - E_r - \tfrac{1}{2}i\Gamma}{E - E_r + \tfrac{1}{2}i\Gamma}. \qquad (3.35)$$

If we write the phase shift δ_l as the sum

$$\delta_l = \tau_l + \eta_l \qquad (3.36)$$

with

$$\exp 2i\tau_l = (\exp il\pi)a_l^*/a_l, \qquad (3.37)$$

the scattering matrix becomes

$$S_l = (\exp 2i\tau_l)\{1 - [i\Gamma/(E - E_r + \tfrac{1}{2}i\Gamma)]\}. \qquad (3.38)$$

τ_l is a potential or background scattering phase shift which varies slowly with energy, and η_l is small except in regions near the resonance energy. In the neighborhood of the resonance level we obtain from Eq. (3.38)

$$\delta_l = \tau_l + \arctan[\Gamma/2(E_r - E)]. \qquad (3.39)$$

If the energy E of the incident particle increases from below E_r to above E_r, the phase shift δ_l changes by π. On putting Eq. (3.39) into Eq. (3.24) (if E_r is the only resonance level for l), we have

$$f(\vartheta) = \frac{1}{2ik} \sum_{l=0}^{\infty} (2l+1)[(\exp 2i\tau_l) - 1]P_l(\cos \vartheta)$$

$$- \frac{1}{2k}(2l+1)(\exp 2i\tau_l) \frac{\Gamma}{E - E_r + \frac{1}{2}i\Gamma} P_l(\cos \vartheta). \qquad (3.40)$$

The first sum is called the potential scattering amplitude, while the second term is called the resonance scattering amplitude. The differential scattering cross section $|f(\vartheta)|^2$ will contain contributions from each, and will also contain an interference term. The resonance cross section becomes

$$\frac{d\sigma_l}{d\omega} = \frac{1}{4k^2}(2l+1)^2 \frac{\Gamma^2}{(E-E_r)^2 + \frac{1}{4}\Gamma^2} [P_l(\cos \vartheta)]^2. \qquad (3.41)$$

The partial total cross section

$$\sigma_l = (4\pi/k^2)(2l+1) \sin^2(\tau_l + \eta_l) \qquad (3.42)$$

becomes

$$\sigma_l = \frac{4\pi}{k^2}(2l+1)\left[(\sin^2 \tau_l) \frac{(E-E_r)^2}{(E-E_r)^2 + \frac{1}{4}\Gamma^2} + (\cos^2 \tau_l) \frac{\frac{1}{4}\Gamma^2}{(E-E_r)^2 + \frac{1}{4}\Gamma^2} \right.$$

$$\left. + (\sin 2\tau_l) \frac{\Gamma(E_r - E)}{(E-E_r)^2 + \frac{1}{4}\Gamma^2} \right], \qquad (3.43)$$

which reduces to the well-known Breit–Wigner formula if the potential phase shift τ_l is small.

The occurrence of resonance scattering is the usual case in atom–atom scattering, since the repulsive barrier necessary for the containment of the decaying state is provided by the centrifugal term, so that the effective potential (see Fig. 5) has the required form shown schematically in Fig. 12b. The collision energy must be lower than the limiting energy for classical orbiting.

Figure 13 shows, for example, the total scattering cross section σ/r_m^2 as a function of the reduced wave number A (which is proportional to the velocity), calculated for a Lennard-Jones (12, 6) potential ($B = 60$) (Düren

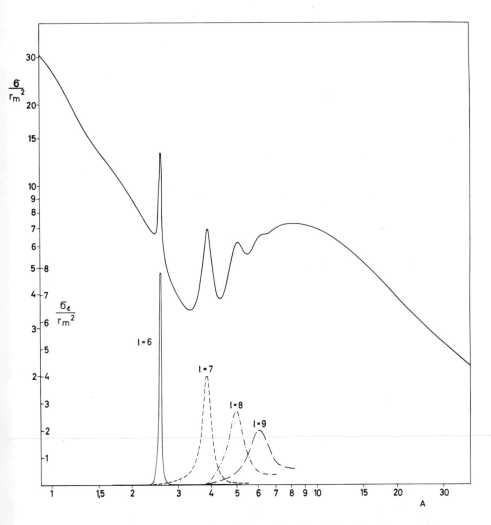

FIG. 13.   Total scattering cross section σ/r_m^2 as a function of the reduced wave number A (proportional to the relative velocity), calculated for a Lennard-Jones (12, 6) potential with $B = 60$. The total cross section exhibits four resonances, which belong to the angular momentum quantum numbers $l = 6$, 7, 8, and 9. The lower half of the figure shows the four partial cross sections $\sigma_l/r_m^2(A)$ responsible for the resonances.

et al., 1965). Four resonances, belonging to angular momenta $l = 6$, 7, 8, and 9, are superimposed on the glory structure. The lower half of Fig. 13 shows the four partial cross sections $\sigma_l/r_m^2(A)$ for $l = 6$, 7, 8, and 9 which are responsible for the various resonances.

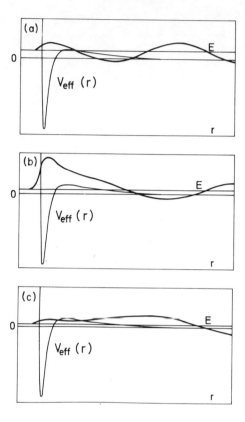

FIG. 14.   The radial wave function $\chi_l(r)$ as a function of the distance r, calculated for a
Lennard-Jones (12, 6) potential for three energies E_i in the vicinity of a resonance at
$E = E_r$. (a) $E_1 < E_r$, (b) $E_2 = E_r$, and (c) $E_3 > E_r$. For $E = E_r$ the large amplitude of χ_l
in the region of the potential well (the effective potential is also plotted in the figures)
shows the high probability density $\chi_l^* \chi_l$ due to the existence of a decaying state. The
energies E_i are indicated by horizontal lines.

Figure 14 illustrates the behavior of the radial wave function $\chi_l(r)$ in
the vicinity of a resonance. In Fig. 14a the energy E is below the resonance
energy E_r, in Fig. 14b we have $E = E_r$, and in Fig. 14c the energy is
above the resonance energy. Also plotted in Fig. 14 is the effective potential
and the collision energy (horizontal line). In the resonance case the radial
wave function obtains large values within the region of the potential well,
indicating clearly the high probability $\chi_l^* \chi_l$ of finding the colliding particles
close together, corresponding to the existence of the decaying state.

Results of a numerical study of the phase shift behavior due to barrier penetration and resonance effects are discussed by Bernstein *et al.* (1966) for a Lennard-Jones (12, 6) potential. The connection between the inverse process, predissociation, and the pattern of resonances also has been investigated (Bernstein, 1966; Waech and Bernstein, 1967).

4. *Scattering of Identical Particles*

In the case of identical particles, the total wave function has to be symmetric (Bose statistics) or antisymmetric (Fermi statistics) with respect to the coordinates. Thus the asymptotic form of the wave function can be written as

$$\psi \xrightarrow[r\to\infty]{} e^{ikr} \pm e^{-ikr} + (e^{ikr}/r)[f(\vartheta) \pm f(\pi - \vartheta)]. \tag{3.44}$$

The positive sign (symmetric wave function) is valid for Bose statistics, the negative sign (antisymmetric wave function) for Fermi Statistics. The differential scattering cross section becomes (if we normalize, as before, to one incoming particle)

$$d\sigma/d\omega = \tfrac{1}{2}|f(\vartheta) \pm f(\pi - \vartheta)|^2, \tag{3.45}$$

and contains an additional interference term if we compare with the classical result [Eq. (2.36)]. Since $P_l(-\cos\vartheta) = (-1)^l P_l(\cos\vartheta)$, the partial wave expansion of the cross sections becomes

$$\frac{d\sigma}{d\omega} = \frac{1}{4k^2}\left|\sum_{l=0}^{\infty} \omega_l(2l+1)[(\exp 2i\delta_l) - 1]P_l(\cos\vartheta)\right|^2 \tag{3.46a}$$

and

$$\sigma = \frac{4\pi}{k^2}\sum_{l=0}^{\infty} w_l(2l+1)\sin^2\delta_l \tag{3.46b}$$

with the following relations for the weight factor w_l:

for bosons (symmetric wave function)	for fermions (antisymmetric wave function)
$w_l = 2$ for l even;	$w_l = 0$ for l even;
$w_l = 0$ for l odd;	$w_l = 2$ for l odd.

TABLE IV

POSSIBLE TOTAL SPIN STATES FOR A SYSTEM OF TWO PARTICLES WITH SPIN s

Spin	Number of states with total spin even	Number of states with total spin odd
Half-integer	$s(2s+1)$	$(s+1)(2s+1)$
Integer	$(s+1)(2s+1)$	$s(2s+1)$

The cross sections for the two cases are designated as $(d\sigma/d\omega)_s$, σ_s (bosons) and $(d\sigma/d\omega)_a$, σ_a (fermions), respectively.

Equations (3.46a) and (3.46b) can only be used for a calculation of the cross sections if the two colliding particles are in the same spin state, so that the total spin of the two-particle system has a definite value. Consequently, these cross sections can only be measured in a molecular beam experiment with two state-selected beams (if the spin of the particles is unequal to zero). Without spin selection one has to average over all possible spin states of the two-particle system, which are assumed to have equal probability. If s is the spin of the individual particles, then the total number of possible spin states of the two-particle system is $(2s+1)^2$. Table IV shows the number of states for which the total spin is even and the number of states for which the total spin is odd.

Let us now consider the scattering of two identical particles with spin s, where s is a half-integer. The probability for the two-particle system to have an even spin is

$$2(2s+1)/(2s+1)^2 = s/(2s+1),$$

and the probability for the system to have an odd spin is

$$(s+1)(2s+1)/(2s+1)^2 = (s+1)/(2s+1).$$

The differential cross section becomes a sum of a symmetric and an antisymmetric contribution, weighted with these statistical weights:

$$\frac{d\sigma}{d\omega} = \frac{s}{2s+1}\left(\frac{d\sigma}{d\omega}\right)_s + \frac{s+1}{2s+1}\left(\frac{d\sigma}{d\omega}\right)_a \qquad (3.46c)$$

and

$$\sigma = \frac{s}{2s+1}\sigma_s + \frac{s+1}{2s+1}\sigma_a. \qquad (3.46d)$$

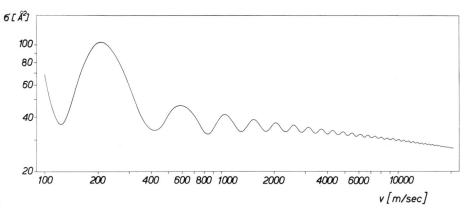

FIG. 15. Total scattering cross section as a function of the relative velocity for the ^{4}He–^{4}He system (Bose statistics).

If s is an integer, we have accordingly

$$\frac{d\sigma}{d\omega} = \frac{s+1}{2s+1}\left(\frac{d\sigma}{d\omega}\right)_{\mathrm{s}} + \frac{s}{2s+1}\left(\frac{d\sigma}{d\omega}\right)_{\mathrm{a}} \qquad (3.46e)$$

and

$$\sigma = \frac{s+1}{2s+1}\,\sigma_{\mathrm{s}} + \frac{s}{2s+1}\,\sigma_{\mathrm{a}}. \qquad (3.46f)$$

For an example of the interference effects due to identical particles, Fig. 15 shows the velocity dependence of the ^{4}He–^{4}He total scattering cross section, calculated for a Lennard-Jones (12, 6) potential. This system is best suited to demonstrate these oscillations, since no glory undulations exist due to the low B value of this system.

D. SCATTERING BY A COMPLEX POTENTIAL

The possibility of inelastic or reactive scattering in addition to elastic scattering can be described phenomenologically by an absorption model: All particles that are scattered out of the elastic channel are described as being absorbed by the target. As in optics, where the absorption of electromagnetic waves may be described by a complex index of refraction, we introduce a complex potential, which leads to complex phase shifts

$$\delta_l = \eta_l + i\zeta_l \qquad (3.47)$$

yielding for the S matrix

$$S_l = \exp 2i\eta_l \exp -2\zeta_l. \tag{3.48}$$

Thus in Eq. (3.25), which describes the asymptotic behavior of the wave function $\psi(r)$, the absolute value of the amplitude of the outgoing wave becomes smaller than the absolute value of the incoming wave, in agreement with the assumption of absorption.

The net outgoing spherical wave (after having removed all portions belonging to the plane wave) is then

$$\psi_s \xrightarrow[r \to \infty]{} (e^{ikr}/2ikr) \sum_{l=0}^{\infty} (2l+1)(S_l - 1)P_l(\cos \vartheta) \tag{3.49}$$

and the integral elastic cross section follows from

$$\sigma_{el} = \int |\psi_s|^2 r^2 d\,\omega = (\pi/k^2) \sum_{l=0}^{\infty} (2l+1)|1 - S_l|^2. \tag{3.50}$$

The integral inelastic cross section (absorption cross section) is the difference between the incoming and outgoing intensities:

$$\sigma_{inel} = \int (|\psi_s|^2 - |\psi_0|^2) r^2 \, d\omega = (\pi/k^2) \sum_{l=0}^{\infty} (2l+1)(1 - |S_l|^2). \tag{3.51}$$

The total cross section is the sum of (3.50) and (3.51)

$$\sigma_{tot} = (2\pi/k^2) \sum_{l=0}^{\infty} (2l+1)[1 - \text{Re } S_l] = (4\pi/k) \, \text{Im } f(0). \tag{3.52}$$

The optical theorem is still satisfied for the total scattering cross section.

The existence of inelastic or reactive channels may reduce the amplitudes of the glory undulations in the total elastic scattering cross section (quenching of glory undulations), depending on the choice of the opacity function

$$P(l, E) = 1 - |S_l|^2 = 1 - \exp -4\zeta_l \tag{3.53}$$

(Marriott and Micha, 1969; Micha, 1969; Eu and Ross, 1967; Mizuno and Chen, 1971; Düren *et al.*, 1972). Calculations of differential scattering cross sections for simple models of $P(l, E)$ have been used for the interpretation of the elastic wide-angle scattering from reactive systems (Hundhausen and Pauly, 1965; Bernstein and Levine, 1968). The influence of the reaction is manifested as a loss in the elastic scattering intensity at large angles (Greene *et al.*, 1966) corresponding to small impact parameters. This corresponds to a more or less abrupt gain in opacity for angular momentum less than some critical value l_c. With increasing l_c the angle at which the intensity loss occurs decreases and a quenching of the rainbow structure may occur.

E. SCATTERING BY NONSPHERICAL POTENTIALS

The quantum mechanical treatment of the scattering by nonspherical potentials is immensely more complex than the spherical case. The orbital angular momentum quantum number l of the relative motion is no longer conserved. Therefore the angular and radial motions are no longer separable and all angular momentum waves contained in the total wave function are coupled to one another through the nonspherical potential.

The simplest case of elastic scattering by a nonspherical potential which also allows a treatment similar to the partial wave expansion is obtained if the potential is fixed in space (Boardman *et al.*, 1967). This condition causes the total angular momentum of the system to remain unconserved and can therefore only be used as an approximation for atom-molecule collisions in such events where the rotational recoil of the target may be neglected. This is possible if the mass of the target molecule is large compared with that of the incident atom or if the collision time is much shorter than a rotational period.

The solution of the Schrödinger equation (3.5), where $U(r)$ is replaced by $U(\mathbf{r})$, can be expanded in terms of the complete set of spherical harmonics

$$\psi_k(\mathbf{r}) = \sum_{l=0}^{\infty} \sum_{m=-l}^{l} [\chi_{lm}(r)/r] Y_{lm}(\hat{\mathbf{r}}). \tag{3.54}$$

The coefficients $\chi_{lm}(r)$ depend implicitly on the incident wave vector **k** due to the asymmetry of the potential. Substituting Eq. (3.54) into the Schrödinger equation, multiplying the resulting equation by the complex-conjugate harmonic $Y^*_{l'm'}(\hat{\mathbf{r}})$, and integrating over the solid angle (expansion in terms of target states), we obtain the following set of coupled radial equations:

$$\left[\frac{d^2}{dr^2} + k^2 - \frac{l(l+1)}{r^2}\right]\chi_{lm}(r) = \sum_{l'=0}^{\infty} \sum_{m'=-l'}^{l'} \chi_{l'm'}(r) \langle lm | U | l'm' \rangle \tag{3.55}$$

where

$$\langle lm|\,U\,|l'm'\rangle = \int d\hat{\mathbf{r}}\; Y_{lm}^*(\hat{\mathbf{r}})U(\mathbf{r})Y_{l'm'}(\hat{\mathbf{r}})\,.$$

These equations reduce to the uncoupled equations (3.14) if $U(\mathbf{r}) = U(r)$. The asymptotic form of $\chi_{lm}(r)$ can be expressed in terms of spherical Hankel functions of the first and second kinds, provided that the potential goes to zero more rapidly than $1/r^2$ along any radial direction:

$$\chi_{lm}(r) \xrightarrow[r\to\infty]{} A_{lm}\,rh_l^+(kr) + B_{lm}\,rh_l^-(kr) \qquad (3.56\text{a})$$

or, using the asymptotic forms of the spherical Hankel functions,

$$\chi_{lm}(r) \xrightarrow[r\to\infty]{} (A_{lm}/k)e^{i(kr-l\pi/2)} + (B_{lm}/k)e^{-i(kr-l\pi/2)}\,. \qquad (3.56\text{b})$$

Thus, the asymptotic behavior of the wave function $\psi_k(\mathbf{r})$ becomes, in complete analogy to Eq. (3.25),

$$\psi_k(\mathbf{r}) \xrightarrow[r\to\infty]{} \sum_l \sum_m B_{lm}(e^{-i(kr-l\pi/2)} - S_{lm}\,e^{i(kr-l\pi/2)})Y_{lm}(\hat{\mathbf{r}}) \qquad (3.57)$$

where we have introduced the S matrix

$$S_{lm}(k) = -A_{lm}/B_{lm}\,.$$

Comparing Eq. (3.57) with the physically required asymptotic behavior, Eq. (3.6) shows immediately that

$$B_{lm} = 2\pi i^{l-1}Y_{lm}^*\,. \qquad (3.58)$$

Since the expansion of the plane wave $\exp i(\mathbf{kr})$ into spherical harmonics gives

$$\exp i(\mathbf{kr}) = 4\pi \sum_l \sum_m i^l Y_{lm}^*(\hat{\mathbf{k}})Y_{lm}(\hat{\mathbf{k}}')j_l(kr)\,. \qquad (3.59)$$

The scattering amplitude becomes

$$f(\mathbf{k},\,\mathbf{k}') = (2\pi/ik) \sum_l \sum_m Y_{lm}^*(\hat{\mathbf{k}})Y_{lm}(\hat{\mathbf{k}}')[S_{lm}(k) - 1]\,. \qquad (3.60)$$

For special nonspherical potentials the problem of solving a set of many coupled equations can be circumvented. If the static potential is of spheroidal symmetry, the introduction of spheroidal coordinates (oblate or prolate, depending on the potential) allows an expansion of the total wave function in terms of spheroidal functions, and the Schrödinger equation can be separated into ordinary differential equations (Li, 1971; Geltman, 1969). If the potential is not fixed in space, the elastic scattering and the whole procedure become even more complicated.

As an example we consider the scattering of an atom by a molecule, which we assume to be a rigid rotator. Instead of expanding the solution of the Schrödinger equation in terms of l, we now expand the solution in terms of the total angular momentum $\mathbf{J} = \mathbf{j} + \mathbf{l}$, where $\mathbf{j}$ is the angular momentum of the rigid rotator (Arthurs and Dalgarno, 1960). $j\hbar$ is the rotational angular momentum and $m_j\hbar$ its projection on an axis fixed in space. The total Hamiltonian is

$$H = H_{\text{rot}} - (\hbar^2/2\mu)\, V_r^2 + V(\mathbf{r}, \hat{\mathbf{q}}). \tag{3.61}$$

H_{rot} is the operator for a rigid rotator whose eigenfunctions are the spherical harmonics $Y_{jm_j}(\hat{\mathbf{q}})$ ($\hat{\mathbf{q}}$ is a unit vector specifying the orientation of the rotator axis with respect to a coordinate system fixed in space, $\mathbf{r}$ specifies the direction of the incident particle ($\hat{\mathbf{r}}$ is a unit vector) and V_r^2 is its Laplacian in the center-of-mass system).

Since the total wave function depends on the quantum numbers j, l (entrance channel), J, and M ($M\hbar$ being the projection of the total angular momentum $J\hbar$ on an axis fixed in space), the Schrödinger equation becomes

$$H\psi_{l;\,j}^{J;\,M}(\mathbf{r}, \hat{\mathbf{q}}) = E_j\psi_{l;\,j}^{J;\,M}(\mathbf{r}, \hat{\mathbf{q}}) \tag{3.62}$$

where

$$E_j = E + (\hbar^2/2I)j(j+1) \tag{3.63}$$

is the total energy of the system (I is the moment of inertia of the rotator). We expand the solution of Eq. (3.62) according to

$$\psi_{l;\,j}^{J;\,M}(\mathbf{r}, \hat{\mathbf{q}}) = \sum_{l',j'} (1/r)u_{j';\,l'j'}^{J;\,l\,j}(r)\mathscr{Y}_{J,\,l',\,j'}^{M}(\hat{\mathbf{r}}, \hat{\mathbf{q}}) \tag{3.64}$$

with

$$\mathscr{Y}_{J,\,l,\,j}^{M} = \sum_{m_l=-l}^{+l} \sum_{m_j=-j}^{+j} (jlm_lm_j|jlJM)\,Y_{lm_l}(\hat{\mathbf{r}})\,Y_{jm_j}(\hat{\mathbf{q}}), \tag{3.65}$$

where $(jlm_l m_j | jlJM)$ are the Clebsch–Gordon coefficients. Substitution of Eqs. (3.64) and (3.65) into Eq. (3.62) gives a set of coupled differential equations for the $u_{j';l'}^{J;j,l}(r)$:

$$\frac{\hbar^2}{2\mu}\left[-\frac{d^2}{dr^2}+\frac{l'(l'+1)}{r^2}-k_{jj'}^2\right]u_{j';l'}^{J;j,l}$$
$$=-\sum_{l''}\sum_{j''}\langle j'l',J|V|j''l'',J\rangle u_{j'';l''}^{J;j,l},\qquad(3.66)$$

where $k_{jj'}$ is the channel wave number

$$k_{jj'}^2=(2\mu/\hbar^2)[E_j-(\hbar^2/2I)j'(j'+1)].\qquad(3.67)$$

The boundary conditions require that the radial wave function $u_{j';l'}^{J;j,l}(r)$ vanishes at $r=0$. For $r\to\infty$ the radial wave function should consist of an incoming plane wave of molecules in the state jl and outgoing waves of molecules in some other state $j'l'$. This condition leads to

$$u_{j';l'}^{J;j,l}(r)\sim\delta_{jlj'l'}\exp[-i(k_{jj}r-\tfrac{1}{2}l\pi)]$$
$$-(k_{jj}/k_{jj'})^{1/2}S^J(j,l;j',l')\exp[i(k_{jj'}r-\tfrac{1}{2}l'\pi)].\qquad(3.68)$$

Equation (3.68) defines the scattering matrix S, which is diagonal in J and independent of M. To calculate the cross sections we combine the solutions (3.64) and (3.65) to yield an incoming plane wave in the entrance channel j, m_j:

$$\psi_j(\mathbf{r},\hat{\mathbf{q}})=\frac{i\sqrt{\pi}}{k_{jj}}\sum_{J=0}^{\infty}\sum_{M=-J}^{+J}\sum_{l=|J-j|}^{J+j}(jlM_,0|jlJM)i^l(2l+1)^{1/2}\psi_{l;j}^{J;M}(\mathbf{r}\,\hat{\mathbf{q}}).\qquad(3.69)$$

$\psi_j(\mathbf{r},\hat{\mathbf{q}})$ behaves asymptotically as

$$\psi_j\sim[\exp i(\mathbf{k}_{jj}\mathbf{r})]Y_{jm_j}(\hat{\mathbf{q}})+\sum_{j'}\frac{i}{k_{jj}}\left(\frac{k_{jj}}{k_{j'j}}\right)^{1/2}\frac{\exp ik_{j'j}r}{r}$$
$$\times\sum_{m_{j'}=-j'}^{+j'}f(j',m_{j'};j,m_j|\hat{\mathbf{r}})Y_{j'm_{j'}}(\hat{\mathbf{q}}),\qquad(3.70)$$

where $f(j',m_{j'};j,m_j|\hat{\mathbf{r}})$ is the reaction amplitude, given by

$$f(j',m_{j'};j,m_j|\hat{\mathbf{r}})=\sum_{J=0}^{\infty}\sum_{M=-J}^{+J}\sum_{l=|J-j|}^{J+j}\sum_{l'=|J-j'|}^{J+j'}\sum_{m_{l'}=-l'}^{+l'}$$
$$\times\sqrt{\pi}\,i^{(l-l')}(2l+1)^{1/2}(jlm_j0|jlJM)(j'l'm_{j'}m_{l'}|j'l'JM)$$
$$\times[\delta_{jj'}\delta_{ll'}-S^J(jl;j'l')]Y_{l'm_{l'}}(\hat{\mathbf{r}}).\qquad(3.71)$$

Equation (3.70) describes an incident plane wave in the entrance channel jm_j together with outgoing spherical waves in the various possible exit channels $j'm_{j'}$. The differential cross section for excitation from the state (j, m_j) to the state $(j', m_{j'})$ is obtained by calculating the outgoing flux in channel $(j', m_{j'})$ from Eq. (3.71). The result is

$$d\sigma(jm_j, j'm_{j'} | \hat{\mathbf{r}}) = (1/k_{jj}^2) | f(jm_j; j'm_{j'} | \hat{\mathbf{r}})|^2 \, d\hat{\mathbf{r}}. \qquad (3.72)$$

The integral cross section for excitation from any j state to the final j' states is obtained by averaging over m_j and summing over $m_{j'}$. Due to the unitarity of the Clebsch–Gordon coefficients and spherical harmonics, the integral cross section reduces to

$$\sigma_J(j', j) = \frac{\pi}{(2j+1)k_{jj}^2} \sum_{l=|J-j|}^{J+j} \sum_{l'=|J-j'|}^{J+j'} +(2J1)| \delta_{jj'} \delta_{ll'} - S^J(jlj'l')|^2. \qquad (3.73)$$

The total cross section is obtained by summing over all J:

$$\sigma_{\text{tot}} = \sum_{J=0}^{\infty} \sigma_J(j', j). \qquad (3.74)$$

The elastic cross sections are included in the Eqs. (3.72) and (3.73) for the special case that entrance and exit channels are the same.

A generalization of the rigid rotor theory to the scattering of a structureless atom by a Σ-state vibrating rotor diatomic molecule has been developed by Eastes and Secrest (1971, 1972) and by Lester and Schaefer (1973).

In the treatment of Arthurs and Dalgarno the coordinate system which is used to describe the collision is held fixed in space throughout the whole collision process. An equivalent formulation, which uses body-fixed coordinate axes between the molecules, has been derived by Curtiss and co-workers (Curtiss and Adler, 1952; Curtiss, 1953, 1968; Gioumonsis and Curtiss, 1961; Hunter and Curtiss, 1973).

For exact numerical calculations of cross sections the space-fixed axes formulation is more convenient; all attempts at actually computing quantum mechanical cross sections for molecular scattering have used this formulation (Allison and Dalgarno, 1967; Lester and Bernstein 1967, 1968; Erlewein et al., 1968; Johnson and Secrest, 1968; von Seggern and Toennies, 1969; Hayes et al., 1971; Wolken et al., 1972; McGuire and Micha, 1972; Lester and Schaefer, 1973; Zarur and Rabitz, 1973, 1974). In connection with certain approximations, however, the body-fixed axes formulation has computational advantages (Pack, 1974).

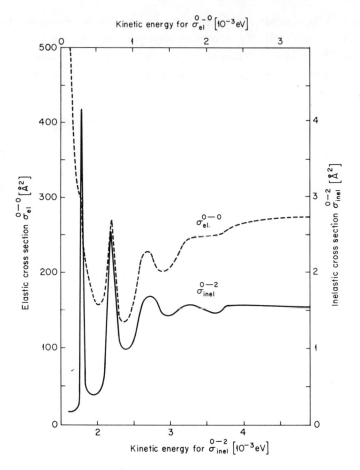

FIG. 16.   Integral elastic and rotational excitation ($j = 0$ to $j' = 2$, summed over all $m_{j'}$) cross sections as a function of the collision energy. The inelastic cross section has been shifted by $\Delta E(0 \to 2)$.

Computational procedures for solving the coupled equations (3.66) are described by Gordon (1969) and Lester (1971). An example of such calculations for the He–N_2 scattering at very low relative energies (below 5×10^{-3} eV; 58 K) is shown in Fig. 16. These calculations have been made in the so-called close coupling approximation, in which only the energetically attainable channels are taken into account. As with pure elastic scattering, orbiting resonances occur in the elastic as well as in the inelastic channel. When energetically inaccessible closed channels are included in the coupled equations further resonances occur due to the formation of temporary bound systems arising from internal excitations during the collision (Micha, 1967; Levine et al., 1968, 1969; Muckermann and Bernstein, 1970).

IV. Semiclassical Approximation

A. General Assumptions

We now turn to the semiclassical approximations,* which offer an important method of solving atomic and molecular scattering processes.† To begin the consideration we note that the partial wave sum (3.24) can be transformed into a rapidly converging sum, using a modification of the Poisson sum rule (Berry, 1966). This yields

$$f(\vartheta) = -\frac{i}{k} \sum_{m=-\infty}^{\infty} e^{-im\pi} \int_0^\infty \lambda [(\exp 2i\delta_{\lambda-\frac{1}{2}}) - 1][\exp(2im\pi\lambda)] P_{\lambda-\frac{1}{2}}(\cos \vartheta) \, d\lambda$$

$$(4.1)$$

where $\lambda = l + \frac{1}{2}$ is now a continuous variable. Now we introduce a set of approximations (Ford and Wheeler, 1959):

(a) Equation (4.1) is a sum over integrals, the integrands of which oscillate rapidly over large regions of the variable λ. The main contributions arise from stationary points on the positive real axis, whenever these exist, and therefore the integrals may be evaluated by the method of stationary phase.

(b) The Legendre polynomials are replaced by their asymptotic expressions: For $\sin \vartheta \lesssim 1/\lambda$

$$P_{\lambda-\frac{1}{2}}(\cos \vartheta) \cong J_0(\lambda \vartheta).$$ $$(4.2a)$$

For $\sin \vartheta \gtrsim 1/\lambda$

$$P_{\lambda-\frac{1}{2}}(\cos \vartheta) \cong [2/\pi\lambda \sin \vartheta]^{1/2} \sin(\lambda \vartheta + \tfrac{1}{4}\pi).$$ $$(4.2b)$$

---

* We consider here only the case of spherically symmetric potentials. For semiclassical methods in the case of angle-dependent potentials and applications to inelastic collision processes, see, for example, Cross (1970), Miller (1970a,b, 1971, 1972), Doll et al. (1973), Marcus (1971, 1972a,b,c).

† For a recent review on semiclassical mechanics see Berry and Mount (1972).

(c) The phase shift δ_l is replaced by its JWKB approximate value

$$\delta_l = A\left(\int_\beta^\infty [1-(\beta^2/\rho^2)]^{1/2}\,d\rho - \int_{\rho_0}^\infty \{1-[f(\rho)/K]-(\beta^2/\rho^2)\}^{1/2}\,d\rho\right) \quad (4.3)$$

where ρ_0 is the largest zero of the radicand (classical turning point). For large values of the reduced energy K and large impact parameters β the classical turning point approaches β, and the second integral can be expanded with the result

$$\delta_l \approx \frac{1}{2K}\int_\beta^\infty \frac{f(\rho)\,d\rho}{[1-(\beta^2/\rho^2)]^{1/2}}. \quad (4.3a)$$

The approximation (4.3) requires for its validity the physical condition of a slowly varying potential,

$$(1/k|E-V|)|dV/dr| \ll 1. \quad (4.4)$$

For understanding the relation between quantum and classical results, the most important property of the JWKB phase shift is its simple relation to the classical deflection function $\vartheta(\lambda)$:

$$d\delta(\lambda)/d\lambda = \tfrac{1}{2}\vartheta(\lambda). \quad (4.5)$$

B. Application to the Differential Scattering Cross Section

1. Discussion of the Interference Structure

We first discuss the differential scattering cross section for angles $0 < \vartheta < \pi$. Here we can use the identity $\sum (2l+1)P_l(\cos\vartheta)=0$ and instead of Eq. (4.1) we obtain for the scattering amplitude

$$f(\vartheta) = -\frac{i}{k}\sum_{m=-\infty}^{\infty}(\exp-im\pi)\int_0^\infty d\lambda\,\lambda\{\exp[i(2\delta_{\lambda-\frac{1}{2}}+2m\pi\lambda)]\}P_{\lambda-\frac{1}{2}}(\cos\vartheta) \quad (4.6)$$

or, using Eq. (4.2b),

$$f(\vartheta) = -\frac{1}{k(2\pi\sin\vartheta)^{1/2}}\sum_{m=-\infty}^{\infty}(\exp-im\pi)$$

$$\times \int_0^\infty \sqrt{\lambda}\,\{\exp[i\varphi_+^{(m)}(\lambda)] - \exp[i\varphi_-^{(m)}(\lambda)]\}\,d\lambda \quad (4.6a)$$

where

$$\varphi_\pm^{(m)}(\lambda) = 2\delta(\lambda) + 2m\pi\lambda \pm \lambda\vartheta \pm \tfrac{1}{4}\pi.$$

The stationary points are those values of λ that satisfy the equation

$$d\varphi_\pm^{(m)}/d\lambda = 0$$

or, using Eq. (3.5),

$$\vartheta(\lambda) = \pm\vartheta - 2m\pi. \qquad (4.7)$$

For realistic interatomic potentials the classical deflection angle ϑ is always smaller than π (except for zero impact parameter). Thus the integrals with $m < 0$ have no stationary points and vanish in the stationary phase approximation. In order to make the following discussion easier, we first assume that ϑ is never less than $-\pi$. Then all integrals with $m > 0$ have no stationary points and we end up with

$$f(\vartheta) = -\frac{1}{k(2\pi \sin \vartheta)^{1/2}} \int_0^\infty d\lambda \sqrt{\lambda}\{\exp[i\varphi_+(\lambda)] - \exp[i\varphi_-(\lambda)]\}, \qquad (4.8)$$

where

$$\varphi_\pm(\lambda) = 2\delta(\lambda) \pm \lambda\vartheta \pm \tfrac{1}{4}\pi.$$

Figure 17 shows as an example the classical deflection function and the phase shift curve δ versus the reduced impact parameter $\beta = \lambda/A$ for a given reduced energy. Furthermore, the two functions φ_+ and φ_- are plotted here for a certain angle which is indicated in the classical deflection function. In general, φ_+ has two points of stationary phase, and φ_- has one point of stationary phase. The three angular momenta which belong to the stationary points correspond to the three classical impact parameters leading into the same angle of deflection.

In the classical case the differential cross section is a sum over these three contributions. In the semiclassical theory, however, the scattering amplitude is a sum over three contributions

$$f(\vartheta) = \sum f_i(\vartheta), \qquad (4.9)$$

each term $f_i(\vartheta)$ belonging to a certain point of stationary phase. By calculating the differential cross section, we get, in addition to the classical value, interference terms.

604

H. Pauly

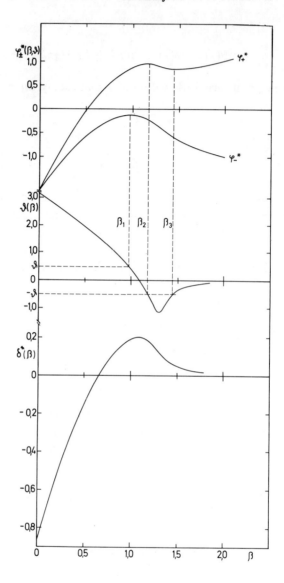

FIG. 17. Typical behavior of the classical deflection function $\vartheta(\beta)$ (in the center of figure), the reduced phase shift function $\delta^*(\beta) = \delta(\beta)/A$ (lower half), and the reduced functions $\varphi^*_\pm(\beta, \vartheta) = \varphi_\pm(\beta, \vartheta)/A$ (upper half) with $\vartheta = 28.6°$, as is indicated by the dashed lines in the deflection function. The curves are calculated for a Lennard-Jones (12, 6) potential with $K = 2$. The relationship between the points of stationary phase [extrema in $\varphi_\pm(\beta, \vartheta)$] and the three impact parameters that lead classically to the same angle of deflection is clearly demonstrated.

To evaluate the scattering amplitude $f_i(\vartheta)$, we expand $\varphi(\lambda)$ in the vicinity of a stationary point λ_i:

$$\varphi(\lambda) = \varphi(\lambda_i) + \tfrac{1}{2}\varphi''(\lambda_i)(\lambda - \lambda_i)^2 \qquad (4.10)$$

and we obtain

$$f_i(\vartheta) = \frac{\exp[i\varphi(\lambda_i)]}{k(2\pi \sin \vartheta)^{1/2}} \int_{-\infty}^{\infty} \sqrt{\lambda} \, \exp[\tfrac{1}{2}i\varphi''(\lambda_i)(\lambda - \lambda_i)^2] d\lambda \qquad (4.11)$$

or

$$f_i(\vartheta) = \frac{1}{k} \left[\frac{\lambda_i}{\varphi''(\lambda_i) \sin \vartheta} \right]^{1/2} \exp\{[\varphi(\lambda_i) - \alpha]\} . \qquad (4.12)$$

α depends on the sign of $\varphi''(\lambda_i)$:

$$\alpha = \tfrac{1}{4}\pi \qquad \text{for} \quad \varphi''(\lambda_i) < 0$$

$$\alpha = \tfrac{3}{4}\pi \qquad \text{for} \quad \varphi''(\lambda_i) > 0$$

In this approximation the interference terms are

$$\cos[2\delta(l_2) - 2\delta(l_3) + (l_2 - l_3)\vartheta - \tfrac{1}{2}\pi] \qquad (4.13)$$

for $i = 2, 3$ and

$$\cos[2\delta(l_1) - 2\delta(l_{2,3}) + (l_1 + l_{2,3})\vartheta + \eta] \qquad (4.14)$$

for $i = 1, 2$ or $1, 3$, respectively, with

$$\eta = 0 \qquad \text{for} \quad i = 1, 2$$

$$\eta = \pi/2 \qquad \text{for} \quad i = 1, 3 .$$

The most rapidly changing portion in these terms is $(l_2 - l_3)\vartheta$, $(l_1 + l_2)\vartheta$, or $(l_1 + l_3)\vartheta$, respectively. Thus, to a first approximation, the angular separation of the interference oscillations is

$$\varDelta\vartheta_{2,3} = 2\pi/|l_2 - l_3| = 2\pi/k|b_2 - b_3| \qquad (4.15)$$

and

$$\varDelta\vartheta_{1;2,3} = 2\pi/|l_1 + l_{2,3}| = 2\pi/k|b_1 + b_{2,3}| . \qquad (4.16)$$

From these expressions we expect two types of oscillations in the pattern of the differential cross section. The interference of f_2 and f_3 yields oscillations with large angular separations, whereas the interferences of f_1 with f_2 and of f_1 with f_3 yield oscillations with small angular separations. This is just the interference structure which is shown in Fig. 7.

If the angle exceeds the classical rainbow angle, φ_+ no longer has a point of stationary phase. So we have only one contribution to the scattering amplitude, resulting from the stationary point in φ_-. The interferences die out with increasing angle, in agreement with the exact calculations shown in Fig. 7.

If the angle of deflection ϑ becomes less than $-\pi$ (for instance, in the case of orbiting) additional stationary points in the integrals with $m > 0$ occur according to Eq. (4.7) (see, for example, Section IV,B,4). These correspond to the additional impact parameters, which classically lead to the same angle of deflection in this case. Thus, further contributions to the scattering amplitude and additional interference terms in the differential scattering cross section are observed.

2. Rainbow Scattering

We consider the function $\varphi_+(\lambda)$, which has, for angles smaller than the classical rainbow angle, two points of stationary phase. Near the rainbow angle the amplitude contributions $f_2(\vartheta)$ and $f_3(\vartheta)$ from the two branches overlap and cannot be calculated independently. Moreover, it is no longer sufficient to fit the phase shift curve by means of a parabola, since $d^2\delta/d\lambda^2$ is approaching zero and the third derivative term must therefore be included.

If we take the approximation (2.23) for the deflection function near the rainbow angle ϑ_r, then, making use of Eq. (4.5), the phase shift will be given near l_r by

$$\delta(\lambda) = \delta_r + \tfrac{1}{2}\vartheta_r(\lambda - \lambda_r) + (\tilde{q}/6A^2)(\lambda - \lambda_r)^3 . \tag{4.17}$$

Substitution of Eq. (4.17) into Eq. (4.8) leads to

$$\varphi_+(\lambda) = 2\delta_r + (\vartheta_r + \vartheta)(\lambda - \lambda_r) + (\tilde{q}/3A^2)(\lambda - \lambda_r)^3 + \tfrac{1}{4}\pi - \vartheta\lambda_r. \tag{4.18}$$

This leads to the rainbow scattering amplitude

$$f_r(\vartheta) = -\frac{\sqrt{\overline{\lambda_r}}}{k(2\pi \sin \vartheta)^{1/2}} (\exp i\Delta) \int_{-\infty}^{\infty} \exp\Big\{ i[(\vartheta_r + \vartheta)(\lambda - \lambda_r)] $$
$$+ \frac{i\tilde{q}}{3A^2}(\lambda - \lambda_r)^3 \Big\} \, d\lambda \tag{4.19}$$

where the phase Δ is given by the expression

$$\Delta = 2\delta_r - \lambda_r \vartheta - \tfrac{1}{4}\pi . \tag{4.20}$$

The integral (4.19) can be expressed by the Airy integral Ai(x) with the final result

$$f_r(\vartheta) = \frac{1}{k}\left(\frac{2\pi\lambda_r}{\sin\vartheta}\right)^{1/2}\left(\frac{\tilde{q}}{A^2}\right)^{1/3} e^{i\Delta}(\mathrm{Ai}x) \tag{4.21}$$

where

$$x = (\tilde{q}/A^2)^{-1/3}(\vartheta - \vartheta_r) . \tag{4.22}$$

If we neglect the interference of the rainbow amplitude with the amplitude of the repulsive branch of the deflection function (β_1), the differential cross section near the rainbow angle has the form

$$\left(\frac{d\sigma}{d\omega}\right)_r = \frac{2\pi\lambda_r}{k^2\sin\vartheta}\left|\frac{\tilde{q}}{A^2}\right|^{-2/3}\mathrm{Ai}^2(x) = \frac{2\pi\beta_r r_m{}^2 A^{1/3}}{(\sin\vartheta)\tilde{q}^{2/3}}\,\mathrm{Ai}^2(x) . \tag{4.23}$$

For $x \to -\infty$

$$\mathrm{Ai}(x) \approx \pi^{-1/2}(-x)^{-1/4}\cos[\tfrac{2}{3}(-x)^{3/2} - \tfrac{1}{4}\pi] . \tag{4.24}$$

Thus the rainbow interference structure reduces to the general case [Eq. (4.14)] when the two points of stationary phase are not close together. Substituting the asymptotic behavior of the Airy integral into Eq. (4.23) and averaging over the interference oscillations

$$\cos^2[\tfrac{2}{3}(-x)^{3/2} - \tfrac{1}{4}\pi] = \tfrac{1}{2}$$

yields the classical expression (2.25) for the rainbow cross section.

An extension of the foregoing treatment of the rainbow scattering which includes a cubic term in the Taylor-series expansion of the deflection function about its minimum has been given by Greene *et al.* (1967).

A more general treatment of the rainbow scattering which yields an uniform expression for the rainbow cross section $|f_2(\vartheta) + f_3(\vartheta)|^2$ which is valid for all angles has been derived by Berry (1966). He obtains

$$(d\sigma/d\omega)_r = P^2\,\mathrm{Ai}^2(-|z|) + Q^2\,\mathrm{Ai}'^2(-|z|) \tag{4.25}$$

where

$$P = \sqrt{\pi}\,|z|^{1/4}[(d\sigma/d\omega)_2^{1/2} + (d\sigma/d\omega)_3^{1/2}]$$
$$Q = \sqrt{\pi}\,|z|^{-1/4}[(d\sigma/d\omega)_3^{1/2} - (d\sigma/d\omega)_2^{1/2}]$$
$$z = \{\tfrac{3}{4}[2\delta(b_2) - 2\delta(b_3) + k\vartheta(b_2 - b_3)]\}^{2/3}.$$

The term

$$\left(\frac{d\sigma}{d\omega}\right)_i = \frac{b_i}{\sin\vartheta}\left|\frac{db_i}{d\vartheta}\right|$$

is the classical differential cross section belonging to branch i of the deflection function. If the contribution of the stationary point (b_1) is included, the complete differential cross section in the semiclassical approach becomes

$$\frac{d\sigma}{d\omega} = \left(\frac{d\sigma}{d\omega}\right)_1 + \left(\frac{d\sigma}{d\omega}\right)_r + 2\left(\frac{d\sigma}{d\omega}\right)_1^{1/2}[Q\,\mathrm{Ai}'(-|z|)\cos\alpha - P\,\mathrm{Ai}(-|z|)\sin\alpha]$$

(4.26)

where

$$\alpha = 2\delta(b_1) - \delta(b_2) - \delta(b_3) - k\vartheta(b_1 + \tfrac{1}{2}b_2 + \tfrac{1}{2}b_3) - \tfrac{1}{4}\pi.$$

A comparison of numerical calculations of differential cross sections according to Eq. (4.26) with those according to Eq. (3.24) shows that the uniform approximation, Eq. (4.26), yields highly accurate results if the reduced wave numbers and angles are not too small $(A > 50, \vartheta > 2\pi/A)$ (Mullen and Thomas, 1973).

Equation (4.25) can be used to construct the deflection function $\vartheta(b)$ in the region $\vartheta(b) < 0$ from experimental observations of the rainbow structure. In this way a practical solution of the inversion problem (see Section IV,E,2) is possible.

3. Small-Angle Scattering

Introducing the approximations outlined in Section IV,A and using Eq. (4.2a), the scattering amplitude at small angles becomes

$$f(\vartheta) = -(i/k)\int_0^\infty \lambda[\exp(2i\delta_{\lambda-\frac{1}{2}}) - 1]J_0(\lambda\vartheta)\,d\lambda.$$

(4.27)

Two regions in the phase shift versus angular momentum curve (compare Fig. 8) make the dominant contributions to the integral in equation (4.27) if the method of stationary phase is used: the vicinity of the maximum phase shift δ_0 $(d\delta/d\lambda = 0)$, corresponding to the impact parameter b_0, and the asymptotic region, where the phase shift becomes a slowly varying function of λ. The first contribution is due to a forward glory and is discussed in the next section.

To evaluate the second contribution, we only need to consider the asymptotic behavior of the phase shift curve, which is determined by the long-range attractive part of the potential. For an inverse power law $V(r) = -C_s/r^s$, we obtain the asymptotic behavior of the phase shift curve from Eq. (2.12) if we use Eq. (4.5) [or by Eq. (4.3a)]. The result is

$$\delta = \tfrac{1}{2} f(s)(C_s/E)k^s \lambda^{-(s-1)} = a/\lambda^{s-1} \tag{4.28}$$

with

$$a = \tfrac{1}{2} f(s)(C_s/E)k^s.$$

The scattering amplitude at small angles (neglecting the forward glory) becomes

$$f(\vartheta) = -(i/k) \int_0^\infty \lambda[\exp(2ia/\lambda^{s-1}) - 1]J_0(\lambda\vartheta)\, d\lambda. \tag{4.29}$$

Since this integral cannot be solved in closed form, we divide the interval of integration into two parts (a) and (b), in order to find an approximate solution:

$$\text{(a)} \qquad 0 \leq \lambda \leq m$$
$$\text{(b)} \qquad m < \lambda < \infty.$$

In interval (a), $\exp(2ia/\lambda^{s-1})$ is a rapidly oscillating function of λ and thus makes no contribution to the integral. In the second interval (b), the phase shifts are small, so that we can use the expansion

$$\exp(2ia/\lambda^{s-1}) = 1 + (2ia/\lambda^{s-1}) - (2a^2/\lambda^{2(s-1)}) + - \cdots. \tag{4.30}$$

Thus we obtain

$$f(\vartheta) = \frac{i}{k}\left[\int_0^m \lambda J_0(\lambda\vartheta)\, d\lambda + 2a^2 \int_m^\infty \lambda^{2s-3}J_0(\lambda\vartheta)\, d\lambda\right] + \frac{2a}{k}\int_m^\infty \lambda^{-s+2}J_0(\lambda\vartheta)\, d\lambda. \tag{4.31}$$

The boundary m is, to a certain extent, arbitrary. It should be small enough to guarantee that the random phase approximation in the interval (a) introduces no appreciable error. On the other hand, it should be large enough that the expansion (4.30) can be used in interval (b). Following Massey and Mohr (1933), m is defined by

$$a/m^{s-1} = \tfrac{1}{2} \tag{4.32}$$

with the result

$$m = [C_s f(s) k^s/E]^{1/(s-1)} \tag{4.33a}$$

or in reduced notation with

$$C_s = C_{0s}\, \varepsilon r_m{}^s$$

we obtain

$$m = A[C_{0s} f(s) v_c/v]^{1/(s-1)}, \tag{4.33b}$$

where v_c is the characteristic velocity introduced in Section III,C,2. The final result for the scattering amplitude at small angles is

$$f(\vartheta) = k r_m{}^2 \left(\frac{C_{0s} f(s) v_c}{v}\right)^{2/(s-1)} \left[\frac{i}{x} J_1(x) + \frac{i}{4(s-2)} G_{2s-4}(x) + \frac{1}{s-3} G_{s-3}(x)\right] \tag{4.34}$$

with $x = m\vartheta$. The functions $G_{2s-4}(x)$ and $G_{s-3}(x)$ are special cases of the functions

$$G_n(x) = n x^n \int_x^\infty J_0(t) t^{-n-1} \, dt \tag{4.35}$$

which may be expanded in the following forms: For $n = 2v$

$$G_n(x) = v \sum_{\substack{j=0 \\ j \neq v}}^{\infty} \left(\frac{ix}{2}\right)^{2j} \frac{1}{(v-j)(j!)^2} - \left(\frac{ix}{2}\right)^{2v} \frac{2v}{(v!)^2} \left[\log \frac{x}{2} - \sum_{j=1}^{v} \frac{1}{j} + C_v\right],$$

where C_e is Euler's constant. For $n = 2v+1$

$$G_n(x) = \frac{(-1)^{v+1} 2^{2v} v! \, x^{2v+1}}{(2v+1)(2v!)^2} - (2v+1) \sum_{v=0}^{\infty} \left(\frac{ix}{2}\right)^{2j} \frac{1}{(2j-2v-1)(j!)^2}.$$

This result together with the expansion of the Bessel function $J_1(x)$ permits a calculation of the scattering amplitude $f(\vartheta)$ and, of course, the differential cross section $d\sigma/d\omega = |f(\vartheta)|^2$ for small angles.

For very small angles requiring only the first terms in the series of $f(\vartheta)$ the result for the differential cross section may be reduced in good approximation to

$$\frac{1}{r_m^2}\frac{d\sigma}{d\omega} = A^2\left(\frac{C_0 f(s)v_c}{v}\right)^{4/(s-1)} g_1(s)\exp\left[-A^2\left(\frac{C_0 f(s)v_c}{v}\right)^{2/(s-1)} g_2(s)\vartheta^2\right]$$

(4.36)

with $g_1(6) = 0.4275$ and $g_2(6) = 0.6091$ (Helbing and Pauly, 1964; Mason *et al.*, 1964). In constrast to the classical result, Eq. (2.13), $d\sigma/d\omega$ remains finite for $\vartheta = 0$.

A uniform approximation for the small-angle scattering is discussed by Berry (1969) and Mount (1973).

4. *Glory Scattering*

a. Forward Glories. As we have pointed out in Section II,B, the vanishing of $\sin\vartheta(b)$ (vanishing of element of solid angle) where b is finite and $d\vartheta/db$ is finite leads classically to a singularity in the cross section for forward or backward scattering. We first consider the forward glory which arises from the fact that the deflection function passes through zero at $b = b_0$, and which we neglected in the preceding section in the small-angle scattering amplitude. From Eqs. (2.14) and (4.5) the phase shift in the vicinity of l_0 becomes

$$\delta = \delta_0 + (\gamma_0/4A)(l - l_0)^2.$$ (4.37)

Introducing this into Eq. (4.27) and using again the method of stationary phase, the glory contribution to the scattering amplitude becomes

$$f_g(\vartheta) = -(i/k)\int_0^\infty \lambda(\exp\{2i[\delta_0 + (\gamma_0/4A)(\lambda - \lambda_0)^2]\})J_0(\lambda\vartheta)\,d\lambda.$$ (4.38)

Within the method of stationary phase we can extend the lower limit of the λ integral to $-\infty$. Then the evaluation of the integral yields

$$f_g(\vartheta) = \frac{r_m}{A}\lambda_0\left(\frac{2\pi A}{\gamma_0}\right)^{1/2}\left\{\exp\left[i\left(2\delta_0 - \frac{3\pi}{4}\right)\right]\right\}J_0(\lambda_0\,\vartheta)$$ (4.39)

$$= \beta_0 r_m\left(\frac{2\pi A}{\gamma_0}\right)^{1/2}\left\{\exp\left[i\left(2\delta_0 - \frac{3\pi}{4}\right)\right]\right\}J_0(A\beta_0\,\vartheta).$$ (4.40)

Thus the contribution of the glory effect to the differential cross section in the forward direction becomes

$$(d\sigma/d\omega)_g = (2\pi\beta_0{}^2 r_m{}^2 A/|\gamma_0|) J_0{}^2(A\beta_0 \vartheta). \tag{4.41}$$

The classical singularity, Eq. (2.15), reduces to a finite peak. If we replace J_0 by its asymptotic expression and average over the oscillations, Eq. (4.41) reduces to the classical value (2.15). Additional glory contributions to the scattering amplitude in the forward direction appear if the deflection function passes through multiplies of -2π. This occurs at low reduced energies K, when the orbiting region is approached. In this case we use Eq. (4.1) with Eq. (4.2a). The regions of stationary phase are characterized by

$$d\delta/d\lambda = -m\pi \qquad \text{or} \qquad \vartheta(\lambda) = -2m\pi.$$

In the vicinity of $\vartheta = -2m\pi$ we approximate the deflection function by

$$\vartheta(\beta) = -2m\pi - \gamma_m(\beta - \beta_m). \tag{4.42}$$

Thus we obtain for the phase shift $\delta(\lambda)$

$$\delta = \delta_m - m\pi(\lambda - \lambda_m) - (\gamma_m/4A)(\lambda - \lambda_m)^2. \tag{4.43}$$

For each angle $\vartheta = -2m\pi$ there are two points $\lambda_m^{(1)}$ and $\lambda_m^{(2)}$ of stationary phase, as can be easily seen from the deflection function. Thus we obtain

$$f_g(\vartheta) = -(i/k) \sum_{v=1}^{2} \sum_{m=1}^{N} \{\exp i[2\delta_m + m\pi(2\lambda_m^{(v)} - 1)]\}$$

$$\times \int_0^\infty \lambda \{\exp[-i(\gamma_m^{(v)}/2A)(\lambda - \lambda_m^{(v)})^2]\} J_0(\lambda\vartheta)\, d\lambda \tag{4.44}$$

where N extends to infinity in the orbiting case. The evaluation of the integrals yields finally

$$f_g(\vartheta) = -\frac{i}{k} \sum_{v=1}^{2} \sum_{m=1}^{N} \left(\exp\left\{i\left[2\delta_m + m\pi(\lambda_m^{(v)} - 1) - \frac{\pi}{4}\right]\right\}\right) \lambda_m^{(v)} \left(\frac{2\pi A}{\gamma_m^{(v)}}\right)^{1/2} J_0(\lambda_m \vartheta).$$

$$\tag{4.45}$$

The main contribution to this sum arises from the first term, since with increasing angle

$$\left(\frac{d\vartheta}{d\beta}\right)_{\beta^{(v)}{}_m} = \gamma_m^{(v)} \to \infty \,.$$

Furthermore, to a first approximation we have

$$\beta_m^{(1)} \approx \beta_m^{(2)} \approx \beta_{\mathrm{orb}} \,,$$

where β_{orb} is the impact parameter at which orbiting occurs. Thus this glory contribution reduces to

$$
\begin{aligned}
f_{\mathrm{g}}(\vartheta) = -\frac{i}{k} \bigg\{ \exp\bigg[i\pi(\lambda_{\mathrm{orb}} - 1) - \frac{i\pi}{4} \bigg] \bigg\} \lambda_{\mathrm{orb}} J_0(\lambda_{\mathrm{orb}} \,\vartheta) \\
\times \bigg\{ [\exp(2i\delta_1^{(1)})] \left(\frac{2\pi A}{\gamma_1^{(1)}}\right)^{1/2} + [\exp(2i\delta_1^{(2)})] \left(\frac{2\pi A}{\gamma_1^{(2)}}\right)^{1/2} \bigg\} \,.
\end{aligned}
\tag{4.46}
$$

b. Backward Glories and Large-Angle Scattering. To consider angles in the vicinity of $\vartheta = \pi$, we put $\vartheta = \pi - \alpha$ (with α small) and obtain from Eq. (4.1)

$$
f(\pi - \alpha) = -(i/k) \sum_{m=-\infty}^{\infty} e^{-i(\pi/2)(2m-1)} \int_0^{\infty} \lambda (e^{2i\delta(\lambda)} - 1) e^{i\pi\lambda(2m-1)} J_0(\lambda\alpha)\, d\lambda \,.
$$

$$\tag{4.47}$$

The points of stationary phase are given by

$$(d/d\lambda)[2\delta(\lambda) + \pi\lambda(2m-1)] = 0 \tag{4.48a}$$

or

$$\vartheta(\lambda) = -(2m-1)\pi \,. \tag{4.48b}$$

In the vicinity of these points the phase shift function can be written as

$$\delta(\lambda) = \delta_m - (2m-1)(\pi/2)(\lambda - \lambda_m) - (\gamma_m/4A)(\lambda - \lambda_m)^2 \,. \tag{4.49}$$

For $m = 0$ the relevant collisions are head-on collisions with $\lambda_0 = \frac{1}{2}$ ($l = 0$).

For repulsive potentials obeying an inverse power law, $V(r) = c_0 \varepsilon r_m{}^n/r^n$, γ_0 is given by Eq. (2.26). In this case the scattering amplitude becomes

$$f(\pi - \alpha) = -\frac{i}{k}\left[\exp(2i\delta_0)\right]\int_0^\infty \lambda\left\{\exp\left[-\frac{i\gamma_0}{2A}\left(\lambda - \frac{1}{2}\right)^2\right]\right\} J_0(\lambda\alpha)\, d\lambda. \quad (4.50)$$

The approximate evaluation of this integral yields (Helbing, 1969)

$$f(\pi - \alpha) \approx -\frac{i}{4k}\left[\left(\frac{4A}{\gamma_0}\right)^2 + \frac{4A}{|\gamma_0|}\left(\frac{4\pi A}{|\gamma_0|}\right)^{1/2}\right.$$

$$\left. + \frac{4\pi A}{2|\gamma_0|}\right]^{1/2} J_0\left(\frac{\alpha}{2}\right)\exp\left(2i\delta_0 - \frac{i\pi}{2} + i\varphi\right) \quad (4.51)$$

where

$$\tan\varphi = [1 + 2(4\pi A/|\gamma_0|)^{1/2}]^{-1}.$$

In the limit $A \to \infty$, $|f(\pi - \alpha)|^2$ yields, according to Eq. (4.51), the classical result, Eq. (2.28). For $m > 0$ the relevant collisions are collisions with deflection angles of $-\pi$, -3π, etc., which occur in the orbiting case. Similar to the case of the forward glory scattering, the glory scattering amplitude becomes

$$f_g(\pi - \alpha) = -\frac{i}{k}\sum_{\nu=1}^2\sum_{m=1}^N\left\{\exp\left[2i\delta_m^{(\nu)} + i\pi(2m-1)\left(\lambda_m^{(\nu)} - \frac{1}{2}\right) - \frac{i\pi}{4}\right]\right\}$$

$$\times \lambda_m^{(\nu)}\left(\frac{2\pi A}{\gamma_m^{(\nu)}}\right)^{1/2} J_0(\lambda_m^{(\nu)}\alpha). \quad (4.52)$$

Here again the main contributions arise from the $m = 1$ terms. Taking into account that $\lambda_m^{(1)} \approx \lambda_m^{(2)} \approx \lambda_{orb}$, we finally get for the backward glory contribution

$$f_g(\pi - \alpha) = -\frac{i}{k}\left\{\exp\left[i\pi\left(\lambda_{orb} - \frac{1}{2}\right) - \frac{i\pi}{4}\right]\right\}\lambda_{orb}J_0(\lambda_{orb}\,\alpha)$$

$$\times \left\{[\exp(2i\delta_1^{(1)})]\left(\frac{2\pi A}{\gamma_1^{(1)}}\right)^{1/2} + [\exp(2i\delta_1^{(2)})\left(\frac{2\pi A}{\gamma_1^{(2)}}\right)^{1/2}\right\}. \quad (4.53)$$

If we average over the interference term $\cos(2\delta_1^{(1)} - 2\delta_1^{(2)})$, the differential cross section becomes

$$|f_g(\pi - \alpha)|^2 = 2\pi r_m{}^2\beta_{orb}^2 AJ_0{}^2(\beta_{orb}A\alpha)(\gamma_1^{(1)} + \gamma_1^{(2)})/\gamma_1^{(1)}\gamma_1^{(2)}. \quad (4.54)$$

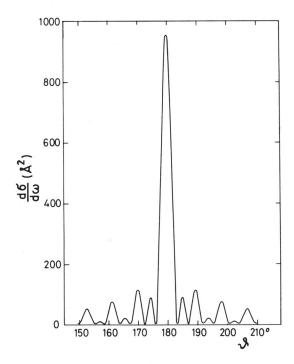

FIG. 18. Differential scattering cross section in the vicinity of $\vartheta = \pi$ in the orbiting region; Lennard-Jones (12, 6) potential, $B = 1842$, $A = 22.3$. The sharp peak at $\vartheta = \pi$ is due to a backward glory.

The differential cross section exhibits a sharp peak at $\vartheta = \pi$ if the deflection function passes through $-\pi$. This is illustrated by Fig. 18, which shows the differential scattering cross section in the backward direction $(d\sigma/d\omega)/(\vartheta)$ calculated for a Lennard-Jones (12, 6) potential in the orbiting case ($K = 0.27$, $A = 22.3$). The irregular interference structure outside the large peak at $\vartheta = \pi$ is due to the superposition of two main contributions [from $\beta_0^{(1)}$ and $\beta_0^{(2)}$, see Eq. (4.52)] to the glory scattering amplitude. The peak at $\vartheta = \pi$ is well represented by the approximate formula (4.54), which yields, however, a regular interference structure outside the peak, since the above-mentioned superposition has been neglected.

Figure 19 shows the velocity dependence of the differential scattering cross section in the backward direction $(d\sigma/d\omega)(\pi)$ calculated for a Lennard-Jones (12, 6) potential. The potential parameters correspond to the He–Kr collision pair (Feltgen, 1970). The large increase in backward

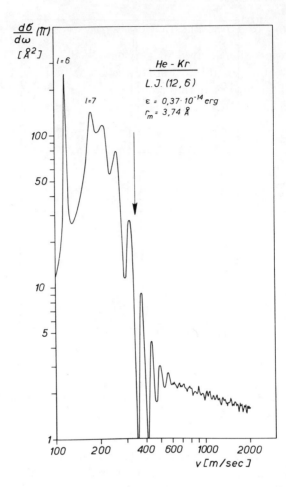

FIG. 19.   Differential scattering cross section $(d\sigma/d\omega)(\vartheta, v)$ at $\vartheta = \pi$ as a function of the relative velocity v. The arrow indicates the velocity at which the deflection function passes through $-\pi$.

scattered intensity at the velocity at which the deflection function passes for the first time through $-\pi$ (indicated by the arrow in Fig. 19) is clearly demonstrated. The oscillations in the differential cross section for $v < 500$ m sec^{-1} are the rapid interference oscillations, the angular dependence of which has been discussed in Section IV,B,1. The sharp spikes which appear at very low velocities characterized by $l = 7$ and $l = 6$, respectively, are due to orbiting resonances.

C. Application to Total Elastic Scattering Cross Sections

From the expression derived in Sections IV,B,3 and IV,B,4 for the scattering amplitude in the forward direction we can easily obtain an expression for the total scattering cross section using the optical theorem, Eq. (3.29). Equations (4.34) and (4.40) yield

$$\frac{\sigma}{\pi r_m^2} = \frac{2s-2}{s-2}\left(\frac{C_0 f(s)v_c}{v}\right)^{2/(s-1)} - 4\beta_0\left(\frac{2\pi}{\gamma_0 A}\right)^{1/2}\cos\left(2\delta_0 - \frac{\pi}{4}\right) \quad (4.55)$$

or

$$\sigma = \sigma_{MM} + \Delta\sigma.$$

The total cross section σ thus contains a contribution σ_{MM} from the attractive long-range part of the potential. The presence of a short-range repulsive potential introduces an additional contribution $\Delta\sigma$ that comes from the glory effect. σ_{MM} is a monotonic function of the velocity, whereas the correction term $\Delta\sigma$ oscillates with the velocity. The result (4.55) can also be derived directly from Eq. (3.28) for the total elastic cross section, using the same approximation as in the case of the scattering amplitude. Since it is possible to integrate

$$\text{Im} f(0) = \frac{1}{2k}\int_0^\infty (2l+1)\sin^2\frac{C_0 f(s)k^s r_m^2}{2Kl^{s-1}}\, dl \quad (4.56)$$

in closed form [this is not possible for $f(\vartheta)$ in the case of $\vartheta \neq 0$], the somewhat arbitrary assumption in the choice of the boundary $\delta_m = 1/2$ [Eq. (4.32)] can be overcome. This method (Landau and Lifschitz, 1959; Schiff, 1956) yields in Eq. (4.55) instead of σ_{MM} a value σ_{LL} which is given by

$$\sigma_{LL} = \frac{2\pi(s-2)}{(s-1)(2s-3)[2/(s-1)]!\sin[\pi/(s-1)]}\sigma_{MM}. \quad (4.57)$$

For $s=6$ the difference between σ_{LL} and σ_{MM} is 7%. Exact quantum mechanical calculations of total cross sections for a monotonic potential function show that the constant obtained with the Landau–Lifschitz approximation is correct within 1.5% (Bernstein and Kramer, 1963). An improvement in the accuracy of Eq. (4.55) is thus possible by using σ_{LL} in place of σ_{MM}.

The glory contribution to the total cross section is classically due to the fact that the deflection function passes through zero at the glory impact parameter b_0 [see Eq. (2.33)]. Thus, according to Eq. (4.5), the phase shift curve $\delta(l)$ exhibits a broad maximum around $\delta(l_0)$, providing a significant fraction of nonrandom phases at intermediate angular momenta. The maximum phase δ_0 increases with decreasing wave number k (see, for example, Fig. 8), and if the attractive well is sufficiently deep, δ_0 can pass successively through multiples of $\pi/2$, giving rise alternately to positive and negative incremental contributions $\Delta\sigma$ to the Massey–Mohr cross section σ_{MM}. From the observed velocities v_N of the extrema the maximum phase δ_0 can be directly determined as a function of the relative velocity v. The condition for an extremum follows from Eq. (4.55):

$$\delta_0(k_N) = \pi(N - 3/8) \tag{4.58}$$

where $N = 1, 2, 3, \ldots$ are indices for maxima, while $N = 1.5, 2.5, 3.5, \ldots$ refer to minima in $\sigma(v)$.

For any assumed potential the velocity dependence of the maximum phase shift may be evaluated numerically, and thus the locations of the extrema in $\sigma(v)$ determined. For large reduced energies K we can use Eq. (4.3a) to evaluate δ_0. For a Lennard-Jones (12, 6) potential we obtain

$$\delta_0 = \frac{v_c}{v} \frac{3\pi n}{32(n-1)} \left(\frac{5\pi n}{32(n-1)f(n)} \right)^{5/(n-6)} = a_1 \frac{v_c}{v}. \tag{4.59a}$$

In this approximation δ_0 depends only on v_c/v (see Fig. 11). Equation (4.59a) is the first term of an expansion of δ_0 in powers of the reciprocal reduced energy K, which was first derived by Bernstein and O'Brien (1965, 1967). This expansion can be written in the following form:

$$\delta_0(K) = (v_c/v)[a_1 - (A_1/K) + (A_2/K^2) + \cdots]. \tag{4.59b}$$

A physical interpretation of the expansion coefficients has been given by Greene and Mason (1972). The coefficient a_1 measures the area of the intermolecular potential well along the glory trajectory, whereas A_1 and A_2 give measures of the square and cube of the well, respectively. Numerical values of the expansion coefficients are tabulated by Bernstein and O'Brien (1965), Greene and Mason (1972) and Bernstein and LaBudde (1973).

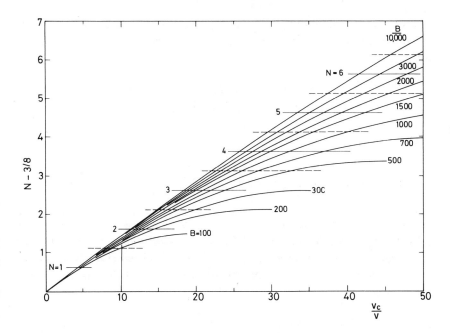

FIG. 20. $N - 3/8$ vs. v_c/v for various values of B; Lennard-Jones (12, 6) potential. The horizontal lines corresponding to different extrema intersect the curves at the appropriate values of v_c/v_N.

More refined methods for the evaluation of potential parameters from total cross-section measurements using the expansion (4.59b) are discussed by Bernstein and O'Brien (1967) and Bernstein and LaBudde (1973).

If the velocities v_N of the extrema are plotted against $N - 3/8$ [see Eqs. (4.58) and (4.59)], a straight line is obtained in the first approximation. Figure 20 shows calculated values of v_N plotted against $N - 3/8$ for various values of the potential well capacity B. With increasing N deviations from the straight line occur due to the higher-order terms in Eq. (4.59b). As B is increased, the deviations occur at higher N values, in agreement with the considerations of Section III,C,2 (see Fig. 11).

To analyze experimental data, the product $v^{2/(s-1)}\sigma(v)$ (usually with $s = 6$) is plotted as a function of $1/v$, yielding an undulatory curve, which is symmetric about a horizontal mean line and in which the extrema are nearly uniformly spaced. From this plot the extremum velocities v_N can be obtained and plotted versus $N - 3/8$. The characteristic velocity v_c can be determined from the initial slope of the resulting line.

From Eqs. (4.55) and (4.57) it follows that the relative amplitudes of the oscillations in the velocity dependence of the total scattering cross section are given by

$$\frac{\Delta\sigma}{\sigma_{\text{LL}}} = \frac{4\beta_0(K)}{g(s)C_0^{2/(s-1)}} \left[\frac{2\pi}{\gamma_0(K)}\right]^{1/2} \frac{K^{2/(s-1)}}{A^{(s+3)/2(s-1)}} \qquad (4.60)$$

with

$$g(s) = 2(2s-2)\Gamma\left(\frac{s}{s-1}\right)\Gamma\left(\frac{s-2}{s-1}\right) f(s)^{2/(s-1)} \Big/ (2s-3)\Gamma\left(\frac{s+1}{s-1}\right).$$

Numerical calculations show that β_0 is only weakly dependent on K (Düren and Pauly, 1963, 1964). The same result holds approximately for γ_0 for reduced energies in the range $1/2 < K < 5$. Thus the relative amplitude depends on the potential parameters ε and r_m and the reduced mass μ in the following way:

$$\frac{\Delta\sigma}{\sigma_{\text{LL}}} \sim \frac{1}{\mu^{1/2}\varepsilon^{2/(s-1)}r_m^{(s+3)/(s-1)}}. \qquad (4.61\text{a})$$

Equation (4.61a) shows that the oscillations are expected to be largest for light atoms. With increasing K, however, γ_0 depends more strongly on K. In the high-energy limit both β_0 and γ_0 can be expanded in inverse powers of the reduced energy to yield

$$\beta_0 = B_0 + \frac{B_1}{K} + \frac{B_2}{K^2} + \cdots, \qquad \frac{\gamma_0}{2} = \frac{c_1}{K} + \frac{C_1}{K^2} + \frac{C_2}{K^3} + \cdots.$$

From these expansions a similar expansion for the relative amplitude is obtained:

$$\frac{\Delta\sigma}{\sigma_{\text{LL}}} = \frac{4B_0}{g(s)}\left(\frac{\pi}{c_1}\right)^{1/2} C_0^{2/(s-1)}\left(\frac{v}{v_c}\right)^{(s+3)/2(s-1)}\left(1 + \frac{H_1}{K} + \frac{H_2}{K^2} + \cdots\right). \qquad (4.61\text{b})$$

In this limit the relative amplitude becomes independent of the reduced particle mass. The coefficients H_j can be interpreted as a measure of the force in the vicinity of the distance of closest approach (Greene and Mason, 1973).

In complete analogy to the classical case discussed in Section II,B,8, the calculations of the scattering amplitude at small angles as described in Sections IV,B,3 and IV,B,4 and the results for the total cross section discussed here are valid only if the maximum phase shift is sufficiently large, $\delta_0 \gg 1$. For large values of the reduced energy the approximations leading to Eq. (4.55) are no longer valid. In this region Eq. (4.3a) can be used to calculate the phase shift curve. For even higher energies, where the repulsive part of the potential determines the scattering, a similar treatment is possible for a repulsive potential which is an inverse power law, $V_{\text{rep}} = c/r^n$. In this limit the total cross section is given by

$$\sigma/\pi r_m{}^2 = p(n)(c_0\, v_c/v)^{2/(n-1)} \tag{4.62}$$

with

$$p(n) = 2\sqrt{\pi}\left(\frac{f(n)}{2}\right)^{2/(n-1)} \Gamma\!\left(\frac{n-2}{n-1}\right)\bigg/\Gamma\!\left(\frac{n+1}{2(n-1)}\right)$$

(see the dashed line in the high-velocity region of Fig. 10).

D. Scattering of Identical Particles

As an example for the semiclassical treatment of the scattering of identical particles we consider the velocity dependence of the total scattering cross section in the case of spinless bosons. Using the expressions (4.34), (4.40), and (4.50) for the scattering amplitude in the forward and backward directions, the optical theorem yields

$$\sigma = \sigma_{\text{MM}} + \Delta\sigma - \frac{2\pi r_m{}^2}{A|\gamma_0|}\left[1 + \frac{|\gamma_0|}{2A}\left(\frac{2\pi A}{|\gamma_0|}\right)^{1/2}\right.$$
$$+ \frac{\pi|\gamma_0|}{4A}\bigg]^{1/2}\cos\!\left(2\delta_0 - \frac{\pi}{2} + \varphi\right) \tag{4.63}$$

with

$$\tan\varphi = [1 + 2(2A/\pi\gamma_0)^{1/2}]^{-1}.$$

The first two terms describe the usual behavior of the cross section which is also observed in the scattering of unlike particles [eq. (4.55)]. Superimposed are oscillations which are due to the symmetrization of the wave function. The amplitudes of these oscillations decrease approximately with $1/A$. The position of the extrema is given by the velocity dependence of the s-phase δ_0. These oscillations can best be seen in the ^{4}He–^{4}He scattering, since this system does not show the normal glory structure, due to the small potential well capacity B (see Fig. 15).

E. SEMICLASSICAL INVERSION PROCEDURES

1. Determination of the Repulsive Part of the Potential from the s Phase As a Function of the Energy

The determination of the energy dependence of the s-phase shift from the measured total cross section as a function of velocity for identical particles makes an inversion procedure for the evaluation of the repulsive part of the interaction potential possible. In a continuum version of the Rydberg–Klein–Rees method for obtaining $V(r)$ from diatomic rotation–vibration spectra it is possible to determine $r(V)$ for $V > 0$ from the empirically determined function $\delta_0(E)$. The expression for the JWKB phase shift can be inverted to yield the classical turning point

$$r_0(E) = \frac{1}{2k} - \frac{2}{\pi}\left(\frac{\hbar}{2\mu}\right)^{1/2}\left\{\pi\int_{-1/2}^{n(0)}\frac{dn}{[E-E(n)]^{1/2}} + \int_{\eta_0(0)}^{\eta_0(E)}\frac{d\eta_0}{[E-E(\eta_0)]^{1/2}}\right\}$$

$$= \frac{1}{2k} + r_1(E) + r_2(E) \tag{4.64a}$$

and the potential energy at $r = r_0$ is then

$$V(r_0) = E - (\hbar^2/2\mu)(1/4r_0^2). \tag{4.64b}$$

The first integral $r_1(E)$ is a contribution from the bound states, where $n(E)$ is given by

$$\left[n(E) + \frac{1}{2}\right]\pi = \left(\frac{2\mu}{\hbar^2}\right)^{1/2}\int_{r_<(E)}^{r_>(E)}\left[E - V(r) - \frac{\hbar^2}{2\mu}\frac{1}{4r^2}\right]^{1/2}dr. \tag{4.65}$$

For purely repulsive potentials we have $r_1(E) = 0$. For a Morse potential $r_1(E)$ can be calculated in closed form, yielding

$$r_1(E) = -(1/2\gamma)r_m \arcsin(1 + E/\varepsilon)^{-1/2}. \tag{4.66}$$

For other potentials a numerical calculation is required. The contribution $r_1(E)$ shows that the potential well must be known in order to determine the repulsive part of the potential. For $E \gg \varepsilon$, however, $r_1(E)$ becomes a small correction to $r_2(E)$, so that an approximate knowledge of the potential well is sufficient to determine $V(r)$ in the region $V > 0$ with adequate accuracy (Feltgen *et al.*, 1973). δ_0 can be determined according to Eq. (4.63) from the observed oscillatory structure.

2. Determination of the Classical Deflection Function from an Analysis of the Rainbow Structure in the Differential Scattering Cross Section

In order to construct the classical deflection function from the measured differential cross section, we divide the deflection function into different parts as shown in Fig. 21. For impact parameters corresponding to angles larger than ϑ_r the determination of the deflection function has already been discussed in Section II,D [Eq. (2.44)]. In the attractive region an analysis of the interference structure of the differential cross section can be used. We give a short description of the method of Buck, which has been most widely applicated in the analysis of atom–atom scattering data (Buck and Pauly, 1968, 1971; Buck *et al.*, 1974). For a recent review of the other methods see Buck (1974).

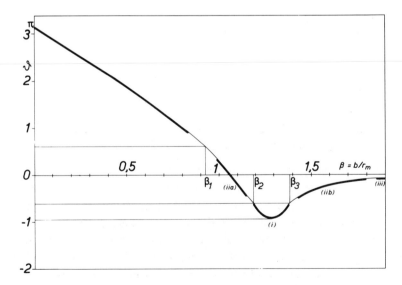

FIG. 21.   The different parts of the classical deflection function which are represented by analytic functions in order to perform the inversion procedure.

Starting point is the semiclassical expression (4.25) for the rainbow cross section. Because of the behavior of A_i^2 and of the smaller amplitude of the second term in this equation, the rainbow maxima z_N (N integer) are given just by the zeros of A_i', whereas the minima z_N (N half-integer) are given by the zeros of A_i. These are tabulated in the literature (Abramowitz and Stegun, 1967). The numbering starts with the primary rainbow. z_N is an implicit function of ϑ_N, the observed extremum angles:

$$z_N = \{\tfrac{3}{4}[2\delta(b_2(\vartheta_N)) - 2\delta(b_3(\vartheta_N))] + k\vartheta_N(b_2(\vartheta_N) - b_3(\vartheta_N))\}^{2/3}. \quad (4.67)$$

Now the deflection function is constructed from simple mathematically invertible functions.

(i) In the region of the minimum

$$\vartheta(b) = -\vartheta_r + q(b - b_r)^2 \qquad\qquad (4.68)$$

$$z_N = k^{2/3}q^{-1/3}(\vartheta_r - \vartheta_N). \qquad\qquad (4.69)$$

(ii) In the regions next to the minimum

$$\vartheta(b) = -q_1(b_2 - b_0) \qquad\qquad (4.70)$$

$$\vartheta(b) = -c_1 b_3^{-c_2} \qquad\qquad (4.71)$$

$$z_N = (\tfrac{3}{4})^{2/3}\{2\delta_0 + kb_0(\vartheta_N) + \tfrac{1}{2}ka_1^{-1}\vartheta_N^2 - kc_1^{1/c_2}[1 - (1/c_2)]^{-1}\vartheta_N^{(1-1/c_2)}\}$$
$$(4.72)$$

δ_0 is the maximum phase shift.

(iii) In the asymptotic region:

The formulas (ii) can be used with $c_1 = 15\pi C/16E$ and $c_2 = 6$ in Eq. (4.71), where C is the van der Waals constant.

For each observed rainbow extremum ϑ_N we obtain an equation $z_N = z_N(b(\vartheta_N))$. This system of equations contains the unknown coefficients ϑ_r, q, b_r, δ_0, b_0, a_1, c_1, c_2, and C. The continuity conditions at the ends of the region of validity of the individual functions reduce the number of unknowns by two. The maximum phase shift δ_0 can be determined from the extrapolation of the z_N vs. ϑ_N curves for $\vartheta = 0$, or more precisely from the oscillatory behavior of the velocity dependence of the total cross section. The van der Waals constant C can be determined from the absolute value of the total cross section [see Eq. (4.55)] or from ab initio calculations [see, for example, Dalgarno (1967)]. Thus five constants remain to be determined from the foregoing system of equations, which can be solved by a least square fit procedure, provided that the number of observed rainbow extrema exceeds the number of unknown quantities.

Finally, the two parts of the deflection function, $\vartheta < 0$ and $\vartheta > 0$, are connected by linear interpolation in order to perform the Firsov integration [Eq. (2.41)].

REFERENCES

ABRAMOWITZ, M., and STEGUN, I. A. (1967). "Handbook of Mathematical Tables." Dover, New York.

ALLISON, A. C., and DALGARNO, A. (1967). *Proc. Phys. Soc.* **90**, 609.

AMDUR, I., and JORDAN, J. E. (1966). *In* "Molecular Beams" (J. Ross, ed.), p. 29. Wiley (Interscience), New York.

ARTHURS, A. M., and DALGARNO, A. (1960). *Proc. Roy. Soc. (London)* **A 256**, 540.

BECK, D. (1970). *In Proc. Int. School Phys.* "*Enrico Fermi*" *Course XLIV* (Ch. Schlier, ed.), "Molecular Beams and Reaction Kinetics," p. 15. Academic Press, New York.

BERNSTEIN, R. B. (1960). *J. Chem. Phys.* **33**, 795.

BERNSTEIN, R. B. (1961). *J. Chem. Phys.* **34**, 361.

BERNSTEIN, R. B. (1962). *J. Chem. Phys.* **37**, 1880.

BERNSTEIN, R. B. (1963). *J. Chem. Phys.* **38**, 2599.

BERNSTEIN, R. B. (1966). *In* "Molecular Beams" (J. Ross, ed.), p. 75. Wiley (Interscience), New York.

BERNSTEIN, R. B. (1966). *Phys. Rev. Lett.* **16**, 385.

BERNSTEIN, R. B., and KRAMER, K. H. (1963). *J. Chem. Phys.* **38**, 2507.

BERNSTEIN, R. B., and LaBUDDE, R. A. (1973). *J. Chem. Phys.* **58**, 1109.

BERNSTEIN, R. B., and LEVINE, R. D. (1968). *J. Chem. Phys.* **49**, 3872.

BERNSTEIN, R. B., and MUCKERMANN, J. T. (1967). *In* "Intermolecular Forces" (J. O. Hirschfelder, ed.), p. 389. Wiley (Interscience), New York.

BERNSTEIN, R. B., and O'BRIEN, T. J. P. (1965). *Discuss. Faraday Soc.* **40**, 35.

BERNSTEIN, R. B., and O'BRIEN, T. J. P. (1967). *J. Chem. Phys.* **46**, 1208.

BERNSTEIN, R. B., CURTISS, C. F., IMAM-RAHAJOE, S., and WOOD, H. T. (1966). *J. Chem. Phys.* **44**, 4072.

BERRY, M. V. (1966). *Proc. Phys. Soc.* **89**, 479.

BERRY, M. V. (1969). *J. Phys. B* **2**, 381.

BERRY, M. V., and MOUNT, K. E. (1972). *Rep. Progr. Phys.* **35**, 315.

BOARDMAN, A. D., HILL, A. D., and SAMPANTHAR, S. (1967). *Phys. Rev.* **160**, 472.

BOBBIO, S. M., RICH, W. G., DOVERSPIKE, L. D., and CHAMPION, R. L. (1971). *Phys. Rev. A* **4**, 957.

BUCK, U. (1971). *J. Chem. Phys.* **54**, 1923.

BUCK, U. (1974). *Rev. Mod. Phys.* **46**, 369.

BUCK, U., and PAULY, H. (1968). *Z. Phys.* **208**, 390.

BUCK, U., and PAULY, H. (1971). *J. Chem. Phys.* **54**, 1929.

BUCK, U., HOPPE, H. O., HUISKEN, F. and PAULY, H. (1974). *J. Chem. Phys.* **60**, 4925.

CROSS, R. J. Jr., (1967). *J. Chem. Phys.* **46**, 609.

CROSS, R. J. Jr., (1970). *J. Chem. Phys.* **52**, 5703.
CROSS, R. J. Jr., and HERSCHBACH, D. R. (1965). *J. Chem. Phys.* **43**, 3530.
CURTISS, C. F. (1953). *J. Chem. Phys.* **21**, 2045.
CURTISS, C. F. (1968). *J. Chem. Phys.* **49**, 1952.
CURTISS, C. F., and ADLER, F. T. (1952). *J. Chem. Phys.* **20**, 249.
DALGARNO, A. (1967). *Advan. Chem. Phys.* **12**, 143.
DATZ, S., HERSCHBACH, D. R., and TAYLOR, E. H. (1961). *J. Chem. Phys.* **35**, 1549.
DOLL, J. D., GEORGE, T. F., and MILLER, W. H. (1973). *J. Chem. Phys.* **58**, 1343.
DÜREN, R., and PAULY, H. (1963). *Z. Phys.* **175**, 227.
DÜREN, R., and PAULY, H. (1964). *Z. Phys.* **177**, 146.
DÜREN, R., and SCHLIER, Ch. (1967). *J. Chem. Phys.* **46**, 4535.
DÜREN, R., HELBING, R., and PAULY, H. (1965). *Z. Phys.* **188**, 468.
DÜREN, R., FRICK, A., and SCHLIER, Ch. (1972). *J. Phys. B* **5**, 1744.
EASTES, W., and SECREST, D. (1971). *Chem. Phys. Lett.* **9**, 508.
EASTES, W., and SECREST, D. (1972). *J. Chem. Phys.* **56**, 640.
ERLEWEIN, W., VON SEGGERN, M., and TOENNIES, J. P. (1968). *Z. Phys.* **211**, 35.
EU, B. C., and ROSS, J. (1967). *Discuss. Faraday Soc.*, **44**, 39.
FELTGEN, R. (1970). Thesis, Univ. of Bonn.
FELTGEN, R., PAULY, H., TORELLO, F., and VEHMEYER, H. (1973). *Phys. Rev. Lett.* **30**, 820.
FIRSOV, O. B. (1953). *Zh. Eksp. Teor. Fiz.* **24**, 279.
FORD, K. W., and WHEELER, J. A. (1959). *Ann. Phys. N.Y.* **7**, 259, 287.
GELTMAN, S. (1969). *In* "Topics in Atomic Collision Theory," p. 73. Academic Press, New York.
GIOUMONSIS, G., and CURTISS, C. F. (1961). *J. Math. Phys.* **2**, 96.
GORDON, R. G. (1969). *J. Chem. Phys.* **51**, 14.
GORDON, R. G. (1971). *Methods Comput. Phys.* **10**, 81.
GREENE, E. F., and MASON, E. A. (1972). *J. Chem. Phys.* **57**, 2065.
GREENE, E. F., and MASON, E. A. (1973). *J. Chem. Phys.* **59**, 2651.
GREENE, E. F., MOURSUND, A. L., and ROSS, J. (1966). *In* "Molecular Beams" (J. Ross, ed.), p. 135. Wiley, New York.
GREENE, E. F., RECK, G. P., and ROSENFELD, J. L. J. (1967). *J. Chem. Phys.* **46**, 3693.
HAYES, E. F., WELLS, C. A., and KOURI, D. J. (1971). *Phys. Rev. A* **4**, 1017.
HELBING, R. (1963). Rep. from the Inst. Applied Physics, Univ. of Bonn.
HELBING, R. (1968). *J. Chem. Phys.* **48**, 472.
HELBING, R. (1969). *J. Chem. Phys.* **50**, 493.
HELBING, R., and PAULY, H. (1964). *Z. Phys.* **179**, 16.
HERSCHBACH, D. R. (1960). Univ. of California, Lawrence Radiation Lab., UCRL Rep. 9379.
HIRSCHFELDER, J. O., CURTISS, C. F., and BIRD, R. B. (1954). "Molecular Theory of Gases and Liquids." Wiley, New York.
HUNDHAUSEN, E., and PAULY, H. (1965). *Z. Phys.* **187**, 305.
HUNTER, L. W., and CURTISS, C. F. (1973). *J. Chem. Phys* **58**, 3884.
JOHNSON, R. B., and SECREST, D. (1968). *J. Chem. Phys.* **48**, 4682.
KELLER, J. B., KAY, I., and SHMOYS, J. (1956). *Phys. Rev.* **102**, 557.
LABUDDE, R. A., and BERNSTEIN, R. B. (1971). *J. Chem. Phys.* **55**, 5499.
LANDAU, L. D., and LIFSCHITZ, E. M. (1959). *In* "Quantum Mechanics," p. 146. Macmillan, New York.
LANE, G. H., and EVERHART, E. (1960). *Phys. Rev.* **120**, 2064.
LANGEVIN, P. (1905). *Ann. Chem. Phys.* **5**, 245.
LEHMANN, C., and LEIBFRIED, G. (1962). *Z. Phys.* **172**, 465.

LESTER, W. A. Jr., (1971). *Methods Comput. Phys.* **10**, 211.
LESTER, W. A. Jr., and BERNSTEIN, R. B. (1967). *Chem. Phys. Lett.* **1**, 207.
LESTER, W. A. Jr., and BERNSTEIN, R. B. (1968). *J. Chem. Phys.* **48**, 4896.
LESTER, W. A. Jr., and SCHAEFER, J. (1973). *J. Chem. Phys.* **59**, 3676.
LEVINE, R. D., JOHNSON, B. R., MUCKERMANN, J. T., and BERNSTEIN, R. B. (1968). *Chem. Phys. Lett.* **1**, 517.
LEVINE, R. D., JOHNSON, B. R., and BERNSTEIN, R. B. (1969). *J. Chem. Phys.* **50**, 1994.
LI, MING CHIANG (1971). *J. Math. Phys.* **12**, 936.
McGUIRE, P., and MICHA, D. A. (1972). *Int. J. Quantum Chem.* **6**, 111.
MARCUS, R. A. (1971). *J. Chem. Phys.* **54**, 3965.
MARCUS, R. A. (1972a). *J. Chem. Phys.* **56**, 311.
MARCUS, R. A. (1972b). *J. Chem. Phys.* **56**, 3548.
MARCUS, R. A. (1972c). *J. Chem. Phys.* **57**, 4903.
MARRIOTT, R., and MICHA, D. A. (1969). *Phys. Rev.* **180**, 120.
MASON, E. A. (1957). *J. Chem. Phys.* **26**, 667.
MASON, E. A., VANDERSLICE, J. T., and RAW, C. J. G. (1964). *J. Chem. Phys.* **46**, 2153.
MASON, E. A., MUNN, R. J., and SMITH, J. F. (1966). *J. Chem. Phys.* **44**, 1967.
MASSEY, H. S. W., and MOHR, C. B. O. (1933). *Proc. Roy. Soc. London* **A141**, 434.
MASSEY, H. S. W., BURKOP, E. H. S., and GILBODY, H. B. (1971). "Electronic and Ionic Impact Phenomena," Vol. III. Oxford Univ. Press (Clarendon), London and New York.
MICHA, D. A. (1967). *Phys. Rev.* **162**, 88.
MICHA, D. A. (1969). *J. Chem. Phys.* **50**, 722.
MILES, J. R. N., and DAHLER, J. S. (1970). *J. Chem. Phys.* **52**, 616.
MILLER, W. H. (1969a). *Int. Conf. Phys. Electron. At. Collisions, 6th* Abstr. of papers, p. 947.
MILLER, W. H. (1969b). *J. Chem. Phys.* **51**, 3631.
MILLER, W. H. (1970a). *J. Chem. Phys.* **53**, 1949.
MILLER, W. H. (1970b). *J. Chem. Phys.* **53**, 3578.
MILLER, W. H. (1971). *J. Chem. Phys.* **54**, 5386.
MILLER, W. H. (1972). *J. Chem. Phys.* **56**, 745.
MIYKAO, R. (1942). *Proc. Phys. Math. Soc. Japan* **24**, 852.
MIZUNO, I., and CHEN, I. C. Y. (1971). *Phys. Rev. A* **4**, 1500.
MORSE, F. A., and BERNSTEIN, R. B. (1962). *J. Chem. Phys.* **37**, 2019.
MOTT-SMITH, H. M. (1960). *Phys. Fluids* **3**, 721.
MOUNT, K. E. (1973). *J. Phys. B* **6**, 1397.
MUCKERMANN, J. T., and BERNSTEIN, R. B. (1970). *J. Chem. Phys.* **52**, 606.
MULLEN, J. M., and THOMAS, B. S. (1973). *J. Chem. Phys.* **58**, 5216.
NEWMAN, W. I., and THORSON, W. R. (1972). *Can. J. Phys.* **50**, 2997.
PACK, R. T. (1974). *J. Chem. Phys.* **60**, 633.
PAULY, H. (1961). *Fortsch. Phys.* **9**, 613.
PAULY, H., and TOENNIES, J. P. (1965). *Advan. At. Mol. Phys.* **1**, 195.
PAULY, H., and TOENNIES, J. P. (1968). *Methods of Exp. Phys.* **7A**, 227.
PECHUKAS, P. (1969a). *Phys. Rev.* **181**, 166.
PECHUKAS, P. (1969b). *Phys. Rev.* **181**, 174.
REMLER, E. A. (1971). *Phys. Rev.* **A3**, 1949.
RICH, W. G., BOBBIO, S. M., CHAMPION, R. L., DOVERSPIKE, L. D. (1971). *Phys. Rev. A* **4**, 2253.
ROSEN, M., and YENNIE, D. R. (1964). *J. Math. Phys.* **5**, 1505.
RUSSEK, A. (1960). *Phys. Rev.* **120**, 1536.
SCHIFF, L. I. (1956). *Phys. Rev.* **103**, 443.

H. Pauly

SCHLIER, Ch. (1963). *Z. Phys.* **173**, 352.
SMITH, F. T., MASCHI, R. P., and DEDRIK, K. G. (1966). *Phys. Rev.* **150**, 79.
STWALLEY, W. C. (1972). Private communication.
VON SEGGERN, M., and TOENNIES, J. P. (1969). *Z. Phys.* **218**, 341.
WAECH, Th. G., and BERNSTEIN, R. B. (1967). *J. Chem. Phys.* **46**, 4905.
WOLKEN, G., Jr., MILLER, W. H., and KARPLUS, M. (1972). *J. Chem. Phys.* **56**, 4930.
ZARUR, G., and RABITZ, H. (1973). *J. Chem. Phys.* **59**, 943.
ZARUR, G., and RABITZ, H. (1974). *J. Chem. Phys.* **60**, 2057.

Chapter 9

Atom Reactions

Juergen Wolfrum

I. Introduction

The reactions of free atoms in the gas phase have attracted numerous investigators during the last half century mainly for two reasons:

Reactions of atoms are among the simplest of chemical processes. They offer favorable conditions for a quantitative theoretical treatment and demonstrate many properties typical of neutral particle reactions. These properties include not only the Arrhenius parameters, but also information about the "activated complex" and the "rearrangement" of the reactants during the reactive process, the probabilities of various reaction pathways and the distribution of the reaction energy over the products, and the influence of electronic excitation and high kinetic energy of the reacting particles.

On the other hand, the practical use of the fast reactions of atoms and free radicals in combustion processes is one of the oldest of all chemical techniques. Since the classical investigations of Bodenstein (1913) and Nernst (1916) it has been well known that even such a very simple combustion reaction as

$$2H_2 + O_2 \quad -- \rightarrow \quad 2H_2O$$

does not actually take place in the form given by the stochiometric relation. Instead, the reaction proceeds through a set of atom and radical reactions like

$$H + O_2 \longrightarrow OH + O$$
$$O + H_2 \longrightarrow OH + H$$
$$H + O_2 + M \longrightarrow HO_2 + M$$
$$H + HO_2 \longrightarrow OH + OH$$
$$\longrightarrow H_2 + O_2.$$

More recently it has become increasingly clear that the rapid expansion of the use of combustion processes has reached the point that the natural atmosphere is being considerably affected. A thorough knowledge of the elementary steps taking place in explosion and combustion processes is therefore clearly needed. Furthermore, the reactions of atoms also play an important part in many photochemically and radiation-initiated processes such as occur in the lower and the upper atmosphere, in chemical lasers, and in many industrial applications.

It has been known for a long time that even careful analysis of the chemically stable starting materials and end products of a gas reaction gives only limited information concerning the elementary steps taking place. The reason for this unsatisfactory result is obvious: Due to the important contribution of atom and radical reactions there are usually many more elementary steps than observed stable components. Thus, efforts have to be made to isolate the individual steps from the overall reaction. Two problems generally arise in the direct investigation of these elementary reactions:

(i) generation of atoms (or radicals) under well-defined conditions;
(ii) measurement of the concentrations of the unstable species.

Generation of atoms by thermal decomposition of their parent molecules can most easily be achieved in the case of alkali metals and halogens due to their relatively low bond dissociation energy. Reactions of halogen and alkali metal atoms have therefore played an important part in the development of reaction kinetics. The importance of halogen atom reactions has recently also been demonstrated (Sullivan, 1967) for the classical iodine–hydrogen reaction.

Since the detection of individual alkali metal atoms was achieved on the basis of surface ionization (Datz and Taylor, 1956) the "atom flame" reactions (Polanyi, 1932) between alkali metal atoms and halogen compounds have been investigated in great detail in crossed molecular beams. This method probably provides the most detailed information on the microscopic course of an atom reaction. As described in Chapter 5, with the development of a mass spectrometric detector (Lee, 1969) molecular beam scattering experiments with other types of atoms are now feasible. Few results, however, are available as yet for the atomic reactions in the practically important $H-C-N-O$ system.

In the following section typical reactions of hydrogen, carbon, nitrogen, and oxygen atoms with simple molecules shall be discussed, including the investigation methods used. Methods of producing these atoms have been known for many years involving the use of photolysis, pyrolysis, radiolysis, and electrical discharges. It is only recently, however, that reliable quantitative results have become obtainable through greatly improved analytical techniques for the accurate determination of atoms and radicals. Nevertheless, with regard to the nearly infinite variety of possible elementary steps in the $H-C-N-O$ system this is still a complex task which requires a high degree of experimental adaptability. With the various experimental methods described in Section II absolute rate coefficients $k(T)$ at temperatures between 200 and 3000 K and pressures between 10^{-4} Torr and 10^3 atm have been measured in a range of many orders of magnitude.

Since an elementary chemical reaction can be quantitatively transferred from one reacting system to another, the measured rate coefficients $k(T)$ are now tabulated in handbooks (e.g., Trotman-Dickenson and Milne,

Juergen Wolfrum

1967; Johnston, 1968; Baulch *et al.*, 1968–1973; Kondratiev, 1970) similar to thermodynamic data of pure substances. However, the straight-forward application of the compiled values to predict the kinetic properties of a chemically reacting gas mixture in a practical situation such as the flame of a combustion engine is often hampered for several reasons:

(i) One can easily fail if an important elementary step has been neglected.

(ii) The complicated interaction of chemical reaction and transport, boundary layer, and heterogeneous effects must be taken into account (see Chapter 12).

(iii) In case of deviations from the equilibrium distribution of states for the reactants the concept of describing the various microscopic processes of an elementary reaction with the few macroscopic parameters of the Arrhenius equation may not be applicable.

The last problem may in principle be overcome by solving the Boltzmann equation to obtain the elementary rate coefficient as function of time and temperature $k(t, T)$. However, in spite of the progress in calculating and measuring elastic, inelastic, and reactive cross sections reported in Chapters 3–8, this has not been possible yet for rather simple elementary steps and this may be so for some time. The rate coefficients $k(T)$ measured for reactants with a Maxwell–Boltzmann distribution of states may therefore continue to be a useful link between the microscopic aspects (described in Chapters 3–8) and the practical applications of collision processes between chemically reactive species.

II. Experimental Techniques

Depending on how the atom reaction is initiated in the thermal environment, one may divide the experimental techniques into three categories: static, flow, and pulse methods.

A. Static Methods

1. Static Isothermal Reactor

The simplest way of measuring reaction rates is the "static," i.e., constant-volume, isothermal reactor. A schematic outline of a typical apparatus is shown in Fig. 1. The reactants are admitted to the reaction

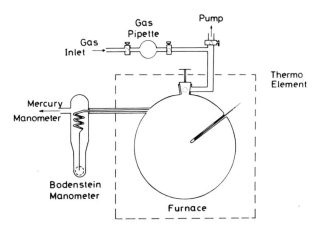

FIG. 1.   Scheme of a static isothermal gas reactor.

vessel (usually Pyrex or silica) through a high-vacuum system and heated to a suitable temperature with a furnace or thermostat. The progress of the reaction is followed by the change in concentration of one or more stable components together with change in pressure (more technical details may be found in the monograph of Melville and Gowenlock, 1964). As already mentioned, however, this type of bulk experiment does not provide unique information on the reaction mechanism. Quite often different sets of elementary steps can account for the observed overall reaction. Therefore, only in a few cases, where the *mechanism is rigorously known already*, can absolute rate constants of elementary steps be extracted in this way. Classical examples are the halogen–atom reactions (for a review, see Fettis and Knox, 1964).

In the case of iodine–atom reactions spectroscopic methods are well suited for "in situ" observation of the concentrations of reactants and products during the reaction in the static vessel. Benson and co-workers (Benson and Golden, 1969) have studied reactions of I atoms with various hydrocarbons (RH) in this manner. The reactions

$$RH + I_2 \; \rightleftharpoons \; RI + HI$$

were investigated between 500 and 800 K in a quartz reaction vessel situated in an aluminum block oven. Starting from the hydrocarbon and iodine, the appearance of hydrogen iodide and RI could be monitored by measurement of optical density in the ultraviolet region (2600–2300 Å).

Around 5000 Å only I_2 absorbs; therefore the absorbance of I_2 at the other wavelengths can be easily accounted for. The overall reaction was interpreted by the mechanism

$$I_2 + M \underset{-a}{\overset{a}{\rightleftharpoons}} 2I + M$$

$$RI + I \underset{-b}{\overset{b}{\rightleftharpoons}} R + I_2$$

$$R + HI \underset{-c}{\overset{c}{\rightleftharpoons}} RH + I$$

which leads by use of the "quasistationary" approximation for the I atoms and hydrocarbon radicals R to the rate expression

$$\frac{d[RI]}{dt} = \frac{k_{-c}(K_{I_2}[I_2])^{1/2}[RH]}{1 + (k_c[HI]/k_{-b}[I_2])} \left\{ 1 - \frac{[HI][RI]}{[I_2][RH]} \frac{1}{K_I^{eq}} \right\}. \qquad (2.1)$$

Since the equilibrium constant K_I^{eq} for the overall reaction lies far to the right between 500 and 800 K, the concentrations of RH and I_2 are essentially constant and also $[I_2] \gg [RI]$ during the observation. The rate constant k_{-c} for the iodine-atom reaction

$$I + RH \xrightarrow{-c} R + HI$$

may then be obtained from

$$\frac{d[RI]}{dt} = k_{-c}(K_{I_2}[I_2])^{1/2}[RH] \left\{ 1 - \frac{[HI][RI]}{[HI]_{eq}[RI]_{eq}} \right\}. \qquad (2.2)$$

It should be noted, however, that this straightforward evaluation rests on some favorable facts of the iodine system. The H—I bond in hydrogen iodide is the strongest bond an I atom can make and one of the weakest of the H atom. Thus, the radical R will always abstract H from HI, not I. In addition, the reaction ($-c$) is usually endothermic by $\Delta H_0^\circ = 20, \ldots,$ 35 kcal mole^{-1} and therefore slow at the temperatures used, so that

$$k_{-a}[I][M] \gg k_{-c}[RH]$$

and the steady-state iodine concentration is given by $(K_a[I_2])^{1/2}$. However, even in this simple case the surface of the reaction vessel cannot be ignored, since at the pressures ($\sim$100 Torr) used dissociation and association of I_2 take place, at least partially, by some heterogeneous mechanism (Benson and Buss, 1958). The situation becomes more complicated for Cl_2 and F_2. Due to the fast chain reaction

$$Cl + RH \xrightarrow{d} R + HCl$$

$$R + Cl_2 \xrightarrow{e} RCl + Cl$$

the steady-state chlorine atom concentration depends on the rates of reactions (d) and (e). In the case of fluorine, moreover, chain branching can occur by intermolecular (Vasilev et al., 1970)

$$H + F_2 \longrightarrow HF\dagger + F$$
$$HF\dagger + F_2 \longrightarrow HF + F + F$$

($\dagger$ represents a vibrationally excited molecule) and intramolecular energy exchange (Rusin et al., 1964).

2. Explosion Limits

Another system where a good deal of material on the reaction mechanism is available is the hydrogen–oxygen reaction (for a review, see, for instance, Richtering, 1965; Foo and Yang, 1971).

The most surprising feature of the H_2–O_2 system was the discovery of several explosion limits at the same temperature but at different pressures. As illustrated in Fig. 2, the reaction of a stoichiometric H_2–O_2 mixture proceeds at 410°C very slowly around 1 Torr. On increasing the pressure to $P_1 \sim 2.5$ Torr, the reaction rate is suddenly increased, i.e., explosion occurs. Starting at 200 Torr, a slow, measurable reaction ($dP/dt \ll -10^{-2}$ Torr min^{-1}) is observed. This reaction proceeds until at *lower* pressure ($P_2 = 7$ Torr) explosion again occurs. At 560°C a second ($P_2 \sim 150$ Torr) and a third ($P_3 \sim 750$ Torr) explosion limit can be reached. The sharp transitions in reactive behavior at P_1, P_2, and P_3 are reproducible quantities well suited for measurement in a static reaction vessel. They may be interpreted in terms of elementary reactions. At the second limit it is usually assumed that the chain branching step

(a) $H + O_2 \longrightarrow OH + O$

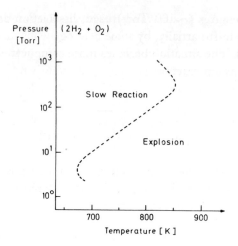

FIG. 2. Explosion limits of a hydrogen–oxygen mixture (spherical reaction vessel; Pyrex coated, with KCl; 7.4 cm diameter) (Lewis and v. Elbe, 1942; Warren, 1952).

competes with the homogeneous chain termination

(b) $H + O_2 + M \longrightarrow HO_2 + M$

$HO_2 \xrightarrow{\text{wall}}$ stable products   (M = inert third body)

and for the total pressure P_2 at the second limit the approximate relation

$$P_2 \simeq 2k_a/k_b \tag{2.3}$$

is used (Nalbandyan and Voevodsky, 1948). At the first limit the reaction (a) competes with heterogeneous chain termination

(c) $H(O, OH) \xrightarrow{\text{wall}}$ destruction

and we have

$$P_1 \simeq k_{cH}/2k_a. \tag{2.4}$$

Clearly, the evaluation of absolute rate constants from the equations for P_1 and P_2 involves several assumptions:

(i) Other chain propagation reactions

$$O + H_2 \longrightarrow OH + H$$
$$OH + H_2 \longrightarrow H_2O + H$$

as well as additional gas-phase and heterogeneous reactions of HO_2 and H_2O_2 are not included.

(ii) The equations for P_1 and P_2 permit estimation of ratios of rate constants only. For the determination of absolute values information on the chain carrier destruction at the vessel wall is needed. Therefore surface conditions, vessel diameter, and surface-to-volume ratio become important.

(iii) The behavior of the system may also be influenced by the H_2/O_2 ratio, the amount of water formed, the presence of inert gases, and the addition of sensitizers and inhibitors.

However, point (iii) on this list of disadvantages led to an interesting extension of the method. Because hydrogen atoms are the rate-controlling radicals in the H_2–O_2 chain reaction, the addition of small amounts of hydrocarbons or other hydrides (RH) leads to a shift in P_2 toward higher temperatures and lower pressures. For rich mixtures (H_2:$O_2 > 4$) the shift of P_2 due to the addition of 0.1–1% RH is accounted for by the occurrence of the new step

(d) $H + RH \longrightarrow H_2 + R$

and is given by

$$\frac{P_2^{RH}}{P_2{}^0} = 1 - \frac{k_d}{2k_a} \frac{[RH]}{[O_2]} \tag{2.5}$$

where $P_2{}^0$ and P_2^{RH} are second limit pressures in the absence and presence of the additive RH, respectively.*

In conclusion, a number of absolute rate constants obtained from the shift of explosion limits show surprisingly good agreement with more direct measured values (see Section III). Indeed, this is one of the most elegant methods when one considers the simple apparatus used and the fact that no measurement of reacting atom and radical concentrations are involved.

In the static reactor, atoms are produced during the course of the overall reaction. In most cases this drastically limits the *pressure, temperature, and time range* where the elementary steps can be investigated. Variation of the surface-to-volume ratio and measurement of temperature gradients

---

* A more refined treatment on the influence exerted by hydrocarbons on P_2 in boric acid-coated vessels has been given by Baldwin and co-workers (1968).

between the center and wall of the reaction vessel by differential calorimetry (Semenov, 1958) often show a large extent of the heterogeneous
contribution to the overall reaction which may introduce additional difficulties. Some of these problems can be circumvented if the atoms are
produced continuously by photolyzing radiation, which is more selective
than thermal energy.

3. *Stationary Photolysis*

Since Nernst's realization that the photochemical hydrogen–chlorine
reaction can be explained by the primary photodissociation of chlorine

$$Cl_2 + h\nu \longrightarrow 2Cl$$

numerous other photolytic atom sources have been found.

At wavelengths shorter than about 4000 Å photodissociation of NO_2
occurs by

$$NO_2(^2A_1) + h\nu \longrightarrow NO(X^2\Pi) + O(^3P).$$

Below 2300 Å it is likely that oxygen atoms in the first electronic excited
state will be formed

$$NO_2(^2A_1) + h\nu(\lambda < 2300 \text{ Å}) \longrightarrow NO(X^2\Pi) + O(^1D).$$

However, with NO_2 as an O-atom source difficulties may arise from the
reactivity of NO_2 in the reaction mixture. In contrast, the mercury-
photosensitized decomposition of nitrous oxide

$$Hg(6\ ^1S_0) + h\nu\ (\lambda = 2537 \text{ Å}) \longrightarrow Hg(6\ ^3P_1)$$

$$Hg(6\ ^3P_1) + N_2O(^1\Sigma^+) \longrightarrow N_2(^1\Sigma^+) + Hg(6\ ^1S_0) + O(^3P)$$

provides a "clean" source of $O(^3P)$ atoms with the additional advantage
that the molecular nitrogen formed gives a measure of the quantum
yield and therefore the number of $O(^3P)$ atoms generated.

Cvetanović and co-workers (1963) have combined this technique with
stable reaction product analysis by gas chromatography and mass spectrometry to obtain ratios of rate constants by competitive measurements.

Reactions of sulfur atoms can be initiated in a similar way either by
Hg photosensitization of carbonyl sulfide

$$COS(^1\Sigma^+) + Hg(6\ ^3P_1) \longrightarrow Hg(6\ ^1S_0) + CO(^1\Sigma^+) + S(^3P)$$

or direct photolysis

$$COS(^1\Sigma^+) + h\nu\ (\lambda < 2500 \text{ Å}) \longrightarrow CO(^1\Sigma^+) + S(^1D)$$

where the sulfur atoms are formed in their first excited state (Gunning and Strausz, 1966). For relative rate measurement of hydrogen atoms with hydrides one component may serve as a photolytic H-atom source (Darwent and Roberts, 1953),

$$H_2S + h\nu \longrightarrow H(^2S_{1/2}) + HS.$$

However, one must carefully take into account that the H atom, due to its light mass, may carry a large fraction of the excess photochemical energy. Thus, the photolysis of hydrogen iodide by

$$HI(^1\Sigma^+) + h\nu \ (\lambda = 2537 \text{ Å}) \longrightarrow H(^2S_{1/2}) + I(^2P_{3/2})$$

gives rise to translationally "hot" hydrogen atoms ($E^* = 41$ kcal mole^{-1}) clearly not in thermal equilibrium with the surroundings at room temperature.

In order to convert the relative rate constants measured by these competitive techniques into absolute values at least one reference reaction must be known absolutely. This requires a determination of the atom concentrations during the reaction. However, the high reactivity of the atoms usually results in very low stationary concentrations in static reaction vessels, which can be detected only in fortunate cases (see Section II,C,1).

As first realized by Wood (1922) and Bonhoeffer (1924), high concentrations of hydrogen atoms can be generated in a low-pressure electrical discharge of molecular hydrogen and separated from the discharge in a fast flow system. It is only during the last decade, however, that more reliable quantitative results for atom reactions have become obtainable in this way through greatly improved analytical techniques for the accurate determination of atoms and radicals. These techniques include various spectroscopic methods, such as sensitive detection of chemiluminescence or resonance fluorescence in the presence of atoms as well as electron paramagnetic resonance and mass spectrometry.

B. Flow Methods

1. Discharge Flow System with Atom Detection by Chemiluminescence

A schematic diagram of a discharge-flow system with atom detection based on the emission spectra of electronically excited molecules formed in the combination reactions of atoms is shown in Fig. 3. A carefully purified

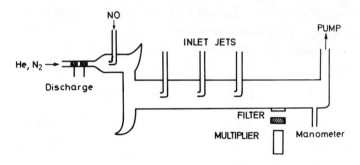

FIG. 3. Schematic diagram of a discharge-flow system with atom detection by chemi-luminescence.

carrier gas (usually argon or helium) is mixed with a few percent of a gas to be dissociated (e.g., H_2, N_2, O_2, halogens) and passed in a quartz tube through an electrodeless discharge. The discharge is maintained either by two thin, metallic foil electrodes wrapped around the discharge tube powered by a radiofrequency oscillator, or by a microwave resonant cavity (Fehsenfeld *et al.*, 1965) supplied by a magnetron operating at 2450 MHz (power $= 50$–200 W). In contrast to the Wood–Bonhoeffer flow discharge, there is no contamination of the discharge products by electrode materials and operation at pressures up to atmospheric is possible due to high energy density and reduced electron recombination rates at the high frequencies used. The discharge region is connected to the main flow reactor via Rayleigh horns in order to prevent photolyzing radiation from the discharge and interference with optical measurements. Stable reactants are mixed with the atoms at various points (mixing time 10^{-3} sec) along the flow tube. In the absence of added reactants the lifetime of the atoms is between 1 and 0.1 sec depending on the pretreatment of the reactor walls (e.g., rinsing with 5% HF solution or syrupy phosphoric acid, or coating with Teflon, which reduces heterogeneous recombination) and the amount of homogeneous recombination at higher pressures (above 5 Torr).

If nitrogen atoms are generated by a discharge in molecular nitrogen, a long-lived yellow afterglow can be observed in the flow tube. Strutt (Lord Rayleigh, 1911) first suggested that this luminescence of "active nitrogen" is associated with the recombination of ground-state nitrogen atoms. The intensity I_{N_2*} of the Lewis–Rayleigh afterglow bands $N_2(B\,^3\Pi_g \rightarrow A\,^3\Sigma_u{}^+)$ can be measured quantitatively with a photomultiplier fitted with a filter around 5500 Å. To determine the absolute

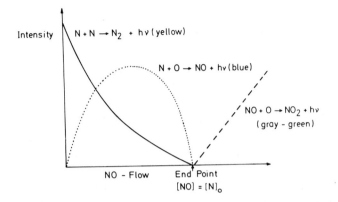

Fɪɢ. 4. Gas phase "titration" of nitrogen atoms with nitric oxide (see text).

concentration of N atoms, the emission is used as an "indicator" for a "titration" of the N atoms in the gas phase (Kaufman and Kelso, 1957; Kistiakowsky and Volpi, 1957). With the addition of nitric oxide, the rapid reaction

$$N(^4S_{1/2}) + NO(^2\Pi) \longrightarrow N_2(^1\Sigma^+) + O(^3P_3)$$

causes the glow to become blue due to emission by electronically excited NO formed by

$$N(^4S_{1/2}) + O(^3P_3) \xrightarrow{+M} NO(B\ ^2\Pi)$$
$$NO(B\ ^2\Pi) \longrightarrow NO(X\ ^2\Pi) + h\nu.$$

When the quantity of NO added corresponds exactly to the original N-atom concentration, the luminescence completely disappears, since all the N atoms have been consumed and the recombination of atomic oxygen gives negligible visible emission. Thus, the "end point" of the titration can be accurately determined.

Since the intensity of the Lewis–Rayleigh afterglow decreases in proportion to the square of the nitrogen atom concentration, as can be seen in Fig. 4, the photomultiplier is readily calibrated for absolute N-atom concentrations by this technique. Further addition of nitric oxide results in the yellow-green "air afterglow," a continuous emission spectrum from 3875 Å to 1.4 μm produced in the reaction

$$NO(X\ ^2\Pi) + O(^3P) \xrightarrow{+M} NO_2{}^*$$
$$NO_2{}^* \longrightarrow NO_2(^2A_1) + h\nu$$

with an intensity proportional to [O][NO] (Becker, Groth, and Thran, 1970, 1972; Golde, Roche, Kaufman, 1973). Similar titration and indicator reactions can also be found for other atoms (Clyne and Thrush, 1961; Gibbs and Ogryzlo, 1965; Clyne and Stedman, 1967).

With this method elementary rate constants for atom-molecule reactions are usually obtained by measuring the changes of the appropriate afterglow emissions due to the addition of an excess of the stable molecule at the various fixed inlet jets (see Fig. 3). Despite their popularity, however, several comments must be made on the use of the discharge-flow methods:

(i) The electrical discharges produce, beside the free atoms, a number of other active species: electrons, ions, electronically excited atoms, and vibrationally excited molecules in the ground and excited electronic states which may cause interfering parallel reactions with the primary reactant or subsequent products.

Under normal experimental conditions ions and electrons are removed within a few centimeters after the discharge region by ambipolar diffusion to the tube walls. Thus, high flow velocities ($\bar{v} > 10^4$ cm sec^{-1}) and large tube diameters ($d > 10$ cm) are necessary for the study of ion reactions in discharge flow systems (Fehsenfeld et al., 1966).

Various excited atoms in metastable electronic states may leave the flow discharge: oxygen and carbon atoms in ^1D and ^1S, nitrogen atoms in ^2P and ^2D, and halogen atoms in $^2P_{1/2}$ states as well as inert gas atoms in metastable ^3P states [$^3P_0$, excitation energy 16.7 eV (Ne*), 11.7 eV (Ar*), 10.6 eV (Kr*), 9.4 eV (Xe*)]. They are usually deactivated by diffusion to the tube walls or collisions with their parent molecules within a few milliseconds after production (see Chapter 10). In contrast, some metastable molecules [e.g., $O_2(^1\Delta_g^+)$, $O_2(^1\Sigma_g^+)$, $N_2(A\ ^3\Sigma_u^+)$ (Wayne, 1970; Wright and Winkler, 1968)] and vibrationally excited ground-state molecules [$H_2(^1\Sigma^+,\ v' > 0)$, $N_2(^1\Sigma^+,\ v' > 0)$] have lifetimes up to several hundred milliseconds (Heidner and Kasper, 1969).

In order to maintain a constant atom flux from the discharge, consistently pure gases must be used. Traces of impurities can alter significantly the yield of atoms. For example, the concentration of atomic nitrogen is increased by two orders of magnitude due to the addition of 0.01 mol % of SF_6 to high-purity nitrogen. There have been indications that if nitrogen could be sufficiently purified, an electrical discharge might not produce nitrogen atoms (Young et al., 1964). In addition, impurities are often completely dissociated in the discharge, giving further reactive species, for instance, hydrogen and oxygen atoms from water vapor.

(ii) As in any absolute measurement, careful attention to the details of evaluation of all experimental variables involved is of course necessary. First one should recognize that variation of reaction time is obtained by varying the distance between atom detector and the inlet of the stable reactant. As discussed in Chapter 12 the exact conversion of distance into reaction time becomes an extremely complicated task if all possible interactions between flow and chemical reaction must be taken into account, such as: development of the boundary layer, radial and axial diffusion, viscous pressure drop, and volume and surface recombination, as well as the elementary step investigated and subsequent steps.

Second, control and measurement of pressure and flow rates must be done with extreme care. This is often strikingly illustrated by the fact that rate constants obtained by various authors with similar flow systems may differ by 100% even though the error claimed by each is less than 20%.

Temperature measurements in the flow reactor may be made with sufficient accuracy with thermocouples constructed from fine wire enclosed in thin Pyrex or silica capillaries. Since atom reactions can be very exothermic, it is possible for thermal gradients to be produced in the flowing mixture during the reaction. Thus, low atom concentrations must be used so that the heat capacity and thermal conductivity of the carrier gas can maintain isothermal conditions.

(iii) The chemiluminescent recombination processes used for the atom detection must be considered in more detail. Since the excited molecules can be formed in two-body association as well as in three-body recombination and removed both by radiation and collisional quenching, the intensity of the observed afterglow may depend on the pressure and the nature of the carrier gas used (Thrush, 1969). Thus, recent experiments on the NO β-band (B $^2\Pi \rightarrow$ X $^2\Pi$) emission produced by the combination of N and O atoms gave, instead of the simple proportionality to [N][O], a more complex dependence, which can be represented as

$$I_{\mathrm{NO}^*} = [\mathrm{N}][\mathrm{O}][\mathrm{M}]/(A + B[\mathrm{N}] + C[\mathrm{O}]) \tag{2.6}$$

(Campbell et al., 1971).

Also, the finer details of the mechanism of the radiative recombination of $N(^4S_{3/2})$ atoms are still not resolved, which is not surprising, since recombination of ground-state nitrogen atoms can occur along 16 different potential curves, only some of which are stable (Becker et al., 1972).

Among the various chemiluminescent reactions used, the "air afterglow" reaction

$$\mathrm{NO} + \mathrm{O} \xrightarrow{\;+\,\mathrm{M}\;} \mathrm{NO_2}^*$$

has gained the widest attention. The absolute intensity–wavelength distribution of the air afterglow has been determined accurately and the pressure dependence investigated down to 10^{-4} Torr (Fontijn et al., 1964; Becker et al., 1970, 1972).

Beside chemiluminescence, absorption and fluorescence of the intense vacuum-ultraviolet atomic resonance lines may be used for sensitive detection of atoms in the discharge-flow reactor (Morse and Kaufman, 1965; Michael and Weston, 1965) (more details are given in Section II,C,1).

2. Measurement of Atom Concentrations by Nonspecific Methods

It was early realized by Bonhoeffer and Harteck that the high atom concentrations obtainable from electrical discharges are sufficient to detect atoms by measuring the heat released or the decrease in pressure in a constant volume when the atoms recombine on a catalytic surface (Bonhoeffer, 1924; Harteck, 1928).

a. Catalytic Probes. The catalytic probe consists of a wire or foil coated with a suitable catalyst and may be movable along the flow reactor. The increase in its temperature due to the atom recombination is measured with an optical pyrometer or by a thermocouple. To make this method quantitative, heat losses from the detector must be accurately known; these are usually difficult to estimate. Tollefson and LeRoy (1948) and Elias et al. (1959) have therefore developed an "isothermal" catalytic probe consisting of several turns of an electrically heated, silver-coated platinum wire which acts as a resistance thermometer. To compensate the heat released by the recombining atoms, the electrical power dissipation is reduced. The atom flow rate can then be simply calculated from the heat of recombination. It is assumed in using this relation that all the atoms recombine on the probe and the efficiency of the catalyst does not change with time. Larkin and Thrush (1964) have overcome this uncertainty by mounting two calorimeters in tandem 3 cm apart, where the downstream calorimeter was used to determine the efficiency of the first one. Thus, the isothermal probe method is absolute, but two disadvantages remain. If all reactive species are scavenged at the detector, diffusion problems can arise (Schulz and LeRoy, 1965), and, more seriously, even in the presence of only one type of atom, interferences due to electronically and vibrationally excited species generated in the discharge are possible (Morgan *et al.*, 1962).

These disadvantages are avoided by a simple gauge first described by Wrede (1928) and Harteck (1928).

b. Wrede–Harteck Gauges. Here the catalyst is placed within a small, closed volume connected to the reaction system by one or more holes having diameter less than the mean free path of the particles at the total pressure used. Atoms and molecules effuse into the enclosed volume, but only molecules effuse out. When sufficient time has been allowed for equilibrium to be set up, mass balance shows that a pressure difference ΔP will develop

$$\Delta P = \alpha P(1 - \sqrt{2}/2),$$

where P is the total gas pressure and α is the fraction of atoms. Clearly, the method is absolute and insensitive to the presence of excited species, and only a small fraction of total atom flux is used for measurement. Its accuracy and sensitivity depend on the accurate measurement of small pressure differences. Groth and Warneck (1957) have employed a diaphragm manometer capable of measuring a pressure difference of 10^{-4} Torr at one Torr with 1% accuracy. This means that atom concentrations of 10^{13} cm^{-3} can be measured quantitatively. However, a shortcoming of the method is the time required to ensure equilibrium, which is several minutes at $P = 1$ Torr. Elias (1966) has circumvented this problem by rapidly isolating a portion of the main flow and following the pressure change due to recombination by a fast pressure transducer.

One point disregarded in the discussion of the discharge-flow reactor is the identification of the primary products of the atom–molecule reaction investigated. For this purpose electronic absorption spectroscopy is suitable only in a few cases, such as OH (Kaufman and DelGreco, 1962) and CN (Boden and Thrush, 1968), but accurate absolute measurements are difficult (see Chapter 10).

In contrast, mass spectrometric detection, unlike other spectroscopic methods, is not tied to special properties of the particles to be detected, and it is possible, in principle, to detect quantitatively all the stable and unstable starting, intermediate, and final species with high sensitivity. Moreover, the mass spectrometer is often able to establish quickly the chemical identity of a particle produced in the reaction.

3. *Mass Spectrometric Detection of Intermediates*

In the application of mass spectrometry to the analysis of reacting gases two problems arise:

(i) Due to the very high pressure difference between reaction vessel and the mass spectrometer ion source (6–10 orders of magnitude), mass spectrometric analysis requires the transfer and quenching of representative samples from the flow system during the progress of the reaction.

(ii) Atoms and radicals must be distinguished from fragment ions of other unstable and stable components of the sample.

a. Molecular Leak Sampling.   Most arrangements for the combination of a mass spectrometer with a gas reactor are based on the principle of the pioneering work of Eltenton (1947). As shown in Fig. 5a, at a short distance from the end of the flow tube there is a plate (10–50 μm thick) with a small orifice ("pinhole" leak, 5–100 μm wide, corresponding to the mean free path of the particles in the flow reactor) through which the gas sample can effuse directly into the ion source. Since the density along the axis of the sample beam decreases with distance according to an inverse square law, the ion source must be located as close as possible to the orifice. Thus, for instance, 1 cm from a pinhole with a 10 μm diameter the pressure in the beam axis falls from 5 Torr in the flow reactor to 10^{-6} Torr, which already corresponds to the total pressure in the ion source.

Atoms and radicals can be observed in this way, but the particles pass into the ion source from a region in the flow system in which the effects of the reactor wall and of the flow boundary layer are already noticeable. For unstable particles this can cause marked differences in concentration compared to that in the actual reaction volume. Some of these disadvantages can be avoided if the gas samples are taken with a conical nozzle that is

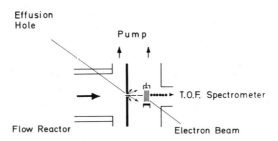

Fig. 5a.   Mass spectrometric analysis in a flow reactor. Molecular leak sampling.

adjusted to the flow and whose aperture is large compared to the mean free path in the flow tube (see Fig. 5b) (Homann *et al.*, 1963; Hoyermann *et al.*, 1967a).

b. Viscous Flow Sampling.   With a conical nozzle (quartz or ceramic; height 10–30 mm, aperture 0.1–1 mm, orifice wall 10–50 μm) the gas samples are taken from a region several millimeters in diameter in front of the tip of the probe, so that only a small percentage of the entering particles can come into contact with the outer probe wall. This can be confirmed by coating the outer surface with a thin layer of carbon and sampling a flowing gas mixture containing oxygen atoms. Very little of the CO formed at the surface is taken in through the nozzle.

The sampling nozzle is attached to an intermediate vacuum chamber, which is evacuated with a large diffusion pump to a pressure between 10^{-2} and 10^{-4} Torr. Due to the large pressure drop the most rapid expansion possible for the gas sample occurs: formation of a supersonic or "free" jet.

As shown in Fig. 6, density and temperature decrease by several orders of magnitude within a few microseconds in the freely expanding jet, and this corresponds to ideal "quenching" of the drawn-off sample. The jet then impinges on a sharp-edged cone of stainless steel (Kantrowitz and Grey, 1952; Becker and Bier, 1954), the "skimmer" (aperture 1 mm, height 10 mm), which "skims" out of the cone of the jet. The apex angle of the cone is so chosen (60–100°) that the particles inside the cone do not undergo collisions with the inner wall and the particles reflected from the outer wall do not pass downstream again. With the optimum distance between sampling orifice and the skimmer (in Fig. 5b, 10 mm) a sharply focused beam of high density enters the ion source.

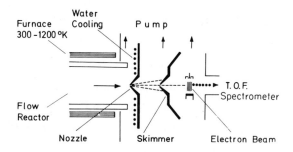

Furnace
300–1200 °K

Water
Cooling

Pump

Flow
Reactor

Nozzle

Skimmer

T.O.F.
Spectrometer

Electron Beam

FIG. 5b.   Nozzle beam sampling.

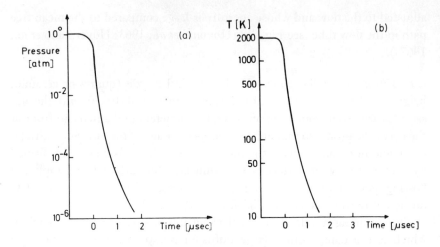

FIG. 6.   Free jet expansion (Greene and Milne, 1966). (a) Pressure drop. (b) Temperature decay.

c. Mass Separation during the Sampling Process.   Whereas for molecular leak sampling the effusion velocity through the sampling orifice varies inversely as the square root of the mass of the particles, the formation of a free jet involves some of the more difficult problems of gas dynamics: subsonic and transonic flow with viscous effects, supersonic flow in transition from continuum to molecular flow, rotational and vibrational relaxation, and partial condensation of the particles.

With the exception of the close vicinity of the orifice, the free jet expansion is usually treated by the method of characteristics for inviscid supersonic flow. According to Sherman (1963, 1965) the results are still valid in the case of jet expansion into a region of finite pressure rather than perfect vacuum. In this case the interaction of the free jet with the background molecules leads to the development of a shock wave system, the well-known " Mach cell " structure. The skimmer must be located upstream of the " Mach disk," i.e., the axial distance X from the orifice must be less than

$$X_M = 0.67d(P_0/P_1)^{1/2} \qquad (2.7)$$

where d is the nozzle diameter and P_0/P_1 is the pressure expansion ratio. The theoretical particle flow rate through the skimmer $\dot{N}_s$ is then given by

$$\dot{N}_s = N_0 a_s \left(\frac{\kappa k T_0}{m}\right)^{1/2} \frac{M_s}{[1 + \frac{1}{2}(\kappa - 1)M_s^2]^{(\kappa+1)/2(\kappa-1)}} \qquad (2.8)$$

where $\kappa = c_p/c_v$ is the specific heat ratio, k is the Boltzmann constant, m is the mass of the molecules, a_s is the skimmer aperture, M_s is the skimmer Mach number as given by Ashkenas and Sherman (1966), and N_0 and T_0 are the stagnation conditions.

Experimental values of $\dot{N}_s$, however, are found to be considerably higher as well as lower than the theoretical values. The situation becomes even more complicated when a multicomponent gas mixture is sampled.

As first suggested by Dirac and experimentally demonstrated by Tahourdin (1946) and Becker and Bier (1954), along the axis of a free jet of a gas mixture the heavier components will be enriched relative to the lighter ones compared with the gas introduced through the nozzle. This so-called "positive separation" can be treated by the theory of diffusive separation (Bier, 1960; Sherman, 1965). The effect can be considerably increased due to the interaction between the skimmer and the supersonic flow, the so-called "probe-induced separation" (Reis and Fenn, 1963). In the case of jet expansion into a vacuum above 10^{-2} Torr, light background molecules may be pumped preferentially through the skimmer and cause the opposite effect of separation enrichment of lighter species (Campargue, 1970).

Thus, a general quantitative treatment of the change in composition of a multicomponent sample during the transit to the ion source is usually extremely difficult. Moreover, the ionization process itself involves further complications.

d. Quantitative Interpretation of Radical Mass Spectra. When the molecular beam enters the ion source, a beam of low-energy electrons (energy 10–100 eV) produced from a heated filament is allowed to collide with the particles. The two beams are usually at right angles and the ion beam is extracted along the third mutually perpendicular direction.

Atoms and radicals are ionized as stable molecules, but several factors make the interpretation of the resulting radical ion currents difficult. Formation of positive ions with an *m/e* ratio corresponding to that of the radical R can occur by several processes:

(i) Electron impact on the radical R in the molecular beam

$$R + e^- \longrightarrow R^+ + 2e^-.$$

(ii) Formation of fragment ions from AR molecules

$$AR + e^- \longrightarrow R^+ + A + 2e^-.$$

(iii) Formation of ions from other stable molecules or radicals with nearly the same mass, e.g., $CH_4{}^+$, $NH_2{}^+$, O^+.

(iv) Ionization of R radicals formed by pyrolysis of sample molecules on the hot ion-source filament.

(v) Ion–molecule or ion–ion reactions in the ion source.

The formation of fragment ions may be suppressed by using electron energies below the "appearance potential" of the R^+ ion from process (ii). The appearance potential $A(R^+)$ is given by

$$A(R^+) \geq I(R) + D(A-R) \tag{2.9}$$

where $I(R)$ is the ionization potential of the radical R and $D(A-R)$ is the dissociation energy of the $A-R$ bond. The inequality is valid if the internuclear distance increases for the molecular ion AR^+ compared with AR, so that the fragments may possess excitation or excess kinetic energy. For radical ions and fragment ions one should find a linear variation of ion current with electron energy (Geltman, 1956) near threshold, by which a unique assignment of the nature of the radical should be possible. However, usually the curves more or less overlap each other due to the Boltzmann energy distribution of the electrons emitted from the hot filament. This may be circumvented by using the retarding potential difference (RPD) method of Fox (1959), which can often also distinguish between species with nearly the same mass [process (iii)] but with different ionization potentials. At the low electron energies used, however, ion currents are very small and phase-sensitive ion counting must be employed (Foner and Hudson, 1962). In a few cases the formation of fragment ions has been suppressed by using charge transfer ionization or field ionization (Talroze, 1960; Beckey and Groth, 1959).

Another way of suppressing the interferences due to processes (ii), (iii), and (iv) is the use of nearly monochromatic photon beams for ionization. In many cases a selective photoionization of radicals is possible, even in the presence of a large excess of stable components with nearly the same mass.

Dibeler et al. (1966) have combined a windowless vacuum-ultraviolet monochromator with a magnetic sector-field mass spectrometer. The photon energy can be varied between 6 and 21 eV (2000–600 Å) by using the monochromator in connection with high-power rare gas continuum lamps. This covers the ionization energies of most of the species present in a reactive gas mixture. However, again problems can arise from the low radical-ion currents obtained, since usually only one ion is formed for 10^3

photons and the photon flux through the ionization chamber is around 10^{10} (quanta sec^{-1}) at 2 Å ($\sim$0.02 eV) bandwidth. Jones and Bayes (1972) have successfully used inert gas resonance lamps (Ar, 1065 Å; Kr, 1165 Å, 1236 Å; Xe, 1470 Å; Laufer and McNesby, 1965; Comes and Schlag, 1959) which give photon fluxes around 10^{13} (quanta sec^{-1}) in connection with pinhole sampling for a quadrupole mass spectrometer for detection of radicals in a discharge flow system. Intensities between 10^{14} and 10^{15} (quanta sec^{-1}) have been obtained by Davis and Braun (1968) for a number of wavelengths down to 1040 Å ($\sim$11.9 eV, the LiF window cutoff) with microwave excitation of various flowing gas mixtures. These lamps can also be used for photoionization.

The presence of surfaces in the ion source can lead to an increase [process (iv)] as well as to a decrease (due to heterogeneous recombination) in radical concentration. To reduce the influence of pyrolysis and wall reactions in the ion source, particles that have hit the walls before entering the ionization region must be removed. This can be achieved by differential filament pumping, construction of relatively open ion sources with reduced wall area, use of a well-collimated molecular beam system, and effective cryopumping with cooled walls of the ion source.

e. Calibration for Free Radicals. The facts described in the preceding sections illustrate that a theoretical determination of the absolute mass spectrometric sensitivity for a certain particle sampled from a reactive gas mixture is a very complicated task. It would not only have to include corrections for the effects described but also data on absolute electron impact (or photon) ionization cross sections as a function of electron (photon) energy, the transmission of the ion optics as a function of the particle mass, and the velocity and internal excitation of the neutral particles, since the ion source is a velocity-sensitive detector and the fragment pattern may depend on internal energy (see Chapter 11). Thus, in most cases the problem can only be solved by extensive calculation. However, particularly for unstable components this is hardly possible if large variations of composition and temperature occur during the reaction, as, for instance, in flames. The situation is more favorable in an isothermal flow reactor, where the high dilution of the reactants with inert carrier gas ensures that temperature and composition are essentially unaffected by the reaction. Defined concentrations of reactive atoms may be generated in the flow reactor by using a microwave discharge in combination with a suitable "titration reaction."

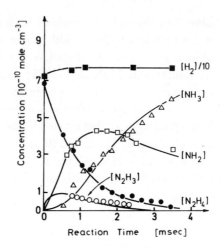

FIG. 7. Computed (lines) and measured (points) concentration–time profiles in the $H + N_2H_4$ reaction; $T = 300$ K, $p = 1$ Torr, $[H]_0/[N_2H_4]_0 = 4.5$ (Gehring *et al.*, 1972).

Significant differences in the mass spectrometric sensitivities have been reported for molecular leak and nozzle beam sampling, e.g., the sensitivity for oxygen atoms relative to that for molecular oxygen increases by a factor of three for the nozzle beam arrangement (Hoyermann *et al.*, 1967), indicating that atom loss occurs for "pinhole" sampling. For the analysis of atoms, electron energies between 15 and 25 eV are usually chosen, since here fragmentation of stable molecules is not too great, while the ionization cross sections are sufficient for accurate detection (ion counting). Accurate data for ionization cross sections are scarce at these low ionization energies (Kieffer and Dunn, 1966). Also, the simple additivity postulate does not seem to be applicable in this energy region (Otvos and Stevenson, 1956).

In some cases absolute radical concentrations may be determined by using fast elementary reactions with known absolute rate constants for the generation or consumption of the radicals (see Fig. 7).

Another possibility is to use the mass balance of reacting systems if only a small number of elementary steps is involved. However, even relative factors obtained by this procedure cannot be used for different experimental arrangements, e.g., sensitivities reported for methyl radicals relative to that for methane vary between 0.45 and 1.7 at 50 eV ionization energy (Le Goff *et al.*, 1966).

A method which is almost free of the problems of interference from other compounds of the reactive gas mixture is electron resonance spectroscopy.

4. *Detection of Gas-Phase Radicals in Flow Systems by Electron Resonance Spectroscopy*

Since the first electron resonance studies of the stable paramagnetic gases O_2 and NO by Behringer and Castle (1949) many free atoms (F, Cl, Br, I; O, S, Se, Te; N, P; H, D), a number of diatomic radicals (e.g., OH, SH, SeH, TeH, SO, ClO, BrO, NS, CN, NF, SF, SeF), and a few polyatomic species (e.g., NO_2, NF_2, NCO) have been detected in the gas phase by this technique (for references see Carrington and Levy, 1967; Carrington *et al.*, 1970; Hoyermann and Wolfrum, 1970).

In the application of electron resonance as an analytical tool for the study of elementary reactions two problems arise:

(i) The chemically labile species must be brought into the microwave resonance cavity in the gap of the magnet.

(ii) As in any absorption spectroscopy, the relationship between the measured absorption signal and the particle concentration is theoretically clear but practically complex and depends on many parameters.

Solution of the first problem depends on utilizing the features of the radical source. Kondratiev, Nalbandyan, and Balakhin (1964) surrounded the whole of a diffusion flame by the resonant cavity. They determined the dependence of the overall concentrations of atoms and some radicals on the composition of the mixture in the rarified flame.

Carrington and Levy (1967) designed a cylindrical quartz mixing cell (46 mm i.d.) in which radicals can be produced by adding a second gas to the products of a microwave discharge. The mixing cell can be surrounded by two cylindrical cavities operating in the TE_{011} mode and is designed so that the electric and magnetic vectors of the microwave field are perpendicular to the dc magnetic field in the sample region. Thus, magnetic as well as electric dipole transitions can be observed. The latter have usually a much higher intensity (the ratios of observed signal heights are of the order of 10^4 in the limit of nonsaturated signals). This is especially valuable for diatomic or polyatomic radicals, which give a complex spectrum due to the interaction of rotational and orbital angular magnetic momentum and possibly spin momentum as well. By this technique it is possible to obtain information about atoms and a number of properties of diatomic radicals (bond length, nuclear hyperfine constant, Λ-doubling intervals, etc.) formed in a microwave discharge or in atom–molecule reactions. For these short-lived species the electron resonance technique has a higher sensitivity

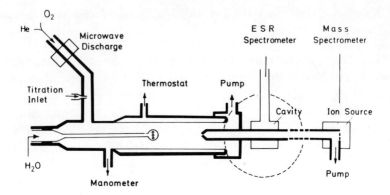

Fig. 8. Discharge-flow system combined with ESR and mass spectrometer (see text).

than ordinary microwave spectroscopy since, due to the use of the resonant cavity, only a few centimeters of sample path length are required. Ground as well as excited states can be observed: atoms in states with different total angular momentum ($^2P_{3/2}$ and $^2P_{1/2}$ halogen atoms, $^3P_{0,1,2}$ oxygen atoms), and electronically [SO($^1\Delta$)] and vibrationally excited radicals (OH, SO). However, no kinetic investigations were carried out with this experimental setup (Carrington et al., 1970).

Measurements of rate constants have involved mostly the discharge-flow system already described. An example is shown schematically in Fig. 8 (Hoyermann et al., 1967). It consists of a glass or quartz flow reactor which can be heated to temperatures between 200 and 1100 K by means of a thermostat or a furnace. Gas samples are taken from the flow reactor by means of a quartz sampling tube. The samples are allowed to expand to 0.1 Torr and are then rapidly pumped through the resonant cavity of an ESR spectrometer and later (after recombination of the radicals on the sampling tube walls) to the ion source of a mass spectrometer for analysis of stable components. The sampling hole is constructed so that contact of the sampled gas with the entrance wall is minimal at sufficiently high pressure and so that mass separation of the gases cannot occur. This can be checked with the mass spectrometer. The magnet and the cavity of the ESR spectrometer can be moved along the sampling tube, so that atom losses can be determined and an extrapolation to the probe tip can be made, which is especially valuable for sampling in low-pressure flames (see Chapter 12).

A number of atom–molecule rate constants have been measured with a similar arrangement described by Westenberg and de Haas (1969) and Brown and Thrush (1967). The ESR cavity is also located at a fixed position outside the flow reactor, but here the total gas flow passes through the cavity. This avoids sampling, but reduces the spatial resolution since the concentration measurements are averaged over the cavity volume, and increases the amount of particles that have reacted in the boundary layer of the flow reactor, since lower pressure (1–3 Torr) and longer (1 m) flow tubes are required.

Relation between Electron Resonance Signal and Atom Concentrations. In a typical electron resonance experiment the amount of microwave energy P_A absorbed by the species is measured at fixed microwave frequency ω_0 while the external magnetic field H is varied (see Vol. IV, Chapter 10). P_A is given in terms of the average value of the microwave power at the sample in the cavity H_1^2, the imaginary part of the magnetic susceptibility $\chi''(\omega)$, and ω_0 as

$$P_A = \tfrac{1}{2}\omega_0 H_1^2 \chi''. \tag{2.10}$$

χ'' is related to the number of particles N available for the microwave transition $i \rightarrow j$ by

$$\chi'' = (N/\beta g_{\text{eff}})|\mu_{ij}|^2 f(H - H_0) \tag{2.11}$$

where β is the Bohr magneton, $g_{\text{eff}} = (\hbar/\beta)(d\omega/dH)$ is the effective g-factor, μ_{ij} is the transition matrix element, and $f(H - H_0)$ is a normalized line shape function.

The actual form of χ'' is affected by several processes:

(i) The reorientation of the net magnetization along the field direction.

If the species maintain an equilibrium during power absorption, χ'' can be related to the total number of absorbing species N_0 and the so-called "longitudinal" relaxation time t_1 for establishing equilibrium with the heat bath at the temperature T:

$$\chi'' = \frac{N_0 \hbar\omega \exp(-E_i/kT)}{kT g_{\text{eff}} \beta Z}|\mu_{ij}|^2 f(H - H_0)$$
$$\times \left[1 + \frac{2t_1 H_1^2}{g_{\text{eff}} \beta\hbar}|\mu_{ij}|^2 f(H - H_0)\right]^{-1} \tag{2.12}$$

where Z is the partition function (Pake, 1962; Carrington and McLachlan, 1967). The case where the absorbing species do not remain equilibrated during microwave power absorption is treated by Potis (1953).

(ii) Line broadening processes, characterized by the so-called "transverse" relaxation time t_2. Assuming a Lorentzian line profile, one can describe $f(H - H_0)$ by

$$f(H - H_0) = (t_2 g_{eff} \beta/\hbar\pi) [1 + t_2{}^2 (H - H_0)^2 g_{eff} \beta/\hbar]^{-1}. \qquad (2.13)$$

(iii) In order to increase the sensitivity of the spectrometer, it is customary to apply a modulating magnetic field in addition to the dc field. The signal detected is therefore proportional to the amplitude of the Fourier component of $\chi''(H)$ at the modulation frequency ω_{MA}. It is displayed in differential form after demodulation with a crystal detector and usually two parameters of the signal are measured: s, the peak-to-peak height in arbitrary units, and w, the distance between the peaks in gauss.

Upon increasing the modulation amplitude, the signal height s increases until a maximum is reached for a modulation amplitude corresponding to the full width of the absorption line. Signal height s can also be maximized with respect to microwave power P_A until saturation occurs ($P_A^{max} \sim 1/t_1 t_2$). The optimal signal-to-noise conditions at s_{max} can be used for relative concentration measurements, provided that t_1 and t_2 are independent of N_0. As discussed by Westenberg and de Haas (1969), this is the case for non-S-state atoms and radicals under normal circumstances. For S-state atoms [mostly H(^{2}S) and N(^{4}S)] this is only true if other paramagnetic species are present in large, constant concentrations compared to the atom concentration.

As suggested by Krongelb and Strandberg (1959), the problem of determining absolute atom and radical concentrations can be solved if the solid standards used in condensed-phase electron resonance investigations are replaced by suitable stable paramagnetic reference gases which fill the resonant cavity in the same manner as the unstable radicals. For atoms a magnetic dipole transition, the so-called F line of molecular oxygen [$O_2(^3\Sigma)$, $K = 1$, $J = 2$, $M = 0 \rightarrow 1$], is suitable. Relative calibration factors Q_{at} for unsaturated and non-modulation-broadened atom lines are given by Westenberg and de Haas (1964, 1965). The absolute atom concentrations determined by ESR from

$$\frac{N_{at}}{N_{O_2}} = Q_{at} \frac{\int_0^\infty \chi''_{at} \, dH}{\int_0^\infty \chi''_{O_2} \, dH} \qquad (2.14)$$

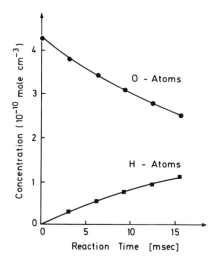

Fig. 9.   Decrease of oxygen atom and increase of hydrogen atom concentrations with reaction time for

$$O(^3P) + H_2O \longrightarrow OH + OH$$

$$O(^3P) + OH \longrightarrow O_2 + H$$

measured with ESR spectrometry; $T = 849$ K, $p = 5.5$ Torr, $[H_2O]_0 = 7.7 \times 10^{-9}$ mole cm^{-3}.

can be compared with concentrations measured by gas-phase titration. Figure 9 shows as an example the consumption and formation of atoms in the $O + H_2O$ reaction as measured by electron resonance spectrometry.

C. Pulse Methods

Within the isothermal flow reactor an atom reaction is started by mixing the two reactive components in a carrier gas. If the reaction is complete in less than 1 msec, reaction and mixing processes are normally difficult to distinguish from each other (see Chapter 12).

Moreover, due to the low pressure usually employed, wall reactions and decomposition of addition complexes formed in the primary step may take place to an appreciable extent, so that many subsequent steps mask the primary step completely. Some of these problems be can avoided if the atoms or radicals are homogeneously generated in the presence of the second reactive component on a very short time scale.

1. *Flash Photolysis*

One of the most successful examples of such a pulse method is "flash photolysis," developed by Norrish and Porter (1949), Herzberg and Ramsay (1951), and others.

By discharging a bank of condensers (charged to 10–20 kV) through a quartz tube containing a rare gas at low pressure, a pulse of high-intensity light (10^{-3}–10^{-1} Einstein per flash) is generated and passed into an absorbing system. Under these conditions large concentrations of atoms and radicals may be formed, so that conventional spectroscopic means can be used to follow their concentration as a function of time after the photolysis flash (for more details see Chapter 10). However, several comments must be made about the application of the classical flash-photolysis arrangement for the measurements of elementary rate constants.

The absorption of the large flash energies may raise the temperature of the absorbing system and also generate nonuniform regions and shock waves in the reaction vessel. Also, at high radical concentrations second-order recombination processes play a dominant role. This requires a determination of absolute concentrations by optical methods, which is often difficult to achieve, since absolute optical transition probabilities and extremely high resolution are required. In addition, the half-life of the flash may no longer be short compared with the reaction time, which demands an accurate knowledge of the time and wavelength dependences of the flash intensity.

Application of flash photolysis to the measurement of rate constants of atom reactions has therefore led to an experimental arrangement quite different from the original apparatus (see Fig. 10).

(i) The discharge energies are reduced by a factor of 100 to 5–50 J, by which light pulses of around 10^{-6} sec half-width with a reduced afterglow can be produced.

(ii) The decrease in photon flux of the flash lamp is partially compensated by increasing the photon energy using reactor windows with lower wavelength cutoff in the vacuum-ultraviolet region (LiF $\lambda > 1050$ Å, Suprasil $\lambda > 1650$ Å), where high absorption coefficients for atom generation by photodissociation of small molecules exist.

(iii) The photographic plate is replaced by one or more photomultipliers and the spectroscopic flash by a high-intensity microwave-excited atomic resonance lamp (Braun, 1968).

The high transition probabilities (10^7–10^9 sec^{-1}) of the atomic resonance

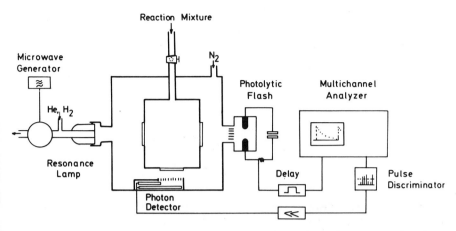

Fig. 10. Scheme of a repetitive flash photolysis-resonance fluorescence apparatus (Davis *et al.*, 1972).

lines allow the detection of low atom concentrations either by absorption or resonance fluorescence. Determination of absolute concentrations by absorption measurements are hampered by the high spectral resolution needed in the vacuum-uv region and the strong, broadened lines emitted from the microwave plasma of the lamps. Fortunately, the low atom concentrations usually allow a high excess of stable reactants, so that absolute rate constants of atom–molecule reactions can be determined by the pseudo-first-order atom decay on a relative concentration scale. However, the Lambert–Beer law must often be used in a modified form (Donovan and Husain, 1971),

$$I = I_0 \exp[-(l\varepsilon N)^\gamma] \tag{2.15}$$

where l is the optical path length, ε is the extinction coefficient, N is the atom concentration, and $\gamma \leq 1$ is an empirical constant.

Some difficulties in the absorption measurements may be circumvented by using atomic resonance fluorescence. This requires detection of low-level light signals as a function of reaction time. Since noise is a statistical quantity measuring accuracy it increases at N measurements proportionally to $\sqrt{N}$. Repetitive flashing in connection with photon counting and averaging in a multichannel analyzer, or boxcar integration of the analog signal of the multiplier, allows measurements down to concentrations as low as 10^7 hydrogen atoms per cm^3 (Braun *et al.*, 1970).

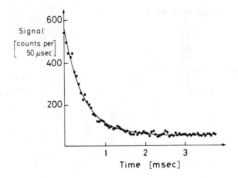

FIG. 11. Lyman-α fluorescence curve of the hydrogen atom decay in the addition of hydrogen atoms to propylene; $T = 298$ K, $p = 50$ Torr, $[C_3H_6]_0 = 2.5 \times 10^{-9}$ mole cm^{-3}, 50 flashes with 75 J energy, (Kurylo et al., 1971).

Since for many atomic resonance lines the wavelength cutoff of the photolyzing radiation can be chosen so that photolysis and fluorescence light are spectrally separated, the noise from scattered light is sufficiently low (Fig. 11).

Besides fluorescence radiation, the various chemiluminescent reactions used for atom detection in flow systems (see Section B,1) and emission from metastable atoms can also be utilized in connection with the repetitive technique (Welge, 1970, 1971; Stuhl and Niki, 1971).

Atom–Radical Reactions. Absolute rate constants of atom–radical reactions can be obtained with the arrangement shown in Fig. 12 (Reinhardt et al., 1969) where flash photolysis is combined with a fast discharge flow system. By a short, intense photolysis flash (3000 J) radicals are generated in a flow reactor in the presence of an excess of atoms which are continuously produced by a microwave discharge. Thus, only relative measurements of radical concentrations as a function of time after the photolysis flash are necessary for the determination of absolute rate constants of atom–radical reactions.

To maintain isothermal conditions and to avoid radical–radical reactions during the experiment the sensitivity of the kinetic absorption spectroscopy is increased by a multiple-pass mirror system. Multilayer coated mirrors allow over 100 traversals of the analyzing light beam along the flow tube without appreciable light loss. Further increase of sensitivity may

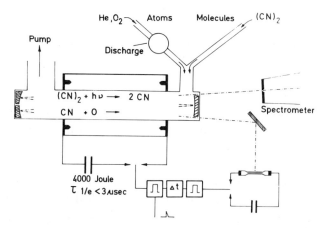

FIG. 12. Schematic diagram of a discharge flow system combined with flash photo-lysis for the investigation of atom–radical reactions (Reinhardt *et al.*, 1969).

be achieved by using a tunable dye laser and placing the flow tube into the laser resonant cavity (Peterson *et al.*, 1971; Thrash *et al.*, 1971).

2. *Photolysis by Intermittent Illumination*

Absolute rate constants of radical reactions can be successfully evaluated with a technique which employs much lower light flux ($\sim 10^{-10}$ Einstein sec^{-1}) than flash photolysis experiments. Johnston and co-workers (1967) have described a "molecular modulation" technique in which ultraviolet fluorescent lamps are periodically turned on and off at frequencies between 0.1 and 40 Hz. In the reaction cell (220 cm in length, 40 cm i.d.) gold-coated mirrors are used to obtain an optical path of 72 m in the infrared. By a 400-Hz modulation of the absorption light beam a phase-sensitive detection of infrared (and ultraviolet) absorption spectra is possible. Besides spectroscopic information, rate constants of radical reactions can be derived from the measured phase shifts of the modulated signal relative to the "square-wave" ultraviolet radiation.

A similar technique has been employed by Atkinson and Cvetanović (1971). They used a modulated low-pressure mercury arc for generation of oxygen atoms by mercury photosensitization of nitrous oxide. The phase shift of the NO_2 "air-afterglow" emission relative to the intermittent mercury resonance radiation can then be related to the decay of oxygen atoms.

3. *Pulse Radiolysis*

In pulse radiolysis, ionizing radiation (electrons from a linear accelerator, x-ray pulses) is used instead of light to generate the radicals. Compared with flash photolysis, it is easier to obtain short ($\sim 10^{-8}$ sec) radiation pulses with high intensity. Thus, rate constants of fast addition reactions of atoms to unsaturated molecules can be measured up to pressures of several atmospheres by pulse radiolysis in combination with atomic resonance absorption or fluorescence spectrophotometry (Bishop and Dorfman 1970, 1971).

As in flash photolysis, care must be taken that the absorption of ionizing radiation is uniform throughout the reaction cell if the reactions studied are not first order. Further complications may arise from interfering reactions with the charged species initially produced and traces of impurities at the high densities employed.

4. *Shock Waves*

A shock wave can change the physical state of matter drastically on a very short time scale. A gas sample may be heated from room temperature to 10^4 K within 10^{-9} sec, and pressures up to 10^3 atm can be reached. These conditions may be held between 10^{-6} and 10^{-3} sec.

Application of shock waves to the study of elementary chemical processes is possible most conveniently in a shock tube, first described by Vieille in 1899. The design of the shock tube is very simple. A metal or glass tube is divided into a high-pressure ("driver" gas) and a low-pressure (reaction mixture) region by a diaphragm (Mylar, aluminum foil). The diaphragm can be destroyed by increasing the pressure of the "driver" gas or by directly puncturing it with a needle. Formation of the shock wave after the diaphragm is broken may best be visualized with a model proposed by Becker (1922). For a quantitative determination of the physical properties of the gas mixture behind the shock wave, the shock front velocity is measured and the conservation relations for mass, momentum, and energy are applied to the thermodynamic data of the reaction mixture. These calculations are strictly valid only for an "ideal," one-dimensional shock front and experimental conditions for kinetic measurements must therefore be selected with great care. At the least the dilution of the reactive component should be high. (Further details may be found in monographs by Bradley (1962); Gaydon and Hurle (1963); Green and Toennies (1964).)

It should be noted that the time scale obtained by monitoring the particle concentration at a fixed observation point along the shock tube is not identical with the reaction time scale for incident shock wave experiments, since the heated gas is moving along the shock tube behind the shock front. Strictly speaking, the use of a shock tube is therefore also a flow method, but since separate mixing of the atoms with their reactants is not necessary, the main advantage of a pulse technique is obtained. Net motion of the gas sample under observation can be avoided if the shock wave reflected at the shock tube end plate is utilized for kinetic measurements. In this case shock front curvature and boundary layer effects must be accounted for.

In order to use the controlled temperature conditions offered by the shock tube for the measurement of rate constants of atom reactions, two techniques have been applied.

(i) Atoms are produced by thermal dissociation of small molecules containing a weak atom–molecule bond, e.g., oxygen atoms from the thermal decomposition of ozone

$$O_3 + M \xrightarrow{\ a\ } O_2 + O + M.$$

At high concentrations of M and at relatively high temperatures the decomposition reaction can be made sufficiently fast so that the reaction

$$O + O_3 \xrightarrow{\ b\ } 2O_2$$

plays a minor role compared to the reaction of the oxygen atoms with an added molecule RX,

$$O + RX \xrightarrow{\ c\ } \text{products}.$$

Usually only the concentration–time history of the molecule RX is followed behind the shock wave, by monitoring the infrared emission of RX with a fast infrared detector (InSb, GeAu). Thus, the accuracy of k_c depends on the calculated atomic oxygen concentration.

(ii) The majority of rate data deduced from shock tube experiments have been obtained by comparing observed concentration–time profiles for species—which can be followed by ultraviolet absorption, infrared emission, or mass spectroscopy—with profiles calculated by numerical integration of a postulated mechanism.

Thus, elementary steps in the hydrogen/oxygen reaction have been investigated by Schott and Getzinger (1972), Wakefield *et al.* (1969), and others by following the ultraviolet absorption due to the hydroxyl radical and infrared emission of water vapor.

Mass spectrometric sampling from shock tubes is much more difficult than from the isothermal flow reactor (Bradley and Kistiakowsky, 1961; Dove and Moulton, 1965).

On the other hand, analysis of stable end products of a shock wave experiment can usually be done more precisely outside the shock tube. This is employed in the "single pulse" shock tube, where rapid cooling of the heated gas is achieved through the expansion wave generated either by intersection of the reflected shock wave with the contact surface or use of a separate expansion chamber (Lifshitz et al., 1963).

A similar technique which may be applied is the adiabatic compression method (Jost, 1949; Martinengo, 1967). The apparatus consists of a cylinder containing the diluted reaction mixture and a compressing piston which is driven by a falling weight or expanding gas and stopped as fast as possible. Compared to the shock tube, the time range for kinetic measurements is increased to 10^{-1}–1 sec and the temperature range closes the gap between the isothermal flow reactor and shock tube experiments.

III. Reactions of Hydrogen Atoms

A. The Reaction with Molecular Hydrogen

The exchange reaction between a hydrogen atom and a hydrogen molecule is the classical example of an atom–molecule reaction. This reaction provides the simplest case where the fundamental kinetic process of bond breaking under the influence of new bond formation can be studied theoretically. For this reason much effort has been given to experimental and theoretical investigations of the $H + H_2$ exchange reaction over the past four decades. However, for a long time it was not clear whether discrepancies between experiment and theory were to be blamed more on shortcomings of one than on those of the other.

For the experimental determination of the rate of the reaction

$$H + H_2 \longrightarrow H_2 + H$$

some labeling of reactants and products is required. This can be obtained by observing the para–ortho hydrogen interconversion or the appropriate isotopic exchange reactions.

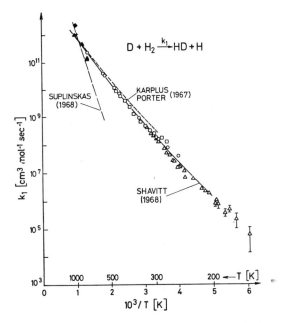

FIG. 13.   Calculated (curves) and measured (points) rate constants for the reaction of deuterium atoms with molecular hydrogen (for symbols see Wagner and Wolfrum, 1971).

Figure 13 shows in Arrhenius form experimental data (points) and theoretical results (curves) for the reaction

$$D + H_2 \longrightarrow HD + H$$
$$\Delta H_0^\circ = -0.8 \quad \text{kcal mole}^{-1}. \tag{3.1}$$

Ridley *et al.* (1966) (Fig. 13, open squares) produced D atoms in a flow system by passing D_2 over a hot tungsten filament. Atom concentrations were measured with a wire calorimeter (see Section II,B,2) and concentrations of H_2, HD, and D_2 were obtained by thermal conductivity. Westenberg and de Haas (1969a) (Fig. 13, open circles) employed a discharge flow system coupled to an ESR spectrometer see Section II B,4.

Later on Mitchell and LeRoy (1973, open triangles) have also used ESR detection.

Figure 13 shows that the direct measurements of k_1 cover a wider temperature range and give more reliable data than earlier investigations (solid points) which used a complex analysis of the overall conversion

$$H_2 + D_2 \longrightarrow 2HD.$$

The curvature of the data from Ridley et al. around 300 K can be explained by an apparent increase of the measured reaction rate due to back diffusion of reagent gases into the atom production region (Ridley, 1968).

The theoretical determination of the thermal rate constant $k_1(T)$ for reaction (3.1) can be divided into three steps:

(i) Construction of the Born–Oppenheimer potential energy hypersurface for the D–H–H (H_3) complex. (Within the framework of the Born–Oppenheimer approximation the isotopic substitution has no effect on the surface.)

(ii) Description of the microscopic behavior of the three atoms on this hypersurface.

(iii) Evaluation of the macroscopic reaction rate constant $k_1(T)$ assuming an equilibrium Maxwell–Boltzmann distribution of velocities and internal energy states for D and H_2.

The ultimate goal in the theory of chemical reactions is to proceed in these steps by accurate a priori quantum calculations. However, even for the simple $H + H_2$ case this has so far not been achieved completely.

For the first step two approaches have been used in the H_3 system:

(a) "Ab initio" calculations.
(b) Semiempirical treatments.

(a) Shavitt et al. (1968) have given one of the most complete a priori variational calculations of the H_3 potential energy surface. The calculations have been made for optimized-exponent basis sets consisting of 15 orbitals (1s, 1s', $2p_x$, $2p_y$, $2p_z$ on each nucleus). From the energy profile along the minimum potential energy path on this surface a potential barrier height E_c of 11 kcal mole^{-1} is obtained for the linear H_3 complex.

The calculated E_c increases to 12.6 (18.2) kcal mole^{-1} if the H atom approaches the axis of the hydrogen molecule at an angle of 150° (120°) indicating that the collinear configuration is energetically the most favorable one (see Fig. 14a).

Ironically, the height of the potential energy barrier for $H + H_2$ calculated in 1968 with the aid of high-speed electronic computers is not far from the results of the ultrasimple valence bond treatment for $H + H_2$ given over 40 years ago. In 1928 London regarded the H_3 complex as the superposition of three H_2 molecules

$$H \leftarrow r_1 \rightarrow H \leftarrow r_2 \rightarrow H$$

$$\longleftarrow\!\!\!\!\longrightarrow r_3 \longleftarrow\!\!\!\!\longrightarrow$$

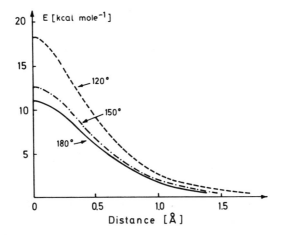

FIG. 14a. Energy profiles along the minimum-energy path for the H_3 system. Variation of nuclear geometry (Shavitt *et al.*, 1968).

The potential energy of the H_3 system was expressed simply in terms of the three Coulombic interaction integrals Q and the three exchange integrals A, B, C:

$$E(r_1, r_2, r_3) = Q_1 + Q_2 + Q_3$$
$$\pm [\tfrac{1}{2}(A - B)^2 + (B - C)^2 + (A - C)^2]^{1/2}. \quad (3.2)$$

As shown in Fig. 14b, this calculation leads to a barrier of $E_c = 8.8$ kcal mole^{-1} between reactants and products. However, a more precise treatment of the London method (including terms resulting from overlap and three-center terms) gives $E_c = 33$ kcal mole^{-1} and destroys the good, accidental agreement with modern results. In addition, the basin on the top of the pass that represents a metastable H_3 complex at $r_1 = r_2 = 0.8$ Å (Fig. 14b) could not be confirmed in molecular beam experiments (Fite *et al.*, 1972) or by the variational calculations.

(b) The unsatisfactory results of the early ab initio approaches led to the development of "semiempirical" treatments. In the earliest surface for H_3 derived from such a treatment (London–Eyring–Polanyi, LEP, surface) the integrals Q and A, B, C were approximated by the Morse function V

$$Q = fV, \qquad A = (1 - f)V$$

where f is a constant factor. However, Sato (1955) pointed out that not only does the LEP surface of H_3 possess the basin at $r_1 = r_2 = 0.8$ Å

($\Delta E_c = 3$ kcal mole^{-1} for $f = 0.14$), but it possesses a further basin at $r_1 = r_2 = 0.3$ Å ($\Delta E_c = 75$ kcal mole^{-1} for $f = 0.12$). As an adjustable parameter Sato replaced f by S^2, the square of the Heitler–London overlap integral

$$E(r_1, r_2, r_3) = \frac{1}{1 + S^2} \Big\{ Q_1 + Q_2 + Q_3$$
$$\pm \Big[\frac{1}{2}(A - B)^2 + (B - C)^2 + (A - C)^2 \Big]^{1/2} \Big\}. \qquad (3.3)$$

For $S^2 = 0.18$ the h_3 potential surface has no basin and gives $E_c = 15.8$ kcal mole^{-1} (see Fig. 14b).

The best semiempirical H_3 surface was generated by Porter and Karplus (1964). They used the complete formulas for the nonionic valence-bond treatment for the three-orbital, three-electron system corresponding to H_3 as given by Slater (1931). The integrals were evaluated by a combination of theoretical and semiempirical treatments. This gives $E_c = 9.1$ kcal mole^{-1} at $r_1 = r_2 = 0.91$ Å.

As can be seen from Fig. 14b, the difference between ab initio and semiempirical calculations for E_c in linear H_3 is now ± 2 kcal mole^{-1} and these values bracket the experimental ones (see Fig. 15). Of course, as illustrated by the London method, energy difference considerations alone are a very poor basis for judging the accuracy of ab initio calculations.

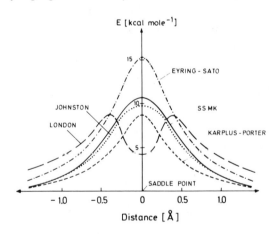

FIG. 14b. Various calculations for the linear H—H—H system (London, 1928; Sato, 1955; Porter and Karplus, 1964; Johnston, 1966; Shavitt et al., 1968).

Once the H_3 potential energy surface is constructed, the calculation of $k_1(T)$ through steps (ii) and (iii) can be divided into the categories:

(a) Solution of the reactive scattering problem.

(b) Introduction of simplifying models.

(a) A complete quantum mechanical determination of $k_1(T)$ which can be compared with the experimental results is still not available. Nevertheless, calculations by numerically "exact" stationary-wave methods should be possible in the near future (Wolken and Karplus, 1974; Baer and Kouri, 1971). Comparison can be made with the quasiclassical trajectory results of Karplus and Porter (1967). In these calculations the Hamiltonian equations for the three-dimensional motion of the three atoms on the semi-empirical Porter–Karplus (1964) surface were integrated by the Runge–Kutta–Gill method. By means of Monte Carlo averages over a large number of appropriately chosen trajectories, the total reaction cross section was determined as a function of the initial relative velocity of D and H_2 and the initial molecular rotation–vibration state of H_2. The thermal rate constant $k_1(T)$ can then be calculated by the Laplace transform of the product of the center-of-mass energy and the state-averaged total reaction cross section. Figure 13 shows the result for $k_1(T)$. (For more details about the trajectory calculations, see Chapter 6.)

(b) The best-known model which avoids the dynamical evaluation of cross sections by the introduction of a statistical formulation is the transition-state theory (TST) of Eyring, Polanyi, Wigner, and others. Here only the form of the potential energy surface in the neighborhood of the "transition region" and the height of the potential barrier must be known to construct an "activated complex" (see Chapter 3).

The properties of the linear DH_2 complex have been derived from the Shavitt et al. (SSMK) surface (1968) by Shavitt (1968). Shavitt also calculated $k_1(T)$ (see Fig. 13) from the transition-state theory by scaling the SSMK surface (E_c is decreased by 11% to 9.8 kcal mole^{-1}) and including a one-dimensional tunneling correction for a specially fitted Eckart barrier.

Suplinskas (1968) has applied a very simple kinematic model to reaction (3.1) and the other isotope variants. This model, suggested by Cross and Wolfgang (1961), represents the H_2 molecule by two hard spheres nearly in contact and the D atom by a third hard sphere, so that the reaction takes place by a direct billiard-ball-type collision between D and H_2. With a kinetic energy threshold for reaction (3.1) of 6 kcal mole^{-1} (see Fig. 15) and a hard-sphere radius of 0.37 Å for H and D the reaction cross sections

$\sigma(v)$ were obtained by calculating the results of a large number of collisions with varied impact parameters and orientations. The thermal rate constant $k_1(T)$ (see Fig. 13) was calculated from the expression

$$k(T) = (2/\pi)^{1/2}(\mu/kT)^{3/2} \int_{v_0}^{\infty} v^3 \sigma(v) \exp(-\mu v^2/2kT)\, dv \qquad (3.4)$$

where μ is the reduced mass, k the Boltzmann constant, and v the relative velocity.

An inspection of Fig. 13 now seems to indicate that the best agreement between experiment and theory is obtained by the transition-state treatment using the ab initio SSMK surface. However, this cannot be regarded as a successful quantitative test for the validity of the transition-state theory (TST). As already mentioned, the calculations of Shavitt involve beside the fundamental assumptions of the TST (equilibrium, separability of the reaction coordinate), further parameters (scaling, tunneling) which are difficult to justify on a priori theoretical grounds. The situation is more favorable for the collinear $H + H_2$ model. Exact quantum mechanical calculations which may be considered as accurate "experimental" one-dimensional rate constants have been compared with TST (Truhlar and Kuppermann, 1971; Truhlar, Kuppermann, Adams, 1973) as well as classical trajectory calculations (Bowman and Kuppermann, 1971). The results generally diverge by a factor of two around 500 K and by an order of magnitude at 200 K. Both collinear and three dimensional calculations of the $H + H_2$ reaction have been carried out in semiclassical calculations by analytic continuation of classical mechanics (George and Miller, 1972; Doll, George, Miller, 1973).

We now discuss the relations between experimental and theoretical approaches to reaction (3.1) in terms of the characteristic energies E_c, the barrier height of the potential energy surface; E_A, the experimental (Arrhenius) activation energy; and E_R, the energy threshold of the reaction.

For $E_c(3.1)$ ab initio calculations give 11 kcal mole^{-1} (Shavitt et al., 1968), 7.6 kcal mole^{-1} (Conroy and Bruner, 1967), and 10.1 kcal mole^{-1} (Liu, 1971). On the semiempirical surface of Porter and Karplus (1964) $E_c(3.1)$ is 9.1 kcal mole^{-1}. As pointed out by Tolman (1920), the Arrhenius activation energy E_A

$$E_A = -R\frac{d \ln k(T)}{d(1/T)} = \langle E^* \rangle - \langle E \rangle \qquad (3.5)$$

is the "difference between the average energy of the molecules which actually react ($\langle E^* \rangle$) and the average energy of all the molecules of that kind ($\langle E \rangle$)." From the experimental points of Fig. 13, $E_A(3.1) = 7.6$ kcal mole^{-1} is derived. From an empirical fit (variation of the Sato parameter S^2) of a semiempirical LEPS potential energy surface to $E_A(3.1)$ Westenberg (1967) obtained $E_c(3.1) = 8.8$ kcal mole^{-1}. However, as already mentioned, Shavitt's scaling of the SSMK surface to the same $E_A(3.1)$ gives $E_c(3.1) = 9.8$ kcal mole^{-1}.

In Fig. 15 the short horizontal lines represent the average energies $\langle E^* \rangle$ and $\langle E \rangle$; also given are the zero-point energies of H_2 and the DH_2 complex. According to TST, E_R, the minimum translational relative kinetic energy for a reactive collision of D with H_2 ($v = 0$, $J = 0$), should correspond to the distance between the zero-point energy of H_2 and the zero-point energy of the DH_2 complex. However, the quasiclassical trajectory calculations (Morokuma and Karplus, 1967) indicate that E_R is usually less than this value. Thus, more energy will be available for crossing the barrier than is suggested by the adiabatic TST model. The only experimental result on $E_R(3.1)$ comes from a photochemical experiment. Kuppermann and White (1966) produced monoenergetic D atoms from DI or DBr photolysis in DI(DBr)/H_2 mixtures. From the amount of HD

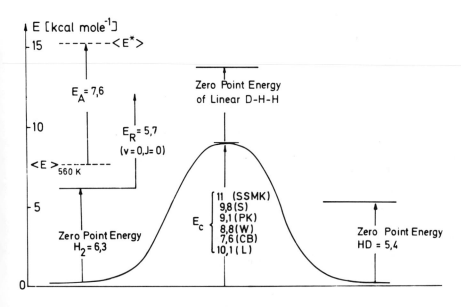

FIG. 15.   Characteristic energies in the $D + H_2$ reaction (see text).

produced by reaction (3.1) they found $E_R(3.1) = 7.6 \pm 0.5$ kcal mole^{-1} for H_2 molecules in thermal equilibrium at 300 K.

Turning from the $H + H_2$ exchange reaction to reactions of H atoms with other molecules, the situation for making a priori predictions changes drastically.

It is theoretically very satisfying to follow the program described in the $H + H_2$ case. However, the needed computer time for making calculations of potential energy surfaces increases with the fourth power of the number of electrons of the reacting species.

It is therefore clear that in spite of the excellent progress that has been made in methods for obtaining polyatomic wave functions, predictions for reactions other than $H + H_2$ are mainly based on empirical or semi-empirical methods and rules. What kind of predictions must be made for the reaction of an H atom with an arbitrarily chosen molecule? To describe a reaction in a thermal system through $k(T)$ the following questions have to be answered:

(a) What are the reaction channels?

(b) What are the rate constants for the possible pathways? How do these rate constants depend on temperature and pressure?

For the univalent hydrogen atom the following categories of reactions can be distinguished.

(i) *Abstraction*
   (a) Hydrogen atom abstraction

$$H + HX \longrightarrow H_2 + X, \quad \text{e.g.:}$$
$$H + CH_4 \longrightarrow H_2 + CH_3.$$

(b) Abstraction of other atoms

$$H + AX \longrightarrow AH + X, \quad \text{e.g.:}$$
$$H + N_2O \longrightarrow OH + N_2.$$

(c) Abstraction of radicals or groups

$$H + RX \longrightarrow RH + X, \quad \text{e.g.:}$$
$$H + CH_3OH \longrightarrow H_2O + CH_3.$$

(ii) *Addition*
(a) Addition to unsaturated systems

$$H + M \longrightarrow HM^*, \quad e.g.:$$

$$H + C_2H_4 \longrightarrow C_2H_5^*.$$

(b) Association with radicals

$$H + R \longrightarrow HR^*, \quad e.g.:$$

$$H + C_2H_5 \longrightarrow C_2H_6^*.$$

(iii) *Substitution*
(a) H-atom displacement

$$D(T) + HX \longrightarrow H + D(T)X, \quad e.g.:$$

$$T + CD_4 \longrightarrow D + CD_3T.$$

(b) Substitution of other atoms and groups

$$T + AX \longrightarrow A + TX, \quad e.g.:$$

$$T + CH_3F \longrightarrow F + CH_3T.$$

Only categories (i) and (ii) will be discussed here since the substitution reactions have a significantly higher activation energy (E_R for $T + CD_4 \approx$ 35 kcal mole^{-1}) than abstraction or addition and are consequently of minor importance in thermally activated systems.

B. Atom Abstraction by Hydrogen Atoms

1. *Abstraction of Hydrogen Atoms*

From the various reaction types mentioned in the preceding section the category (i),(a) looks rather similar to the $H + H_2$ case. One is therefore forced to apply semiempirical methods developed for $H + H_2$ to predict rate constants of such reactions. In this spirit, Johnston and co-workers (1963, 1966) have devised a simple procedure termed the bond-energy bond-order (BEBO) method in which the collinear valence bond model for

$$H\uparrow + H\downarrow\uparrow X \longrightarrow H\uparrow \cdots ① \cdots H\downarrow \cdots ② \cdots \uparrow X \longrightarrow H\uparrow\downarrow H + \uparrow X$$
$$\cdots\cdots\cdots ③ \cdots\cdots\cdots$$

is used. It is supposed that the energy of the system can be decomposed into two partial bonds ① and ② with the order n and $1-n$ and one antibond ③ as suggested by the sign of the electron spin orientations,

$$E(r_1, r_2) = E(n) = E_1(H{\uparrow}{\downarrow}H) + E_2(H{\uparrow}{\downarrow}X) + E_3(H{\uparrow}{\uparrow}X). \qquad (3.6)$$

The reaction is then described in terms of the bond-order coordinate n. Initially n is zero and as the reaction proceeds it approaches one. Since only one parameter is used, the BEBO method does not permit calculation of the whole collinear potential energy surface. Instead, the energy profile $E(n)$ along a path where the sum of bond orders of ① and ② remains unity is obtained. It is assumed that the reaction path is this collinear minimum-energy path leading from reagents to products. Using Pauling's (1947) empirical relationships

$$E = E_s n^{p(q)} \qquad (3.7)$$

$$r = r_s - 0.26 \ln n \qquad (3.8)$$

between bond energy E, bond length r, and bond order n, where $p(q)$ are empirical constants and E_s is the energy and r_s the distance of the single bond, E_1 and E_2 can be represented by

$$E_1 = E_{1s} n^p \qquad (3.9)$$

$$E_2 = E_{2s}(1-n)^q. \qquad (3.10)$$

The third term E_3 in Eq. (3.6) describes the repulsion between the attacking hydrogen atom and the remaining atom or radical X. Sato (1955) has suggested the anti-Morse function V_{tr} as a convenient expression that fits the triplet $^3\Sigma$ repulsion potential curve (Hirschfelder and Linnet, 1950) of the H_2 molecule:

$$V_{tr} = E_s[\exp(-\beta_{H_2} r^*)][1 + 0.5 \exp(-\beta_{H_2} r^*)] \qquad (3.11)$$

where β_{H_2} is the Morse parameter for H_2 ($\beta_{H_2} = 1.94$ Å^{-1}), $r^* = r - r_s$ is the difference between the actual internuclear distance r and the bond length at equilibrium r_s.

Johnston and Parr (1963) pointed out that the fit between Sato's function and the theoretical $H_2(^3\Sigma)$ curve can be improved if a constant factor α is applied to the Sato function. Equation (3.6) can now be written as

$$E(n) = E_{2s}[1 - (1-n)^q] - E_{1s} n^p$$
$$- E_{3s}[\alpha \exp(-\beta_{H_2} r_3^*)][1 + 0.5 \exp(-\beta_{H_2} r_3^*)]. \qquad (3.12)$$

Once Eq. (3.12) is written down, the BEBO method applies the transition-state model to the calculation of $k(T)$. The properties of the activated complex are evaluated by the following procedure: The condition

$$dE(n)/dn = 0 \quad \text{at} \quad E(n) = \text{max} \quad (3.13)$$

gives the value of n at the saddle point (n^+). The bond lengths r_1^+ and r_2^+ of the activated complex are then calculated from Pauling's relations. Force constants and vibration frequencies for the bending and the symmetric and asymmetric stretching modes of the activated complex are obtained from the second derivatives of E with respect to n at $E(n^+) = $ max.

Table I shows a comparison between observed and BEBO-calculated rate constants for some H-atom transfer reactions. In view of the sometimes astonishingly good agreement between BEBO calculations and

TABLE I

COMPARISON OF EXPERIMENTAL AND CALCULATED[a] RATE CONSTANTS FOR
REACTIONS OF HYDROGEN ATOMS WITH SIMPLE HYDRIDES

Reaction	$\log k_{calc}$ (cm^3 $mole^{-1}$ sec^{-1}) $\log k_{exp}$			
	200 K	300 K	400 K	500 K
$H + HCl \rightarrow H_2 + Cl$	8.7	10.2	11.0	11.4
	9.5	10.8	11.4	11.8[b]
	—	10.4[c]	—	—
$H + H_2S \rightarrow H_2 + SH$	9.9	11.1	11.7	12.1
	11.0	11.6	11.9	12.1[d]
$H + CH_4 \rightarrow H_2 + CH_3$	5.9	7.8	9.0	9.8
	—	—	7.4	8.7[e]
$H + N_2H_4 \rightarrow H_2 + N_2H_3$	13.2	13.6	13.8	14.0
	10.3	11.3	11.7	12.0[f]

[a] BEBO method, with $\alpha = 0.5$ and tunneling corrections.
[b] Westenberg and de Haas (1968).
[c] Glass (1974).
[d] Michelcic and Schindler (1970); Braun et al. (1971).
[e] Kurylo and Timmons (1969).
[f] Gehring et al. (1972).

experimental results, a word of caution is necessary. Besides the assumptions of the transition-state model, the BEBO method uses the very simple collinear representation of the reaction. The extension of the Sato function to describe the repulsive energy between H↑ ··· ↑X and A↑ ··· ↑X pairs, where A and X are atoms as well as radicals, has no theoretical justification. The calculated potential barrier heights depend strongly upon the factor α applied to the Sato function. With $\alpha = 0.5$ good agreement for the energy profile of the linear H_3 complex with more sophisticated treatments is obtained (see Fig. 15) and this value is also used in Table I. However, although the mismatch between the Sato function and the theoretical $H_2(^3\Sigma)$ repulsion is reduced in the 0.5–1.3-Å range if $\alpha = 0.65$ is used, the agreement with experimental activation energies may become worse in this case. The BEBO model will also fail if the vibrational amplitudes of the activated complex become large, so that the small-vibration approximation (neglect of cubic and higher terms in the Taylor expansion around the saddle point) breaks down (Johnston, 1966).

As with the LEPS method, the BEBO model permits calculation of $k(T)$ with empirical parameters from the molecular structure of the reactants. There is, of course, also the possibility of considering a series of similar reactions and looking for purely empirical correlations of the Arrhenius parameters. For a homologous series of reactions a relationship between the Arrhenius activation energy E_A and the heat of reaction ΔH_r was given by Polanyi (1935, 1938) and Semenov (1958) as

$$E_A = E_0 + c\, \Delta H_r. \qquad (3.14)$$

Two reactions must be chosen in the homologous series to derive the two parameters E_0 and c. Further Arrhenius activation energies can then be predicted from known bond energies. However, for sufficiently exothermic members of the series negative E_A values are obtained. This can be avoided by a logarithmic expression given by Mok and Polanyi (1969)

$$\Delta \log E_A = -c'\, \Delta(\Delta H_r). \qquad (3.15)$$

The concept of relating a thermodynamic quantity to an Arrhenius parameter can also be used for the preexponential A factor. According to the simple transition-state model with the one-dimensional reaction coordinate, the thermal rate constant $k(T)$ can be put in the form ($\kappa = 1$)

$$k(T) = kT/h \, \exp(-\Delta G_0^{\ddagger}/RT) \qquad (3.16)$$

where $\Delta G_0^\ddagger$ is the Gibbs energy of activation.

$\Delta G_0^\ddagger$ may be expressed in terms of enthalpy and entropy changes. Thus,

$$k(T) = (kT/h) \exp(\Delta S_0^\ddagger/R) \exp(-\Delta H_0^\ddagger/RT). \qquad (3.17)$$

Using the mid-temperature $\bar{T}$ of the measured rate constants, the Arrhenius A factor can be related to the "entropy of activation" $\Delta S_0^\ddagger$ by

$$A = (k\bar{T}/h) \exp(\Delta S_0^\ddagger/R). \qquad (3.18)$$

Calculations of $\Delta S_0^\ddagger$ are usually started by postulating a "tight activated complex" (Benson, 1968). Entropy changes are then estimated with respect to a known molecule by considering changes due to symmetry, spin, additional rotation, etc. Thus, for example, for the reaction

$$H + C_2H_6 \longrightarrow H_2 + C_2H_5 \qquad (3.19)$$

$$S_0^\ddagger(C_2H_7^{\cdot}) \geq S_0^\ddagger(C_2H_6) + \overset{\text{symmetry}}{R \ln 6} + \overset{\text{spin}}{R \ln 2} \qquad (3.20)$$

$$\Delta S_0^\ddagger \geq S_0^\ddagger(C_2H_7^{\cdot}) - S^\circ(C_2H_6) - S^\circ(H)$$

$$\Delta S_0^\ddagger \geq - S^\circ(H) + R \ln 12$$

with $\bar{T} = 400$ K, the following lower limit for the A factor is obtained:

$$A \geq (k\bar{T}/h) \exp(\Delta S_0^\ddagger/R) = 10^{13.1} \text{ cm}^3 \text{ mole}^{-1} \text{ sec}^{-1}. \qquad (3.21)$$

The difference between this and the observed value ($10^{13.6}$ cm^3 mole^{-1} sec^{-1}, Dove and Clark (1973)) may now be explained by assuming some "looseness" of the activated complex. However, any discussion of properties of the activated complex in terms of entropy changes derived from experimental A factors must recognize that Eq. (3.16) involves very drastic assumptions.

While rate constants for H-atom transfer from simple hydrides can usually be obtained in a straightforward manner, direct measurements for larger molecules are often hampered due to the complexity of subsequent atom–radical and radical–molecule reactions. As an example, Fig. 16 illustrates the reactions occurring after mixing H_2O_2 with H atoms at room temperature. At the first step HO_2 as well as OH radicals can be produced. The HO_2 radicals react quickly with further H atoms to form mainly OH radicals. At 300 K the attack of OH on H_2O_2 occurs 10^2 times faster than the reaction with H atoms. Thus, in the presence of H atoms

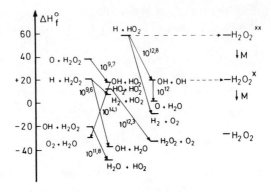

FIG. 16. $\Delta H_f°$ diagram of reactants and products for the elementary steps in the $H + H_2O_2$ reaction. The rate constants are given in $cm^3\ mole^{-1}\ sec^{-1}$ at room temperature.

a chain reaction takes place. A direct measurement of the rate constant of the first step is possible only under rather extreme conditions, such as, for example, the following:

1. Measurements of H-atom decay with an excess of H_2O_2

$$[H_2O_2] : [H] \gg k_{H+H_2O_2}/k_{OH+H_2O_2}.$$

This might be achieved with Lyman-α-fluorescence detection of H atoms (see Section II,C,1).

2. Measurements of H_2O_2 decay with an excess of H atoms

$$[H] : [H_2O_2] \gg k_{H+H_2O_2}/k_{H+HO_2}$$

with a molecular beam sampling mass spectrometer (Section II,B,3).

Actual rate constant measurements on this reaction have been carried out in a different way. Hydrogen atoms were replaced by D atoms and the chain reaction was suppressed with added O atoms (Albers et al., 1971).

Studies on the influence of H_2 on the homogeneous decomposition of H_2O_2 indicate that at higher temperatures (700–1200 K), in addition to H abstraction, the formation of OH and H_2O become important in the $H + H_2O_2$ reaction. It appears that this reaction channel requires a higher activation energy than the H-atom abstraction. It would therefore be interesting to study the products from reactions of H atoms with H_2O_2 at different initial H-atom energies.

TABLE II

RATE CONSTANTS FOR REACTIONS OF HYDROGEN ATOMS WITH THE ISOELECTRONIC
MOLECULES H_2O_2, N_2H_4, AND C_2H_6 AT ROOM TEMPERATURE

Reaction	$-\Delta H^{\circ}_{298}$ (kcal mole^{-1})	$\log k$ (cm^3 mole^{-1} sec^{-1})
$H + H_2O_2 \rightarrow HO_2 + H_2$	14.6	9.6[a]
$H + HO_2 \rightarrow OH + OH$	38.3	12.4[b]
$OH + H_2O_2 \rightarrow H_2O + HO_2$	29.6	12.2[c]
$H + N_2H_4 \rightarrow N_2H_3 + H_2$	28	11.3[d]
$H + N_2H_3 \rightarrow NH_2 + NH_2$	15	12.2[d]
$NH_2 + N_2H_4 \rightarrow NH_3 + N_2H_3$	29	11.5[d]
$H + C_2H_6 \rightarrow C_2H_5 + H_2$	5.9	7.6[e]
$H + C_2H_5 \rightarrow CH_3 + CH_3$	10.1	13.6[f]
$CH_3 + C_2H_6 \rightarrow CH_4 + C_2H_5$	4.7	6.3[e]

[a] Albers et al. (1971).   [d] Gehring et al. (1971).
[b] Lloyd (1974).   [e] Dove et al. (1973).
[c] Greiner (1968); Hack et al. (1974).   [f] Kurylo et al. (1971).

Sometimes it is instructive to consider the behavior of groups forming an isoelectronic sequence. Table II shows that the isoelectronic molecules H_2O_2, N_2H_4, and C_2H_6 react with H atoms quite similarly : formation of H_2 in the first step and rupture of the central bond after an excited original molecule is reformed by addition of an H atom in the second step. However, in contrast to the H_2O_2 case, the NH_2 and CH_3 radicals react more slowly than H atoms with their parent molecules and no analogous chain reaction is possible.

Turning to hydrides of elements from the second row of the periodic table, an increased ability of H-atom addition to the saturated molecules is observed. This may be related to the possibility of such atoms to expand their valence shells more readily. The rate constant measurements for $H + HCl$ should especially be mentioned, since they can be compared with results for the reverse reaction (Westenberg and de Haas, 1968). Surprisingly the ratio h_{H+HCl}/k_{Cl+H_2} is higher than the equilibrium constant by a factor of 2–3 ($T = 250$–456 K). This discrepancy lies outside the reported experimental error. Nonetheless, the influence of vibrationally excited H_2 molecules, which can be generated in discharge-flow systems (Heidner and Kasper, 1969), as an acceleration of the measured rate k_{H+HCl} by additional H-atom consumption in reactions ($H + HCl_2 \rightarrow 2\ HCl$, Glass (1974)) induced by the Cl atoms produced in $H + HCl \rightarrow H_2 + Cl$, must be carefully studied.

2. *Abstraction of Other Atoms*

Another class of atom reactions where a great deal of experimental and theoretical work has been directed comprises the reactions of H atoms with halogens. Measured rate constants are given in Fig. 17. The asterisks indicate vibrational and rotational excitation of the hydrogen halides produced in the reaction. From the infrared chemiluminescence spectra of HX* the fraction of reaction energy that is released in the vibrational and rotational degrees of freedom can be obtained. These data, together with results from crossed molecular beam experiments and the thermal rate studies shown in Fig. 17, can then be compared with classical trajectory and quantum calculations on varied potential energy surfaces, so that a detailed picture of these reactions is available (see Chapter 6). However, if one looks at the experimental rate data shown in Fig. 17 in light of the empirical and semiempirical methods discussed in Section III,B the agreement is seen to be poor in absolute magnitude and trend. Clearly, the Arrhenius activation energy *increases* with increasing exothermicity in contrast to Eq. (3.15). Mok and Polanyi (1969) have pointed out that Eq. (3.15) might not be applicable to series of reactions where abstracted and rejected atoms or groups are changed simultaneously.

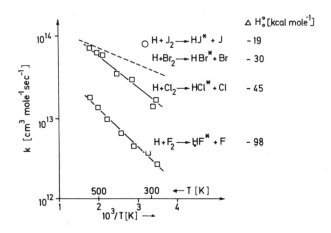

FIG. 17.   Rate constants for the reactions of hydrogen atoms with halogen molecules; □, Albright *et al.* (1969); – –, Jost (1929); ○, Penzhorn and Darwent (1968).

The high reaction rates observed for halogen abstraction through H atoms, which produces hydrogen halides with a population inversion for several vibration–rotation states, have stimulated an important practical application of atom reactions. Kasper and Pimentel (1965) first demonstrated that laser action can be observed from the reaction $H + Cl_2$ in a suitable optical cavity. Since then continuous and pulsed laser action has been reported for many fast reactions of H atoms with halogen compounds ($NOCl$, SCl_2, $COCl_2$, C_2Cl_2, Cl_2O, F_2O, etc.), O_3, and in other atom reactions (Kompa, 1973).

Among the most important reactions in combustion and explosion processes is the interaction of H atoms with molecular oxygen. At lower temperatures ($T < 1000$ K) the addition of H to O_2 in the presence of a third body predominates*

$$H(^2S) + O_2(^3\Sigma) \xrightarrow{\;+M\;} HO_2(^2A') \qquad (3.22)$$

$k_{22} = 10^{15.4} \exp(0.5/RT) \text{ cm}^6 \text{ mole}^{-2} \text{ sec}^{-31}, \quad \Delta H_0^\circ = -47 \text{ kcal mole}^{-1}.$

As shown in Fig. 16, HO_2 can quickly react with further H atoms to form OH radicals. At low H-atom concentrations disproportionation of the HO_2 radicals becomes possible

$$HO_2 + HO_2 \longrightarrow H_2O_2 + O_2$$

$$k = 10^{12.3} \text{ cm}^3 \text{ mole}^{-1} \text{ sec}^{-1} \quad \text{at} \quad 298 \text{ K}.$$

At the second explosion limit of a H_2–O_2 mixture, reaction (3.22) competes with the chain branching step

$$H(^2S) + O_2(^3\Sigma) \longrightarrow OH(^2\Pi) + O(^3P) \qquad (3.23)$$

$k_{23} = 2 \times 10^{14} \exp(-16.8/RT), \qquad \Delta H_0^\circ = 16.7 \text{ kcal mole}^{-1}.$

As one expects from the small energy barrier observed in reaction (3.22), the Arrhenius activation energy of reaction (3.23), is very close to endothermicity. The absence of an additional energy barrier is also confirmed by the low activation energy of the reverse process $O + OH \rightarrow O_2 + H$. At room temperature k_{23} is below 10^3 cm^3 mole^{-1} sec^{-1} and reaction (3.22)

---

* The Arrhenius activation energy E_A is given here and in the following discussion in kcal mole^{-1}.

will dominate. However, reaction (3.23) can take place if the reactants are electronically excited (Wauchop and Phillips, 1967)

$$H(^2P) + O_2(^3\Sigma) \longrightarrow OH(^2\Sigma) + O(^3P)$$

$$OH(^2\Sigma) \longrightarrow OH(^2\Pi) + h\nu.$$

The reaction of hydrogen atoms with ozone

$$H(^2S) + O_3(^1A_1) \longrightarrow OH^*(^2\Pi, \nu \leq 9) + O_2(^3\Sigma) \qquad (3.24)$$

$$k_{24} = 10^{13.2} \text{cm}^3 \text{ mole}^{-1} \text{ sec}^{-1}, \qquad \Delta H_0° = -77 \text{ kcal mole}^{-1}$$

is believed to be the source of OH vibration–rotation bands in the night airglow spectrum. Since the mean radiative lifetime for the hydroxyl radicals in the ninth vibrational level has been found to be as long as 6.4×10^{-2} sec, the influence of vibrational energy on the rate of the secondary reaction (Potter *et al.*, 1971)

$$OH(\nu = n) + O_3 \longrightarrow HO_2^* + O_2$$

$$k_{\nu=0} = 10^{11.5} \text{ cm}^3 \text{ mole}^{-1} \text{ sec}^{-1}, \qquad k_{\nu=9} = 10^{12.7} \text{ cm}^3 \text{ mole}^{-1} \text{ sec}^{-1},$$

can be obtained within the time resolution of a discharge flow system. Del Greco and Kaufman (1962) have introduced the reaction

$$H + NO_2 \longrightarrow NO + OH \qquad (3.25)$$

$$k_{25} = 10^{13.5} \text{ cm}^3 \text{ mole}^{-1} \text{ sec}^{-1}, \qquad \Delta H_0° = 29.5 \text{ kcal mole}^{-1},$$

as a source of hydroxyl radicals for kinetic studies. In contrast to reaction (3.24) very few, if any, vibrationally excited OH radicals are formed in reaction (3.25). This indicates that the potential energy surface of $H + O_3$ involves a greater percentage of attractive energy release than the $H + NO_2$ surface (see Chapter 6). Further information on the structure of the complex formed by H-atom reaction with NO_2 can be obtained from matrix-isolation experiments (see Vol. IV, Chapter 5). Studies of reaction (3.25) in an argon matrix ($T = 4$–14 K) show spectra of *cis* and *trans* nitrous acid (HONO) in agreement with the rapid formation of OH and NO in the gas phase. This is in contrast to the prediction of Walsh (1953), who had postulated a nitrite (HNO_2) formation in reaction (3.25). The intermediate of the $H + CO_2$ reaction, *cis*- and *trans*-HO—C=O, could also be detected in matrix studies of OH with CO. It is interesting to note that the BEBO method accurately predicts the activation barrier for the reaction of H atoms with the isoelectronic molecules CO_2 and N_2O although for the first reaction E_A is close to endothermicity and the second reaction is 62 kcal mole^{-1} exothermic.

However, in concluding this discussion of atom abstraction by H atoms, attention again should be drawn to the fact that predictions of rate constants by empirical and semiempirical methods are often only a qualitative guide.

C. Addition of Hydrogen Atoms

The addition of an H atom to an unsaturated molecule yields an excited radical which can (i) redissociate, (ii) dissociate into different products, or (iii) be collisionally stabilized. This leads to a pressure dependence of the measured rate constants. Significant collisional stabilization of the HO_2 radical formed through the addition of H atoms to O_2 occurs above 10 atm. At and below atmospheric pressure reaction (3.22) is always third order. Addition of H atoms to polyatomic molecules leads to excited radicals where the excess energy can be distributed among an increased number of oscillators; therefore the change from third- to second-order kinetics can occur before atmospheric pressure is reached.

Figure 18 shows a logarithmic plot of measured rate constants at room temperature for the consumption of hydrogen atoms in the presence of acetylene as a function of pressure. The reaction is characterized by a first-order decay of the H atoms with reaction time without consumption of C_2H_2. This can be explained by the following reaction mechanism:

$$H + C_2H_2 \rightleftharpoons C_2H_3^* \tag{3.26}$$

$$C_2H_3^* + M \longrightarrow C_2H_3 + M \tag{3.27}$$

$$C_2H_3 + H \longrightarrow C_2H_2 + H_2. \tag{3.28}$$

The asterisk indicates a vibrationally excited vinyl radical formed 39 kcal mole^{-1} above its ground state. According to this mechanism, which can be confirmed by isotopic studies, the experimental rate constant k_{exp} is given by (t = reaction time)

$$k_{exp} = \Delta(\ln[H])/(\Delta t)[C_2H_2]_0 = 2k_{26}\{(k_{27}[M]/k_{-26}) + k_{27}[M]\}.$$

The term in curly braces represents the relative first-order rate constant

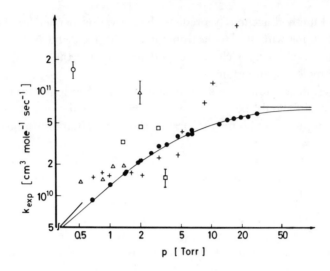

Fig. 18. Dependence of the experimental rate constants k_{exp} for the reaction of hydrogen atoms with acetylene on pressure at 298 K (for symbols see Wagner and Wolfrum, 1971).

for the unimolecular decomposition of the vibrationally excited vinyl radical,

$$k_{exp} = 2k_{26}\{k_{uni}^{C_2H_3}/k_{\infty}^{C_2H_3}\}.$$

At high pressures k_{exp} approaches $2k_{26}$. The pressure dependence of the addition reaction parallels that of the reverse unimolecular decomposition. Thus, the extrapolation schemes from the theory of unimolecular reactions can be applied to obtain k_{26}. In Fig. 18 a "falloff" curve as suggested by Slater ($s = 1$) has been used (see Chapter 11).

If H atoms are replaced by D atoms in reaction (3.26) practically no pressure dependence is observed up to 20 Torr. This large isotope effect illustrates the importance of step (ii) mentioned at the beginning of this subsection.

$$\text{D} + \text{C}_2\text{H}_2 \longrightarrow \text{C}_2\text{H}_2\text{D}^* \longrightarrow \text{C}_2\text{HD} + \text{H} \qquad (3.26')$$

$$\Delta H_0^\circ = -1.6 \text{ kcal mole}^{-1}.$$

Due to the difference of the zero-point energies of the C—D and the corresponding C—H bonds, dissociation of the $\text{C}_2\text{H}_2\text{D}^*$ radical into

C_2HD and H becomes 1.6 kcal mole^{-1} exothermic. This difference in excess energy favors the isotopic exchange against the redissociation into C_2H_2 and D atoms.

The addition of H atoms to ethylene has been the subject of numerous investigations. Although nearly all techniques for monitoring the H-atom decay (catalytic detectors, Lyman-α photometry and resonance fluorescence, mass and ESR spectrometry) have been employed in this case, until recently the reported rate constants showed differences of up to two orders of magnitude. The reason for the even greater discrepancies compared with $H + C_2H_2$ lies in the complex pressure dependence of subsequent reactions. As indicated in Table II, ethyl radicals can react quickly with further H atoms to form two methyl radicals. Thus, the measured H-atom consumption can be governed by a variety of pressure-dependent steps

$$H + C_2H_4 \rightleftharpoons C_2H_5{}^* \xrightarrow{+M} C_2H_5 \qquad (3.29)$$

$$H + C_2H_5 \rightleftharpoons C_2H_6{}^* \xrightarrow{+M} C_2H_6 \qquad (3.30)$$
$$\downarrow$$
$$CH_3 + CH_3$$

$$H + CH_3 \rightleftharpoons CH_4{}^* \xrightarrow{+M} CH_4 \qquad (3.31)$$

$$CH_3 + C_2H_5 \longrightarrow C_3H_8{}^* \xrightarrow{+M} C_3H_8 \qquad (3.32)$$
$$\downarrow$$
$$CH_4 + C_2H_4$$

$$C_2H_5 + C_2H_5 \longrightarrow C_4H_{10}^* \xrightarrow{+M} C_4H_{10} \qquad (3.33)$$
$$\downarrow$$
$$C_2H_6 + C_2H_4$$

However, the reactions (3.30–3.33) are suppressed if rate measurements are carried out with an initial ratio $[C_2H_4]_0/[H]_0 \gg k_9/k_{10}$ (Kurylo et al., 1970). In order to compare experimental data with theoretical results, $\log(S/D)$ versus $\log p$ is plotted, where S is the fraction of stabilized and D the fraction of decomposed ethyl radicals formed in reaction (3.29). In view of the often unsatisfactory absolute agreement of theory and experiment, Rabinovitch and Setser (1964) have suggested semiempirical extrapolation schemes to obtain the limiting high-pressure rate constants. Nevertheless, the linear $\log(S/D)$ against $\log p$ relationship is obeyed for a change in pressure of eight orders of magnitude as shown in the $H + cis$-2-butene case, where experiments can be extended from 10^{-3} Torr to 205 atm. For more details on the application of the theory of unimolecular decomposition to recombination see Chapter 11.

If one now turns to the temperature dependence of such addition reactions, one must carefully avoid any mixing of pressure and temperature influences during the rate constant measurements. Going from C_2 to C_3 and larger unsaturated hydrocarbons the temperature decreases where H-atom abstraction becomes important compared to the addition process. Also, the addition process itself becomes more complex since pathways such as nonterminal addition, isomerization, and decomposition into different products must be taken into account

$$H + CH_2=C=CH_2 \rightleftharpoons C_3H_5^* \xrightarrow{+M} C_3H_5 \qquad (3.34)$$
$$\downarrow$$
$$CH_3-C\equiv CH + H$$

$$H + C_3H_5 \rightleftharpoons C_3H_6^* \xrightarrow{+M} C_3H_6 \qquad (3.35)$$
$$\downarrow$$
$$CH_2=C=CH_2 + H_2$$

$$H + C_3H_6 \rightleftharpoons C_3H_7^* \xrightarrow{+M} C_3H_7 \qquad (3.36)$$
$$\downarrow$$
$$CH_3 + C_2H_4$$

(Wagner and Zellner, 1972).

IV. Reactions of Carbon Atoms

In view of the great number of known carbon compounds, quantitative investigations of carbon atom reactions are notable for their scarcity. Although many sources of atomic carbon, such as nuclear transformations (Wolfgang, 1965), carbon arc burning under vacuum (Skell and Engel, 1965), explosion and evaporation of graphite filaments (Sprung, et al., 1965), and photolysis (Braun et al., 1969), radiolysis (Meaburn and Perner, 1966), and plasmolysis (Martinotti et al., 1968) of carbon compounds have been used, in most cases only mechanistic conclusions could be drawn from these studies.

An important step toward the quantitative understanding of the kinetics of carbon atom reactions was made by Braun and co-workers (1969), who showed that C atoms in the ground [$C(2 \,^3P_J)$]*, the first [$C(2 \,^1D_2)$, $E = 30$ kcal mole^{-1}], and the second [$C(2 \,^1S_0)$, $E = 62$ kcal mole^{-1}] electronic

---

* J = total angular momentum quantum number.

TABLE III

RATE CONSTANTS FOR REACTIONS OF CARBON ATOMS IN VARIOUS ELECTRONIC STATES AT ROOM TEMPERATURE

	Rate constant (cm^3 $mole^{-1}$ sec^{-1})		
Reaction	$C(2\ ^3P_J)$	$C(2\ ^1P_2)$	$C(2\ ^1S_0)$
$C + H_2 \rightarrow CH + H$	$<10^6$	$10^{14.2}$	$<10^{12.5}$
$C + O_2 \rightarrow CO + O$	$10^{13.3}$	$<10^{12.5}$	—
$C + NO \rightarrow CN + O$	$10^{13.8}$	$10^{13.8}$	—

For references see Wagner and Wolfrum (1971).

excited states can be detected by their resonance absorption in the far ultraviolet after flash photolysis of C_3O_2.

Also, C atoms generated in a flow system by dissociation of carbon suboxide or allene in a microwave discharge can be observed by absorption spectroscopy.

Table III shows a comparison of measured rate constants for some reactions of C atoms in the three low-lying electronic energy levels.

The reaction with H_2 to form $CH(X\ ^2\Pi)$ and $H(1\ ^2S_{1/2})$ is endothermic for $C(2\ ^3P_J)$ and is therefore very slow for thermal atoms at room temperature. It may be possible for translationally "hot" C atoms.

For $C(2\ ^1D_2)$ atoms this pathway is exothermic and the reaction proceeds rapidly at 300 K, whereas $C(2\ ^1S_0)$ atoms are significantly less reactive, in spite of the greater exothermicity of these reactions. This example demonstrates that energy and spin considerations alone [$C(2\ ^1D_2)$ and $C(2\ ^1S_0)$ have the same spin state and the reaction with $H_2(^1\Sigma^+)$ to form $CH(X\ ^2\Pi)$ and $H(1\ ^2S_{1/2})$ is "spin allowed"] are often insufficient for the prediction of the reactive behavior. The result, however, can be understood on the basis of the adiabatic correlations of reactants and products in terms of their symmetry (Shuler, 1953; Herzberg, 1966). As shown in the correlation diagram (Donovan and Husain, 1970) in Fig. 19, there is no adiabatic potential energy surface for the analogous reaction of $C(^1S_0)$ atoms.

For $C(2\ ^3P_J)$ and $C(2\ ^1D_2)$ atoms, besides the surfaces ($^3A'$, $^1A''$) leading directly to $CH(X\ ^2\Pi)$ and $H(1\ ^2S_{1/2})$, two surfaces ($^3A''$, $^1A'$) correlating to these products via formation of $CH_2(^3B_1, ^1A_1)$ are available. In fact, experimental results indicate that "insertion" of C atoms into the H_2 molecule

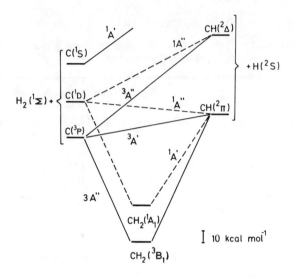

F<small>IG</small>. 19. Correlation diagram for the reactions of molecular hydrogen with carbon atoms in various electronic states (Donovan and Husain, 1970). For the $^3B_1$–$^1A_1$ energy difference of the CH$_2$ radical the value suggested by Herzberg (1966) is used. There is, however, still discrepancy between experimentally and theoretically predicted values for the $^3B_1$–$^1A_1$ splitting (Schaefer, 1972).

can occur and the vibrationally hot CH$_2$ molecules are stabilized at pressures around 1 atm. However, since for the adiabatic orbital correlation rules the least symmetric complex formed during the reaction—which will in general be of rather low symmetry, quite often only point group C_s— must be considered, the predictive power of these correlation rules for a priori assessment of prefered reaction pathways is rather limited. Thus, in contrast to the reaction with H$_2$, formation of CO$_2$ by "insertion" of C(2 ^3P_J) atoms into O$_2$ molecules could not be observed at high pressures nor in the liquid phase (Wolfgang, 1965; Braun et al., 1969) in spite of the fact that a surface of symmetry $^1A'$ correlates directly with CO$_2$(X $^1\Sigma^+$).

Although attack on both ends of the NO molecule may occur on several surfaces for ground-state C atoms at 300 K

$$C(2\ ^3P_J) + NO(X\ ^2\Pi) \xrightarrow{\substack{2A'/22A'' \\ 4A'/24A''}} O(2\ ^3P_J) + CN(^2\Sigma^+)$$

$$\xrightarrow{22A'/32A''} N(2^2D_J) + CO(X\ ^1\Sigma^+)$$

$$\xrightarrow{4A''} N(2\ (^4S_{3/2}) + CO(X\ ^1\Sigma^+)$$

$\Delta H_0^{\circ} = -33,\ -51,\ -106$ kcal mole^{-1}, respectively, the preferential reaction products ($\geq 85\%$) are O atoms and CN, formed in the least exothermic reaction channel. In addition, for reactions involving polyatomic reactants, the adiabatic correlation rules are further weakened through the vibrational–electronic interaction.

Surprisingly, $C(2\ ^3P_J)$ atoms react relatively slowly with hydrocarbons at room temperature. The rate constants for the reactions with CH_4, C_2H_2, and C_2H_4 are less than $10^7\ cm^3\ mole^{-1}\ sec^{-1}$ (Martinotti et al., 1968). The corresponding reactions of $C(2\ ^2D_2)$ and $C(2\ ^1S_0)$ (Meaburn and Perner, 1966) are fast. The reaction with CH_4 leads directly to the formation of C_2H_2. However, as already mentioned, most of the results of carbon-atom–hydrocarbon studies are only of qualitative nature.

V. Reactions of Nitrogen Atoms

A. GENERATION OF NITROGEN ATOMS

Because of the high bond dissociation energy and optical transparency ($\lambda > 1100\ \text{Å}$) of molecular nitrogen, no other convenient thermal or photochemical sources of nitrogen atoms have been found since 1911 when Strutt first suggested that the electrical discharge in N_2 creates N atoms. As shown in Table IV, however, this "active" nitrogen contains many energetic species other than ground-state ($2\ ^4S_{3/2}$) nitrogen atoms. It is not surprising, therefore, that in spite of the great number of papers devoted to reactions of "active" nitrogen (Wright and Winkler, 1968), only few reactions are kinetically well understood.

In contrast to earlier theories (Mitra, 1945), it is now generally agreed that the chemical reactivity of "active" nitrogen is not due to the presence of charged species, although the delayed increase of electron and ion (Brömer and Hesse, 1969) number density indicates some electron- and

TABLE IV

APPROXIMATE CONCENTRATIONS (IN PARTICLES CM^{-3}) OF THE VARIOUS REACTIVE SPECIES PRODUCED BY A MICROWAVE DISCHARGE IN MOLECULAR NITROGEN

$[N_2(X\ ^1\Sigma_g^+)]_0$	$N_2(^1\Sigma_g^+, v>0)$	$N_2(A\ ^3\Sigma_u^+)$	$N_2^+(^4\Sigma_u^+)$	e^-	$N(2\ ^4S_{3/2})$	$N(2\ ^2D_J)$	$N(2\ ^2P_J)$
10^{17}	$10^{16.3}$	10^{12}	10^9	$10^{9.9}$	10^{15}	10^{13}	10^{12}

ion-producing processes. Also, nitrogen atoms in the low-lying metastable states—$N(2\,^2D_J,\ E=55\ \text{kcal mole}^{-1})$ and $N(2\,^2P_J,\ E=137\ \text{kcal mole}^{-1})$— play a minor role since they are rapidly (~ 1 msec) deactivated at the wall of the discharge flow system (Foner and Hudson, 1962).

The generation of appreciable concentrations of vibrationally excited nitrogen molecules $N_2(^1\Sigma_g^+,\ v>0)$ has found an important technical application in the carbon dioxide laser. Since the vibrational energy stored by the nitrogen molecules is transferred to the asymmetric stretch mode of CO_2 by a very efficient near-resonant exchange process

$$N_2(^1\Sigma_g^+,\ v=1)+CO_2(^1\Sigma_g^+,\ 00^\circ 0)$$
$$\longrightarrow\quad CO(^1\Sigma_g^+,\ 00^\circ 1)+N_2(^1\Sigma_g^+,\ v=0) \tag{5.1}$$

the inverted population against the $CO_2(10^\circ 0)$ symmetric stretching level can be used for stimulated emission

$$CO_2(00^\circ 1)\quad\longrightarrow\quad CO_2(10^\circ 0)+h\nu(\lambda=10.6\ \mu m)$$

(for further details see Chapter 10).

While vibrationally excited N_2 may be eliminated by processes like (5.1) or wall collisions, metastable electronically excited $N_2(A\,^3\Sigma_u^+)$ are formed continuously during the $N(2\,^4S_{3/2})$ atom recombination (Becker *et al.*, 1972). Although their steady-state concentration is kept low

$$\{[N_2(A\,^3\Sigma_u^+)]\sim 10^{-3}[N(^4S_{3/2})]\},$$

predominantly by the removal process

$$N(^4S_{3/2})+N_2(A\,^3\Sigma_u^+)\quad\longrightarrow\quad N_2(X\,^1\Sigma_g^+)+N(^4S_{3/2}) \tag{5.2}$$
$$k_2=10^{13.5}\ \text{cm}^3\ \text{mole}^{-1}\ \text{sec}^{-1}\quad\text{at}\quad 298\ \text{K},$$

due to their large excitation energy ($E=143$ kcal mole^{-1}) and long radiative lifetime ($\tau\sim 2$ sec), decomposition of additives that do not react with ground-state N atoms may occur. Thus, dissociation of CO_2 takes place by (Campbell and Thrush, 1968)

$$CO_2(^1\Sigma_g^+)+N_2(A\,^3\Sigma_u^+)\quad\longrightarrow\quad CO(^1\Sigma^+)+N_2(X\,^1\Sigma_g^+)+O(2\,^3P_J)$$

while the reaction (Herron and Huie, 1968)

$$N(^4S_{3/2})+CO_2(^1\Sigma_g^+)\quad\longrightarrow\quad NO(^2\Pi)+CO(^1\Sigma^+) \tag{5.3}$$
$$k_3<10^8\ \text{cm}^3\ \text{mole}^{-1}\ \text{sec}^{-1}$$

is slow at room temperature, probably due to the "forbidden" spin change involved. In addition, $N_2(A\,^3\Sigma_g{}^+)$ molecules can act as triplet sensitizers for reactants with low-lying triplet states [metal atoms, CS_2, $(CN)_2$, SO_2, etc.] and exhibit triplet–triplet disproportionation

$$N_2(A\,^3\Sigma_u{}^+) + N_2(A\,^3\Sigma_u{}^+) \longrightarrow N_2(^1\Sigma_g{}^+) + N_2(C\,^3\Pi_u) \qquad (5.4)$$

$$k_4 = 10^{13.1}\ \mathrm{cm^3\ mole^{-1}\ sec^{-1}}.$$

From this account it is quite obvious that agreement of measured kinetic parameters can only be expected if the reactions of $N(^4S_{3/2})$ atoms with the added molecules are fast compared to the N-atom recombination. This is the case if the reaction leads directly to the formation of a multiple nitrogen bond such as NO ($D = 151$ kcal mole^{-1}), CN ($D = 184$ kcal mole^{-1}), or N_2 ($D = 225$ kcal mole^{-1}).

B. Oxygen Atom Abstraction by Nitrogen Atoms

As shown in Fig. 20, there is good agreement of measured rate constants for the reaction

$$N(2\,^4S_{3/2}) + O_2(^3\Sigma_g{}^-) \longrightarrow NO(X\,^2\Pi) + O(2\,^3P_J) \qquad (5.5)$$

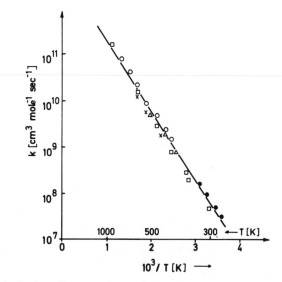

FIG. 20. Arrhenius diagram of experimental rate constants for the reaction of N(^{4}S) atoms with molecular oxygen: ●, Becker *et al.* (1969); □, Wilson (1967); △, Kistiakowsky and Volpi (1957); ○, Clyne and Thrush (1961); ×, Vlasturas and Winkler (1967) (for references see Baulch *et al.*, 1968-1973).

where N-atom decay has been followed by mass spectrometry, ESR, chemi-luminescence, and HCN "titration" (see Section V,C). The appreciable activation energy found in the exothermic reaction (5.5) makes this step too slow for ground-state reactants to explain the considerable concentrations of nitric oxide found in the sub-100-km region of the earth's atmosphere (Hunten and McElroy, 1968). From the measured NO, O_2, and N-atom concentrations at 200 K a value of $k_5 > 10^{11}$ cm^3 mole^{-1} sec^{-1}— six orders of magnitude larger than the measured value—is required. Since the electronically excited reactants $[O_2(^1\Delta_g),$ N(2 ^{2}D)] correlate directly with the products of reaction (5.5), one might speculate that the activation barrier could easily be overcome by their excitation energy. However, the measured quenching rate constant of $10^{9.2}$ cm^3 mole^{-1} sec^{-1} for $O_2(^1\Delta_g)$ by N(^{4}S) cannot be applied to the reaction (Westenberg et al., 1970)

$$\text{N}(2\ ^4\text{S}_{3/2}) + \text{O}_2(^1\Delta_g) \xrightarrow{\text{4A', 4A''}} \text{NO}(\text{X}\ ^2\Pi) + \text{O}(2\ ^3\text{P}_J). \tag{5.5'}$$

For N(^{2}D) atoms the reaction

$$\text{N}(2\ ^2\text{D}) + \text{O}_2(\text{X}\ ^3\Sigma_g{}^-) \longrightarrow \text{NO}(\text{X}\ ^2\Pi) + \text{O}(2\ ^3\text{P}_J) \tag{5.5''}$$

$$k_5'' = 10^{13.6}\ \text{cm}^3\ \text{mole}^{-1}\ \text{cm}^{-1} \quad \text{at} \quad 300\ \text{K}$$

apparently dominates compared to the quenching process of N(2 ^{2}D) by molecular oxygen.

In contrast to the reaction with O_2, reactions of N(2 ^{4}S$_{3/2}$) atoms with many other oxygen compounds exhibit very low activation barriers (see Table V). The reaction with NO_2 is particularly interesting because of the variety of reaction channels available. The major primary process is the formation of N_2O. This exothermic displacement reaction is one of the few examples where vibrational excitation can be determined in a triatomic product molecule:

$$
\begin{aligned}
\text{N}(^4\text{S}_{3/2}) + \text{NO}_2(\text{X}\ ^2\text{A}_1) \ & \longrightarrow \ \text{O}(^3\text{P}_J) + \text{N}_2\text{O}(^1\Sigma^+ v_1 = 0;\ 1 \leq v_2 \leq 10;\ v_3 \leq 1) && 70\% \\
& \longrightarrow \ \text{O}(^3\text{P}_J) + \text{N}_2\text{O}(^1\Sigma^+ v_1 \geq 1;\ v_2 \geq 1;\ v_3 = 0) && 25\% \\
& \longrightarrow \ \text{O}(^3\text{P}_J) + \text{N}_2\text{O}(^1\Sigma^+ v_1 \geq 1;\ v_2 \geq 1;\ v_3 \geq 1). && 3\%
\end{aligned}
$$

Around 40% of the reaction energy enters the vibrational modes of N_2O (Clough and Thrush, 1969).

TABLE V

RATE CONSTANTS FOR REACTIONS OF N(^{4}S) ATOMS WITH SMALL OXYGEN-
CONTAINING MOLECULES AT ROOM TEMPERATURE

Reaction	$-\Delta H_0^\circ$ (kcal mole^{-1})	log k (cm^3 mole^{-1} sec^{-1})
N(^{4}S) + NO → N$_2$ + O	75	13.1[a]
N(^{4}S) + SO → NO + S	27	12.7[b]
N(^{4}S) + HO → NO + H	49	13.6[c]
N(^{4}S) + O$_3$ → NO + O$_2$	126	11.5[d]
N(^{4}S) + Cl$_2$O → NCl + ClO	57	12.7[e]
N(^{4}S) + NO$_2$ → N$_2$O + O (0.43)	42	13.0[f]
→ NO + NO(0.33)	78	—
→ N$_2$ + O$_2$ (0.13)	121	—
→ N$_2$ + 2O (0.1)	2	—

[a] Lin *et al.* (1970).　　　　　　[d] Phillips and Schiff (1962).
[b] Jacob (1968).　　　　　　　　　[e] Freeman and Phillips (1968).
[c] Campbell and Thrush (1968).　　[f] Phillips and Schiff (1965).

C. REACTIONS WITH HYDROCARBONS

The bond dissociation energy of the NH radical (Seal and Gaydon, 1966; $D_{NH} = 74$ kcal mole^{-1}) is rather low compared to the C—H bond dissociation energies of hydrocarbons ($D_{C-H} \sim 90$–128 kcal mole^{-1}). Consequently, abstraction of H atoms by N(^{4}S$_{3/2}$) is an endothermic process and is very slow at room temperature. This creates a situation where the influence of the various energetic species of the "active" nitrogen as well as of atoms and radicals produced in subsequent reaction steps predominate and explains the conflicting observations often reported for the reactions of "active" nitrogen with hydrocarbons. In earlier work the concentration of N atoms was estimated from the amount of HCN produced by addition of an excess of the hydrocarbon. However, with the "NO titration" N-atom concentrations approximately twice that obtained by HCN yield have been found. This discrepancy was removed only recently (Safrany and Jaster, 1968) by the addition of H atoms from a second discharge to the hydrocarbon "active" nitrogen mixture. As discussed in Section III, the initial step is then the formation of alkyl radicals either by H-atom abstraction or, in the case of alkenes, by addition. Nitrogen atoms are converted to HCN by

$$N(^4S) + C_nH_{2n+1} \longrightarrow HCN + C_{n-1}H_{2n-1} + H$$
$$\longrightarrow NH + C_nH_{2n}.$$

In the case $[H]_0 \gg [N]_0$, N atoms are regenerated from the NH radicals

$$H + NH \longrightarrow N + H_2$$

while for $[H]_0 \ll [N]_0$ the HCN yield decreases since N_2 is formed by

$$N(^4S) + NH \longrightarrow N_2 + H$$
$$NH + NH \longrightarrow N_2 + H_2 \text{ or } 2H.$$

The situation is similar with many proposed sets of elementary reactions, in which some facts are explained and others are not. Thus, to understand the observed formation of NH_3 in the presence of large concentrations of N atoms, it is assumed that NH radicals react much faster with H atoms than with N atoms. However, no direct observation of the proposed NH radicals has been made. In the absence of quantitative rate measurements no particular reason for the postulated reactivity of NH is available. Again, this mirrors the simple fact that the number of observed species is much less than the number of equations involved.

VI. Reactions of Oxygen Atoms

The reactions of free oxygen atoms determine the course of many oxidation and combustion processes. As biradicals they exhibit a great variety of possible reaction channels so that the primary products and rate constants of many of their reactions have only recently been definitely established by direct investigation.

A. The Reactions with H_2, H_2O, and H_2O_2

The reaction of atomic oxygen with H_2

$$O(^3P) + H_2(^1\Sigma) \longrightarrow OH(^2\Pi) + H(^2S) \tag{6.1}$$
$$\Delta H_0^\circ = +1.9 \text{ kcal mole}^{-1}$$

is an important chain-branching step in the oxygen/hydrogen reaction and numerous other oxidation reactions. Apparent activation energies of between 6 and 12 kcal mole^{-1} were reported for this reaction some years ago (Kaufman, 1961). Figure 21 shows that most of the data obtained between 320 and 1000 K by different methods (discharge flow systems

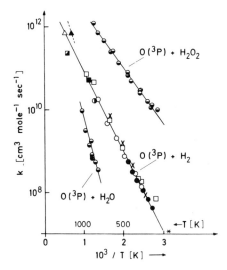

FIG. 21.   Arrhenius diagram of experimental rate constants for the reaction of O(^{3}P) atoms with hydrogen, water, and hydrogen peroxide; ◓, Albers *et al.* (1971); for remaining symbols see Wagner and Wolfrum (1971). Experimental methods: □, ◓, ○, discharge-flow reactor with ESR atom detection; ○, *, discharge flow with chemiluminescence atom detection; ×, stirred reactor with molecular leak sampling; ◑, ■, explosion limits; ◪, flames; △, ▲, shock waves.

with ESR and chemiluminescent atom detection, stirred reactor coupled to mass spectrometer, explosion limits) agree now within ±25% and may be represented by an Arrhenius expression

$$k_1 = 10^{13.2} \exp(-9.4/RT) \text{ cm}^3 \text{ mole}^{-1} \text{ sec}^{-1}.$$

Since on a plot of log k vs. $1/T$ the experimental data at low temperatures cover a large portion of the graph, the Arrhenius activation energy E_A can be evaluated in this region with good precision. The question arises as to whether the simple Arrhenius equation

$$k = A \exp(-E_A/RT)$$

may be used for a confident extrapolation from the lower temperature data to rate constants at elevated temperatures (1000–3000 K). Clearly, one suspects that the Arrhenius equation with two temperature-independent parameters cannot give the whole story. An unequivocal prediction about the exact behavior of the Arrhenius parameters of reaction (6.1), however, can only be made if sufficiently accurate information on the energy dependence of the reactive cross section $\sigma(E)$ for this reaction is available, from which a calculation of the thermal rate constant over a wide temperature range is possible.

The question is also difficult to answer from the experimental results available at present for the 1500–3000 K region. A direct comparison of Arrhenius activation energies measured at low and high temperatures is not useful since it is difficult to achieve a precision better than about RT, which is already 3–6 kcal mole^{-1} in this regime. Recent shock tube experiments, by Schott and Getzinger (1972) give $k_1 = 4 \times 10^{12}$ cm^3 mole^{-1} sec^{-1} at 1600 K, which is a factor of four above the Arrhenius line in Fig. 21. The simple hard-sphere collision model

$$k' = A'\sqrt{T} \exp(-E_0/RT)$$

only predicts an increase of 20% compared to the Arrhenius line for k_1 at 1600 K. The transition state model, on the other hand, gives stronger deviations. With the frequencies for the $OH_2^\ddagger$ complex from the BEBO procedure the TST model predicts $E_A(6.1) = 10.3$ kcal mole^{-1} in the temperature range 200–800 K and $E_A(6.1) = 15.8$ kcal mole^{-1} between 800 and 2000 K.

Through variation of the frequencies of the active complex $HO_2^\ddagger$ one can of course "explain" any increase in the Arrhenius activation energy with increasing temperature. Nevertheless, this is a dangerous procedure before more experimental data are available and the correct application of the transition-state model has been tested.

In addition to k_1, rate data from the two other H-atom abstraction reactions in the H_2/O_2 system

$$O(^3P) + H_2O \longrightarrow OH + OH \tag{6.2}$$
$$\Delta H_0{}^\circ = +16.7 \text{ kcal mole}^{-1}$$

$$O(^3P) + H_2O_2 \longrightarrow OH + HO_2$$
$$\Delta H_0{}^\circ = -12.7 \text{ kcal mole}^{-1} \tag{6.3}$$

$$\longrightarrow O_2 + H_2O$$
$$\Delta H_0{}^\circ = -85.1 \text{ kcal mole}^{-1}$$

are also shown in Figure 21. A comparison with values from a BEBO calculation is given in Table VI. While good agreement is obtained

TABLE VI

COMPARISON OF EXPERIMENTAL AND CALCULATED[a] RATE CONSTANTS FOR
H-ATOM ABSTRACTION BY $O(^3P)$ ATOMS

Reaction	$\dfrac{\log k_{\text{calc}}}{\log k_{\text{exp}}}$ (cm^3 mole^{-1} sec^{-1})			
	300 K	500 K	800 K	1000 K
$O(^3P) + H_2 \rightarrow OH + H$	$\begin{cases}4.4\\7.0\end{cases}$	7.6 9.0	9.7 10.6	10.5 11.2[b]
$O(^3P) + H_2O \rightarrow OH + HO$	$\begin{cases}1.7\\-\end{cases}$	6.6 —	9.4 8.9	10.3 9.8[c]
$O(^3P) + H_2O_2 \rightarrow OH + HO_2$ $\rightarrow H_2O + O_2$	$\begin{cases}10.1\\9.7\end{cases}$	11.3 11.0	12.0 12.1[c]	12.3 —

[a] BEBO method, with $\alpha = 1$ and tunneling corrections.
[b] Wagner and Wolfrum (1971).
[c] Albers et al. (1971).

for reaction (6.2), the discrepancies for reactions (6.1) and (6.3) reflect the limitation of the simple model used in the BEBO procedure.

As in the reactions of carbon and nitrogen atoms, electronic excitation of oxygen atoms can be effectively used to surmount potential energies of activation found for ground-state reactions. Table VII gives some examples.

TABLE VII

RATE CONSTANTS FOR REACTIONS OF OXYGEN ATOMS IN VARIOUS ELECTRONIC
STATES AT ROOM TEMPERATURE

Reaction	$\log k$ (cm^3 mole^{-1} sec^{-1})		
	$O(^3P_J)$	$O(^1D_2)$	$O(^1S_0)$
$O(X) + H_2 \rightarrow OH + H$	$<7^a$	12.7[d]	8.8[d]
$O(X) + H_2O \rightarrow OH + OH$	1[b]	13.3[e]	—
$O(X) + O_3 \rightarrow O_2 + O_2$	9.7[c]	14.2[e]	14.5[f]

[a] Wagner and Wolfrum (1971).
[b] Albers et al. (1971).
[c] McCrumb and Kaufman (1972).
[d] Donovan and Husain (1970).
[e] Biedenkapp, et al. (1970); Scott and Cvetanović (1970).
[f] London et al. (1971).

B. Reactions with Alkanes

As in the reaction with H_2, an H atom is apparently transferred from saturated hydrocarbons to the attacking $O(^3P)$ atom,

$$O(^3P) + RH \longrightarrow R + OH.$$

While the measured Arrhenius activation energies E_A decrease with decreasing R—H bond strength, the rate of the overall consumption of O atoms increases in proportion to the nature and the number of the C—H bonds of the higher paraffins. For the attack of $O(^3P)$ atoms on primary, secondary, and tertiary C—H bonds of the alkanes, many of the experimental results can be described by the expressions (Herron and Huie, 1969)

$$k_{pri} = 5 \times 10^{12} \exp(-5.8/RT) \quad cm^3 \, mole^{-1} \, sec^{-1},$$

$$k_{sec} = 1.3 \times 10^{13} \exp(-4.5/RT) \quad cm^3 \, mole^{-1} \, sec^{-1},$$

$$k_{tert} = 1.6 \times 10^{13} \exp(-3.3/RT) \quad cm^3 \, mole^{-1} \, sec^{-1}.$$

Attack by $O(^1D)$ atoms, on the other hand, takes place without an activation barrier with insertion of $O(^1D)$ into the C—H bond

$$O(^1D) + RH \longrightarrow ROH^*.$$

TABLE VIII

Reactions of $O(^1D)$ Atoms with Alkanes

Reaction	Yield (%)	Conditions
$O(^1D) + CH_4 \xrightarrow{+M} CH_3OH$	70	87 K, Liquid Ar
$\rightarrow CH_3 + OH$	30	
$O(^1D) + C_2H_6 \xrightarrow{+M} C_2H_5OH$	97	87 K, Liquid Ar
$\rightarrow C_2H_4 + H_2O$	3	
$O(^1D) + i\text{-}C_4H_8 \xrightarrow{+M} i\text{-}C_4H_7OH$	90	298 K, $10^{3.1}$ Torr N_2
$\xrightarrow{+M} t\text{-}C_4H_7OH$	10	
$O(^1D) + CH_3Cl \rightarrow H_2CO + HCl \, (v = 0)$	$N_{v=1}/N_{v=0} = 0.6$	298 K, 30 Torr
$\rightarrow H_2CO + HCl \, (v = 1)$		($O_2 : CH_3Cl : SF_6$
		$= 1 : 1 : 20$)

For references see Wagner and Wolfrum (1971).

The resulting alcohol molecule exhibits strong vibrational excitation and can be stabilized only at high pressures or in the liquid phase. In the reaction of $O(^1D)$ with haloalkanes the elimination of vibrationally excited halogen hydrides can be observed (see Table VIII).

C. THE REACTION WITH ACETYLENE

Although acetylene is the simplest hydrocarbon with respect to the number of atoms in the molecule, the number of reaction channels in the reaction with $O(^3P)$ atoms increases compared with the alkane reactions just described. The $O(^3P)$ atoms first form an addition complex $(C_2H_2O)^*$ with C_2H_2. The Arrhenius activation energy required for this step ($E_A = 3$ kcal mole^{-1}) agrees with the value obtained in the addition of H atoms to C_2H_2 (see Section III,C). However, whereas the excited $C_2H_3^*$ radicals can decompose only in a reversal of their formation reaction, several decomposition paths are conceivable for the $(C_2H_2O)^*$ complex in which either the acetylene C—C bond is conserved by elimination of H_2 or H atoms (in analogy to the $D + C_2H_2$ reaction) or is broken:

$$O(^3P) + C_2H_2 \longrightarrow (C_2H_2O)^* \qquad (6.4)$$

$$
\begin{array}{ccc}
\overset{a}{\swarrow} & \downarrow b & \overset{c}{\searrow} \\
C_2O + H_2 & HC_2O + H & CH_2 + CO \\
\Delta H_0{}^\circ = -21 & -22 & -48 \\
\text{(kcal mole}^{-1}) & &
\end{array}
$$

$$k_4 = 10^{13.1} \exp(-3.00/RT) \text{ cm}^3 \text{ mole}^{-1} \text{ sec}^{-1}.$$

Indirect as well as direct evidence for all three processes exists:

1. The direct formation of CH_2 and CO was observed mass spectrometrically in an experiment with crossed, free jets (Gehring, 1971).

2. A small steady-state concentration of HC_2O and CH_2 radicals was found by using photoionization for mass spectrometric analysis of intermediates in the $O + C_2H_2$ reaction in a discharge flow system (Jones and Bayes, 1972).

3. C_2O as well as HC_2O have been postulated as precursors for the strong CO vacuum-uv chemiluminescence, which can be observed in the $O + C_2H_2$ reaction (Becker and Bayes, 1968) and might be produced by the reaction

$$O(^3P) + C_2O(^3\Sigma) \longrightarrow CO(A\,^1\Pi, d\,^3\Delta, e\,^3\Sigma) + CO(^1\Sigma).$$

4. Two hydrogen atoms are detected with an ESR spectrometer for every acetylene molecule reacted (Hoyermann *et al.*, 1967, 1969; Brown and Thrush, 1967). This overall stoichiometry is in accordance with fast subsequent reactions following step (b) or (c)

$$O + HC_2O \xrightarrow{\text{b}'} 2CO + H$$

$$O + CH_2 \xrightarrow{\text{c}'} CO + 2H.$$

Strong vibrational excitation is found for the CO formed (Clough and Thrush, 1968; Poss, 1971).

5. In an excess of C_2H_2 the methylene radical reacts with acetylene to form C_3H_4, which is present mainly as methylacetylene and allene and can react quickly with oxygen atoms according to

$$O(^3P) + CH_3-C_2H \longrightarrow CH_3CH^* + CO \tag{6.5}$$

$$k_5 = 10^{11.6} \text{ cm}^3 \text{ mole}^{-1} \text{ sec}^{-1} \quad \text{at} \quad 298 \text{ K}$$

$$O(^3P) + CH_2{=}C{=}CH_2 \longrightarrow C_2H_4 + CO \tag{6.6}$$

$$k_6 = 10^{12.9} \exp(-1.6/RT) \quad \text{cm}^3 \text{ mole}^{-1} \text{ sec}^{-1}$$

(Herbrechtsmeier and Wagner, 1972).

6. Appreciable stabilization of the $(C_2H_2O)^*$ complex to ketene

$$(C_2H_2O)^* + M \longrightarrow CH_2CO$$

$$\Delta H_0{}^\circ = -127 \text{ kcal mole}^{-1}$$

occurs only at very high pressures ($p > 500$ atm) (Troe and co-workers, 1972) or in an argon matrix (Haller and Pimentel, 1962).

Further studies of this reaction are clearly needed to assess quantitatively the extent of the observed reaction channels (which may also vary with temperature), to explain the small amount of ketene observed at low pressures (1 Torr), the absence of an isotope effect even at low temperatures (Quickert, 1972), and the reactions that lead to the formation of free electrons (Bradley and Tse, 1968) and ions (Fontijn *et al.*, 1965) and to chemiluminescence of OH, CH, and C_2 (Becker *et al.*, 1965; Quickert, 1972).

Excellent agreement exists, however, among various investigators about the rate constant at room temperature (see comparison by Stuhl and Niki, 1971)

$$k_4 = (0.96 \pm 0.05) \times 10^{11} \text{ cm}^3 \text{ mole}^{-1} \text{ sec}^{-1}$$

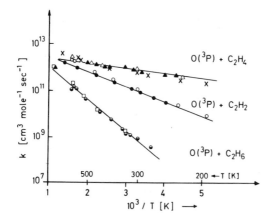

FIG. 22. Arrhenius diagram of experimental rate constants for the reactions of O(^{3}P) atoms with C_2 hydrocarbons; ▲, Davis *et al.*, 1972; for the remaining symbols see Wagner and Wolfrum, 1971.

and the Arrhenius activation energy (see Fig. 22). If the rate data for the addition of O(^{3}P) atoms to C_2H_2 are extrapolated to high temperatures (1500–2500 K), H-atom abstraction from acetylene by O(^{3}P) atoms (Bradley and Kistiakowsky, 1961)

$$O(^3P) + C_2H_2 \longrightarrow C_2H + OH \qquad (6.4')$$

$$\Delta H_0^\circ = +26 \text{ kcal mole}^{-1}$$

appear far too endothermic (Okabe, 1973) to be the chain-branching process in the high-temperature oxidation of acetylene.

D. Reactions with Alkenes

The reactions of oxygen atoms with olefins are very similar to the corresponding reactions of the methylene radical, which is isoelectronic with O atoms (Kirmse, 1964; Frey, 1964; Closs, 1968). According to Cvetanović (1963, 1970), the addition of O(^{3}P) atoms to olefins first yields triplet biradicals whose lifetime is comparable with the period of rotation about the C—C bond, and which isomerize by ring closure and migration of H atoms or alkyl groups to form epoxides, aldehydes, and ketones. On the basis of studies on the addition of O(^{3}P) atoms to condensed olefins (at 90 K) Klein and Scheer (1970) concluded, however, that the isomerization and the localization of the oxygen atom must take place simultaneously.

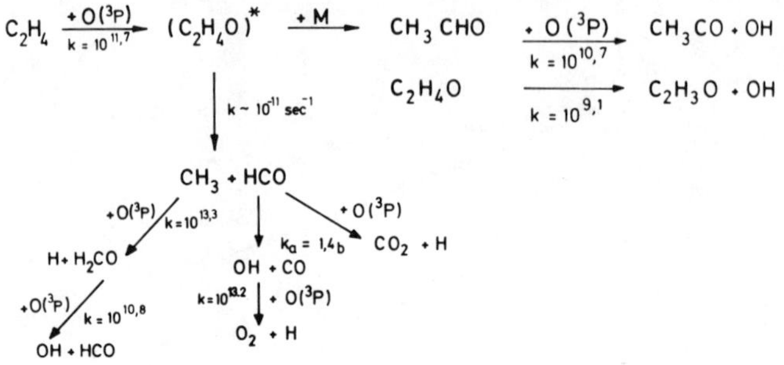

$$C_2H_4 \xrightarrow[k=10^{11.7}]{+O(^3P)} (C_2H_4O)^* \xrightarrow{+M} CH_3CHO \xrightarrow[k=10^{10.7}]{+O(^3P)} CH_3CO \cdot OH$$

$$C_2H_4O \xrightarrow[k=10^{9.1}]{} C_2H_3O \cdot OH$$

$$\downarrow k \sim 10^{11} \text{ sec}^{-1}$$

$$CH_3 + HCO$$

$$H + H_2CO \xleftarrow[k=10^{13.3}]{+O(^3P)} \qquad \xrightarrow{+O(^3P)} CO_2 + H$$

$$\downarrow k_a = 1.4b$$

$$OH + CO$$

$$OH + HCO \xleftarrow[k=10^{10.8}]{+O(^3P)} \qquad \downarrow k=10^{13.2} \quad +O(^3P)$$

$$O_2 + H$$

FIG. 23. Elementary steps in the reaction of O(³P) atoms with ethylene. Rate constants at 298 K in cm³ mole⁻¹ sec⁻¹.

Figure 23 shows the elementary steps occurring in the reaction of $O(^3P)$ atoms with ethylene. As in the reactions of H atoms, the energy barrier to be overcome is lower than in the case of acetylene.

Stabilization of the $(C_2H_4O)^*$ complex to form acetaldehyde and small amounts of ethylene oxide takes place to a considerable extent at atmospheric pressure. The high-pressure limit is reached around 50 atm (Eusuf and Wagner, 1972; Troe et al., 1972). At the lower pressures normally employed in discharge flow systems decomposition of the addition complexes predominates. An identification of the decomposition products has been made recently by Kanofsky and Gutman (1972).

As shown in Fig. 23, CH_3 and HCO are formed in the $O(^3P) + C_2H_4$ case. The subsequent atom–radical reaction

$$O(^3P) + CH_3 \longrightarrow H_2CO + H \qquad (6.7)$$

$$k_7 = 10^{13.3} \text{ cm}^3 \text{ mole}^{-1} \text{ sec}^{-1} \quad \text{at} \quad 298 \text{ K}$$

was investigated directly by Morris and Niki (1972) using the reaction of H atoms with diazomethane

$$H + CH_2N_2 \longrightarrow CH_3 + N_2$$

as the source of methyl radicals.

For the reaction of $O(^3P)$ atoms with the higher homologs of ethylene the addition products can be readily detected as stable end products and used for the determination of relative rate constants. Table IX gives relative rate constants for some olefins. These values clearly show an electrophilic character of the $O(^3P)$ addition to olefins which is also evident in the

TABLE IX

RELATIVE RATE CONSTANTS (BASED ON ETHYLENE) FOR THE ADDITION OF OXYGEN, SULFUR, AND SELENIUM ATOMS TO SOME OLEFINS AT ROOM TEMPERATURE

	$k_{olefin}/k_{C_2H_4}$		
	$O(2\ ^3P)$	$S(3\ ^3P)$	$Se(4\ ^3P)$
$H_2C=CH_2$	$\equiv 1$	$\equiv 1$	$\equiv 1$
$H_2C=CH-CH_3$	4.3	7.8	2.6
$H_2C=CH-CF_3$	0.06	—	—
$H_2C=CH-C_2H_5$	5.8	11	7.1
$H_2C=C(CH_3)_2$	23	56	447
$H_2C=C(CH_3)CF_3$	0.5	—	—
$\log k_{C_2H_4}$ (cm^3 mole^{-1} sec^{-1})	11.7	11.8	11.0

[a]For references see Wagner and Wolfrum (1971).

analogous reactions of S(3 ^3P) and Se(4 ^3P) atoms. Attack of the aromatic ring by the electrophilic oxygen atom requires a somewhat higher activation energy (Timmons et al., 1972)

$$O(^3P) + C_6H_6 \longrightarrow (C_6H_6O)^* \qquad (6.8)$$

$$k_8 = 10^{13.6} \exp(-4.4/RT) \quad cm^3 \ mole^{-1} \ sec^{-1}.$$

E. REACTIONS WITH SULFUR COMPOUNDS

During the oxidation of simple sulfur compounds (S_2, CS_2, OCS, H_2S) the presence of oxygen atoms can be seen from an intense blue-violet SO_2 chemiluminescence which was assigned to the recombination of SO with oxygen atoms as early as 1934 by Gaydon. A definite identification of the elementary steps and the determination of their rate constants became possible only through the isolated investigations of these reactions in flash photolysis and discharge flow reactor experiments. Table X lists some rate constants found at room temperature. Attack of O(^3P) on CS_2 and OCS can lead to abstraction as well as exchange of sulfur atoms. The relative importance of the two channels at various temperatures is not yet established quantitatively. About 10% of the reactions are reported (Homann et al., 1968, 1970) to proceed through the exchange channel at 1000 K. Thus, though the main reaction paths followed in the reaction of

TABLE X

RATE CONSTANTS FOR REACTIONS OF $O(^3P)$ ATOMS WITH SIMPLE
SULFUR COMPOUNDS AT ROOM TEMPERATURE[a]

Reaction	$-\Delta H_0^\circ$ (kcal mole^{-1})	$\log k$ (cm^3 mole^{-1} sec^{-1})
$O(^3P) + CS_2 \rightarrow CS + SO$	22	12.3
$\rightarrow OCS + S$	53	<8
$O(^3P) + OCS \rightarrow CO + SO$	55	9.8
$\rightarrow CO_2 + S$	57	<7
$O(^3P) + H_2S \rightarrow SH + OH$	14	10.4
$O(^3P) + SO_2 \rightarrow SO + O_2$	13	−2.3
$O(^3P) + SO_3 \rightarrow SO_2 + O_2$	35	5.6
$O(^3P) + CS \rightarrow CO + S$	76	12.9

[a]For references see Wagner and Wolfrum (1971).

$O(^3P)$ with CS_2 and OCS are analogous, a higher Arrhenius activation energy is found for the more exothermic reaction with OCS. Vibrational excitation of the diatomic product molecules (CO, SO, CS) has been detected in some reactions (Smith, 1967; Hancock and Smith, 1971; Poss, 1971) and successfully used for chemical CO laser operation initiated by atomic oxygen (Wittig et al., 1970; Stuart et al., 1970) and in free-burning flames (Pilloff et al., 1971).

CS_2/O_2 mixtures show three explosion limits similar to the H_2/O_2 system, which indicates the importance of branching reactions. One branching step is the reaction of sulfur atoms with molecular oxygen (Fair and Thrush, 1969)

$$S(^3P) + O_2(^3\Sigma) \longrightarrow SO(^3\Sigma) + O(^3P)$$

$$k = 10^{12.3} \text{ cm}^3 \text{ mol}^{-1} \text{ sec}^{-1} \quad \text{at} \quad 298 \text{ K}$$

with no detectable pressure and temperature dependence (Davis, Klemm and Pilling, 1972).

Sulfur superoxide (SOO), which was observed as an unidentified continuous absorber in exploding mixtures of CS_2, OCS, and H_2S with O_2 (Myerson et al., 1957), has been postulated as a possible intermediate of this reaction. As shown by Norrish and Zeelenberg (1957) and more recently by Basco and Morse (1971), however, these spectra are the result of temperature broadening of the SO_2 spectrum. Formation of SO_2 by

$$SO + O_2 \longrightarrow SO_2 + O$$
$$k = 10^{12} \exp(-7.9/RT) \quad cm^3 \, mole^{-1} \, sec^{-1}$$

and the reverse reaction are particularly interesting steps in connection with the problems of air pollution.

F. Reactions with Nitrogen Compounds

A serious air pollutant, nitric oxide, which triggers photochemical smog formation, is formed in combustion processes by breaking of the N—N bond of N_2 by the reaction with oxygen atoms. The rate for the direct attack of N_2 by $O(^3P)$ atoms

$$O(^3P) + N_2(^1\Sigma) \longrightarrow NO(^2\Pi) + N(^4S) \qquad (6.9)$$
$$k_9 = 10^{13.8} \exp(-75.5/RT) \quad cm^3 \, mole^{-1} \, sec^{-1}$$

can be derived from the reverse reaction. The high Arrhenius activation energy of reaction (6.9) ensures that even at 3000 K it proceeds several orders of magnitude more slowly than attack of H_2 (or hydrocarbons) by $O(^3P)$ (see Fig. 21). Therefore, formation of nitric oxide occurs to a large extent in the post-flame gases after passage of the flame front. The nitrogen atoms formed in (6.9) may further react with O_2 [see reaction (5.5)]. Using the rate constants of this simple two-step chain mechanism (Zeldovich, 1946), quantitative predictions for the formation of NO in high-pressure flames have been made (Newhall and Shaded, 1971).

Since reaction (6.9) is so endothermic, it is interesting to ask whether the vibrational energy of the nitrogen molecule can be efficiently utilized to overcome the endothermic barrier. Morgan, Phillips and Schiff (1962) and Black, Sharpless and Slanger (1973) have found some vibrational excitation of N_2 while investigating the reverse step to (6.9). A shock tube study of Wray and co-workers (1970), however, leads to the result that the rate of (6, 9) does not depend on the vibrational temperature of the nitrogen. This discrepancy may be explained by the fact that oxygen atoms are very effective in transferring vibrational energy from molecular nitrogen while the reactive cross section is small. (Breshears and Bird, 1968; McNeal et al., 1972; Nikitin and Umanski, 1972 (see also Chapter 4)).

Another way of breaking the bonds of molecular nitrogen is the formation of N_2O by the reaction

$$O(^3P) + N_2 + M \longrightarrow N_2O + M \qquad (6.10)$$

$$k_{10} = 10^{14} \exp(-18.0/RT) \quad cm^3 \, mole^{-1} \, sec^{-1}$$

followed by

$$O(^3P) + N_2O \longrightarrow NO + NO \qquad (6.11)$$

$$\longrightarrow N_2 + O_2$$

$$k_{11} = 10^{14} \exp(-28.0/RT) \quad cm^3 \, mole^{-1} \, sec^{-1}.$$

Reaction (6.10) can play a role in the nitric oxide formation in combustion processes at high pressures and temperatures below 1500 K.

A third possibility for breaking the N_2 bond in hydrocarbon combustion processes is offered by the reactions of molecular nitrogen with carbon atoms or hydrocarbon radicals which result in the formation of carbon–nitrogen compounds.

Surprisingly, the attack of cyanogen compounds by $O(^3P)$ atoms requires a significantly higher activation energy than the attack of compounds with a carbon–carbon triple bond. For the reactions

$$O(^3P) + XCN \longrightarrow OX + CN \qquad (X = H, Cl, Br, CN) \qquad (6.12)$$

Arrhenius activation energies of 7 (ClCN), 8 (HCN), 10 (BrCN), and 11 (C_2N_2) kcal mole^{-1} have been measured. In the $O(^3P) + C_2N_2$ case the primary addition complex $(C_2N_2O)^*$ was observed in the gas phase by visible and infrared absorption spectroscopy (Hand and Hexter, 1970). From the cyanogen radicals formed in reaction (6.12) free nitrogen atoms are then generated by

$$O(^3P) + CN \longrightarrow CO + N \qquad (6.13)$$

$$k_{13} = 10^{13.2} \, cm^3 \, mole^{-1} \, sec^{-1} \quad at \quad 298 \, K,$$
$$\Delta H_0^\circ = -73 \, kcal \, mole^{-1}.$$

Figure 24 shows the effect of vibrational excitation of the cyanogen radical on the rate of reaction (6.13). In spite of the fact that one vibrational quantum of CN exceeds the reported Arrhenius activation energy (Boden and Thrush, 1968) for reaction (6.13) by a factor of two, $k_{13}(v')$ shows no significant increase until $v' = 7$ is reached.

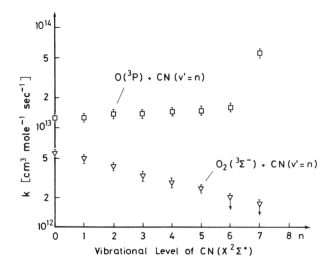

FIG. 24. Effect of vibrational excitation on the rate constants of the reaction of cyanogen radicals with $O(^3P)$ atoms and molecular oxygen at room temperature.

As shown in Fig. 25, a possible explanation for this increase is an effective use of the vibrational excitation for the endothermic reaction

$$O(^3P) + CN \longrightarrow C(^3P) + NO \qquad (6.13')$$

$$\Delta H_0^\circ = +33 \text{ kcal mole}^{-1}$$

which might have a "late" energy barrier (see Chapter 6). The rate of

$$CN + O_2 \longrightarrow NCO + O \qquad (6.14)$$

$$k_{14} = 10^{13.5} \exp(-1.0 \pm 0.2/RT) \quad \text{cm}^3 \text{ mole}^{-1} \text{ sec}^{-1}$$
$$\Delta H_0^\circ = -4 \text{ kcal mole}^{-1}$$

decreases with increasing vibrational quantum number of the cyanogen radical.

Turning to the oxidation of simple hydrides of nitrogen, a large number of elementary steps follow the initial attack of these molecules by $O(^3P)$ atoms. As can be seen from Fig. 26, hydrazine reacts extremely rapidly with atomic oxygen even at low temperatures. The primary products formed in this reaction were observed directly with the mass spectrometer (Foner and Hudson, 1968; Gehring *et al.*, 1969). It was found that the reaction leads directly to diimine and water

$$O(^3P) + N_2H_4 \longrightarrow N_2H_2 + H_2O. \qquad (6.15)$$

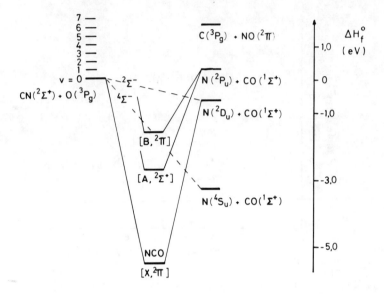

Fig. 25.   Correlation diagram for the reaction of cyanogen radicals with ground-state oxygen atoms.

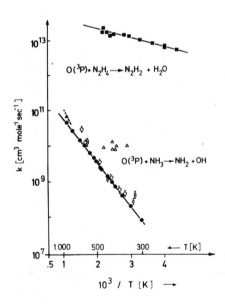

Fig. 26.   Arrhenius diagram of experimental rate constants for the reaction of $O(^3P)$ atoms with ammonia and hydrazine (for symbols see Wagner and Wolfrum, 1971).

This reaction thus provided the first direct evidence that $O(^3P)$ atoms can take up two hydrogen atoms in one elementary step. Only one hydrogen atom is apparently transferred from ammonia to the $O(^3P)$ atom,

$$O(^3P) + NH_3 \longrightarrow NH_2 + OH. \qquad (6.16)$$

Formation of a nitrogen–oxygen bond can occur in the subsequent reactions of $O(^3P)$ atoms with the amine and diimine radicals (Gehring *et al.*, 1972)

$$O + NH_2 \longrightarrow HNO + H \qquad (6.17)$$
$$\longrightarrow NH + OH$$
$$O + N_2H_2 \longrightarrow NH_2 + NO \qquad (6.18)$$
$$\longrightarrow N_2 + OH + H.$$

The nitric oxide, however, is not a stable end product in this system since the reaction

$$NO + NH_2 \longrightarrow H_2O + N_2 \qquad (6.19)$$
$$k_{19} = 10^{12.7} \text{ cm}^3 \text{ mole}^{-1} \text{ sec}^{-1} \quad \text{at} \quad 298 \text{ K}$$

can reduce it to molecular nitrogen.

List of Symbols

A	Appearance potential of molecular ions	K	Equilibrium constant
D	Dissociation energy	M_s	Mach number
$E(r)$	Potential energy	N	Particle concentration
E^*	Excitation energy	$\dot{N}$	Particle flux
E_A	Experimental (Arrhenius) activation energy	P	Pressure
		P_A	Microwave energy
E_c	Barrier height of the potential energy surface	Q_{at}	Atom calibration factor of the ESR signal
E_R	Energy threshold of the reaction	R	Gas constant
$\Delta G_0^\ddagger$	Gibbs energy of activation	S^2	Sato parameter
ΔH_r	Heat of reaction	$\Delta S_0^\ddagger$	Entropy of activation
$\Delta H_0^\ddagger$	Enthalpy of activation	T	Temperature
H_1	Magnetic field	V	Morse function
I	Light intensity	a_s	Skimmer aperture
J	Total angular momentum quantum number	c	Empirical constant
		d	Nozzle diameter
		g_{eff}	Effective g-factor

h	Planck constant	α	Correction factor of the Sato function
k	Boltzmann constant		
$k(T)$, k_i	Rate coefficient	β	Bohr magneton
l	Optical path length	β_{AB}	Morse parameter of the molecule AB
m	Particle mass	ε	Extinction coefficient
n	Bond order	κ	Transmission coefficient
p, q	Empirical constants	λ	Wavelength
r	Internuclear distance	μ	Reduced mass
s	Peak-to-peak height of the ESR signal	μ_{ij}	Transition matrix element
		χ	Magnetic susceptibility
t	Reaction time	σ	Reaction cross section
t_i	Relaxation time	ν	Frequency
v	Velocity	ω	Microwave frequency
w	Linewidth of the ESR signal	[ ]	Concentration

REFERENCES

ALBERS, E. A., HOYERMANN, K., WAGNER, H. GG., and WOLFRUM, J. (1971). *Int. Symp. Combust.* 13*th* p. 77. Combust. Inst., Pittsburgh, Pennsylvania.

ALBRIGHT, R. G., DODONOV, A. F., LAVROSKAYA, G. K., MOROSOV, I. I., and TALROZE, V. L. (1969). *J. Chem. Phys.* **50**, 3632.

ASHKENAS, H., and SHERMAN, F. S. (1966). *In* "Rarefied Gas Dynamics" (J. A. Lauermann, ed.), Vol. 2, p. 84. Academic Press, New York.

ATKINSON, R., and CVETANOVIĆ, R. J. (1971). *J. Chem. Phys.* **55**, 659.

BAER, M., and KOURI, D. J. (1971). *Phys. Rev. A* **4**, 1924.

BALAKHIN, V. P., GERSHENZON, Y. M., KONDRATIEV, V. N., and NALBANDYAN, A. B. (1964). *Dokl. Akad. SSSR* **154**, 883, 1142.

BALDWIN, R. R., EVERETT, C. J., HOPKINS, D. E., and WALKER, R. W. (1968). *Advan. Chem. Ser.* 76 (R. F. GOULD, ed.). Amer. Chem. Soc. Publ., Washington, D.C.

BASCO, N., and MORSE, R. D. (1971). *Proc. Roy. Soc. (London)* **A321**, 129.

BAULCH, D. L., DRYSDALE, D. D., and LLOYD, A. C. (1968–1970). "Critical Evaluation of Rate Data for Homogeneous Gas Phase Reactions of Interest in High Temperature System," Vol. 1–5, Leeds.

BAULCH, D. L., DRYSDALE, D. D., HORNE, D. G., and LLOYD, A. C. (1973) "Evaluated Kinetic Data for High Temperature Reactions" Vols. 1, 2, Butterworths, London.

BECKER, E. W., and BIER, K. (1954). *Z. Naturforsch.* **9a**, 975.

BECKER, K. H., and BAYES, K. D. (1968). *J. Chem. Phys.* **48**, 653.

BECKER, K. H., KLEY, D., and NORSTROM, R. J. (1965). *Int. Symp. Combust.* p. 405. Combust. Inst., Pittsburgh, Pennsylvania.

BECKER, K. H., GROTH, W., and KLEY, D. (1969). *Z. Naturforsch.* **24a**, 1280.

BECKER, K. H., GROTH, W., and THRAN, D. (1970). *Chem. Phys. Lett.* **6**, 583.

BECKER, K. H., FINK, E. H., GROTH, W., JUD, W., and KLEY, D. (1972). *Discuss. Faraday Soc.* **53**, 35.

BECKER, R. (1922). *Z. Phys.* **8**, 321.

BECKEY, H. D., and GROTH, W. (1959). *Z. Phys. Chem.* **NF20**, 307.

BEHRINGER, R., and CASTLE, J. G. (1949). *Phys. Rev.* **75**, 1963; **76**, 869.

BENSON, S. W. (1968). "Thermochemical Kinetics." Wiley, New York.
BENSON, S. W., and BUSS, J. H. (1958). *J. Chem. Phys.* **28**, 301.
BENSON, S. W., and GOLDEN, D. M. (1969). *Chem. Rev.* **69**, 125.
BIEDENKAPP, D., HARTSHORN, L. G., and BAIR, E. J. (1970). *Chem. Phys. Lett.* **5**, 379.
BIER, K. (1960). *Z. Naturforsch.* **15a**, 714.
BISHOP, W. P., and DORFMAN, L. M. (1970). *J. Chem. Phys.* **52**, 3210.
BISHOP, W. P., and DORFMAN, L. M. (1971). *J. Chem. Phys.* **54**, 3422.
BLACK, G., SHARPLESS, R. L., and SLANGER, T. G. (1973). *J. Chem. Phys.* **58**, 4792.
BODEN, J. C., and THRUSH, B. A. (1968). *Proc. Roy. Soc. (London)* **A305**, 93.
BODENSTEIN, M. (1913). *Z. Phys. Chem.* **85**, 329.
BONHOEFFER, K. F. (1924). *Z. Phys. Chem.* **113**, 199, 492.
BOWMAN, J. M., and KUPPERMANN, A. (1971). *Chem. Phys. Lett.* **12**, 1.
BRADLEY, J. N. (1962). "Shock Waves in Chemistry Physics." Wiley, New York.
BRADLEY, J. N., and KISTIAKOWSKY, G. B. (1961). *J. Chem. Phys.* **35**, 1.
BRADLEY, J. N., and KISTIAKOWSKY, G. B. (1961). *J. Chem. Phys.* **35**, 264.
BRADLEY, J. N., and TSE, R. S. (1968). *J. Chem. Phys.* **49**, 1968.
BRAUN, W., KURYLO, M. J., and PETERSON, N. C. (1971). *J. Chem. Phys.* **54**, 943.
BRAUN, W., BASS, A. M., DAVIS, D. D., and SIMMONS, J. D. (1969). *Proc. Roy. Soc. (London)* **A312**, 417.
BRESHEARS, W. D., and BIRD, P. F. (1968). *J. Chem. Phys.* **48**, 4768.
BRÖMER, H. H., and HESSE, J. (1969). *Z. Phys.* **219**, 269.
BROWN, J. M., and THRUSH, B. A. (1967). *Trans. Faraday Soc.* **63**, 630.
CALVERT, J. G., and PITTS, J. N. (1966). "Photochemistry." Wiley, New York.
CAMPARGUE, R. (1970). *J. Chem. Phys.* **52**, 1795.
CAMPBELL, I. M., and THRUSH, B. A. (1968). *Trans. Faraday Soc.* **64**, 1265.
CAMPBELL, I. M., NEAL, S. B., GOLDE, M. F., and THRUSH, B. A. (1971). *Chem. Phys. Lett.* **8**, 612.
CARRINGTON, A., and LEVY, D. H. (1967). *J. Phys. Chem.* **71**, 2.
CARRINGTON, A., and McLACHLAN, A. D. (1967). "Introduction to Magnetic Resonance," p. 8. Harper, New York.
CARRINGTON, A., LEVY, D. H., and MILLER, T. A. (1970). *Advan. Chem. Phys.* **18**, 149.
CLOSS, G. L. (1968). Structures of carbenes and the stereochemistry of carbene additions to olefins, *In* "Topics in Stereochemistry," Vol. 3, Wiley, New York.
CLOUGH, P. N., and THRUSH, B. A. (1968). *Chem. Commun.* 1351.
CLOUGH, P. N., and THRUSH, B. A. (1969). *Proc. Roy. Soc. (London)* **A309**, 419.
CLYNE, M. A. A., and STEDMAN, D. H. (1967). *Chem. Phys. Lett.* **1**, 36.
CLYNE, M. A. A., and THRUSH, B. A. (1961). *Trans. Faraday Soc.* **57**, 1305.
CLYNE, M. A. A., and THRUSH, B. A. (1962). *Discuss. Faraday Soc.* **33**, 139.
COMES, E. J., and SCHLAG, E. W. (1959). *Z. Phys. Chem.* **NF21**, 212.
CONROY, H., and BRUNER, B. L. (1967). *J. Chem. Phys.* **47**, 921.
COOLIDGE, A. S., and JAMES, H. M. (1934). *J. Chem. Phys.* **2**, 811.
CROSS, R. J., and WOLFGANG, R. (1961). *J. Chem. Phys.* **35**, 2002.
CVETANOVIĆ, R. J. (1963). *Advan. Photochem.* **1**, 115.
CVETANOVIĆ, R. J. (1970). *J. Phys. Chem.* **74**, 2730.
DARWENT, B. DE B., and ROBERTS, R. (1953). *Discuss. Faraday Soc.* **14**, 55.
DATZ, S., and TAYLOR, E. H. (1956). *J. Chem. Phys.* **25**, 389.
DAVIS, D. D., and BRAUN, W. (1968). *Appl. Opt.* **7**, 2071.
DAVIS, D. D., HUIE, R. E., HERRON, J. T., KURYLO, M. J., and BRAUN, W. (1972). *J. Chem. Phys.* **56**, 4868.
DAVIS, D. D., KLEMM, R. B., and PILLING, M. (1972). *Int. J. Chem. Kinet.* **4**, 367.

DEL GRECO, F. P., and KAUFMAN, F. (1962). *Discuss. Faraday Soc.* **33**, 128.

DIBELER, V. H., REESE, R. M., and KRAUSS, M. (1966). *Advan. Mass Spectromet.* **3**, 471; **4**, 767.

DOLL, J. D., GEORGE, T. F., and MILLER, W. H. (1973). *J. Chem. Phys.* **58**, 1343.

DONOVAN, R. J., and HUSAIN, D. (1970). *Chem. Rev.* **70**, 489.

DONOVAN, R. J., and HUSAIN, D. (1971). *Trans. Faraday Soc.* **67**, 375, 2025.

DOVE, J. E. and CLARK, T. C. (1973), *Can. J Chem.* **51**, 2147.

DOVE, J., and MOULTON, D. (1965). *Proc. Roy. Soc.* (*London*) **A283**, 216.

DRYER, F., NAEGELI, D., and GLASSMAN, I. (1971). *Combust. Flame* **17**, 270.

ELIAS, L. (1966). *J. Chem. Phys.* **44**, 3810.

ELIAS, L., OGRYZLO, E. A., and SCHIFF, H. I. (1959). *Can. J. Chem.* **37**, 1692.

ELTENTON, G. C. (1947). *J. Chem. Phys.* **15**, 455.

EUSUF, M., and WAGNER, H. GG. (1972). *Ber. Bunsenges. Phys. Chem.* **76**, 437.

EVANS, M. G., and POLANYI, M. (1938). *Trans. Faraday Soc.* **34**, 11.

EYRING, H., and POLANYI, M. (1931). *Z. Phys. Chem.* **B12**, 279.

FAIR, R. W., and THRUSH, B. A. (1969). *Trans. Faraday Soc.* **65**, 1557.

FAIR, R. W., VAN ROODSELAAR, A., and STRAUSZ, O. P. (1971). *Can. J. Chem.* **49**, 1659.

FEHSENFELD, F. C., EVENSON, K. M., and BROIDA, H. P. (1965). *Rev. Sci. Instrum.* **36**, 294.

FEHSENFELD, F. C., SCHMELTEKOPF, A. L., GOLDAN, P. D., SCHIFF, H. I., and FERGUSON, E. E. (1966). *J. Chem. Phys.* **44**, 4087.

FETTIS, G. C., and KNOX, J. H. (1964). *Progr. Reaction Kinet.* **2**, 2.

FITE, W. L., GEDDES, J., and KRAUSE, H. F. (1972). *J. Chem. Phys.* **56**, 3298.

FONER, S. N., and HUDSON, R. L. (1962). *J. Chem. Phys.* **36**, 2681; **37**, 1662.

FONER, S. N., and HUDSON, R. L. (1968). *J. Chem. Phys.* **49**, 3724.

FONTIJN, A., MEYER, C. B., and SCHIFF, H. I. (1964). *J. Chem. Phys.* **40**, 64.

FONTIJN, A., MILLER, W. J., and HOGAN, J. M. (1965). *Int. Symp. Combust.* 10th p. 545. Combust. Inst., Pittsburgh, Pennsylvania.

FOO, K. K., and YANG, C. H. (1971). *Combust. Flame* **17**, 223.

FOX, R. E. (1959). *Advan. Mass Spectromet.* **1**, 397.

FREEMAN, C. G., and PHILLIPS, L. F. (1968). *J. Phys. Chem.* **72**, 3028.

GAEDTKE, H., GLÄNZER, K., HIPPLER, H., LUTHER, K., and TROE, J. (1972). *Int. Symp. Combust.* 14th Combust. Inst., Pittsburgh, Pennsylvania.

GARDINER, W. C., Jr., MALLARD, W. G., McFARLAND, M., MORIGANA, K., OWEN, J. H., RAWLINS, W. T., TAKEYAMA, T., and WALKER, B. F. (1972). *Int. Symp. Combust.*, 14th Combust. Inst., Pittsburgh, Pennsylvania.

GAYDON, A. G. (1934). *Proc. Roy. Soc.* (*London*) **A146**, 901.

GEHRING, M. (1971). PhD Thesis, Georg-August-Univ., Göttingen.

GEHRING, M., HOYERMANN, K., WAGNER, H. GG., and WOLFRUM, J. (1969). *Ber. Bunsenges. Phys. Chem.* **73**, 956.

GEHRING, M., HOYERMANN, K., WAGNER, H. GG., and WOLFRUM, J. (1971). *Ber. Bunsenges. Phys. Chem.* **75**, 1287.

GEHRING, M., HOYERMANN, K., SCHACKE, H., and WOLFRUM, J. (1972). *Int. Symp. Combust.* 14th Combust. Inst. Pittsburgh, Pennsylvania.

GELTMAN, S. (1956). *Phys. Rev.* **102**, 171.

GEORGE, T. F., and MILLER, W. H. (1972). *J. Chem. Phys.* **56**, 5722.

GIBBS, D. B., and OGRYZLO, E. A. (1965). *Can. J. Chem.* **43**, 1905.

GLASS, G. P. (1974). *J. Phys. Chem.* to be published.

GREEN, E. F., and TOENNIES, J. P. (1964). "Chemical Reactions in Shock Waves." Arnold, London.

GREENE, F. T., and MILNE, T. A., (1966). *Advan. Mass Spectromet.* 841.
GREINER, N. R. (1968), *J. Phys. Chem.* **72**, 406.
GROTH, W., and WARNECK, P. (1957). *Z. Phys. Chem.* **NF10**, 323.
GUILLORY, W. A., and HUNTER, C. E. (1971). *J. Chem. Phys.* **54**, 598.
GUNNING, H. E., and STRAUSZ, O. P. (1966). *Advan. Photochem.* **4**, 143.
HACK, W., HOYERMANN, K., and WAGNER, H. GG. (1974). *Z. Naturforsch.* **29a**, 1236.
HALLER, I., and PIMENTEL, G. C. (1962). *J. Amer. Chem. Soc.* **84**, 2855.
HANCOCK, G., and SMITH, I. W. M. (1971). *Chem. Phys. Lett.* **8**, 41.
HAND, C. W., and HEXTER, R. M. (1970). *J. Amer. Chem. Soc.* **92**, 1828.
HARTECK, P. (1928). *Z. Phys. Chem.* **139**, 98.
HEIDNER, R. F., and KASPER, J. V. V. (1969). *J. Chem. Phys.* **51**, 4163.
HERBRECHTSMEIER, P., and WAGNER, H. GG. (1972). *Ber. Bunsenges. Phys. Chem.* **76**, 517.
HERRON, J. T., and HUIE, R. E. (1968). *J. Chem. Phys.* **72**, 2235.
HERRON, J. T., and HUIE, R. E. (1969). *J. Phys. Chem.* **73**, 3327.
HERZBERG, G. (1966). "Molecular Spectra and Molecular Structure," Vol. III. Electronic Spectra and Electronic Structure of Polyatomic Molecules. Van Nostrand-Reinhold, New York.
HIRSCHFELDER, J. O., and LINNET, J. W. (1950). *J. Chem. Phys.* **18**, 130.
HOMANN, K. H., MOCHIZUKI, M., and WAGNER, H. GG. (1963). *Z. Phys. Chem. (Frankfurt)* **37**, 299.
HOMANN, K. H., KROME, G., and WAGNER, H. GG. (1968). *Ber. Bunsenges. Phys. Chem.* **72**, 998.
HOMANN, K. H., KROME, G., and WAGNER, H. GG. (1970). *Ber. Bunsenges. Phys. Chem.* **74**, 645.
HOYERMANN, K., and WOLFRUM, J. (1970). "New Experimental Techniques in Propulsion and Energetics Research" (D. Andrews and S. Surugue, ed.), Agard. Conf. Proc. No. 83.
HOYERMANN, K., WAGNER, H. GG., and WOLFRUM, J. (1967a). *Ber. Bunsenges. Phys. Chem.* **71**, 603.
HOYERMANN, K., WAGNER, H. GG., and WOLFRUM, J. (1967b). *Ber. Bunsenges. Phys. Chem.* **71**, 599.
HOYERMANN, K., WAGNER, H. GG., and WOLFRUM, J. (1967c). *Z. Phys. Chem. (Frankfurt)* **55**, 72.
HOYERMANN, K., WAGNER, H. GG., and WOLFRUM, J. (1969). *Z. Phys. Chem. (Frankfurt)* **63**, 193.
HOYERMANN, K., WAGNER, H. GG., WOLFRUM, J., and ZELLNER, R. (1971). *Ber. Bunsenges. Phys. Chem.* **75**, 22.
HUNTEN, D. M., and McELROY, M. B. (1968). *J. Geophys. Res.* **73**, 2421.
HUSAIN, D., and KIRSCH, L. J. (1971). *Chem. Phys. Lett.* **8**, 543.
JACOB, A. (1968). Ph.D. Thesis, McGill University, Montreal.
JOHNSTON, H. S. (1966). "Gas Phase Reaction Rate Theory." Ronald Press, New York.
JOHNSTON, H. S. (1968). Tables of Bimolecular Gas Reactions and Supplements, NSRDS-NBS 9. U.S. Dept. of Commerce, Washington, D.C.
JOHNSTON, H. S., and PARR, C. J. (1963). *J. Amer. Chem. Soc.* **85**, 2544.
JOHNSTON, H. S., McGRAW, G. E., PANKERT, T. T., RICHARDS, L. W., and VAN DEN BOGAERDE, J. (1967). *Proc. Nat. Acad. Sci. U.S.* **57**, 1146.
JONES, I. T. N., and BAYES, K. D. (1972). *J. Amer. Chem. Soc.* **94**, 6869.
JOST, W. (1929). *Z. Phys. Chem.* **B3**, 95.
JOST, W. (1939). "Explosions- und Verbrennungsvorgänge in Gasen." Springer, New York

JOST, W. (1949). *Int. Symp. Combust.* 3rd p. 424. Comb. Inst., Pittsburgh, Pennsylvania.

KANOFSKY, J. R., and GUTMAN, D. (1972). *Chem. Phys. Lett.* **15**, 236.

KANTROWITZ, A., and GREY, J. (1952). *Rev. Sci. Instrum.* **22**, 328.

KARPLUS, M., and PORTER, R. N. (1967). *Discuss. Faraday Soc.* **44**, 164.

KASPER, J. V. V., and PIMENTEL, G. C. (1965). *Phys. Rev. Lett.* **14**, 352.

KAUFMAN, F. (1958). *Proc. Roy. Soc. (London)* **A 247**, 123.

KAUFMAN, F. (1961). *Progr. Reaction Kinet.* **1**, 3.

KAUFMAN, F., and DEL GRECO, F. P. (1962). *Discuss. Faraday Soc.* **33**, 128.

KAUFMAN, F., and KELSO, J. R. (1957). *J. Chem. Phys.* **27**, 1209.

KAUFMAN, F., and LIN, C. L. (1971). *J. Chem. Phys.* **55**, 3760.

KIEFFER, L. J., and DUNN, G. H. (1966). *Rev. Mod. Phys.* **38**, 1.

KIRMSE, W. (1964). "Carbene Chemistry." Academic Press, New York.

KISTIAKOWSKY, G. B., and VOLPI, G. G. (1957). *J. Chem. Phys.* **27**, 1141.

KLEIN, R., and SCHEER, M. D. (1970). *J. Phys. Chem.* **74**, 613, 2732.

KOMPA, K. (1973). Chemical Lasers. *In* "Topics of Current Chemistry." Springer, New York.

KONDRATIEV, V. N. (1970). "Rate Constants of Elementary Gas Reactions." NAUKA, Moscow.

KONDRATIEV, V. N. (1972). *Kinetics and Catalysis* **13**, 3.

KRONGELB, S., and STRANDBERG, W. M. P. (1959). *J. Chem. Phys.* **31**, 1196.

KUPPERMANN, A., and WHITE, J. M. (1966). *J. Chem. Phys.* **44**, 4352.

KURYLO, M. J., and TIMMONS, R. B. (1969). *J. Chem. Phys.* **50**, 5076.

KURYLO, M. J., PETERSON, N. C., and BRAUN, W. (1970). *J. Chem. Phys.* **53**, 2776.

KURYLO, M. J., PETERSON, N. C., and BRAUN, W. (1971). *J. Chem. Phys.* **54**, 4662.

LARKIN, F. S., and THRUSH, B. A. (1964). *Discuss. Faraday Soc.* **37**, 112.

LAUFER, H. A., and McNESBY (1965). *J. Chem. Phys.* **42**, 3329.

LEE, Y. T. (1969). *Rev. Sci. Instrum.* **40**, 1402.

LEGAY, F. (1967). *J. Chem. Phys.* **64**, 9.

LEGOFF, P., CASSUTO, A., and PENTENERO, A. (1966). *Advan. Mass Spectrom.* **3**, 853.

LEWIS, B., and v. ELBE, G. (1942). *J. Chem. Phys.* **10**, 366.

LIFSHITZ, A., BAUER, S. H., and RESLER, E. (1963). *J. Chem. Phys.* **38**, 2056.

LIN, C., PARKES, D. A., and KAUFMAN, F. (1970). *J. Chem. Phys.* **53**, 3896.

LIU, B. (1971). *Int. J. Quantum Chem.* **5S**, 123.

LLOYD, A. C. (1974). *Int. J. Chem. Kinet.* **6**, 169.

LONDON, F. C. (1928). "Probleme der Modernen Physik," Sommerfeldfestschrift, p. 104. Hirzel, Leipzig.

LONDON, G., GILPIN, R., SCHIFF, H. I., and WELGE, K. H. (1971). *J. Chem. Phys.* **34**, 1971.

McCRUMB, L., and KAUFMAN, F. (1972). *J. Chem. Phys.* **57**, 1270.

McNEAL, R. J., WHITSON, M. E., and COOK, G. R. (1972). *Chem. Phys. Lett.* **16**, 507.

MARTINENGO, A. (1967). *In* "Oxidation and Combustion Reviews" (C. F. H. Tipper, ed.), Vol. 2, p. 209. Elsevier, Amsterdam.

MARTINOTTI, F. F., WELCH, M. J., and WOLF, A. P. (1968). *Chem. Commun.* 115.

MAYER, S. W. (1967). *J. Phys. Chem.* **71**, 4159.

MAYER, S. W., SCHIELER, L., and JOHNSTON, H. S. (1967). *Int. Symp. Combust.* 11th p. 837. Combust. Inst., Pittsburgh, Pennsylvania.

McGRATH, W. D., and MORROW, T. (1966). *Trans. Faraday Soc.* **62**, 642.

MEABURN, G. M., and PERNER, D. (1966). *Nature* (London) **212**, 1042.

MELVILLE, H. W., and GOWENLOCK, B. G. (1964). "Experimental Methods in Gas Reactions." Macmillan, New York.

MICHAEL, J. V., and WESTON, R. E. (1965). *J. Chem. Phys.* **45**, 3632.

MICHELCIC, D., and SCHINDLER, R. N. (1970). *Ber. Bunsenges. Phys. Chem.* **74**, 1280.
MITCHELL, D. N., and LeROY, D. J. (1973). *J. Chem. Phys.* **58**, 3449.
MITRA, S. K. (1945). "Active Nitrogen—A New Theory." Chem. Soc., Calcutta.
MOK, M. H. and POLANYI, J. C. (1969). *J. Chem. Phys.* **51**, 1451.
MORGAN, J. E., PHILLIPS, L. F., and SCHIFF, H. I. (1962). *Discuss. Faraday Soc.* **33**, 118.
MOROKUMA, K., and KARPLUS, M. (1967). *Discuss. Faraday Soc.* **44**, 78.
MORRIS, E. D., and NIKI, H. (1972). *Int. J. Chem. Kinet.* **5**, 47.
MORSE, F. A., and KAUFMAN, F. (1965). *J. Chem. Phys.* **42**, 1785.
MYERSON, A. L., TAYLOR, F. R., and HANST, P. L. (1957). *J. Chem. Phys.* **26**, 1309.
NALBANDYAN, A. B., and VOEVODSKY, V. V. (1948). "The Mechanism of Hydrogen Combustion," Russ., Moscow.
NERNST, W. (1916). *Z. Elektrochem.* **22**, 62.
NEWHALL, K. H., and SHADED, S. M. (1971). *Int. Symp. Combust., 13th.* p. 365, Combust. Inst., Pittsburgh, Pennsylvania.
NIKITIN, E. E., and UMANSKI, S. J. (1972), *Farad. Disc. Chem. Soc.* **53**, 7,
NORRISH, R. G. W., and ZEELENBERG, A. P. (1957). *Proc. Roy. Soc. (London)* **A240**, 293.
OGG, R. A., and POLANYI, M. (1935). *Trans. Faraday Soc.* **31**, 604.
OKABE, H., and DIBELER, V. H., (1973). *J. Chem. Phys.* **59**, 2430.
O'NEIL, S., SCHAEFER, H. F. III, and BENDER, C. F. (1971). *J. Chem. Phys.* **55**, 162.
OTVOS, J. W., and STEVENSON, D. P. (1956). *J. Amer. Chem. Soc.* **78**, 546.
PAKE, G. E. (1962). "Paramagnetic Resonance," p. 8. Benjamin, New York.
PAULING, L. (1947). *J. Amer. Chem. Soc.* **69**, 542.
PETERSON, N. C., KURYLO, M. J., BRAUN, W., BASS, A. M., and KELLER, R. A. (1971). *J. Opt. Soc. Amer.* **61**, 746.
PHILLIPS, L. F., and SCHIFF, II. I. (1962). *J. Chem. Phys.* **36**, 1509.
PHILLIPS, L. F., and SCHIFF, H. I. (1962). *J. Chem. Phys.* **37**, 1233.
PHILLIPS, L. F. and SCHIFF, H. I. (1965). *J. Chem. Phys.* **42**, 3171.
PILLOFF, H. S., SEARLES, S. K., and DJEU, N. (1971). *Appl. Phys. Lett.* **19**, 9.
POLANYI, M. (1932). "Atomic Reactions." Williams and Norgate, London.
PORTER, R. N., and KARPLUS, M. (1964). *J. Chem. Phys.* **40**, 1105.
POSS, R. (1971). PhD Thesis, Georg-August-Univ., Göttingen.
POTTER, A. E. Jr., COLTHARP, R. N., and WORLEY, S. D. (1971). *J. Chem. Phys.* **54**, 992.
QUICKERT, K. A. (1972). *J. Phys. Chem.* **76**, 825.
RABINOVITCH, B. S., and SETSER, D. W. (1964). *Advan. Photochem.* **3**, 1.
RAMSAY, D. A. (1952). *J. Chem. Phys.* **20**, 1920.
REINHARDT, K. H., WAGNER, H. Gg., and WOLFRUM, J. (1969). *Ber. Bunsenges. Phys. Chem.* **73**, 638.
REIS, V. H., and FENN, J. B. (1963). *J. Chem. Phys.* **39**, 3240.
RICHTERING, H. (1965). *In* "Low Temperature Oxidation" (W. Jost, ed.). Gordon and Breach, New York.
RIDLEY, B. A. (1968). PhD Thesis, Univ. of Toronto.
RIDLEY, B. A., SCHULZ, W. R., and LeROY, D. J. (1966). *J. Chem. Phys.* **44**, 3344.
RIPLEY, D. L., and GARDINER, W. C. Jr. (1966). *J. Chem. Phys.* **44**, 2285.
ROSS, J., and MAZUR, P. (1961). *J. Chem. Phys.* **35**, 19.
RUSIN, L. Y., CHAIKIN, A. M., and SHILOV, A. E. (1964). *Kinet. Katal.* **5**, 1121.
SAFRANY, D. R., and JASTER, W. (1968). *J. Phys. Chem.* **72**, 518.
SATO, S. (1955). *J. Chem. Phys.* **23**, 592, 2465.
SCHAEFER, H. F. III (1972). "The Electronic Structure of Atoms and Molecules." Addison-Wesley, Reading, Massachusetts.

SCHOTT, G. L., and GETZINGER, R. W. (1972). In "Physical Chemistry of Fast Reactions" (B. P. Levitt, ed.). Plenum Press, New York.

SCHULZ, W. R., and LeROY, D. J. (1965). J. Chem. Phys. 42, 3869.

SCOTT, P. M. and CVETANOVIĆ, R. J. (1970). J. Chem. Phys. 45, 1440.

SEAL, K. E., and GAYDON, R. G. (1966). Proc. Phys. Soc. (London) 89, 459.

SEMENOV, N. N. (1958). "Some Problems in Chemical Kinetics and Reactivity." Princeton Univ. Press, Princeton, New Jersey.

SHAVITT, I., (1968). J. Chem. Phys. 49, 4048.

SHAVITT, I., STEVENS, R. M., MINN, F. L., and KARPLUS, M. (1968). J. Chem. Phys. 48, 2700.

SHERMAN, F. S. (1963). In "Rarified Gas Dynamics" (J. A. Lauermann, ed.) Vol. 2, p. 228. Academic Press, New York.

SHERMAN, F. S. (1965). Phys. Fluids 8, 773.

SHULER, K. E. (1953). J. Chem. Phys. 21, 624.

SKELL, P. S., and ENGEL, S. K. (1965). J. Amer. Chem. Soc. 87, 1135.

SLATER, J. C. (1931). Phys. Rev. 38, 1109.

SMITH, I. W. M. (1967). Discuss. Faraday Soc. 44, 196.

SPRUNG, J. L., WINSTEIN, S., and LIBBY, W. F. (1965). J. Amer. Chem. Soc. 87, 1812.

STEDMAN, D. H., STEFFENSON, D., and NIKI, H. (1970). Chem. Phys. Lett. 7, 173.

STRUTT, R. J. (1911). Proc. Roy. Soc. (London) A 85, 219.

STUHL, F., and NIKI, H. (1971). J. Chem. Phys. 55, 3943, 3954.

SUART, R. D., ARNOLD, S. J., and KIMBELL, G. H. (1970). Chem. Phys. Lett. 7, 337.

SULLIVAN, J. H. (1967). J. Chem. Phys. 46, 73.

SUPLINSKAS, R. J. (1968). J. Chem. Phys. 49, 5046.

TAHOURDIN, P. A. (1949). Oxford Rep. 36, Oxford.

TALROZE, V. L. (1960). Prib. Tekhn. Eksp. 6, 78.

THRUSH, B. A. (1969). Ann. Rev. Phys. Chem. 19, 371.

THRASH, R. J., v. WEYSSENHOFF, H., and SHIRK, J. S. (1971). J. Chem. Phys. 55, 4659.

TIKHOMIROVA, N. N., and VOEVODSKY, V. V. (1955). "Chain Oxidation of Hydrocarbons in the Gas Phase," Moscow.

TIMMONS, R. B., LEE, J. H., KIM, P., and BONANNO, R. A. (1972). J. Chem. Phys. 57, 1377.

TOLLEFSON, E. L., and LeROY, D. J. (1948). J. Chem. Phys. 16, 1057.

TOLMAN, R. C. (1920). J. Amer. Chem. Soc. 42, 2506.

TROTMAN-DICKENSON, A. F., and MILNE, G. S. (1967). Tables of Bimolecular Gas Reactions, and Supplements, NSRDS-NBS 9. U.S. Dept. Commerce, Washington, D.C.

TRUHLAR, D. G., and KUPPERMANN, A. (1971). Chem. Phys. Lett. 9, 269.

TRUHLAR, D. G., KUPPERMANN, A., and ADAMS, J. T. (1973). J. Chem. Phys. 59, 395.

VASILEV, G. K., NAKAROV, E. F., PAPIN, V. G., and TALROZE, V. L. (1970). Dokl. Phys. Chem. 191, 296.

VIEILLE, P. (1899). C. R. Acad. Sci. Paris 129, 1228.

WAGNER, H. GG., and WOLFRUM, J. (1971). Angew. Chem. Int. Ed. 10, 604.

WAGNER, H. GG., and ZELLNER, R. (1972). Ber. Bunsenges. Phys. Chem. 76, 440.

WAKEFIELD, C. B., RIPLEY, D. L., and GARDINER, W. C. Jr. (1969). J. Chem. Phys. 50, 325.

WALSH, A. D. (1953). J. Chem. Soc. 2272.

WARREN, D. R. (1952). Proc. Roy. Soc. (London) A 211, 86.

WAUCHOP, T. S., and PHILLIPS, L. F. (1967). J. Chem. Phys. 47, 4281.

WAYNE, P. (1970). Advan. Photochem. 7, 311.

WELGE, K. H. (1970). J. Chem. Phys. 52, 239.

WESTENBERG, A. A. (1967). *Discuss. Faraday Soc.* **44**, 169.
WESTENBERG, A. A., and DE HAAS, N. (1964). *J. Chem. Phys.* **40**, 3087.
WESTENBERG, A. A., and DE HAAS, N. (1965). *J. Chem. Phys.* **43**, 1544.
WESTENBERG, A. A., and DE HAAS, N. (1967). *J. Chem. Phys.* **47**, 1393.
WESTENBERG, A. A., and DE HAAS, N. (1968). *J. Chem. Phys.* **48**, 4405.
WESTENBERG, A. A., and DE HAAS, N. (1969a). *J. Chem. Phys.* **50**, 707.
WESTENBERG, A. A., and DE HAAS, N. (1969b). *J. Chem. Phys.* **51**, 5215.
WESTENBERG, A. A., ROSCOE, J. M., and DE HAAS, N. (1970). *Chem. Phys. Lett.* **7**, 597.
WITTIG, C., HASSLER, J. C., and COLEMAN, P. D. (1970). *Nature (London)* **226**, 845.
WOLFGANG, R. (1965). *Progr. Reaction Kinet.* **3**, 97.
WOLKEN, G., and KARPLUS, M. (1971). Abstr. of Papers of the VII. I. C. P. E. A. C., p. 302. North Holland Publ., Amsterdam.
WOLKEN, G. and KARPLUS, M. (1974). *J. Chem. Phys.* **60**, 351.
WOOD, R. W. (1922). *Proc. Roy. Soc. (London)* **A102**, 1.
WRAY, K. L., FELDMAN, E. V., and LEWIS, P. F. (1970). *J. Chem. Phys.* **53**, 4131.
WREDE, E. (1928). *Z. Instrum.* **48**, 201.
WRIGHT, A. N., and WINKLER, C. A. (1968). "Active Nitrogen" (E. M. Loebl, ed.). Academic Press, New York.
YOUNG, R. A., SHARPLESS, R. L., and STRINGHAM, R. (1964). *J. Chem. Phys.* **40**, 117.
ZELDOVICH, J. (1946). *Acta Physicochim. SSSR.* **4**, 577.

Chapter 10

Relaxation Methods in Gases

A. B. CALLEAR

I. General Introduction

A. RELAXATION METHODS

In this chapter, techniques are described with which a static gas can be disturbed; from the time dependence of the relaxation to equilibrium, information on the mechanism and rates of kinetic processes is obtained. Two general methods of inducing a departure from equilibrium are optical excitation and excitation by electron impact. For rate measurements, the radiation is pulsed or modulated. In the first category, we shall discuss techniques involving radiations from the microwave to the vacuum-ultraviolet regions. Pulsed radiolysis and electric discharges will be included under electron impact methods. Applications will be described to the kinetics of both energy transfer processes and chemical reactions. Ultrasonic methods are not included.

The blackbody flash-photolysis technique has been applied extensively to problems of structure and kinetics, and a complete survey will not be attempted. A few basic applications will be described. To sustain interest and continuity in selected topics, occasionally material is included which has only a peripheral relationship to relaxation methods.

B. DEFINITION OF RELAXATION TIME

If a displacement from equilibrium δ decays with first-order kinetics, then

$$-d\delta/dt = k\delta,$$

where k is a constant. In the case of first-order decay, a "relaxation time" can be defined and it is simply k^{-1}; it is the time interval during which the displacement decays by a factor e.

The relaxation time is independent of the direction of the displacement. This can be seen as follows for the kinetics of a two-level system where both reactions are pseudo first order. Consider molecules A occupying only states i (lower) and j (upper), with transitions between the states induced in collision with an inert species M:

$$A_i + M \underset{k_{ji}}{\overset{k_{ij}}{\rightleftharpoons}} A_j + M.$$

The rate equation is

$$-d[A_i]/dt = d[A_j]/dt = k_{ij}[A_i][M] - k_{ji}[A_j][M].$$

The solution is

$$[A_i] = \{k_{ji}[A]/(k_{ij} + k_{ji})\}(1 - \exp\{-(k_{ij} + k_{ji})[M]t\})$$

when $[A_i] = 0$ at $t = 0$; and

$$[A_i] = \{[A]/(k_{ij} + k_{ji})\}(k_{ji} + k_{ij} \exp\{-(k_{ij} + k_{ji})[M]t\})$$

when $[A_i] = [A]$ at $t = 0$. $[A] = [A_i] + [A_j]$ is the total concentration. With either of the initial conditions, the reciprocal relaxation time is seen to be $(k_{ij} + k_{ji})[M]$. Usually there is a large disparity between k_{ij} and k_{ji} when a gas is excited with radiation (the exception being microwave excitation) and the reciprocal relaxation time can be identified with the first-order coefficient for the exothermic step. Thus the rate coefficient can be deduced without knowledge of the absolute concentrations corresponding to the displacement, if the reactions which restore equilibrium are first order.

Measurement of rate coefficients is usually more difficult if the rate of reaction is second order in the concentration of nonequilibrium states, because the absolute extent of the displacement is now required as a function of time. A simple example is the measurement of the rate coefficient for the termolecular recombination of atomic iodine I, which is pseudo second order in [I] in the presence of a large excess of inert gas. The termolecular rate coefficient is given by $[M]^{-1} d[I]^{-1}/dt$.

Obviously before any inference can be drawn from an observed relaxation-time profile, the mechanism needs to be established. Erroneous results have frequently been deduced when the understanding of the mechanism proved to be incomplete.

C. Early Experiments

Relaxation techniques in gases date back to the work of Meisner (1925) and Dorgelo (1925), involving kinetic absorption spectroscopy of the metastable states of the inert gases. The metastable atoms were produced in a sinusoidally varying electric discharge, and absorption of lines from a discharge background source was recorded photographically, with the background 180° out of phase with the voltage applied to the reaction vessel. By varying the frequency, it was possible to show qualitatively that the metastable species persisted for a few msec (10^{-3} sec). Pool (1929) appears to have conducted the first experiment with kinetic spectroscopy using optical excitation. A mixture of mercury vapor and nitrogen was illuminated with 2537-Å resonance radiation [$Hg(6\ ^3P_1) \leftarrow Hg(6\ ^1S_0)$]. In N_2 the $Hg(6\ ^3P_1)$ undergoes spin–orbit relaxation:

$$Hg(6\ ^3P_1) + N_2 \longrightarrow Hg(6\ ^3P_0) + N_2 .$$

Pool detected the metastable $Hg(6\ ^3P_0)$ photographically by reversal of the 4047-Å line (7 $^3S_1$–6 $^3P_0$), and, by employing a rotating wheel as a fast shutter, he observed the decay profiles. Pool (1931) invoked the participation of a long-lived, metastable N_2* in his reaction mechanism.

The first study of a free radical by kinetic absorption spectroscopy appears to be the experiment of Oldenberg (1934) inspired by observations (of others) of free radical spectra from outer space. He subjected H_2O vapor to a repetitively pulsed electric discharge and detected the free OH radical in absorption with a 21-ft grating spectrograph. A carbon-arc continuum was employed as background and the absorption spectrum was taken at various times following excitation by means of a slit set in a rotating wheel. Strong absorption spectra of OH X $^2\Pi$ were observed with time delays of 1/8 and 1/300 sec. Presumably substantial heating of the water vapor did occur in these experiments, though it was reported that the band heads were weak compared to those of the emission spectra observed from flames. The detection of the absorption spectrum of OH at the "steady state" at high temperature had previously been reported by Bonhoeffer and Reichhardt (1928).

Present-day relaxation techniques are essentially refinements of these early methods of excitation by means of light or electron impact.

II. Blackbody Flash Photolysis

A. THE BASIC EXPERIMENT

In 1949, Norrish and Porter described an experiment in which gases were subjected to an intense flash of light, obtained by discharging ~10,000 J of electrical energy from a bank of capacitors through a 1-m-long discharge lamp with robust electrodes at each end. The duration of the flash was about 4 msec. The nature of the photochemical reactions was shown to be different from that obtained with conventional, low-intensity photolysis, which was attributed to the high concentration of intermediates produced by flash photolysis.

In 1950, Porter (1950a,b) described the combination of flash photolysis and direct observation of transients by kinetic absorption spectroscopy. The technique for the latter was in some respects similar to that which had been used earlier by Pool and by Oldenberg, except that the spectra were recorded on single shot. Many of the features of the apparatus originally described by Porter are still in use in laboratories throughout the world. The flash lamp was filled with Kr at 50–100 Torr and was triggered with a central electrode. It was located parallel to a quartz reaction vessel, inside a reflector coated with magnesium oxide. A mechanical shutter provided the time delay between the initiating photoflash and the spectroscopic background flash. The latter consisted of an electroded discharge lamp similar to the photoflash. Time delays between the two flashes were recorded with a photocell located inside the spectrograph. The duration of the photoflash was ~1 msec. Transient absorption was observed due to CS and S_2 in flashed CS_2; SH and HS_2 in flashed H_2S; and ClO in flashed Cl_2/O_2 mixtures. Two regions of absorption were detected in flashed biacetyl.

Christie and Porter (1952) examined the spectral distribution from the discharge lamps and found that the energy per unit wavelength in the 2600–4400-Å region is independent of wavelength, corresponding to a very high-temperature black body. Some 7% of the energy is converted to ultraviolet light. In fact the spectral distribution is not strictly blackbody; the continuum is overlaid with emission and absorption lines, mainly of atomic silicon.

By 1952 (Herzberg and Ramsay, 1952), refinements to the experiment included replacement of the mechanical timer with an electronic device, and the incorporation of small, capillary discharge lamps (Lyman discharge) for the background source. The basic features of the experiment

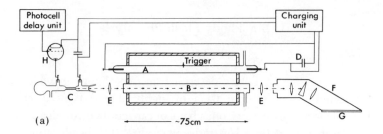

(a)   ~75cm

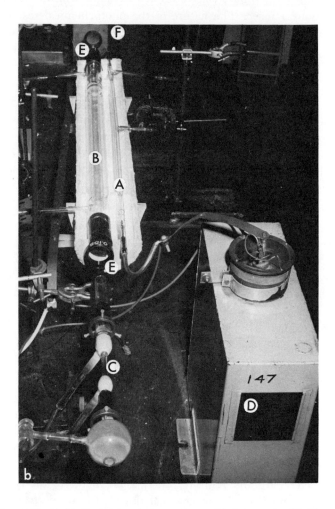

FIG. 1. A blackbody flash photolysis apparatus. (a) Schematic. (b) Photograph. A, flash lamp. B, reaction vessel. C, Lyman flash lamp. D, capacitor. E, lenses. F, spectrograph. G, photographic emulsion. H, thyratron. (Callear, unpublished.)

are illustrated in Fig. 1; the top of the reflector has been removed. This apparatus was designed for a photolysis flash of 2000 J at 10 kV, and the duration of the emission is shown in Fig. 2. For the same energy, the time constant of the emission can be reduced by about a factor of four by operating at 20 kV, which is recommended for modern equipment. In the far ultraviolet ($\sim$2000 Å) the flash duration is $\sim$20% shorter than for visible light. The spectroscopic flash is normally operated at about 100 J, and effectively terminates 10 μsec (10^{-5} sec) after triggering. This simple design (Fig. 1) operating at 20 kV is highly practicable, with the flash lamp filled with $\sim$100 Torr of Kr plus $\sim$10 Torr of N_2.

Techniques for very high flash energies have been developed by Claesson and co-workers (Claesson and Lindqvist, 1957).

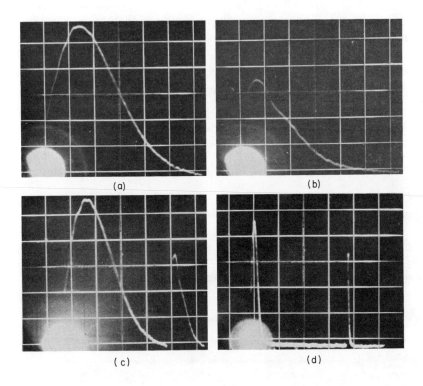

(a)   (b)

(c)   (d)

FIG. 2.   Oscilloscope traces (2000-J photoflash at 10 kV : 100-J spectroscopic flash at 10 kV). (a) Photoflash; scale, one division = 10 μsec. (b) Spectroscopic flash; scale, one division = 4 μsec. (c) Photoflash + spectroscopic flash; scale, one division = 15 μsec; set delay 66 μsec. (d) Photoflash + spectroscopic flash; scale, one division = 120 μsec; set delay 498 μsec. (Billingsley and Callear, unpublished.)

Relaxation rates can be measured by time-resolved absorption or emission spectroscopy. The former can be achieved by exposing a strip of photographic emulsion for each time delay, and also by monitoring reversal of a continuous background source at selected wavelengths with a photomultiplyer.

B. Measurement of Relative Concentrations by Plate Photometry

Transient species are generally observed directly by flash photolysis and therefore the experiments reveal some aspects of the mechanism. This function of at least partial determination of the mechanism is inherent in each of the applications which are detailed below. One simple case is shown in Fig. 3, where the formation of the CH_3 radical (Herzberg, 1961) and the β-methallyl radical $CH_2\dot{=}C(CH_3)\dot{=}CH_2$ (Callear and Lee, 1968) has been recorded photographically in the flash photolysis of isobutene. The parent absorbs light in the far ultraviolet, below 2200 Å, and the observed production of the two radicals demonstrates clearly that following electronic excitation of isobutene, both C—H and C—C bond scission occur. However, the experiment gives no clue as to whether the fragmentation of the isobutene occurs in an electronically excited state or following a crossing to the ground state.

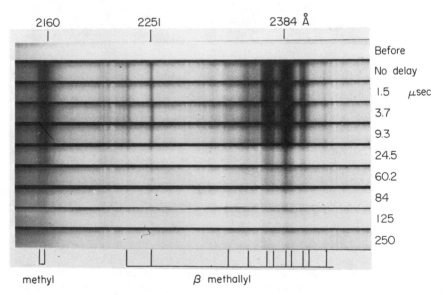

Fig. 3.   Methyl and β-methallyl radicals in the flash photolysis of isobutene. 0.5 Torr i-C_4H_8 + 100 Torr Ar. 100 J. (Callear and Lee, 1968.)

From plates or films of the kind shown in Fig. 3, the time dependence of the relative concentrations of the radicals can be determined by plate photometry. Between about 0.4 and 1.2, the densities ($\log_{10}$ incident/transmitted intensity) of photographic emulsions are proportional to the log of the light intensity I to which the film or plate was exposed. The plate density can be measured directly by microdensitometry. Thus if the Beer–Lambert law is obeyed by a particular electronic band, the recorded change of plate density is proportional to the concentration of the carrier of the band. In a favorable case relative concentrations can be measured with an accuracy of about $\pm 7\%$. The linearity of plate density with $\log_{10} I$ can be checked with neutral filters or a step wedge placed between the spectroscopic source and spectrograph slit. A wire gauze or mesh is a simple form of neutral filter.

The Beer–Lambert law is only obeyed if the width of the spectroscopic feature is large compared to the width of the image of the spectrograph slit on the film or plate. This condition holds for the 2160-Å band of CH_3 (Fig. 3) because it is diffuse due to predissociation. If an electronic band exhibits rotational fine structure, at low pressure the line shape approximates to the Gaussian form given by the Doppler equation. The Doppler width is generally very small compared to the width of the slit image in applications of flash spectroscopy to kinetics (frequently conducted with high-aperture, low-dispersion instruments). In this case an equation of the form

$$I = I_0 \exp(-k_v C^n L^n)$$

is usually found to hold (without theoretical justification), where k_v is an effective extinction coefficient, C is the concentration of the carrier, L is the optical path length, and n is the Beer–Lambert factor. Experimental measurements, for example, with the band heads of molecular electronic spectra, do conform to this expression and n is generally determined by blanking off various lengths of the reaction vessel with an opaque material. Relative concentrations are determined by raising the observed plate density changes to the power n^{-1}. It is found that n invariably lies in the 0.5–1 range.

Plate photometry is not very accurate and is laborious. The technique of monitoring transient absorption with a continuously operated background source and photomultiplyer provides a complete time history on single shot. However, the method is difficult to apply experimentally, especially at short wavelength, if the relaxation time is ≤ 100 μsec, because of the great intensity of the scattered light from the initiating flash. By far the most accurate technique is to monitor time-resolved emission, though the occurrence of convenient emission from flashed gases is unusual (see Section II,J).

C. RECOMBINATION OF ATOMS AND RADICALS

Application of flash photolysis to the recombination of transient species will be illustrated with atomic iodine and the free CH_3 radical.

1. *Combination of* $I(5 \ ^2P_{3/2})$

A study of the recombination of ground-state atomic iodine $I(5 \ ^2P_{3/2})$ by flash spectroscopy was first reported by Davidson *et al.* (1952). They employed a 50-J flash (1 μF at 10 kV) with a duration of 10^{-5} sec to dissociate iodine into atoms, and the concentration was monitored with time by observing the absorption of a continuous background source by the $B \ ^3\Pi_{0_u+}$–$X \ ^1\Sigma_g{}^+$ main system of I_2. Simultaneously, similar experiments had been conducted by Christie *et al.* (1953, 1955). They employed a high-energy flash but filtered the exciting light through dichromate solution to avoid scatter in the wavelength region where the return of the $I_2 \ X \ ^1\Sigma_g{}^+$ was monitored. Molecular iodine is a very efficient third body for I atom combination and in an excess of inert gas M the full mechanism is

$$I + I + M \longrightarrow I_2 + M$$
$$I + I + I_2 \longrightarrow 2I_2.$$

It is easily seen that by monitoring the $[I_2]$ as a function of time at various initial $[I_2]/[M]$ values, the two rate coefficients can be measured.

A study of the temperature dependence of the recombination rates in various gases was described by Porter and Smith (1961) and results are listed in Table I. If the rate coefficients are expressed in Arrhenius form, $k = A \exp(-E/RT)$, the activation energies are found to be negative since the recombination rate coefficients decrease with increase of temperature.

The negative temperature coefficients for atomic recombination have been interpreted with two rather different models, the atom molecule complex theory and the energy transfer theory. This is one of the most interesting problems in kinetics and we shall digress briefly to examine

TABLE I

ACTIVATION ENERGIES E_a FOR COMBINATION OF ATOMIC IODINE
(Porter, 1962)

Third body	He	Ar	H_2	O_2	I_2	CO_2	C_6H_6
E_a (kcal)	−0.4	−1.3	−1.2	−1.5	−4.4	−1.7	—1.7

each point of view. The former theory postulates the existence of an equilibrium concentration of weakly bound complexes IM. Collision of the atoms with the complexes leads to recombination

$$I + M \rightleftharpoons IM$$
$$I + IM \longrightarrow I_2 + M.$$

This model has been supported by Porter (1962) by rationalizing the magnitudes of the negative activation energies with the expected binding energies of the atom molecule complexes. The concentration of the IM decreases with increasing temperature, to slow down the rate of combination. It is reasonably obvious that the atom molecule complex theory is the correct model for very efficient third bodies, such as I_2 and NO.

The energy transfer model (Hornig and Palmer, 1957) was devised to account for the observation that the activation energies of the dissociation of diatomic molecules (shock tube experiments) are generally less than the dissociation energies (the atom molecule complex theory would suppose that the IM binding energy contributes to bond rupture). The energy transfer theory postulates that the energy required to rupture the bond can be supplied from rotations of the I_2–M system, as well as from relative translation. The probability that energy in excess of E is available in a bimolecular collision is

$$P_E = \left[\sum_{i=0}^{s-1} (E/RT)^i (1/i!) \right] \exp(-E/RT),$$

where s is the number of classical oscillators plus the number of doubly degenerate rotators plus one for a translational coordinate. For the simple case of dissociation of I_2 by Ar,

$$[\tfrac{1}{2}(D/RT)^2 + (D/RT) + 1] \exp(-D/RT)$$

is the probability that energy in excess of the dissociation energy D is available from relative translation, the I_2 rotation, and the two-particle orbital rotations ($s = 3$, ignoring vibration of the I_2).

The energy of the internal rotations cannot contribute fully toward bond rupture because the total angular momentum has to be conserved. However, the system will tend to take advantage of the entropy increase accompanying dissociation, if the energy is available. Since $D/RT \gg 1$ at ambient temperature, the rate coefficient for dissociation of I_2 should be, according to the energy transfer model,

$$k = \tfrac{1}{2}PZ(D/RT)^2 \exp(-D/RT),$$

where P is a steric factor and Z is the collision frequency. The corresponding Arrhenius activation energy $d(\log k)/d(RT)^{-1}$ is $D - 1.5\,RT$ since Z is proportional to $T^{1/2}$.

The difference between the Arrhenius activation energies for decomposition of I_2 and recombination of I at a particular temperature must equal the internal energy change at that temperature, which is $D + 0.5RT$ (ignoring vibration). Thus the energy transfer model predicts an activation energy of $\sim -2RT$ for the I atom recombination. At 300°K this equals -1.2 kcal, compared to -1.3 (± 0.1) kcal found experimentally (Table I). Thus the energy transfer model is not easily dismissed in this case since it accounts for the magnitude of the observed activation energy perfectly well. Furthermore, Wong and Lee (1974) have recently shown from crossed beam scattering that the depth of the potential well between H_2 and atomic iodine is 0.33 kcal mole^{-1}, only one-fourth of the magnitude of the negative activation energy.

These problems have been attacked by flash photolysis, in a somewhat different experiment. Figure 4 shows the formation of $I(5\ ^2P_{1/2})$ in the flash photolysis of I_2 under various conditions (Broadbent et al., 1968). Light was absorbed in the $B\ ^3\Pi_{0u+}$–$X\ ^1\Sigma_g^+$ system, which converges at 4995 Å; the $B\ ^3\Pi_{0u+}$ state correlates with one $I(5\ ^2P_{1/2})$ and one $I(5\ ^2P_{3/2})$ atom. However, when the flash photolysis of I_2 was confined to the banded region of the spectrum with light filters, absorption due to excited atoms was observed quite strongly; there is a high quantum yield for production of excited atoms below the thermochemical limit, and it appears that the highly vibrationally excited $I_2\ B\ ^3\Pi_{0u+}$ efficiently absorbs energy from the inert gas atoms. This phenomenon was termed "collisional release." Figure 5 (Broadbent and Callear, 1972) shows the quantum

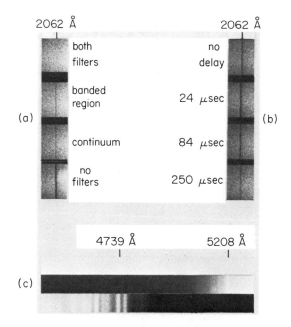

FIG. 4.   Formation of excited atomic iodine I(5 $^2P_{1/2}$) in the flash photolysis of I_2 in an excess of CO_2. (a) Production of I* with excitation limited either to the B $^3\Pi_{0_u^+}$− X $^1\Sigma_g^+$ continuum below 5000 Å, or to the banded region above 5000 Å. (b) Decay of excited atoms with time. (c) Transmission of the filters under flash conditions. (Broadbent *et al.*, 1968.)

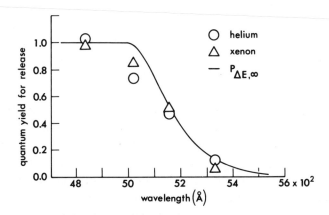

FIG. 5.   Dependence of the quantum yield of I(5 $^2P_{1/2}$) formation on wavelength in the photolysis of iodine–helium and iodine–xenon mixtures. The solid line is derived from the energy transfer theory assuming all the rotations contribute to bond rupture. (Broadbent and Callear, 1972.)

yield versus wavelength dependence for the formation of excited atoms by the endothermic process. The system shows identical behavior in excess He or Xe, which is contrary to what would be expected with the atom–molecule complex theory. The solid line of Fig. 5 is the function

$$[\tfrac{1}{2}(E/RT)^2 + (E/RT) + 1] \exp(-E/RT),$$

where E is energy deficiency for direct formation of excited atoms. There is striking agreement between the experiments and the prediction from the energy transfer model, though it is curious that the system takes every advantage when the energy is available. If this picture is correct, it implies that recombining collisions will have low total energy, high impact parameters, and consequently anomalously high angular momentum for the low-energy states.

Steinfeld and co-workers (Steinfeld and Schweid, 1970) have studied quenching and vibrational relaxation of I_2 B $^3\Pi_{0_u+}$ up to $v' = 53$ ($\sim 2kT$ below the dissociation limit at 300°K). They found that cross sections for quenching increase sharply as the limit is approached, and vibrational relaxation becomes relatively less important. They attributed the effects at high v' as being due to the onset of collisional release, though the experiments give no direct indication of the mechanism. However, the quenching cross sections for He are much smaller than for Xe, so that although the $I(5\,{}^2P_{1/2})$ quantum yields are the same in the two gases, the actual rate of release is much faster in Xe than in He. This is due to the small mass of the He atom and its difficulty to transfer energy to the heavy iodine. The activation energy of -0.4 kcal for combination of $I(5\,{}^2P_{1/2})$ in He is surprisingly small.

Recently Burde et al. (1974) reported the detection of $I(5\,{}^2P_{1/2})$ produced by laser photolysis of I_2 in the banded region of the B $^3\Pi$–X $^1\Sigma_g{}^+$ system. The excitation, with a narrow-band dye laser pulse of duration 10^{-8} sec, is a considerable advance over previous techniques. The method should reveal much detail of the effects of collisional release.

Burns and co-workers (Chang et al., 1971; Blak and Burns, 1971) have reported measurements of the $I(5\,{}^2P_{3/2})$ combination in Ar up to 1164°K, and concluded that at 1064°K, three-fourths of the combination occurs via atom molecule complexes, and one-fourth by the energy transfer route. The $Br(4\,{}^2P_{3/2})$ combination was studied up to 1273°K.

Some properties of I_2 B $^3\Pi_{0_u+}$ will be discussed in more detail in the section on fluorescence and lifetimes.

2. Combination of CH_3 Radicals

Measurement of the recombination rate of CH_3 radicals by kinetic spectroscopy of the 2160-Å band (Fig. 3) was first reported by van den Bergh *et al.* (1969). This is an awkward experiment because the absolute $[CH_3]$ has to be determined. Methyl radicals were generated by the flash photolysis of small partial pressures of both mercury dimethyl and azomethane with Ar added to $\sim$100 Torr to maintain isothermal conditions. The optical path length was 80.5 cm and the photoflash was operated at 20 kV with energies between 50 and 3000 J. Nearly all intensities were measured photographically on film (a suitably fast emulsion is Kodak Panchroroyal) sensitized with sodium salicylate. If an emulsion is not sensitized, the sensitivity usually falls off below 2300 Å. It is frequently desirable to coat the film with a layer of some fluorescent material which shifts the far-ultraviolet light to longer wavelength, where the emulsion is sensitive. A simple method of sensitizing is to dip the film in a solution of 5% sodium salicylate in methanol, allow it to drain off for a few minutes, and then dry with a warm air blower before loading into the film holder

The 2160-Å CH_3 band is strong (oscillator strength 1.3×10^{-2}) and its absorption obeys the Beer–Lambert law. Conditions were found where there was very little combination during the flash and where the free radical concentration and decay responded to variation in flash energy according to the equation

$$[CH_3]_t^{-1} - [CH_3]_{t'}^{-1} = 2k(t - t').$$

These conditions corresponded to low flash energies, typically 85 J, with $[HgMe_2] = 0.03$ Torr or $[N_2Me_2] = 0.10$ Torr. With the former, 98% of the photolysis was complete 11 μsec after initiation of the flash with a computed 88% of the total generated CH_3 remaining free. Thus the analysis was not critically dependent on the intensity profile of the generating flash.

The degree of photolysis was measured for each of the parent compounds by recording the absorption at 2160 Å at very short delay times (negligible loss due to recombination) when single gas samples were repetitively flashed. The experiments with $HgMe_2$ were the most accurate because it undergoes a greater degree of photolysis for a given flash energy (23% with 85 J). Results are shown in Fig. 6 and the rate coefficient was recorded as $2.43\ (\pm0.24) \times 10^{13}$ cm^3 mol^{-1} sec^{-1} at 293°K. Good agreement was

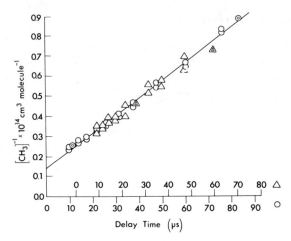

FIG. 6. Second-order decay of methyl radicals following the flash photolysis of HgMe₂–inert gas mixtures (○) and N₂Me₂–inert gas mixtures (△). 300°K. (van den Bergh *et al.*, 1969.)

later reported by Basco *et al.* (1970) in similar experiments. See also Parkes *et al.* (1973).

In the flash photolysis of HgMe₂, if the inert gas pressure was reduced below about 3 Torr, the CH₃ with zero-point vibration was found to be formed slowly following flash termination, as shown in Fig. 7 (Callear

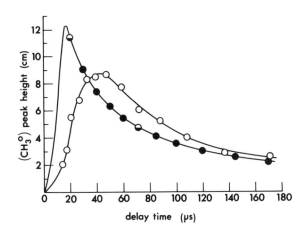

FIG. 7. Time behavior of vibrationally relaxed methyl radicals at 100 Torr (●) and at 3 Torr (○) of added helium. [HgMe₂] = 0.02 Torr, flash energy 100 J. (Callear and van den Bergh, 1971.)

and van den Bergh, 1971). Apparently photolysis of $HgMe_2$, in its banded system between 1850 and 2150 Å, produces the CH_3 radical in excited vibrational and/or electronic states. The results of Fig. 7 indicate that only the vibrationally cold CH_3 recombine; up to any particular concentration of CH_3 at late delay times, the area under a plot of $[CH_3]^2$ was indistinguishable in experiments at high and low pressure. The measurements shown in Fig. 7 were obtained with a flash unit having a 2-m-long reaction vessel, specially designed to slow down methyl recombination for a given optical density at 2160 Å. Combination of allyl radicals has been studied by Callear and van den Bergh (1970) and combination of CF_3 by Basco and Hathorn (1971).

D. MEASUREMENT OF THE RATES OF SOME PSEUDO-FIRST-ORDER REACTIONS

The reaction of atomic Se with olefins has been studied in detail by flash photolysis, by monitoring both the Se atom decay (1960 Å) and also the appearance of olefin selenides which absorb strongly in the far ultraviolet (Callear and Tyerman, 1966a, b). Atomic selenium was produced by the flash photolysis of CSe_2, which has a strong system at ~2300 Å. Figure 8 shows the decay of the atoms and the simultaneous appearance of ethylene selenide. By conducting experiments at various temperatures, the rate parameters were determined. The olefins were always present in great excess of the atomic Se, so that the Se decay was exponential, and the reciprocal relaxation time was identified with k[olefin], where k is the rate coefficient for addition to the olefin. Figure 9 shows that a striking correlation exists between the activation energies for addition of atomic selenium to olefins and the ionization potential of the olefin. The degree of polarization in the transition complex is greatest with olefins of low ionization potential, and polarization tends to reduce the energy of the abnormal electronic structure of the transition complex. This type of correlation was recognized earlier by Cvetanović (1963) for reaction of O(2 ^{3}P) atoms with olefins.

Smith (1968a) measured the absolute rate of reaction of O(2 ^{3}P) with CS_2, NO_2, and olefins, by flash spectroscopy. The principle of the method was to produce CS in the reaction

$$O + CS_2 \longrightarrow CS + SO.$$

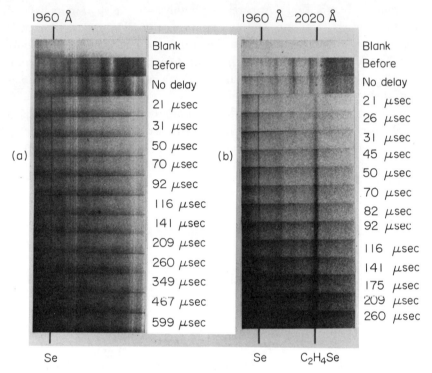

FIG. 8.   Kinetic absorption spectra showing product formation and simultaneous consumption of reactant. (a) 0.04 Torr CSe_2 + 50 Torr N_2. (b) 0.04 Torr CSe_2 + 2.5 Torr C_2H_4 + 47 Torr N_2. (Callear and Tyerman, 1966a.)

The (0, 0) band of the main system of CS at 2570 Å is intense and its rate of formation provides a convenient marker for [O(2 ³P)]. The atomic oxygen was produced by the flash photolysis of NO_2 through a Pyrex filter, which ensured that only the O(2 ³P) ground state was produced. The rate coefficient for the above reaction was expressed as (in liter mol^{-1} sec^{-1})

$$\log_{10} k = 9.8 \,(\pm 0.2) - 600 \,(\pm 300)/2.3 \times 1.98T.$$

Rate coefficients for reaction of O(2 ³P) with butene-1 and isobutene were recorded by adding them at various partial pressures to CS_2/NO_2 mixtures and studying the inhibition of the CS. The CS molecule persists for a few seconds in the gas phase at 300°K. The results of these experiments are shown in Fig. 10.

Absolute rates of reaction of S(3 ³P) have also been measured by flash photolysis (Donovan et al., 1970).

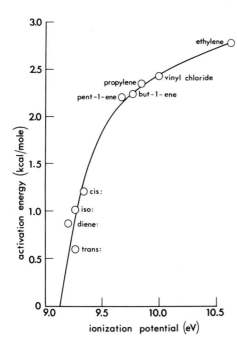

Fig. 9. Correlation of activation energies for addition of atomic selenium to olefins with ionization potential of the olefin. cis: *cis*-but-2-ene; trans: *trans*-but-2-ene; iso: isobutene; diene: 1,4-butadiene. (Callear and Tyerman, 1966a.)

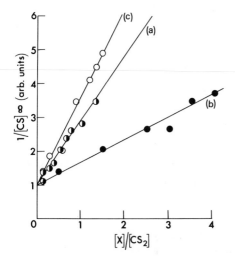

Fig. 10. The reciprocal of the yield of carbon monosulfide at long delay times ($[CS]_\infty$) plotted against $[X]/[CS_2]$ at 298°K. (a) ◑, NO_2; (b) ●, butene-1; (c) ○, isobutene. (Smith, 1968a; reproduced by permission of Dr. I. W. M. Smith.)

Greiner (1970) has measured rate parameters for reaction of OH and OD radicals with 12 hydrocarbons, by producing the radicals in the flash photolysis of water, and monitoring the decay by kinetic absorption spectroscopy. The Beer–Lambert factor was deduced by comparing the

TABLE II

Arrhenius Parameters for Reaction of OH with some Hydrocarbons
(Greiner, 1970)

	$\log_{10} A$ (cm^3 mol^{-1} sec^{-1})	E_a (cal)
Methane	12.52	3772 ($\pm$102)
Ethane	13.05	2447 ($\pm$106)
Neopentane	12.93	1677 ($\pm$88)
2,2,3,3-Tetramethyl butane	12.99	1595 ($\pm$125)
Cyclohexane	13.15	634 ($\pm$145)
Propane	12.86	1349 ($\pm$76)
n-Butane	12.93	1041 ($\pm$185)
n-Octane	13.25	724 ($\pm$120)
i-Butane	12.72	769 ($\pm$125)
2,3-Dimethyl butane	12.46	-257 ($\pm$133)
2,2,3-Trimethyl butane	12.68	228 ($\pm$145)
2,2,4-Trimethyl pentane	12.97	847 ($\pm$126)

absorption of particular rotational lines with the theoretical line strengths. Some of Griener's rate coefficients are listed in Table II.

Rates of reaction of OH with H_2, D_2, and CO have been measured by Stuhl and Niki (1972a) by flash photolysis and resonance fluorescence.

Reactions of the NH radical were reported by Mantei and Bair (1968). They discovered that the NH radical is produced in the isothermal flash photolysis of NH_3 but only in a narrow pressure range. The NH is formed in either one or other of the secondary reactions

$$2NH_2 \longrightarrow NH + NH_3$$

$$H + NH_2 \longrightarrow H_2 + NH .$$

A high proportion of the radicals occupied the first excited vibrational level. The NH appeared to decay by the insertion reaction

$$NH + NH_3 \longrightarrow N_2H_4$$

with a rate coefficient of $\sim 2 \times 10^{-11}$ cm^3 molecule^{-1} sec^{-1}.

Relaxation and reaction of atomic carbon in the ^3P and ^1D states, produced in the flash photolysis of C_3O_2, was reported by Braun et al. (1969). It was found that C(^1D) inserts into CH_4, to form vibrationally hot C_2H_4, which splits out H_2:

$$C(^1D) + CH_4 \longrightarrow C_2H_2 + H_2 .$$

Braun *et al.* (1970) made the first spectroscopic study of the kinetics of CH_2 radical reactions, by flash photolysis. The radicals were produced in the flash photolysis of ketene and the CH_2 triplet was monitored via the Herzberg (1966) system at 1415 Å. The singlet to triplet deactivation appeared to occur quite rapidly in collisions with He.

Reaction of CH_3 radicals with nitric oxide was studied via kinetic spectroscopy of the 2160-Å band by Basco *et al.* (1970) and also by Callear and van den Bergh (1971). Figure 11 shows how the apparent bimolecular rate

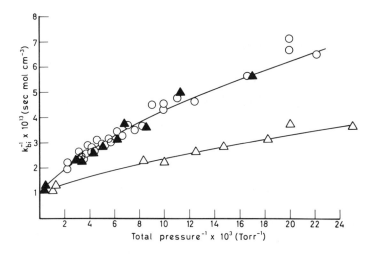

FIG. 11. Dependence on total pressure of the reciprocal pseudo-second-order rate coefficient for reaction of CH_3 with NO. $\bigcirc$, N_2; $\triangle$, propane; $\blacktriangle$, propane results scaled by 2.9^{-1} to achieve coincidence with the N_2 data. Solid lines derived using Rice–Marcus theory with $D_0(CH_3-NO) = 46.8$ kcal mole^{-1}. (Callear and van den Bergh, 1971.)

coefficient for combination of CH_3 with NO varies with total gas pressure in N_2 and C_3H_8. The solid lines show the "falloff" predicted by the Rice–Marcus (Marcus and Rice, 1951) theory, with $D_0(CH_3-NO) = 46.8$ kcal mole^{-1}.

E. ENERGY PARTITIONING IN PHOTOCHEMICAL REACTIONS

The flash photolysis experiment is frequently capable of revealing initial vibrational and electronic states in photochemical reactions. Photolysis of triatomic molecules, photolysis of polyatomic molecules, and energy distribution in secondary reactions will be discussed briefly.

1. *Dissociation of Triatomic Molecules*

In the photodissociation of most triatomic molecules,

$$XYZ + h\nu \longrightarrow XY + Z,$$

it has been established by flash spectroscopy and beam studies that only a small fraction of the energy excess usually appears as vibration in the diatomic fragment. The experimental systems that have been studied appear to fall into two classes. In the first, the upper electronic state persists for $>10^{-12}$ sec before decomposition, and CS_2 $\tilde{A}$ $^1B_2$ seems to belong to this case. In the other class, the upper state dissociates in $\sim10^{-14}$ sec. The corresponding spectra are diffuse or broadened because of predissociation (Herzberg, 1966).

Flash photolysis of $CS_2(\tilde{A}\ ^1B_2-X\ ^1\Sigma_g{}^+, \sim2000$ Å) produces CS with up to seven quanta of vibration (Callear, 1963) (Fig. 12)

$$CS_2 \mid h\nu \longrightarrow CS(v \leq 7) + S(3\ ^3P).$$

It is difficult to measure the "nascent" distribution of the CS because if the total CS concentration is high enough for the $v'' = 7$ state to be detected photographically in absorption, vibrational relaxation is extremely fast due to inelastic interaction of CS with atomic S. The fraction of molecules which initially populate $v'' = 0$ can be measured, however, by observing the intensity of the (0, 0) band (2570 Å) at short delay times with and without the addition of small partial pressures of CH_4. The excited CS is rapidly deactivated by the CH_4 by V–V transfer. Thus it was shown (Callear, unpublished) that about 0.25 of the CS initially populates $v'' = 0$.

The CS_2 absorbs light in a sharp band system extending from 1850 to 2200 Å. Since the spectrum is only very weakly predissociated, the excess energy should partition statistically among the three oscillators of the bent, electronically excited state before dissociation. Considering the oscillators to be classical, the probability of finding a single oscillator of $CS_2{}^*$ with energy between E' and $E' + dE'$ is proportional to the total number of states of the other two oscillators in the range $E - E'$, $E - E' + dE'$, where E is the excess energy. The normalized probability is easily seen to be

$$2E^{-2}(E - E')\ dE'.$$

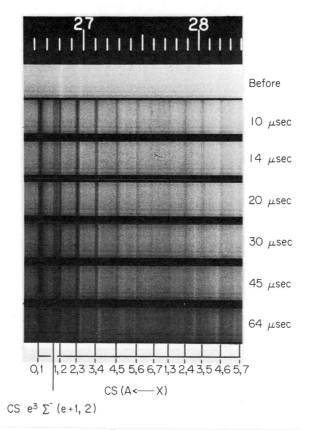

FIG. 12. Production of CS X $^1\Sigma_g^+$ with up to seven quanta of vibration, in the flash photolysis of CS_2. $[CS_2] = 0.5$ Torr. $[O_2] = 50$ Torr. $[N_2] = 450$ Torr. 2000 J and 1.5 m path length. (Callear, 1963.)

The distribution into the vibrational levels $v = 0, 1, 2, 3, 4, 5, 6, 7$, corresponding to relative populations 8, 7, 6, 5, 4, 3, 2, 1, would be roughly consistent with that found experimentally (Fig. 12) and corresponds to 0.22 produced initially with $v'' = 0$. While much detail of the mechanism remains to be discovered, it seems evident that CS_2 Ã $^1B_2$, or a perturbing state of lower energy, does survive long enough for energy partitioning to occur.

We next consider the second case, where the electronic transition is diffuse or continuous. In this case the electronically excited molecule breaks up before the excess energy partitions between the internal degrees of freedom, and only a small fraction of the excess energy appears as vibration in the diatomic fragment. There are two reasons for this. The recoil accompanying separation of the products on the repulsive potential energy surface should be rather inefficient in exciting the diatomic part; this is because the "force constant" between the product species is usually small compared to the force constant of the diatomic molecule, and the recoil forces tend to act on the center of mass of the diatomic molecule rather than on a particular atom (Kalman *et al.*, 1970). Second, there is a general law that the nuclear separations of diatomic molecules in the ground states are very nearly the same as those of the ground states of the triatomic molecules from which they are produced, as indicated in Table III.

TABLE III

COMPARISON OF INTERNUCLEAR SEPARATIONS (Å) IN DIATOMIC AND TRIATOMIC MOLECULES (Herzberg, 1966)

H_2O	H_2S	CO_2	CS_2	NO_2	O_3	SO_2
0.956	1.328	1.162	1.554	1.193	1.278	1.432
OH	SH	CO	CS	NO	O_2	SO
0.970	1.350	1.128	1.534	1.151	1.207	1.492

Consequently the nuclear separation of the diatomic fragment tends to be coupled only weakly to the overall dynamics of the dissociation, and this is the main feature of the photolysis of triatomic molecules.

Flash photolysis of H_2O in the vacuum ultraviolet produces $OH(v = 0)$ almost entirely (Welge and Stuhl, 1967). The H_2S molecule absorbs continuously in the far ultraviolet, producing electronically excited molecules with a wide range of energies; only $SH(v = 0)$ is observed in the flash photolysis. Basco and Norrish (1962a) detected a small yield of $NO(v = 1)$ in the flash photolysis of NO_2. Norrish and Oldershaw (1959) showed that flash photolysis of SO_2 in the 1850–2350-Å region produces a very small yield of $SO(v = 1)$, the vast excess having $v = 0$; there appear to be several systems of SO_2 in this wavelength region and resonance fluorescence of one of the states has been observed (Herzberg, 1966). Basco and Norrish (1962a) detected a very small yield of vibration of the CN radical in the flash photolysis of CNBr.

To examine the photolysis of triatomic molecules via diffuse systems in greater depth, we need to consider two subcases, one in which there is little change of nuclear separation of the diatomic part in the intermediate, electronically excited molecule, and the other in which a substantial, transient change occurs. In the first case the coupling of the excess energy to the diatomic fragment is extremely weak and may account, for example, for the low yield of vibrational energy in the H_2S photolysis. In the second subcase, at the Franck–Condon maximum of the transition the nuclear separations are unchanged by the electron jump but if, for example, the equilibrium separation of the diatomic part is greater in the electronically excited molecule, the nuclei will start to spring apart. However, this means that the potential energy of the diatomic spring is reduced in the electronically excited molecule, and the bond has to regain this potential energy when dissociation has been completed. This will tend to dampen out any vibration of the diatomic part in the overall dissociation, though the yield of vibration will tend to be higher than in the first subcase since now the vibration is more strongly coupled to the translational recoil.

The second subcase also differs from the first in that if the nuclear separation of the diatomic part does change appreciably in the electronically excited state, then that coordinate will be excited by the electronic transition. In the short wavelength of the transition, potential energy is fed directly into the diatom and can result in highly vibrationally excited fragments. It should be noted that at the wavelength of the intensity maximum and to longer wavelengths, only low-v'' states of the diatom can be produced; the resulting distribution should be heavily weighted into the low vibrational levels with a tail into the high levels.

The photolysis of NOCl in the far ultraviolet seems to provide an example of this subcase; Mitchell and Simons (1967) have estimated that the NO bond distance is greater by 0.2 Å in the upper state. Basco and Norrish (1962b) detected $NO(v \le 11)$ in the NOCl flash photolysis, as shown in Fig. 13. The author has attempted to estimate the yields into the various vibrational levels and the approximate results are listed in Table IV.

Pollack (1966) has observed stimulated infrared emission from flashed NOCl from the levels $v = 6$, 7, 8, and 9. Insufficient information is available to rationalize why the gain is highest in the $v = 6$–9 range.

TABLE IV

APPROXIMATE YIELDS OF THE VIBRATIONAL STATES OF NO X $^2\Pi$ IN THE BLACKBODY FLASH PHOTOLYSIS OF NOCl

v''	0	1	2	3	4	5	Σ (6–11)
$F_{v''}$	0.24	0.2	0.2	0.08	0.04	0.04	0.20

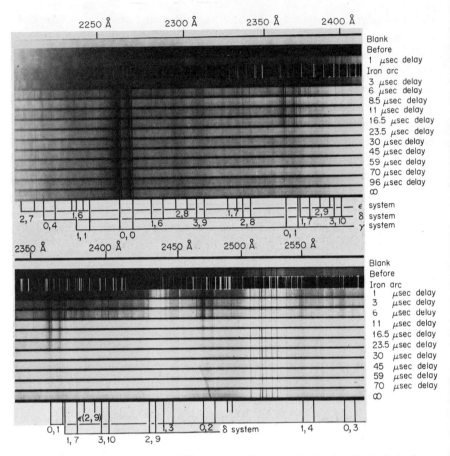

FIG. 13. Production of NO X $^2\Pi$ with up to 11 quanta of vibration, in the flash photolysis of NOCl. Upper: [NOCl] = 1 Torr, [N_2] = 375 Torr. Lower: [NOCl] = 2 Torr, [N_2] = 420 Torr. 1600 J and 300°K. (Basco and Norrish, 1962b; reproduced by permission of Professor R. G. W. Norrish.)

Processes of photodissociation have been discussed in some detail by Simons (1971).

2. Energy Distribution in the Photolysis of Polyatomic Molecules

An example has been mentioned of the formation of vibrationally excited fragments in the photolysis of a polyatomic molecule; in the flash photolysis of HgMe$_2$ at least 80% of the CH$_3$ radicals are formed in excited states. There is no general technique available for the determination of the quantum states of polyatomic fragments, though the problem has been attacked from two points of view.

In the flash photolysis of CH_3SSCH_3, CH_3SCH_3, and related compounds Callear and Dickson (1970) were able to rationalize the occurrence or nonoccurrence of secondary decomposition of product fragments by postulating statistical energy partitioning in the initially formed electronically excited molecule. The energy distributions were examined with the classical formula

$$P_{F,F+dF}^{n,s} = [\lceil s / \lceil n \lceil s - n]F^{n-1}(1-F)^{s-n-1}\, dF.$$

$P_{F,F+dF}^{n,s}$ is the probability that a fragment containing n classical oscillators of a molecule originally containing s classical oscillators carries a fraction of between F and $F + dF$ of the excess energy. It is only applicable to the case where the back reaction has zero activation energy. Thus it was possible to account for the observation that if CH_3SSCH_3 dissociates to give CH_3SS, the radical carries sufficient energy to undergo decomposition to $CH_3 + S_2$. However, if the initial split produces $2CH_3S$, the stability of the CH_3S against $CH_2S + H$ formation could also be rationalized. In that work it was valuable to be able to formulate the classical limit, and the comparison with experiment gave some cohesion and guidance in the choice of elementary steps.

Pimentel and co-workers have pioneered the development of photochemical lasers, which is the second, but not lesser, experimental method. For example, Berry and Pimentel (1968) observed stimulated emission from HF on the lowest two fundamentals in the flash photolysis of CH_3CF_3. The experiments obviously prove that $HF(v \leq 2)$ is produced, probably without full population inversion. Later Berry and Pimentel (1969) discovered a general source of photoelimination lasers in the photolysis of C_2H_3X, where X is a halogen atom.

3. Energy Distributions in Secondary Photochemical Reactions

In his study of the reaction

$$O(2\ ^3P) + CS_2 \longrightarrow OS + CS,$$

Smith (1967) was able to record the initially formed quantum states of both the SO and CS product species. It is the only case of product energy distribution which has been studied quantitatively by flash spectroscopy.

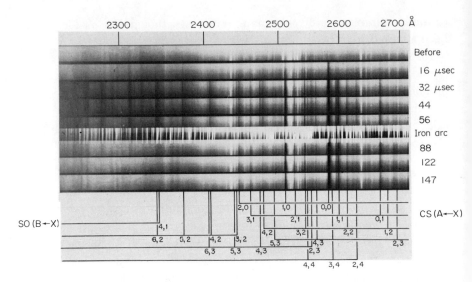

FIG. 14. Formation of vibrationally excited CS and SO in the reaction of O(2 ³P) with CS₂. [NO₂] = 0.25 Torr. [CS₂] = 1.25 Torr. [Ar] = 80 Torr. 2500 J. (Smith, 1967; reproduced by permission of Dr. I. W. M. Smith.)

Figure 14 shows that with moderately high concentrations of CS_2 and NO_2, $CS(v \leq 3)$ and $SO(v \leq 4)$ can be detected. The SO is removed by

$$NO_2 + SO \longrightarrow NO + SO_2$$

but the relative intensities of the SO bands were constant in the short interval during which they were observed. From the Beer–Lambert and Franck–Condon factors it was shown that some 18% of the heat of reaction is retained by the SO and 8% by the CS. The distributions were Boltzmann corresponding to vibrational temperatures of 2870 and 1775°K, respectively. Investigations of the kinematics by computer simulation on various potential energy surfaces showed that the excitation of the CS is due to the recoil accompanying the energy release.

F. Vibrational Relaxation of Some Diatomic Molecules

The vibrational relaxation of two diatomic molecules, CS and NO, has been studied in some detail by flash photolysis and kinetic absorption spectroscopy.

1. *Relaxation of* CS X $^1\Sigma^+(v=1)$

By producing CS by the reaction described in the previous subsection, Morley and Smith (1971) measured the rate coefficients for vibrational relaxation of $CS(v=1)$ by H_2, $p\text{-}H_2$, HD, ^{3}He, D_2, ^{4}He, N_2O, NO_2, CS_2, CO_2, H_2O, D_2O, H_2S, and D_2S. The measurements were made photoelectrically by reversing the light from a high-pressure mercury lamp at the A $^1\Pi$–X $^1\Sigma^+$ (2, 1) band, with photoelectric detection following dispersion with a medium quartz spectrograph. Corrections were made for cascading from $CS(v=2)$. The photoflash light was filtered through Pyrex, which eliminated scatter at 2534 Å, in the region of the CS(2, 1) band. Results are listed in Table V. The triatomic molecules appear to cause

TABLE V

RATE COEFFICIENTS AND PROBABILITIES FOR DEEXCITATION OF
$CS(v=1)$ (Smith, 1968b; Morley and Smith, 1971)

M	k (cm^3 molecule^{-1} sec^{-1})	P_{10}^{-1}(exp)	P_{10}^{-1}(calc)
$o\text{-}H_2$	1.4×10^{-13}	5.5×10^3	2×10^3
$p\text{-}H_2$	2.7×10^{-13}	3.1×10^3	2×10^3
HD	5.7×10^{-14}	1.4×10^4	5×10^3
^{3}He	5.7×10^{-15}	1.0×10^5	5.5×10^3
D_2	5.5×10^{-15}	1.0×10^5	1.0×10^4
^{4}He	2.2×10^{-15}	2.2×10^5	9×10^3
N_2O	1.34×10^{-11}	26	2×10^2
CO_2	1.38×10^{-13}	2.7×10^3	1.5×10^3
NO_2	5.0×10^{-13}	8×10^2	3.9×10^2
CS_2	2.1×10^{-14}	2×10^4	2×10^4
H_2O	5.0×10^{-12}	90	—
D_2O	8.1×10^{-12}	55	—
H_2S	6.3×10^{-12}	62	—
D_2S	6.8×10^{-12}	59	—

relaxation by V–V and/or V–R transfer. The experimental $P_{1,0}$ (probability per collision) values were computed from the measured rate coefficients by taking the collision cross section of CS to be 4.7 Å. The result for $o\text{-}H_2$ was calculated from those for H_2 and $p\text{-}H_2$ "by difference."

Relaxation in He is slower than that predicted from standard theory (Callear and Lambert, 1969) by about fiftyfold, and it is well known that the distorted wave theory overestimates V–T relaxation rates for systems of small reduced mass. The difference between the efficiency of o-H_2 and that of p-H_2 was attributed to the occurrence of

$$CS(v = 1) + H_2(J = 4) \longrightarrow CS(v = 0) + H_2(J = 6)$$

which is induced by dipole–quadrupole interaction (Sharma 1969; Sharma and Brau, 1969). It was first recognized by Mahan (1967) that in V–V energy transfer at exact resonance the dominant interaction could be of the long-range dipole–dipole type. Sharma refined the theory and extended it to multipole interactions and V–R transfer. Vibrational exchanges from CS to N_2O and CO_2 are both close to exact resonance. Morley and Smith suggest that the much greater rate of transfer to N_2O occurs because the transition of N_2O is infrared allowed, while that of the CO_2 is not, which is in accord with the requirements of Sharma's theory. The rate of transfer to CO_2 is consistent with what would be expected from standard theory, where the dominant interaction is taken to be the short-range repulsion. A full interpretation of the relaxation rates by the triatomic hydrides was not given.

2. *Relaxation of* NO X $^2\Pi(v = 1)$

Nitric oxide absorbs light in the far ultraviolet; when it is subjected to flash photolysis an excess population of molecules in the first vibrational level is observed (Basco *et al.*, 1961). The mechanism of relaxation of the initially formed electronically excited molecules is complex and is still incompletely understood. Some aspects are discussed further in Section VI.

The formation and relaxation of $NO(v = 1)$ are illustrated by the spectra of Fig. 15. The relaxation was monitored by plate photometry and the results show that the relaxation is dominated by self collisions,

$$NO(v = 1) + NO(v = 0) \longrightarrow 2NO(v = 0).$$

The collision probability of this process was recorded as $\sim 2 \times 10^{-4}$ at $300°K$, and a similar rate had been measured previously by Bauer *et al.* (1959) with ultrasonic absorption. More recently Slobodskaya and Tkachenko (1970) recorded a similar probability with a spectrophone. The nitric oxide molecule provided one of the earliest systems for the study of vibrational exchange reactions, e.g.,

$$NO(v = 1) + CO(v = 0) \longrightarrow NO(v = 0) + CO(v = 1).$$

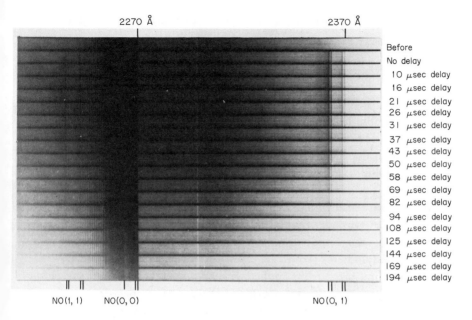

2270 Å   2370 Å

NO(1, 1)   NO(0, 0)   NO(0, 1)

FIG. 15. Vibrational excitation of NO X $^2\Pi$ resulting from blackbody flash photolysis. [NO] $= 5$ Torr. $N_2 = 600$ Torr. 1600 J. (Basco *et al.*, 1961.)

The measurements gave the first correlation of these V–V processes with the energy discrepancy (Callear, 1962).

The relaxation of NO($v = 1$) in self collisions is abnormally fast, which has been attributed by Nikitin (1960) to a crossing between $^3\Sigma_g{}^-$ and $^1\Sigma_g{}^+$ states of the (NO)$_2$ collision complex.

A cleaner and more direct spectroscopic approach to vibrational relaxation is to induce excitation with an infrared laser and to monitor the decay of the fluorescence. Stephenson (1974) has applied such a technique to study NO($v = 1$) relaxation, and the method is capable of greater accuracy and refinement than flash photolysis. A general discussion of laser techniques is given in Section III.

Donovan and Husain (1967) have measured some relaxation rates of CO($v = 1$) by flash photolysis. The CO was excited by absorption of ultraviolet light in the Cameron bands (a $^3\Pi$–X $^1\Sigma^+$). Donovan and Husain (1970) have also studied relaxation of HBr($v = 1$) by various molecules. The HBr was excited by flash photolysis in the vacuum ultraviolet and it was suggested that the first vibrational level is produced by

$$Br(4\ ^2P_{1/2}) + HBr(v = 0) \longrightarrow Br(4\ ^2P_{3/2}) + HBr(v = 1) \ .$$

Leone and Wodarczyk (1974) have described direct evidence for this type of process, using pulsed laser techniques.

G. Production and Relaxation of the Metastable States of Atoms

Atoms produced by photolytic dissociation are frequently formed with a non-Boltzmann distribution among the electronic states. The first example that was discovered and explored by flash photolysis was $Se(4\ ^3P_J)$, generated in the CSe_2 photodissociation (Callear and Tyerman, 1966b). The probability per collision with Ar of inducing the $J = 0 \rightarrow 1$ transition (544 cm^{-1}) was recorded as $\sim 10^{-4}$; collisional deactivation of electronically excited species by the inert gases is usually very slow if the energy to be transferred is greater than a few kT. An attempt to correlate deactivation rates with the magnitude of the energy to be transferred was described by Callear and Lambert (1969).

Flash photolysis can be applied generally to the measurement of the relaxation rates of atoms in metastable states. It is a specialized area with little theoretical cohesion at present, and only one further example will be detailed here. Iron carbonyl has an intense, continuous absorption in the far ultraviolet and, when present to the extent of $\sim 10^{-3}$ Torr in an inert gas, with a blackbody flash the entire carbonyl can be destroyed.

$$Fe(CO)_5 + nh\nu \longrightarrow Fe + 5CO.$$

The removal of the CO groups is sequential. The supersaturated vapor of atomic iron rapidly polymerizes to a smoke of iron particles. However, there is very little loss of atoms at up to 10^{-3} sec delay and during this time relaxation processes of the atomic iron can be followed by kinetic absorption spectroscopy. The atoms are initially produced in a large number of electronic states (Callear and Oldman, 1967). The highly excited states decay rapidly and after 50 μsec delay, only the ground a ^5D_J states are significantly populated. The excitation energies of the $J = 0, 1, 2, 3$, and 4 states are respectively 978, 888, 704, 416, and 0 cm^{-1}.

From photometry of the decay rates it was shown that the upper four substates attain Boltzmann population relative to one another after ~ 100 μsec, to form a coupled (by collision) system overpopulated with respect to the a $^5D_4$ state. It is the $J = 3 \rightarrow 4$ transition, involving the largest energy change, which is the rate-determining step in the final phase of the relaxation. In Ar the collision probability is $\sim 10^{-5}$. The time dependence of relative populations is shown in Fig. 16. This type of behavior

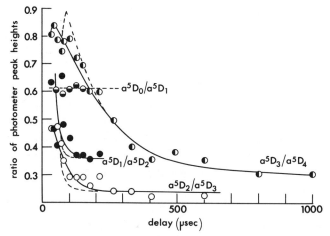

FIG. 16. Relative populations of the Fe a ^5D states in Ar as a function of time following the blackbody flash photolysis of $Fe(CO)_5$. The broken line is the behavior predicted with a model in which the rates of the individual transitions were taken to be proportional to $\exp(k\,\Delta E)$, where the ΔE are the internal energy changes (all negative). The constant k was determined from the measured rate of the $J = 3 \rightarrow 4$ transition. (Callear and Oldman, 1967.)

is similar to the vibrational relaxation of polyatomic molecules in which the excitation of the lowest vibrational frequency is usually the largest energy step and is consequently rate determining with respect to the entire internal energy. Quasi equilibrium between spin–orbit states was first demonstrated for the metastable states of neon, discussed in Section VII.

Relaxation of $I(5\ ^2P_{1/2})$ has been studied by Donovan and Husain (1965, 1966), that of $As(^2D)$ by Callear and Oldman (1968), and that of $Tl(6\ ^2P_{3/2})$ by Bellisio and Davidovits (1970).

A successful theory for collisionally induced spin–orbit relaxation has been proposed by Dashevskaya et al. (1970).

H. Organic Triplets in the Gas Phase

Flash photolysis has been applied extensively to the production and detection of the triplet states of molecules in solution, by Porter and co-workers. Porter and Wright (1955) reported the detection of the triplet states of nine organic molecules in the gas phase, by kinetic spectroscopy. The kinetic behavior of organic triplets in the gas phase remains to be explored in detail. Ashpole et al. (1971) have recently shown that the triplet yields are pressure dependent, which they attributed to the reversibility of intersystem crossing.

I. Combustion

Norrish and co-workers have applied flash photolysis to studies of chemical relaxation associated with combustion and explosion. In the presence of a photosensitizer such as NO_2 or amyl nitrite, hydrocarbon–oxygen mixtures can be exploded on flashing. Provided the initial total pressure is ≤ 50 Torr, the reactions can be conducted in quartz vessels. Kinetic absorption spectroscopy and photoelectric detection of the emitted light usually show the occurrence of a period of induction of ~ 1 msec before the explosion or flame is formed. Generation of heat and chain centers by the flash may propagate sufficiently rapidly to lead to an explosive rate.

Erhard and Norrish (1956) attempted to determine by flash photolysis the mechanism whereby lead tetraethyl inhibits hydrocarbon combustion in spark ignition engines. At top dead center of the compression stroke, the fuel–oxygen mixture has been partly consumed by "slow" movement of the flame front from the point of ignition. The unburnt gases, "end gas," are then subjected to severe stresses due to the high temperature and pressure. If spontaneous ignition breaks out in the end gas, the resulting pressure wave gives rise to the phenomenon of "knocking." Lead compounds inhibit the chain reactions in the end gas and may prevent knocking.

Figure 17 shows the behavior of tetraethyl lead in a flashed mixture of acetylene, amyl nitrite, and oxygen. Like the end gas in an engine, the heated mixture does not immediately explode. The onset of the hot flame or explosion is marked by the appearance of the OH radical at ~ 300 μsec delay. In the absence of lead the same mixture would have exploded after about 50 μsec. During the induction period the spectrum of gaseous PbO can be seen, indicating that the inhibiting effect of lead may be due to reactions of PbO dispersed homogeneously. Prior to these observations the effect of lead was generally considered to be due to the formation of a PbO colloidal smoke, which inhibited the reactions heterogeneously. The controversy has not yet been conclusively settled one way or the other. Both gaseous PbO and colloidal PbO are present in an end gas during autoignition.

J. Blackbody Flash Photolysis in the Vacuum Ultraviolet

Specialized techniques have been described for flash photolysis in the vacuum ultraviolet. In the standard techniques described above (Fig. 1) the flash lamp and reaction vessel are of quartz and are separated by a few

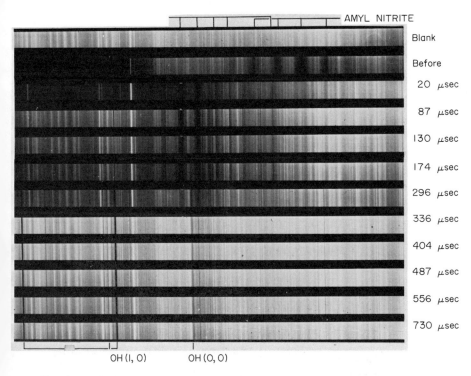

FIG. 17.   The behavior of tetraethyl lead in a flash-initiated explosion of acetylene and oxygen, photosensitized by addition of amyl nitrite. (Erhard and Norrish, 1956; reproduced by permission of Professor R. G. W. Norrish.)

cm path of air, which limits photolysis to $\lambda \geq 1850\,\text{Å}$. Ramsay and Nelson (1956) described the first design specifically for $\lambda < 1850\,\text{Å}$. The lamp and reaction vessel were separated with a sapphire window, with transmission down to $\sim 1500\,\text{Å}$. The CN radical was detected in absorption in flashed HCN. (With low gas pressures electric discharge occurred in the reaction system and the absorption spectra of a variety of diatomic hydrides, C_2, and CN were detected in discharged gases). Another technique was described by Black and Porter (1962) in which the flash was generated in an annular sheath around a central, coaxial vessel of high-grade quartz.

A practicable design for the vacuum ultraviolet was described by Kley et al. (1963). This method has subsequently been successfully applied to several relaxation systems, especially by Braun, McNesby, and co-workers. The design is indicated in Fig. 18 (Braun et al., 1967). The discharge occurs perpendicularly to the lamp axis via five electrode pairs spaced 5 cm

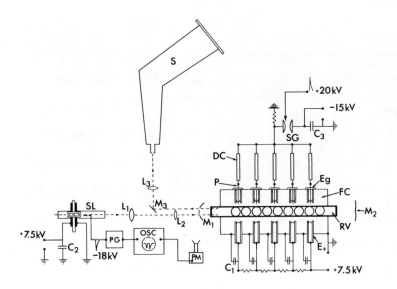

Fɪɢ. 18.   An apparatus for blackbody flash photolysis in the vacuum ultraviolet.
SL, spectroscopic light source. L, lens. C_1, five 8-μF capacitors. C_2, 10-μF capacitor.
C_3, 1-μF capacitor. M_1M_2, multireflection mirrors. DC, delay cables. E_g, ground electrodes. E_+, high-voltage electrodes. P, trigger pins. FC, flash chamber. RV, reaction
chamber. M_3, aluminized mirror. PG, high-voltage pulse generator. OSC, oscilloscope.
PM, photomultiplier. (Reproduced by permission of Dr. J. R. McNesby.)

apart. The lamp was filled with N_2 at about 50 Torr, which held off the
applied potential of $\sim$7.5 kV. The lamp was triggered with a high voltage
spark applied simultaneously to each electrode pair. The resulting flashes
were of short duration, 2–3 μsec half-life, because of the close spacing
between electrode tips which results in a low impedance. Vacuum-ultraviolet radiation ($\lambda > \sim$1200 Å) was admitted to the reaction vessel via
disks of LiF cemented on to a glass frame. It was claimed that $\sim$3 $\times$ 10^{17}
vacuum-ultraviolet quanta per pulse could be delivered to the absorbing
gas.

Transient species were detected with kinetic absorption spectroscopy,
using eight traversals with multiple-pass mirrors. Thereby the CH radical
was detected in flashed CH_4 and some of its absolute reaction rates were
recorded.

An elegant experiment with vacuum-ultraviolet excitation was described
by Filseth *et al.* (1970b) and Stuhl and Niki (1970). Here O(2 ^{1}D) is pro-

duced by flash photolysis of O_2 in the Schuman–Runge continuum. Then $O_2 \, b \, ^1\Sigma_g^+$ is generated by energy transfer from the excited atom:

$$O_2 + h\nu \longrightarrow O(2\,^3P) + O(2\,^1D)$$
$$O(2\,^1D) + O_2 \, X \, ^3\Sigma_g^- \longrightarrow O(2\,^3P) + O_2 \, b \, ^1\Sigma_g^+.$$

It was possible to monitor the decay of the excited molecular emission in the afterglow by detection of the "atmospheric bands" with a photomultiplyer. Rate coefficients for deactivation of $O_2 \, b \, ^1\Sigma_g^+$ are listed in Table VI. Some 10^6 collisions with $O_2 \, X \, ^3\Sigma_g^-$ are required for relaxation. The intensity of the initiating flash is enormously greater than the feeble atmospheric emission, and the experiment is only possible after elaborate care to avoid scattered light, because the $O_2 \, b \, ^1\Sigma_g^+$ is very long-lived compared to the flash duration.

TABLE VI

RATE COEFFICIENTS (cm^3 molecule^{-1} sec^{-1}) FOR DEACTIVATION OF
$O_2 \, b \, ^1\Sigma_g^+(v = 0)$ AT 300°K (Filseth et al., 1970b; Stuhl and Niki, 1970)[a]

CO_2	CO	SF_6	O_2	H_2O	NH_3
4.4×10^{-13}	4.3×10^{-15}	5.7×10^{-16}	4.5×10^{-16}	3.3×10^{-12}	8.6×10^{-14}
			(4.7×10^{-17})	(4.7×10^{-12})	
CH_4	C_2H_6	N_2O	NO	NO_2	H_2
1.1×10^{-13}	3.6×10^{-13}	7.0×10^{-14}	4.1×10^{-14}	3.1×10^{-14}	1.1×10^{-12}
					(4×10^{-13})
N_2	Ar	C_2H_4	C_2H_2	Propylene	Butene-1
1.8×10^{-15}	5.8×10^{-18}	4×10^{-13}	4.5×10^{-13}	6.4×10^{-13}	6.4×10^{-13}
Butene-2 trans	Butene-2 cis	Tetramethyl ethylene			
6.9×10^{-13}	7.6×10^{-13}	9.1×10^{-13}			

[a] The values in parentheses are due to Thomas and Thrush (1975), who show that traces of water vapor have upset some of the earlier measurements.

Filseth et al. (1970a, 1972) produced $O(2\,^1S)$ by the pulsed, vacuum-ultraviolet flash photolysis of CO_2. Rate coefficients for relaxation of the excited atom were recorded by monitoring the decay of the atomic emission at 5577 Å. For deactivation by CO, NO, O_2, and N_2 they recorded 1.0×10^{-14}, 8.0×10^{-10}, 3.6×10^{-13}, and $<2 \times 10^{-16}$ cm^3 molecule^{-1} sec^{-1}, respectively (300°K). Relaxation of $O(2\,^1D)$ has also been studied by flash photolysis. For example, Gilpin et al. (1971) produced the excited atoms by the flash photolysis of O_3 and monitored the atomic emission at 6300 Å. For removal of $O(2\,^1D)$ by O_3 and O_2, rate coefficients of

2.5×10^{-10} and 5×10^{-11} cm^3 molecule^{-1} sec^{-1}, respectively, were recorded (300°K). The fate of O(2 ^{1}D) in its reactions with O$_3$ has been investigated by Bair and his associates (Webster and Bair, 1972; Baimonte et al., 1971).

Reactions of ground-state atomic oxygen have also been studied by Stuhl and Niki (1971a), producing atoms by vacuum-ultraviolet flash photolysis. Absolute reaction rates were measured by observing the decay of chemiluminescence in the afterglow (e.g., from NO$_2$* and CO$_2$*). Rate coefficients for the reactions

$$O + O_2 + O_2 \longrightarrow O_3 + O_2$$

$$O + O_2 + N_2 \longrightarrow O_3 + N_2$$

where recorded as 6.4×10^{-34} and 5.4×10^{-34} cm^6 molecule^{-2} sec^{-1}, respectively (300°K). Stuhl and Niki also applied the method to study reaction of O(2 ^{3}P) with saturated hydrocarbons (1971b) and olefins (1972b).

Hochanadel and Ghormley (1972) flashed H$_2$O vapor in the vacuum ultraviolet and detected a broad absorption region, λ_{max} at 2050 Å, due to the HO$_2$ radical.

The rate coefficient for the attachment of H to O$_2$ with Ar as third body was measured by Wong and Davies (1974) in the range 220–360°K. The H atoms were produced by the vacuum-ultraviolet flash photolysis of CH$_4$.

K. DETECTION OF FREE RADICALS BY INFRARED ABSORPTION

Detection of transients by kinetic absorption infrared spectroscopy was pioneered by both Pimentel and Johnston. Pimentel and Carlso (1966) claimed to have detected the CF$_3$ radical produced, for example, in the flash photolysis of CF$_3$COC$_6$H$_5$. Bands at 1090, 701, and 1259 cm^{-1} were assigned and the radical was shown to be nonplanar. The carrier persisted for $\sim$400 μsec after flashing, which is surprisingly long.

Johnston and co-workers have developed a technique of repetitively pulsing a gas with light to produce transients with repetitive detection in the dark periods. Very long optical path lengths were achieved. With this technique of "modulated kinetic spectroscopy," for example, the ClOO and HO$_2$ radicals have been detected (Johnston et al., 1969; Paukert and Johnston, 1972). Pimentel and his associates have detected infrared absorption due to CH$_3$ (Tan et al., 1972).

L. Detection of Transients by Resonance Fluorescence

Detection of a transient species by resonance fluorescence was first achieved by Azada *et al.* (1928). Mercury vapor in nitrogen was irradiated with a 2537-Å source to produce $Hg(6\ ^3P_0)$, and simultaneously with 4047-Å radiation ($7\ ^3S_1$–$6\ ^3P_0$) from a second source. The intensity of the 5461-Å line ($7\ ^3S_1$–$6\ ^3P_2$) was measured in emission. Crude relaxation rates were measured by studying the decay of the 5461-Å line following cessation of the 2537-Å excitation. Braun and co-workers have resurrected the technique very effectively to study the decay of atoms produced by flash photolysis. For example, by producing H atoms in the low-energy flash photolysis of C_2H_4 and simultaneously irradiating continuously with Lyman α radiation, Kurylo *et al.* (1970) measured the rate coefficient for H addition to C_2H_4 by monitoring the Lyman α fluorescence intensity from the reacting gas. A Rice–Marcus extrapolation permitted the determination of k_∞. Kurylo *et al.* (1971) have also studied the reaction

$$H + H_2S \longrightarrow H_2 + SH$$

with the same technique at various temperatures, and were able to express the rate coefficient in the form

$$k = 1.29 \times 10^{-11} \exp(-1709/1.98T)\ \text{cm}^3\ \text{molecule}^{-1}\ \text{sec}^{-1}.$$

Klemm and Davies (1973) applied the method to measure rate coefficients for reaction of S atoms with olefins. Kurylo and Hui (1973) and Black *et al.* (1972) reported absolute rate coefficients for $O(2\ ^3P)$ reactions.

M. Flash Photolysis and Mass Spectrometry

A few experiments have been described in which chemical relaxation rates, following flash photolysis, have been monitored by mass spectrometry. Thus, for example, Meyer (1968, 1974) employed a rapid-scanning time-of-flight mass spectrometer to yield a complete mass spectrum every 50 μsec. Successive mass patterns were displayed on an oscilloscope and time-resolved with a drum camera. The rate of formation of I_2 was monitored in flashed CH_3I and it was concluded that the I_2 is produced by

$$I(5\ ^2P_{1/2}) + CH_3I \longrightarrow I_2 + CH_3$$

as well as by three-body combination of $I(5\ ^2P_{3/2})$.

III. Excitation with Pulsed Lasers

A. General Comments

Light pulses of extremely short duration can be produced with lasers by q-switching and mode-locking. Consequently laser techniques have the potential of improving the time resolution of kinetic spectroscopy by several powers of ten over the blackbody flash method.

There are two general methods of applying lasers to relaxation measurements. First, when a gas absorbs radiation from a laser pulse, excited species can continue to radiate after cessation of excitation; from the nature and time dependence of the fluorescence, kinetic data can be derived. Second, laser-excited species can be monitored by means of a probe signal. The most general probe device is optical absorption. Excited species have also been monitored by Raman scattering (DeMartini and Ducuing, 1966).

In principle, optical absorption of laser-excited species provides the basis for techniques of wide applicability. In absorption, both radiative and nonradiative states can be detected. The probe source may be monochromatic or a continuum. Use of the former would constitute what is frequently termed a " double resonance " technique. With an intense background continuum, spectra can be recorded photographically (obviously a short duration pulse is required) which is immensely valuable for pioneering new molecular systems.

Relaxation measurements have been conducted with lasers in the infrared, visible, and ultraviolet regions. The application of infrared lasers to rotational energy transfer is discussed in Section V. Application to the measurement of the lifetimes of electronically excited species is discussed in Section VI.

B. Vibrational Relaxation Measurements with Pulsed Lasers

During the last few years many studies of laser vibrational excitation and fluorescence have been published, and it is now the most generally useful technique for studying V–T and V–V energy transfer. Both excitation and fluorescence are selective to particular quantum states, which may be contrasted with ultrasonic methods. Vibrational excitation by flash photolysis is often complicated by the behavior of the initially formed, electronically excited species.

Three groups reported laser-induced vibrational relaxation more or less simultaneously. Hocker *et al.* (1966) q-switched a CO_2 laser with a rotating mirror and observed the decay of the v_3 fluorescence after the pulse termination from an irradiated sample of CO_2. The laser radiation is not a true resonance transition since the lower level is the doubly excited bending mode v_2. However, there is an appreciable population of this level in equilibrium at 300°K:

$$CO_2(020) + hv \longrightarrow CO_2(001).$$

The second of the initial reports of vibrational excitation was the stimulated Raman scattering experiment of DeMartini and Ducuing(1966). With radiation from a q-switched ruby laser (2 MW, 20 nsec) incident on H_2 at high pressure, it was discovered that 1% of the molecules were excited to $J = 1$ of $v = 1$. They employed a relatively long-duration, non-q-switched ruby laser as a probe source and monitored the intensity of the anti-Stokes scattering with time. Thereby the vibrational relaxation time was estimated. This type of experiment obviously has potential for refinement and extension to other molecules.

The third of the initial experiments was conducted by Yardley and Moore (1966), who excited CH_4 to v_3 with the He–Ne laser line at 3.39 μm. The laser beam was chopped mechanically and the phase lag between excitation and fluorescence was observed. The v_3 emission was detected with an InSb photomagnetic detector. The decay of the v_3 emission gave rise to v_4 emission, the lowest vibrational frequency of CH_4, which was recorded with a Ge–Cu detector cooled to 20°K. Molecules are removed very rapidly from v_3 by fast (and complex) V–V and intra- and intermolecular processes. Ultimately the distribution in the excited vibrational levels becomes statistical and the coupled set of levels undergoes slow V–T relaxation via the lowest frequency, v_4. The probability of relaxation of molecules with v_3 excited was recorded as 1.4×10^{-2} per collision, and the v_3 relaxation time was identical to that of the initial rise of the v_4 fluorescence.

In CO_2, the probability of removal of the (001) state per collision is 10^3 slower than CH_4 with v_3 excited. The V–V transfer is usually rapid in hydrides, which is partly due to their large amplitude of vibration, which results in efficient coupling in collision. Moore *et al.* (1967) have studied the rates of V–V transfer from $CO_2(001)$, produced with q-switched laser excitation, to various molecules, e.g.,

$$N_2(v = 0) + CO_2(001) \longrightarrow N_2(v = 1) + CO_2(000),$$

which is the reverse of the V–V process in the CO_2 laser. This reaction rapidly attains statistical equilibrium since the internal energy change is only 19 cm^{-1}. Therefore the $CO_2(v_3)$ fluorescence rapidly decays to a "steady state" level, and the relaxation time yields the rate coefficient for the near-resonant V–V transfer. This is then followed by the slower V–V transfer into the symmetric and bending modes of CO_2. A point of special interest in this research has been the discovery that V–V transfer is particularly fast if the transitions of both molecules are infrared-allowed. This has stimulated the theoretical developments of Mahan (1967) and Sharma (1969) mentioned earlier, which have had both interpretive and predictive value. The laser experiments showed that transfer between isotopic CO_2 molecules occurs at practically every gas-kinetic collision.

Rosser *et al.* (1969) reported a study of the temperature dependence of the reaction

$$CO_2(001) + N_2(v = 0) \longrightarrow CO_2(000) + N_2(v = 1)$$

and recorded $\log_{10} k \,(\text{Torr}^{-1}\,\text{sec}^{-1}) - 6.79 \quad 30.8 T^{-1/3}$ for the 400–1000°K range. This result was shown to be in good agreement with the theory of Sharma and Brau (1969), in which the dominant interaction is taken to be the CO_2 dipole-derivative–N_2 quadrupole. Deactivation rates of $CO_2(001)$ to (010) and (100) were also measured. Rosser *et al.* (1971) have also studied the rate of the reaction

$$CO_2(001) + CO(v = 0) \longrightarrow CO_2(000) + CO(v = 1)$$

as a function of temperature; this process is off resonance and the observed rate coefficients could be equally well accounted for with the dipole–dipole interaction or the short-range repulsion which is the dominant interaction in the standard, distorted-wave theory (Herzfeld and Litovitz, 1959). They also reported the measurement of deactivation rates of CO_2 (001) to (010) due to collisions with CO. Relaxation of $CO_2(001)$ by various molecules was reported recently by Stephenson and Moore (1972).

The vibrational relaxation of a number of diatomic molecules has also been achieved by means of infrared laser excitation. By frequency doubling radiation from a CO_2 laser with a tellurium crystal, Stephenson achieved excitation of both CO (1973) and NO (1974). Relaxation by various collision partners was measured and also the rates of vibrational disproportionation, e.g.,

$$2CO(v = 1) \longrightarrow CO(v = 2) + CO(v = 0).$$

Vibrational relaxation of the hydrogen halides has also been studied extensively (Chen et al., 1968; Airey and Fried, 1971; Chen, 1971; Hopkins et al., 1973; Hancock and Green, 1972).

Laser-induced infrared fluorescence has been applied to investigate the vibrational relaxation of C_2H_4 (Yuan and Flynn, 1973), SF_6 (Knudtson and Flynn, 1973), BCl_3 (Houston et al., 1973), and O_3 (Rosen and Cool, 1973). It is difficult to detect and analyze the weak fluorescence from the polyatomic molecules. In each case excitation was achieved with a pulsed CO_2 laser. When a single vibrational mode is excited in a polyatomic molecule, a general feature is that intramolecular V–V transfer is induced rapidly by collisions, ultimately to populate many modes statistically. This is then followed by the comparatively slow V–T relaxation, the rate of which is usually controlled by the lowest vibrational frequency of the molecule. These general features had already been indicated by ultrasonic measurements (Callear and Lambert, 1969) and are directly confirmed by the laser experiments.

Relaxation of the $HCl(v = 1)$ by atomic chlorine has been investigated by Craig and Moore (1971) and by Ridley and Smith (1971). Energy transfer is rapid because of a chemical interaction.

Successful infrared–infrared double resonance experiments have been reported by Steinfeld et al. (1970) and Yuan et al. (1973). In both experiments vibrational excitation was achieved with a q-switched CO_2 laser, and excited levels were monitored in absorption with a low-power, continuous CO_2 laser. Steinfeld et al. excited the v_3 level of SF_6 (940 cm^{-1}) and observed its fast decay by V–V processes by monitoring the transient change of absorption. It was shown that the final V–T phase of relaxation is controlled by the lowest frequency, v (344 cm^{-1}). Yuan et al. reported a somewhat similar study with C_2H_4, monitoring the initial V–V relaxation by absorption spectroscopy.

In summary, laser-induced infrared fluorescence provides the first general method of studying vibrational exchange processes in gases. A great contribution to molecular relaxation already has been achieved.

In Fig. 19 are plotted $\log_{10}$ of the rate coefficients for V–V transfer against energy discrepancy, for non-hydride diatomic molecules at 295°K. All species are in the ground electronic states except for the point close to exact resonance, involving NO $A^2\Sigma^+$ in collision with ground state N_2 (see Section VI C). The left-hand ordinate indicates the approximate probability per collision, which has been obtained simply by taking the collision frequency to correspond to $\sim 2.9 \times 10^{-10}$ cm^3 molecule^{-1} s^{-1} for

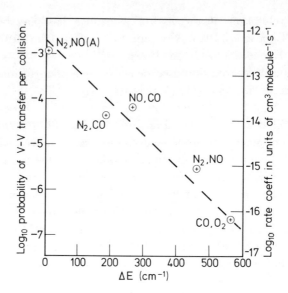

Fig. 19. Gross dependence of V-V exchange probability on energy discrepancy for non-hydride diatomic molecules (295°K).

all systems. The CO, NO, and N_2, NO data have been obtained by flash photolysis and laser methods, with excellent agreement. The change of internal energy is the dominant factor which controls the rate of vibrational exchange. The scatter about the line drawn through the data obviously reflects differences in the nature of the interactions which induce the transitions.

The data for Fig. 19 were obtained from the following papers: Callear (1962), Stephenson (1973, 1974), Hancock and Smith (1971), Miller and Millikan (1974), and Basco *el al.* (1961). A similar correlation for vibrationally excited carbon monoxide is shown in Fig. 39.

C. LASER ELECTRONIC EXCITATION

1. *General Comments*

Laser excitation is attractive for the investigation of molecular electronic relaxation for two reasons. First, the duration of excitation may be as short as 10^{-11} sec, giving access to the measurement of ultrafast intra- and intermolecular processes. Second, the exciting radiation may have a narrow bandwidth and is consequently selective and clean; the selectivity makes it possible to explore the behavior of molecules prepared over a range of quantum states.

Mechanism and rates can be examined either from the spontaneous emission (usually visible or infrared), or in absorption by reversal of a discrete source or continuum. The subject is still in its infancy but it should gather momentum as the pace of laser development quickens.

It is convenient to categorize the applications as follows: (a) measurement of the lifetimes of electronically excited molecules (discussed in Section VI,B); (b) spontaneous intramolecular relaxation; and (c) collisionally induced processes.

A nanosecond technique for absorption studies (in solution) was first described by Novak and Windsor (1967, 1968) and was further improved by Porter and Topp (1970). Much of the picosecond (10^{-12} sec) technology has been developed and applied by Rentzepis and his associates, for example, Rentzepis et al. (1973).

2. Spontaneous Intramolecular Relaxation

The mechanisms of singlet–triplet intersystem crossing in large molecules in the gas phase are presently being examined with laser fluorescence techniques. Borisevich and Gruzinskii (1967) first showed that the emission from benzophenone exhibits both rapidly decaying and slowly decaying components. Busch et al. (1972) investigated the benzophenone emission with a monochromator and photomultiplier, following excitation with a frequency-doubled ruby laser at 28,800 cm^{-1} ($\sim$2800 cm^{-1} above the 0–0 band of the first singlet). They discovered that the luminescence consists of two exponentially decaying components with lifetimes of $\sim$10 and $\sim$200 μsec at very low pressures; the spectral distributions are slightly different in the two time regimes.

The rapidly decaying component appears to correspond to triplet levels which are strongly coupled to the singlet states initially excited. The lifetime of $\sim$10 μsec, due to the strongly coupled singlet–triplet system, is three times longer than the radiative lifetime of the singlet calculated from the absorption oscillator strength. Other triplet levels (the density of states of the triplet is $\sim$10^5 per wave number at this energy) which are only weakly coupled to the initial states (for reasons of symmetry and the Franck–Condon principle) are responsible for the slow decay, which is presumably the normal phosphorescent emission of the triplet with a time constant determined by wall removal.

Hochstrasser and Wessel (1973) have also investigated the laser-induced luminescence of benzophenone, using a variety of energies from 25,880 to 37,700 cm^{-1}. They confirmed the double exponential decay. However, many puzzling features of these complex systems have not yet been adequately explained and obviously remain to be defined more precisely in future research.

Werkhoven *et al.* (1971) excited pyrene vapor to its first singlet state with a nanosecond ruby laser pulse. The decay of the emission was reported to be nonexponential, being initially faster than in the late afterglow. This was attributed to a faster intersystem crossing to the triplet in the vibrationally excited singlet prepared initially. As the vibrational energy is removed in collision, the crossing rate decreases. Luminescence from the first and second singlets of pyrene and their internal conversion has been studied by Baba *et al.* (1971).

A simple case of intramolecular relaxation was reported by Bradley *et al.* (1973). Atomic magnesium was excited to Mg(3 ^{1}P$_1$) (2852 Å), with the frequency-doubled output of a tuned dye laser pumped with radiation from a doubled neodynium laser (5300 Å). Some 24 members of the n ^{1}D$_2 \leftarrow 3$ ^{1}P$_1$ Rydberg series were detected in absorption by converting part of the laser radiation to a continuum as background. A line at 3009 Å was shown to be broadened due to preionization.

3. *Collisionally Induced Processes*

Collisional relaxation following laser electronic excitation will be exemplified by four experiments: observation of emission in the visible, emission in the infrared, absorption of transients with a continuum background, and finally electronic double resonance.

Jennings *et al.* (1973) described an interesting system for studying molecular energy transfer. They discovered that if sodium is excited to Na(3 ^{2}P) in the presence of a trace of cesium and an excess of H$_2$, electronic energy transfer from the sodium to the cesium occurs giving rise to the Cs(6 ^{2}P $\rightarrow$ 6 ^{2}S) resonance radiation. The electronic energy transfer occurs through the intermediacy of vibrationally excited H$_2$, as follows:

$$\text{Na(3 }^2\text{S)} + h\nu \longrightarrow \text{Na(3 }^2\text{P)}$$

$$\text{Na(3 }^2\text{P)} + \text{H}_2(v = 0) \longrightarrow \text{Na(3 }^2\text{S)} + \text{H}_2(v \leq 4)$$

$$\text{H}_2(v = 3, 4) + \text{Cs(6 }^2\text{S)} \longrightarrow \text{H}_2(v = 0, 1) + \text{Cs(6 }^2\text{P)}$$

$$\text{Cs(6 }^2\text{P)} \longrightarrow \text{Cs(6 }^2\text{S)} + h\nu.$$

Vibrationally excited H_2 with less than three quanta has insufficient internal energy to excite the cesium electronically. The distribution of H_2 among the various vibrational states could not be determined and it should not be supposed that there is an efficient conversion of electronic to vibrational energy; typically the vibrational yields are about $1/3$. The sodium was excited with a chopped, tunable dye laser. From the variation of the decay constant of the visible emission with the H_2 pressure, a rate coefficient of 3.9×10^{-14} cm^3 molecule^{-1} sec^{-1} for collisional removal of $H_2(v = 3, 4)$ by $H_2(v = 0)$ was derived.

Leone and Wodarczyk (1974) discovered that if Br_2 is photodissociated at 4730 Å in the presence of HCl, the first fundamental of HCl is emitted. The mechanism is as follows:

$$Br_2 + h\nu \longrightarrow Br(4\ ^2P_{1/2}) + Br(4\ ^2P_{3/2})$$

$$Br(4\ ^2P_{1/2}) + HCl(v = 0) \longrightarrow Br(4\ ^2P_{3/2}) + HCl(v = n)$$

$$HCl(v = n) + (n - 1)HCl(v = 0) \longrightarrow nHCl(v = 1)$$

$$HCl(v = 1) \longrightarrow HCl(v = 0) + h\nu .$$

They suggest that some 50% of the electronic energy is converted to vibration. Excitation was achieved with a frequency-doubled Nd^{3+} : YAG laser, energy 1 mJ, duration 500 nsec. Slanger and Black (1974) concluded that the yield of vibrationally excited N_2 in the collisional relaxation of $O(2\ ^1D)$ corresponds to conversion of $\sim 1/3$ of the electronic energy to vibration (the process has an important role in the Earth's atmosphere). Vibrationally excited N_2 was detected by stimulated Raman scattering.

With a background continuum, Formosinho et al. (1970) detected the triplet state of anthracene immediately following intersystem crossing. Excitation was achieved with a q-switched, frequency-doubled ruby laser pulse at 3470 Å, 80 mJ energy, duration 20 nsec. Observation of the vibrationally excited triplets was achieved with a pulsed Xe arc as background; the continuum was dispersed and monitored photoelectrically at various wavelengths. Above 4080 Å, absorption due to excited triplets decayed with time (hot bands). At wavelengths below 4020 Å, absorption first increased with time, corresponding to a buildup of vibrationally relaxed triplets. It was concluded that the triplet looses some 800 cm^{-1} of energy per collision with CH_4. Relaxation is less efficient in collision with Ar. The nature of the vibrational relaxation of polyatomic molecules obviously has an important role in unimolecular reactions.

The recently reported experiment of Burde *et al.* (1974) provides an example of what may be termed electronic double resonance. Iodine was excited in the banded region of the main $I_2(B\ ^3\Pi_{0_u^+} - X\ ^1\Sigma_g^+)$ system above 5000 Å, with a pulsed dye laser, 10 nsec duration and 20 pps repetition. The production of excited iodine atoms by endothermic, collisional release was monitored by reversal of the 2062-Å atomic line (from an electrodeless discharge lamp). A signal averager was employed to extract the relaxation profile from background noise. It is an excellent experiment, because of the high selectivity of excitation and because of the good resolution in time; from the experimental viewpoint it should provide much detail concerning the ultimate step in diatomic molecule dissociation, which has already been discussed in Section II,C.

IV. Flash Photolysis with the Resonance Radiation of Atoms

A. Mercury Flash-Photosensitized Reactions

Experiments have been conducted in which the transient species produced in reactions photosensitized by excited atoms were detected photographically by kinetic absorption spectroscopy. The first approach resulted from the discovery that the radiation from a microwave discharge, even at levels of power up to 10^5 W, consists solely of discrete lines with negligible continuum. From a mixture of Hg vapor and He or N_2, emission of the 2537-Å line of Hg was observed strongly (Callear *et al.*, 1965). A flash photolysis apparatus was constructed in which microwave power was coupled to a 50-cm-long, annular lamp via a radiating horn. The reaction cell, diameter 5 mm, was located along the lamp axis, and light from a standard Lyman discharge was directed through the reaction vessel onto the slit of a spectrograph. Thus, for the first time, the formation of HgH in the reaction

$$Hg(6\ ^3P_1) + H_2 \longrightarrow HgH + H$$

was demonstrated (Callear and Hedges, 1970a,b), as shown by the spectra of Fig. 20. By monitoring the transient decrease of the [Hg] with time, the quantum yield of HgH formation was estimated to be roughly 0.8. The

4013 Å

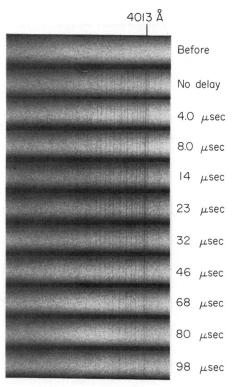

Before

No delay

4.0 μsec

8.0 μsec

14 μsec

23 μsec

32 μsec

46 μsec

68 μsec

80 μsec

98 μsec

FIG. 20. Absorption spectrum of HgH produced in the reaction of Hg(6 ³P₁) with H₂. Monochromatic excitation was achieved with a powerful, single shot of microwave radiation, in a lamp coaxial with a 5-mm-diameter, central reaction vessel. (Callear and Hedges, 1970a.)

formation of mercury halides HgX in the quenching of Hg(6 ³P₁) by RX was also investigated with this technique.

Following these discoveries, it was considered that a similar experiment could be devised with an electroded discharge, with suitable design characteristics. With this object in view, Callear and McGurk (1970b) constructed a multielectrode flash lamp with the discharge occurring transverse to the lamp axis between many electrode pairs; a photograph of the first apparatus is shown in Fig. 21. The 80-cm-long lamp was constructed by sealing (epoxy resin) two quartz tubes, of internal diameter 5 and 20 mm, coaxially into a Pyrex tube 50 mm in diameter. The inner quartz tube was used for filter gases. Twenty-two tungsten electrode pairs, spaced 4 cm apart, were sealed into the Pyrex tube. Each electrode pair was connected by 1 m of coaxial cable to a distributor terminal. The whole assembly was built

768   A. B. Callear

Fig. 21. The multielectrode flash lamp for monochromatic excitation. Twenty-two electrode pairs discharge simultaneously and are fed from the distributor at the bottom of the picture. For optimum excitation at 2537 Å the apparatus is heated to 313°K, [Hg] = 6×10^{-3} Torr. The reaction vessel, 5 mm diameter and length 75 cm, is located along the lamp axis. (Callear and McGurk, 1972.)

inside a large metal box which could be heated to 330°K. In fact optimum quantal absorption was achieved at 313°K, [Hg] = 6×10^3 Torr, with the lamp powered with a 1.5-μF capacitor charged to 20 kV, and triggered with a spark gap. The intensity–time profile of the 2537 Å emission could be approximated to an exponential decay with a time constant of 16 μsec. The lamp was filled with mercury vapor and [He] = 1 Torr.

The characteristics of the multielectrode device are quite different from those of the blackbody-type flash lamps. The former are silent and of low overall luminosity, and the emission consists entirely of discrete lines similar to that from a continuous Hg resonance lamp. The technique indicated in Fig. 21 is highly practicable and reproducible. Some of the design characteristics were inspired by the lamp shown in Fig. 18, though the performance and objectives are quite different.

The quantal absorption in the reaction vessel with the apparatus of Fig. 21 was measured as 2.2×10^{14} quanta cm^{-3} per flash, by determining the CS produced in the sequence

$$Hg(6\,^1S_0) + h\nu \longrightarrow Hg(6\,^3P_1)$$

$$Hg(6\,^3P_1) + N_2O \longrightarrow Hg(6\,^1S_0) + N_2 + O(2\,^3P)$$

$$O(2\,^3P) + CS_2 \longrightarrow CS + SO.$$

The absolute CS can be calibrated by the blackbody flash photolysis of CS_2 at low pressures ($\sim$0.01 Torr) when it can be almost entirely dissociated to $CS + S(3\,^3P)$. With the above reaction sequence, absolute reaction rates of $O(2\,^3P)$ can be measured by monitoring the rate of formation of the CS. By measuring the CH_3 produced in the reaction

$$Hg(6\,^3P_1) + CH_3Br \longrightarrow HgBr + CH_3$$

$$\longrightarrow Hg(6\,^1S_0) + Br + CH_3$$

the quantal absorption was recorded as 1.5×10^{14} quanta cm^{-3} per flash, in a similar apparatus, assuming that the CH_3 is produced with unit quantum efficiency, and employing the known oscillator strength of the 2160-Å CH_3 transition (van den Bergh et al., 1969). In the reactions of $Hg(6\,^3P_1)$ with both CH_3Br and CH_3I, it was noted that the halogen atoms are produced in both the $^2P_{1/2}$ and $^2P_{3/2}$ states (Callear and Wood, 1971b).

A variety of reactions and relaxation processes have been investigated spectroscopically with the new technique. Three simple examples are

$$Hg(6\,^3P_1) + CO(v = 0) \longrightarrow Hg(6\,^3P_0) + CO(v = 1)$$

$$Hg(6\,^3P_1) + H_2S \longrightarrow Hg(6\,^1S_0) + H + SH$$

$$Hg(6\,^3P_1) + \text{ethylene imine} \longrightarrow Hg(6\,^1S_0) + C_2H_4 + NH.$$

The formation and decay of the NH radical produced in the latter reaction is shown in Fig. 22 (Callear and McGurk, 1972), confirming conclusions drawn from steady-state experiments by Klemm (1967).

An interesting result in this research was to discover that the reaction of either $Hg(6\,^3P_1)$ or $Hg(6\,^3P_0)$ with HD produces predominantly HgD, as shown in Fig. 23. This gives an indication of a possible reaction mechanism, which is discussed at the end of this section. Relative yields of mercury

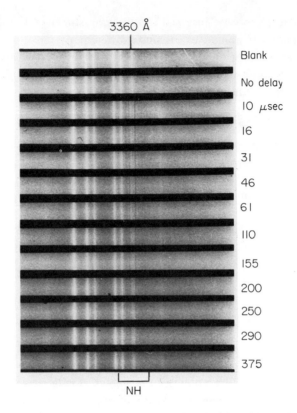

FIG. 22.   Formation of NH in the reaction of Hg(6 $^3P_0$) with ethylene imine. The (0, 0) band of the A $^3\Pi$–X $^3\Sigma^-$ system. 0.1 Torr ethylene imine + 600 Torr N_2. (Callear and McGurk, 1972.)

FIG. 23.   Preferential HgD formation in the reaction of Hg(6 $^3P_1$) with HD. The (1, 0) bands of the A $^2\Pi_{1/2}$–X $^2\Sigma^+$ system. (a) HD, (b) equimolar $H_2 + D_2$, (c) D_2, (d) H_2. Each exposure at 16 μsec and 300 J. Total hydrogen pressure = 2 Torr + [Ar] = 700 Torr. (Callear and McGurk, 1970b.)

hydrides were determined by plate photometry and by calculating the Franck–Condon factors, and the results are listed in Table VII (Callear and McGurk, 1972).

TABLE VII

YIELDS OF MERCURY HYDRIDES IN THE REACTIONS OF
Hg(6 $^3P_{1,0}$) WITH H_2, D_2, AND HD (CALLEAR AND McGURK, 1972)

Reaction	Quantum yield
Hg(6 $^3P_1$) + H_2 → HgH + H	0.67 ± 0.04
Hg(6 $^3P_1$) + D_2 → HgD + D	0.76 ± 0.05
Hg(6 $^3P_1$) + HD → HgH + D	0.13 ± 0.02
Hg(6 $^3P_1$) + DH → HgD + H	0.70 ± 0.09
Hg(6 $^3P_0$) + H_2 → HgH + H	1.00 ± 0.08
Hg(6 $^3P_0$) + D_2 → HgD + D	0.88 ± 0.08
Hg(6 $^3P_0$) + HD → HgH + D	0.175 ± 0.02
Hg(6 $^3P_0$) + DH → HgD + H	0.82 ± 0.08

Accurate measurements of the HgH and HgD yields in the reaction of Hg(6 $^3P_1$) with H_2 and D_2 were made by Callear and Wood (1972). In the Hg flash-photosensitized reaction of H_2 containing small partial pressures of NO, a band system was discovered in the far ultraviolet which was shown to be due to HNO. The HNO persists for a few seconds and could easily be monitored photoelectrically, with a hydrogen lamp as background source. It was discovered further that HgH reacts very rapidly with NO (rate coefficient $\sim 10^{-11}$ cm^3 molecule^{-1} sec^{-1} at 300°K) but HgH reacts quite slowly, if at all, with C_2H_4. Also there is no rapid reaction of HNO with C_2H_4. In the absence of ethylene, the overall reaction is

$$Hg(6 \ ^3P_1) + H_2 + 2NO \longrightarrow Hg(6 \ ^1S_0) + 2HNO,$$

whereas in the presence of ethylene (in large excess over the NO), the only HNO-forming reaction is

$$HgH + NO \longrightarrow Hg(6 \ ^1S_0) + HNO.$$

Oscilloscope traces of the formation and chemical relaxation of HNO, with and without added C_2H_4, are shown in Fig. 24. Thus the initial ratio of the HNO, divided by two, gives the absolute HgH quantum

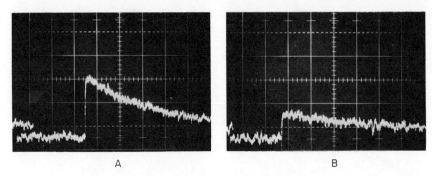

A   B

FIG. 24. Formation of HNO monitored photoelectrically. A, 500 Torr H_2 + 5 Torr NO. B, 500 Torr H_2 + 10 Torr C_2H_4 + 0.2 Torr NO. Under conditions A, formation of HgH and H results in HNO formation. Under conditions B, the H atoms are scavenged by the C_2H_4 and the HNO results only from reaction of HgH with NO. The HNO decay indicates complex kinetics. One division = 1.0 sec. (Callear and Wood, 1972.)

yield. Ethyl radicals are rapidly scavenged to yield C_2H_5NO, which presumably undergoes slow secondary reactions with NO.

The kinetics of the decay of HgH in Hg/H_2 mixtures has not yet been resolved, though

$$HgH + H \longrightarrow Hg(6\,^1S_0) + H_2$$

seems to be one of the main loss processes.

Table VIII lists rate coefficients for deactivation of $Hg(6\,^3P_0)$ by various gases which were measured by monochromatic flash excitation. Most of the experiments were conducted with an excess of N_2, by following the 2537-Å fluorescence in the afterglow. At high N_2 pressures, the

$$[Hg(6\,^3P_1)]/[Hg(6\,^3P_0)]$$

is constant following cessation of the excitation, so that the $Hg(6\,^3P_0)$ decay can be monitored photoelectrically via the 2537-Å emission on single shot. Also listed in Table VIII are quantum yields for $Hg(6\,^3P_0)$ production. These measurements were made by observing the $Hg(6\,^3P_0)$ formation by kinetic absorption spectroscopy via the 4047-Å line ($7\,^3S_1$–$6\,^3P_0$) in various gases at low total pressures where only a small fraction of the $Hg(6\,^3P_1)$ is quenched, always with a large excess of Ar added, which does not deactivate $Hg(6\,^3P_{1\,or\,0})$ to any significant extent, but serves to keep constant the pressure broadening of the atomic lines. The apparatus was calibrated by measuring the plate density change at 4047 Å with N_2

TABLE VIII

QUANTUM YIELDS Φ FOR THE $Hg(6\ ^3P_{1\to0})$ SPIN–ORBIT RELAXATION
AND RATE COEFFICIENTS FOR DEACTIVATION OF $Hg(6\ ^3P_0)$
(Callear and McGurk, 1973; Freeman et al., 1971b) (300°K)

Gas	Φ	Rate coefficient (cm^3 molecule^{-1} sec^{-1}) Callear and McGurk, 1973	Freeman et al., 1971b
H_2	<0.03	5.37 (±0.35) × 10^{-11}	9.2 × 10^{-11}
NO	≲0.10	2.51 (±0.16) × 10^{-10}	2.0 × 10^{-10}
CO	0.85	1.035 (±0.062) × 10^{-11}	3.9 × 10^{-11}
O_2	<0.10	1.81 (±0.07) × 10^{-10}	2.7 × 10^{-10}
CO_2	∼0.01	4.39 (±0.23) × 10^{-13}	—
N_2O	<0.10	1.12 (±0.04) × 10^{-10}	5.8 × 10^{-11}
CH_4	0.15	5.90 (±0.21) × 10^{-15}	—
C_2H_6	0.42	8.88 (±0.43) × 10^{-14}	4.5 × 10^{-13}
C_3H_8	0.38	4.41 (±0.18) × 10^{-13}	—
C_2H_4	<0.1	4.20 (±0.06) × 10^{-10}	—
NH_3	0.62	3.80 (±0.20) × 10^{-13}	3.2 × 10^{-13}

in the range 0–2 Torr; N_2 induces the $Hg(6\ ^3P_{1\to0})$ transition with unit efficiency (Callear and Hedges, 1970a). Similar experiments were conducted with the other gases and the $Hg(6\ ^3P_0)$ yields were determined from known $Hg(6\ ^3P_1)$ quenching rates relative to N_2 (Cvetanović, 1964). The high quantum yields in CO and NH_3 are consistent with results of Vikis et al. (1970), using continuous illumination and product analysis.

Newman et al. (1970) have developed an excellent technique for studying the formation and relaxation of $Hg(6\ ^3P_0)$ by modulating the 2537-Å radiation and measuring the phase shift of sensitized luminescence. The principle of the phase shift technique is detailed in Section VI. Sensitized luminescence of NH_3 by $Hg(6\ ^3P_1)$ was first observed by Mitchell and Dickenson (1927), and was shown to consist of a broad, diffuse band with a maximum at ∼3500 Å. The emission was supposed to be due to excited NH_3 molecules. Newman et al. (1970) showed that there is a time lag between the $Hg(6\ ^3P_1)$ quenching by NH_3 and the diffuse emission. They proposed the mechanism

$$Hg(6\ ^3P_1) + NH_3 \longrightarrow NH_2 + H + Hg(6\ ^1S_0)$$

$$Hg(6\ ^3P_1) + NH_3 \longrightarrow Hg(6\ ^3P_0) + NH_3$$

$$Hg(6\ ^3P_0) + NH_3 \longrightarrow Hg(6\ ^1S_0) + NH_3 + h\nu.$$

The luminescence was supposed to arise from an NH_3Hg^* complex formed in bimolecular collisions. Later, Callear and McGurk (1970a) confirmed their hypothesis in part, by demonstrating that the $Hg(6\,^3P_0)$ and the 3500-Å luminescence exhibit the same relaxation time following excitation with a monochromatic flash. Further, however, they showed that deactivation of the $Hg(6\,^3P_0)$ by NH_3 can occur both in bimolecular and in termolecular collisions. The latter was attributed to the attachment of $Hg(6\,^3P_0)$ to the NH_3 in stabilizing, three-body encounters:

$$M + Hg(6\,^3P_0) + NH_3 \longrightarrow HgNH_3^* + M$$

$$HgNH_3^* \longrightarrow Hg(6\,^1S_0) + NH_3 + h\nu.$$

The occurrence of termolecular relaxation was later confirmed by Freeman *et al.* (1971a) and they also measured the lifetime of the stabilized complex as $\sim$2 μsec. This lifetime, and a similar value for $HgND_3^*$, was later confirmed by Koskikallio *et al.* (1971), and is presumably the radiative lifetime. Pseudobimolecular rate coefficients for relaxation of $Hg(6\,^3P_0)$ by NH_3 and ND_3 are shown as a function of N_2 pressure in Fig. 25; there is a pronounced deuterium isotope effect on the termolecular rates.

Freeman *et al.* (1971b) have measured relaxation rates of $Hg(6\,^3P_0)$ by various gases by adding them to $Hg + NH_3$ mixtures and studying

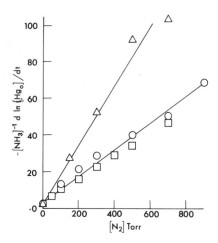

FIG. 25.   Removal of $Hg(6\,^3P_0)$ in NH_3 ($\bigcirc$, $\square$) and ND_3 ($\triangle$) in bimolecular and in termolecular collisions. The pseudobimolecular rate coefficient $-[NH_3]^{-1}\,d\ln[Hg_0]/dt$ is plotted against pressure of N_2. The intercept yields the bimolecular rate coefficient and the slope is the termolecular rate coefficient. (Koskikallio *et al.*, 1971.)

their effect on the phase shifts. They are compared with the flash photolysis results in Table VIII, and there is general agreement to within about a factor of two. Freeman *et al.* also reported rate coefficients for deactivation of $HgNH_3^*$ by various gases. The observation of termolecular kinetics in this system is good evidence that the emitter is an $HgNH_3$ complex, and not an electronically excited state of NH_3. Further, emission from NH_3^* would be banded. At high pressures of ammonia the $Hg(6\ ^3P_0)$ will attach clusters of NH_3 (Callear and Connor, 1974).

Hunziker (1969) has developed a technique for the spectroscopic study of Hg-photosensitized reactions which appears to have considerable potential. A 2537-Å Hg resonance lamp was modulated by excitation with a radiofrequency discharge at 200 kHz. The radiation was absorbed in a reaction cell with multiple-pass mirrors, and the production of transient species was detected in absorption with a continuous xenon arc as background source, and a scanning monochromator. With a lock-in, phase-sensitive amplifier, changes of optical density of considerably less than 1% can be measured. It was shown that $Hg(6\ ^3P_0)$ excites naphthalene to its triplet state, by observing triplet–triplet absorption. The relaxation of $Hg(6\ ^3P_0)$ has been studied in various gases, and it was concluded that deactivation of $Hg(6\ ^3P)$ by C_2H_2 causes electronic excitation of the C_2H_2 (Burton and Hunziker, 1972). Hunziker and Wendt (1971) demonstrated that excited mercury atoms interact with benzene to produce the triplet (which absorbs at 2320 Å) and the kinetics of its deactivation were investigated.

Modulated kinetic spectroscopy has also been applied by Hunziker and Wendt (1974) in the discovery of the $\tilde{A}\ ^2A'$–$\tilde{X}\ ^2A''$ system of HO_2 in the near infrared. Emission bands of the same system were discovered recently by Becker *et al.* (1974).

B. Cadmium Flash-Photosensitized Reactions

Some preliminary experiments have been conducted on flash spectroscopy with the 2288- and 3261-Å cadmium resonance radiations, with the multielectrode flash technique. The main feature of these experiments has been the discovery that the $Cd(5\ ^1P_1)$ produced by excitation at 2288 Å is rapidly deactivated to $Cd(5\ ^3P)$ by various gases. High pressures were employed in most of the experiments, and the $J = 0$, 1, and 2 states of $Cd(5\ ^3P)$ were always in statistical equilibrium. This is indicated by the spectra of Fig. 26, where the $Cd(5\ ^3P)$ were produced in an excess of CH_4

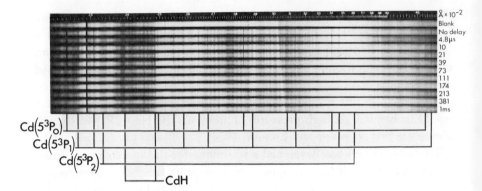

FIG. 26. Production of Cd(5 ^{3}P) and CdH in the deactivation of Cd(5 ^{1}P$_1$) by CH$_4$, with monochromatic excitation at 2288 Å. [Cd] = 2.6 × 10^{-3} Torr, [CH$_4$] = 720 Torr. (Breckenridge and Callear, 1971.)

by excitation at 2288 Å (Breckenridge and Callear, 1971). The relative intensities of the various Cd(5 ^{3}P) lines were invariant with delay time. The CdH results from the reaction

$$\text{Cd}(5\,^1\text{P}_1) + \text{CH}_4 \longrightarrow \text{CdH} + \text{CH}_3,$$

which competes with the 5 ^{1}P$_1 \rightarrow$ 5 ^{3}P deactivation. In CH$_4$ the Cd(5 ^{3}P) decays almost entirely by the 3261-Å (^{3}P$_1 \rightarrow {}^1$S$_0$) emission.

Even in H$_2$, the formation of CdH by irradiation at 2288 Å appears to be largely preceded by deactivation of Cd(5 ^{1}P$_1$) to Cd(5 ^{3}P). With [Cd] = 2.6 × 10^{-3} Torr, transient conversion of most of cadmium to the hydride can be effected, as illustrated in Fig. 27. The light absorption was estimated as 4 × 10^{13} quanta cm^{-3} per flash, about one-fifth of that of the Hg experiments.

Relative hydride yields in the reaction of Cd(5 ^{3}P) with H$_2$ + D$_2$ mixtures and HD are listed in Table IX. The rates into the various reaction channels correlate with the reaction endothermicities in a very simple manner.

The reaction of Cd(5 ^{3}P) with HD provides a curious contrast to the reaction of Hg(6 ^{3}P) with HD; as stated above, the latter yields predominantly HgD. In all the reactions of Hg(6 ^{3}P$_{1,0}$) with H$_2$, D$_2$, and HD the yields of mercury hydrides are greater than are predicted if it is assumed that the excess energy is distributed statistically among the product degrees of freedom; the intermediate HHgH complex is too short-lived

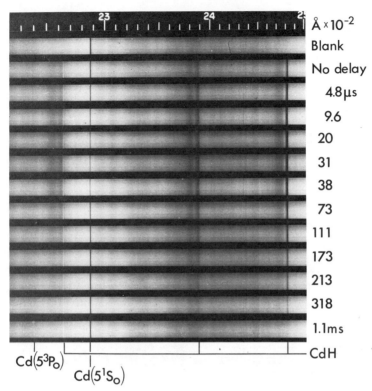

FIG. 27. Transient conversion of cadmium to the hydride in a $Cd/H_2/CH_4$ mixture excited at 2288 Å. $[Cd] = 2.6 \times 10^{-3}$ Torr, $[H_2] = 8$ Torr, $[CH_4] = 150$ Torr. (Breckenridge and Callear, 1971.)

TABLE IX

CORRELATION OF RELATIVE REACTION RATES OF Cd(5 $^3P_1$) WITH
INTERNAL ENERGY CHANGES (Breckenridge and Callear, 1971)

	Relative rate	$\exp(-\Delta E_0/RT)$
Cd(5 $^3P_1$) + H_2 → CdH + H	1.00	1
Cd(5 $^3P_1$) + D_2 → CdD + D	0.37 (± 0.07)	0.31
Cd(5 $^3P_1$) + HD → CdH + D	1.00	0.41
Cd(5 $^3P_1$) + DH → CdD + H	1.90 (± 0.20)	0.74

for statistical energy partitioning to precede fragmentation. If the Hg(6 ^3P) attacks the HD sideways on and induces repulsion between the H and D atoms, because of momentum conservation the H atom would carry two-thirds of the liberated kinetic energy, and would have a greater probability of breaking away than the D atom. Since the Cd (5 ^3P) processes are endothermic, the energy distribution may remain statistical throughout. If this is the correct explanation, it should be found that Zn(4 ^3P) reacts with HD preferentially to form ZnD, since the reactions are again exothermic.

Attempts to study reactions of excited Cd atoms by blackbody flash photolysis have been described by Young et al. (1970) and most of their conclusions are in accord with those deduced from the monochromatic flash experiments.

C. Xenon Flash-Photosensitized Reactions and Relaxation of N_2 A $^3\Sigma_u^+$

Experiments with monochromatic flash excitation with the 1470-Å resonance line of xenon have been described by Callear and Wood (1971a). The initial research was designed to study relaxation processes of N_2 A $^3\Sigma_u^+$,

$$Xe + h\nu(1470 \text{ Å}) \longrightarrow Xe^*$$
$$Xe^* + N_2 \ X\, ^1\Sigma_g^+ \longrightarrow \longrightarrow Xe + N_2 \ A\, ^3\Sigma_u^+.$$

The multielectrode technique was employed to produce an intense pulse of the 1470-Å radiation. The reaction cell was positioned along the lamp axis and was constructed by cementing two rows of rectangular blocks of vacuum-grown LiF onto two strips of Pyrex plate, as shown in Fig. 28. The inner dimensions of the reaction vessel cross section were 7.5×3 mm.

Measurements of rates of energy transfer from N_2 A $^3\Sigma_u^+$ to various acceptors had previously been pioneered by Young and co-workers (Young et al., 1969; Black et al., 1969). Absolute rates were measured by monitoring the Vegard–Kaplan emission (N_2 A $^3\Sigma_u^+$–X $^1\Sigma_g^+$) and also the fluorescence of electronically excited acceptors following a pulsed, electroded discharge, e.g.,

$$N_2 \ A\, ^3\Sigma_u^+(v = 0) + NO \ X\, ^2\Pi(v = 0)$$
$$\longrightarrow N_2 \ X\, ^1\Sigma_g^+(v = 0\text{–}2) + NO \ A\, ^2\Sigma^+(v = 0\text{–}2)$$
$$NO \ A\, ^2\Sigma^+ \longrightarrow NO \ X\, ^2\Pi + h\nu \ (\gamma \text{ bands}).$$

In the flash photolysis experiments, N_2 A $^3\Sigma_u^+$ decay rates were measured

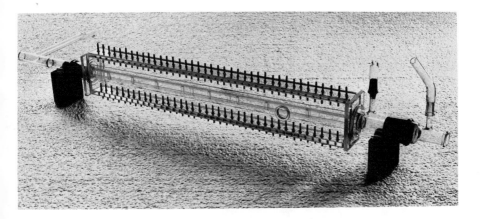

FIG. 28. A lamp and central reaction vessel for monochromatic excitation in the vacuum ultraviolet. LiF rectangular blocks are cemented on to strips of plate glass. The quartz "porthole" is for observation of emission sideways on. (Callear and Wood, unpublished.)

by monitoring either the NO γ bands or the Hg 2537-Å emission photo-electrically on single shot. The reciprocal relaxation times were found to be linearly dependent on the partial pressure of deactivating gas as shown in Fig. 29. Decay rates in C_2H_2 and C_2H_4 were monitored by inclusion of $[Hg] = 1.9 \times 10^{-4}$ Torr. Following termination of the initiating flash, the $N_2 A\ ^3\Sigma_u^+$ decays by

$$N_2 A\ ^3\Sigma_u^+ + Hg(6\ ^1S_0) \longrightarrow N_2 X\ ^1\Sigma_g^+ + Hg(6\ ^3P)$$

and

$$N_2 A\ ^3\Sigma_u^+ + M \longrightarrow N_2 X\ ^1\Sigma_g^+ + M^*.$$

Thus the reciprocal relaxation time is

$$k_{Hg}[Hg] + k_M[M]$$

and the slopes of plots of the type shown in Fig. 29 are bimolecular rate coefficients for deactivation of $N_2 A\ ^3\Sigma_u^+$. Results are compared to those of Young and co-workers in Table X; there is good agreement between the two sets of rate coefficients except in the transfer to Hg and NH_3.

In the monochromatic flash experiments, some resolution of the initial and final quantum states in the transfer to Hg and NO was achieved. In

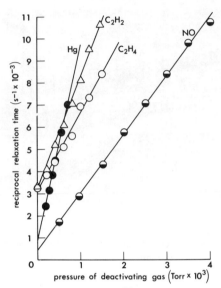

FIG. 29. Rates of relaxation of N_2 A $^3\Sigma_u^+$ produced by monochromatic xenon flash-photosensitization, monitored photoelectrically with the Hg 2537-Å emission or with the NO γ emission. ●, Hg; ◒, NO; △, C_2H_2; ○, C_2H_4. [N_2] = 4 Torr + [He] = 500 Torr + [Xe] = 1 Torr. In C_2H_2 and C_2H_4 the N_2 A $^3\Sigma_u^+$ concentration was monitored by inclusion of [Hg] = 1.9×10^{-4} Torr. (Callear and Wood, 1971a.)

mixtures of Xe + Hg + N_2 flashed at 1470 Å it was possible to monitor the formation of Hg(6 $^3P_0$) by reversal of the 2967-Å Hg line (6 $^3D_1$–6 $^3P_0$) photoelectrically. It was concluded that $\sim$25% of the Hg(6 ^3P) is produced directly with $J = 0$, in the energy acceptance from N_2 A $^3\Sigma_u^+$. This was shown to be consistent with a model in which the reaction channels were weighted with the product of their state densities and the Franck–Condon factors of the nitrogen transitions. It was also possible to show that Xe* excitation produces N_2 A $^3\Sigma_u^+(v = 0, 1)$, and the rate coefficient for vibrational relaxation in He at 300°K was recorded as 1.2×10^{-15} cm^3 molecule^{-1} sec^{-1}, corresponding to $\sim$3 $\times 10^5$ collisions. The N_2 A $^3\Sigma_u^+(v = 0$ and 1) excited the NO γ-progressions in quite different ratios, according to the equations

N_2 A $^3\Sigma_u^+(v = 0)$ + NO X$^2\Pi(v = 0)$

$$\longrightarrow \quad N_2 \text{ X}^1\Sigma_g^+ + \text{NO A }^2\Sigma^+(v = 1\!:\!0 = 1\!:\!9.5)$$

N_2 A $^3\Sigma_u^+(v = 1)$ + NO X$^2\Pi(v = 0)$

$$\longrightarrow \quad N_2 \text{ X}^1\Sigma_g^+ + \text{NO A }^2\Sigma^+(v = 1\!:\!0 = 1\!:\!1.9).$$

TABLE X

RATE COEFFICIENTS FOR DEACTIVATION OF N_2 A $^3\Sigma_u^+$ AT 295°K
(Callear and Wood, 1971a; Young et al., 1969; Black et al., 1969)

	Rate coefficient (cm^3 molecule^{-1} sec^{-1}) Callear and Wood	Young and co-workers
Hg	2.9 ($\pm$0.2) $\times 10^{-10}$	1.4 $\times 10^{-11}$
C_2H_2	1.6 ($\pm$0.2) $\times 10^{-10}$	1.6 $\times 10^{-10}$
C_2H_4	1.1 ($\pm$0.1) $\times 10^{-10}$	1.5 $\times 10^{-10}$
NO	8.0 ($\pm$0.4) $\times 10^{-11}$	8 $\times 10^{-11}$
NH_3	$<2 \times 10^{-11}$	1.8 $\times 10^{-10}$
N_2O	6.1 ($\pm$0.9) $\times 10^{-12}$	6.4 $\times 10^{-12}$
O_2	3.6 ($\pm$0.2) $\times 10^{-12}$	3.8 $\times 10^{-12}$
n-C_4H_{10}	2.7 ($\pm$0.2) $\times 10^{-12}$	—
CO[$N_2^*(v=0)$]	1.5 ($\pm$0.2) $\times 10^{-12}$	$\Big\{$ 2.5 $\times 10^{-12}$
CO[$N_2^*(v=1)$]	2.4 ($\pm$0.5) $\times 10^{-11}$	
C_3H_8	1.3 ($\pm$0.1) $\times 10^{-12}$	—
C_2H_6	2.6 ($\pm$0.2) $\times 10^{-13}$	—
H_2	$\sim 3.0 \times 10^{-15}$	3.0 $\times 10^{-15}$
CH_4	$\leq 1.7 \times 10^{-15}$	$<7 \times 10^{-15}$
CO_2	$\leq 1.3 \times 10^{-15}$	$<2.7 \times 10^{-14}$
C_2N_2	—	5.6 $\times 10^{-11}$

The relationship between the initial and final quantum states could also be partially rationalized with a model in which each channel is weighted with the product of the two Franck–Condon factors and the density of states. From a comparison of the simultaneous NO γ and Hg 2537-Å emissions, it was demonstrated that N_2 A $^3\Sigma_u^+$ excites NO A $^2\Sigma^+$ with close to unit efficiency.

V. Microwave Techniques for Rotational Relaxation

A. INTRODUCTION

Microwave techniques are beginning to show a delightful fine structure to rotational relaxation in gases. Double resonance was first applied to assist in the assignment of microwave transitions; one line was saturated with a powerful source and the effects on other lines supposedly corresponding to the same initial level were examined (Battaglia et al., 1959; Yajima and Shimoda, 1960). The success of these experiments indicated the possibility of investigating rotational relaxation by microwave double resonance; if a powerful pumping source is used to upset the equilibrium of a pair of states, the disturbance should also be manifest in other states which are coupled to the initial states by collision. Realization of such a method for studying rotational relaxation was reported by Cox *et al.* (1965), Unland and Flygare (1966), and Oka (1966). Unland and Flygare described a time-resolved technique for absolute rate measurement. Oka subsequently studied several molecular systems in some detail, and has determined selection rules for rotational relaxation with different kinds of intermolecular interaction. Some of the highlights of this work are summarized in the next section. The time-resolved techniques are described briefly in Section V,C.

B. Steady-State Microwave Double Resonance

1. *The Principle of the Method*

The principle of the method of microwave double resonance for rotational relaxation is indicated by the four-level diagram in Fig. 30a for the inversion doublets of NH_3. The heavy arrow is the pumping radiation at level J, K, and the effect of this on the $J - 1$, K doublet is examined by a weak probing signal indicated by the light arrow. The strongest effects are often found in $J \pm 1$ states with the same initial and final K value. The magnitude of the change of the probing signal due to pumping is designated $\Delta I/I$ and can be as high as 30% in a favorable system.

Figures 30b and 30c show the types of collisional processes which may occur. Both α (far infrared) and β are allowed electric dipole transitions

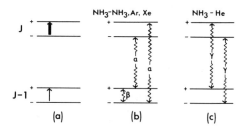

Fig. 30.   Four-level diagrams of NH_3 for microwave double resonance. (a) Pumping radiation, heavy arrow; monitoring radiation, light arrow. (b) Electric dipole-allowed transitions. (c) Electric quadrupole-allowed transitions. (After Oka, 1968a; reproduced by permission of Dr. T. Oka.)

($\Delta J = 0 \pm 1$, $\Delta K = 0$, $+ \leftrightarrow -$), while the processes γ are "electric quad-rupole allowed" (Oka's notation). The intensity of the pumping radiation is sufficient to equalize the population of the pumped pair, and the effect on the $J - 1$, K pair depends on the relative rates of the β processes compared to the $\Delta J = -1$ processes, α. If the former are comparatively very fast, the $\Delta I/I$ is small. Processes of type α will cause $\Delta I/I$ to be positive since they will decrease the population of the upper $J - 1$, K level and increase the population of the lower $J - 1$, K level with respect to Boltzmann equilib-rium. Processes γ will cause $\Delta I/I$ to be negative. Cases exist where α and γ occur with approximately equal efficiency to yield $\Delta I/I \approx 0$.

The absolute cross sections for rotational transitions, for example, in NH_3, can be determined from the dependence of line broadening on pres-sure (lifetime broadening). However, such measurements yield no detail concerning the type of process, except that if the transition has a large cross section, i.e., occurs at long range, it is expected on theoretical grounds to result from dipole–dipole interaction and should show obedience to the electric dipole selection rules (Townes and Schawlow, 1955).

2. *Experimental Results*

The apparatus that Oka (1967) has used for most of his experiments consists of a 3-m K-band Stark cell with phase-sensitive detection. The pumping power of 10–20 W is generated with a klystron. Monitoring signals are produced with various klystrons in the energy range 1–30 μW, which is insufficient to disturb the equilibrium.

Oka's first experiments were conducted by pumping the K-type or l-type doublets of H_2CO, DHCO, HCN, DCN, and H_2CCO (Oka, 1967). Transitions between the doublets occur in the microwave regions and the four-level systems are similar to those of Fig. 30 except that the splittings increase with J. Also, the parities of the upper and lower levels alternate so that the dipole-allowed α transitions produce negative $\Delta I/I$, which was in fact observed in the pure gases. Three conclusions were drawn from these experiments:

1. Collisionally induced transitions obey the optical rules (based essentially on the negative $\Delta I/I$, $\Delta J = -1$, and $\Delta K = 0$).

2. The dominant interaction which causes the transitions is dipole–dipole.

3. The rate coefficients for the processes α and β are approximately equal.

It is considered by Oka that the α-type transitions are probably resonant, i.e., exchange rotational quanta with other molecules rather than dissipate the internal energy change as translation. An example of such a process is

$$(K = 4, J = 5) + (K = 3, J = 4) \rightarrow (K = 4, J = 4) + (K = 3, J = 5).$$

This is optically allowed for each molecule, causes no change in the total rotational angular momentum, and involves only a small change in the internal energy (due to differences in the effect of centrifugal distortion in the various species).

The observed $\Delta I/I$ values were independent of pressure in the high-pressure region ($\sim 2 \times 10^{-2}$ Torr) but fell off below 10^{-2} Torr due to wall collisions which equilibrate the populations. By calculating the frequency of competitive wall processes (diffusion rate), Oka deduced a collision diameter of ~ 20 Å for gas-phase transitions in H_2CO and $HDCO$.

Any effect of pumping the J, K doublet on the $J-1$, K populations is bound to affect the $J-2$, K populations by a cascade effect. Any such effect should fall off as a geometric progression. In HCN and DCN, effects on the $J-2$, K doublets were observed which were too large to be attributed to cascade effects, and it was suggested that $\Delta J = 2$ transitions, with "quadrupole selection rules," also play a dominant role in these systems.

Oka's results with NH_3 are particularly detailed and interesting. The differences between the microwave frequencies corresponding to different inversion doublets are small, and some difficulty was experienced in separating the monitoring signal from the pumping radiation. However, results for pumping 18 different inversion doublets were obtained in pure NH_3 (Oka, 1968a), with $\Delta I/I$ in the range 8.22–0.35%. All the $\Delta I/I$ were positive, corresponding to a dominance of α-type electric dipole transitions. The only $\Delta J = 2$ effects were found pumping the 5, 1 and 4, 1 doublets; in the former case the 3, 1 signal decreased its intensity by 0.55%. The effect of the 5, 1 pumping on the 4, 1 transition was the strongest observed, $\Delta I/I = 8\%$. The $\Delta J = 2$ effects in pure NH_3 were attributed to cascade influences. No evidence was found for $\Delta K \neq 0$ transitions.

Lees and Oka (1968, 1969) later devised an ingenious triple resonance experiment to establish the character of the $\Delta J = 2$ transitions. For the effect of pumping the 5, 1 on the 3, 1 doublet of NH_3, first the 4, 1 doublet was saturated with a strong "clamping" signal, and the absorption of the 3, 1 observed. The pumping radiation was then switched on to the 5, 1 doublet; any direct 5, 1–3, 1 coupling would still be observed, but the

TABLE XI

MICROWAVE TRIPLE RESONANCE WITH SOME SIX-LEVEL SYSTEMS[a]

Collision	Six-level system	Transition	$\Delta I_c/I$	$\Delta I/I$
HCN—HCN	$(J = 11)_p$–$(J = 10)_c$–$(J = 9)_s$	l doublets	-38.3 ± 2	-11.8 ± 2
NH$_3$—NH$_3$	$(4, 1)_p$–$(3, 1)_c$–$(2, 1)_s$	Inversion doublets	$+4.4 \pm 0.2$	0 ± 0.5
NH$_3$—H$_2$	$(4, 1)_p$–$(3, 1)_c$–$(2, 1)_s$	Inversion doublets	$+11.4 \pm 1$	-2.6 ± 1
CH$_3$OH—CH$_3$OH	$(J = 9)_p$–$(J = 10)_c$–$(J = 11)_s$	l doublets	-3.1 ± 1	0 ± 0.5
CH$_3$OH—He	$(J = 9)_p$–$(J = 10)_c$–$(J = 11)_s$	l doublets	-11.3 ± 1	-6.2 ± 1

[a] $\Delta I_c/I$ is the change of intensity of the $J - 2$ doublet due to the clamping radiation on the $J - 1$ doublet. $\Delta I/I$ is the effect on the $J - 2$ doublet of pumping the J doublet with the $J - 1$ clamped (Lees and Oka, 1968).

cascade effect would be obliterated by the clamp on the intermediate level. Some results of these six-level systems are listed in Table XI. The subscripts p, c, and s denote pumping, clamped, and signal. The $\Delta I_c/I$ are the changes observed in the double resonance experiment, and the final column lists absorption changes in the triple resonance experiment. The $\Delta J = 2$ effects in pure NH$_3$ are clearly due to cascade processes. $\Delta J > 1$ cannot occur to the extent of more that 10% of the $\Delta J = 1$ transitions.

Results are included in Fig. 31 (Oka, 1968b) for the $(J + 1, K)$–(J, K) $(J = K)$ four-level systems, where it is seen that $\Delta I/I$ decreases with increasing J. It is interesting to notice that at small J the $\Delta I/I$ are much larger in NH$_3$–inert gas systems than in pure NH$_3$; the $\Delta I/I$ are negative in He. The experiments with the inert gases were conducted with $[NH_3] \simeq 10^{-2}$ Torr $+ 1$ Torr of added gas.

Rotational relaxation in the NH$_3$–rare gas systems was shown not to be restricted by the electric dipole selection rules. From pressure broadening it is known that the effective collision diameters for the NH$_3$–He, NH$_3$–Ar, and NH$_3$–NH$_3$ systems are respectively 2.4, 3.7, and 13.8 Å, indicating that the dominant interaction in the case of the rare gases is the short-range electron–electron repulsion. In these systems the $\Delta J > 1$ and $\Delta K \neq 0$ transitions were observed strongly. The $\Delta J \leq 5$ were observed, but with $\Delta I/I$ decreasing with increasing ΔJ.

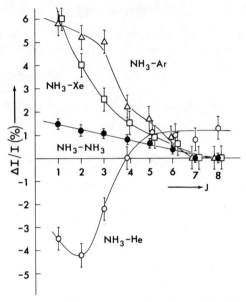

FIG. 31. Dependence of $\Delta I/I$ versus J for the $(J+1, K)_p$–$(J, K)_s$ $(J=K)$ four-level systems in NH_3. Positive $\Delta I/I$ indicates a preference for electric dipole-allowed transitions. Negative $\Delta I/I$ arises from a preference for electric quadrupole transitions. (Oka, 1968b; reproduced by permission of Dr. T. Oka.)

The levels of NH_3 with $K = 3n$ (n integral) are of species A, while the levels with $K = 3n \pm 1$ are of species E (analogous to ortho and para states in linear, symmetric molecules) and the A↔E transitions are forbidden. For pumped inversion doublets with $K = 3n$, $\Delta K = \pm 3n$ was demonstrated, providing the first experimental confirmation of the low probability of A↔E interconversion in gas-phase collisions. Pumped E states had no effect on A states and vice versa. For all states $\Delta k = \pm 3n$ was found, where k is a "signed" quantum number ($2 \leftarrow -1$ allowed). This rule was formulated from all the ΔK processes which occurred. With $K \geq 4$, $\Delta K = +3n$ or -3 was always obeyed. Other transitions for example, $\Delta K = 1$ in states with $K = 1$ or 2, were therefore interpreted to be $\Delta k = \pm 3$ transitions, etc. The discovery of the selection rule for the signed k is a remarkable aspect of this research. The magnitude of $|\Delta I/I|$ decreased as Δk increased, i.e., $\Delta k = 0 \rightleftharpoons 3 > 6 > 9$. No obvious parity rule was found and from Fig. 31 it is seen that in NH_3–NH_3, Ar, and Xe the $+ \leftrightarrow -$ transitions are dominant, whereas the $+ \leftrightarrow +$ and $- \leftrightarrow -$ are more frequent in He. No explanation for these reversed parity effects in helium has been proposed.

3. Interpretation of the Results

We first present Oka's attempts to account for the results in pure NH_3. The dominant interaction which causes transitions is clearly dipole–dipole, which is manifest in the obedience to the electric dipole selection rules, $\Delta J = 0 \pm 1$, $\Delta K = 0$, $+ \leftrightarrow -$ ($\Delta I/I$ positive). Oka shows quantitative agreement between his results and Anderson's theory (1950). The theory requires that the change of internal energy of the system of two molecules must be less than or equal to the interaction energy. This implies that the α transitions must be resonant, or near resonant. The ratio of the matrix elements of the *instantaneous* dipole interaction Hamiltonian for an α–β transition is roughly proportional to $(J^2/K^2 - 1)^{1/2}$. The $\Delta I/I$ were smallest for $J = K + 1$ and for a given K increased with J. Here the numbers J and K refer to the pumped state which undergoes a deactivating collision. (It is obviously impossible to deactivate a state with $J = K$ with the $\Delta K = 0$ restriction.) For a given K, as J increases above 5, $\Delta I/I$ decreases, which was attributed to the decreasing probability of finding a resonant partner for an α-type relaxation. The $J = 4$ are the most populous states at 300°K.

The decrease with J for the $(J + 1, K)$–(J, K) series of Fig. 31 can be attributed partially to the decreasing J^2/K^2 with increasing J, and also to the lack of resonant partners at higher J. From an absolute calculation based on Anderson's theory, Oka concluded that the rather small $\Delta I/I$ values found in pure NH_3 arise because of the occurrence of γ-type transitions, corresponding to consecutive α and β processes in a single collision event.

Interaction of NH_3 with the inert gases corresponds to hard collisions in which $\Delta J > 1$ and $\Delta K \neq 0$ occur readily. It is surprising that the $\Delta I/I$ are larger in the inert gases since the α transitions convert more energy to translation than do the β transitions. The $\Delta k = \pm 3n$ rule arises, according to Oka, because C_3 is still a symmetry operation in the collision complex, and the symmetry of the wave functions is described by the nondegenerate species A, E+, and E−. The interaction Hamiltonian is finite only if $\Delta k = \pm 3n$, where n is integral.

Daly and Oka (1970) studied the rotational relaxation of NH_3 by the nonpolar molecules H_2, O_2, N_2, CH_4, and SF_6, and curiously a general obedience to the electric dipole selection rules was found, in sharp contrast to the inert gas systems. However, in H_2, $\Delta K \neq 0$ transitions do occur (Fabris and Oka, 1972). Dominance of dipole–dipole interaction has also been reported in the relaxation of CH_3Br, by Ronn and Lide (1967). The CH_3Br was excited with a CO_2 laser.

Shimizu and Oka (1970) reported a clear-cut example of measurement of rotational relaxation by infrared–microwave double resonance. With a continuous N_2O laser at 80 mW, the $v_2[^\circ Q-(8, 7)]$ line of NH_3 was pumped, which increased the intensity of the 8, 7 line by two- to eightfold, according to the pressure; the upper level of the inversion doublet was pumped out. The effect on the 9, 7 and 7, 7 doublets was observed. The laser method obviously has the advantage of causing a large deviation from equilibrium.

It has been demonstrated by Freund et al. (1973) that in ammonia vapor the β transitions occur with little change of the translational velocity. This is not surprising because the change of internal energy is small compared to the kinetic energy of translation. The experiments were conducted with an infrared–infrared double resonance technique using two-photon excitation (an infrared line from an N_2O laser plus a microwave transition to achieve near coincidences with v_2 of NH_3). The pumping radiation burnt a hole in the Doppler profile due to excitation of molecules with a particular velocity component and it was demonstrated that the hole is transferred by the β-type transition in self collisions. In collisions with He, the hole is smeared out because rotational energy transfer is induced by the short-range repulsive forces, which must also change the velocity.

In the work described here, Oka and his associates have made a very substantial contribution to the understanding of rotational relaxation in gases.

Redon and Fourier (1972) have developed an infrared–microwave double resonance experiment with NH_3 in which a Stark field was employed to achieve resonance with laser lines.

C. Time-Resolved Measurements

Modulated and fully time-resolved microwave techniques have been developed recently which yield relaxation times for rotational relaxation. Perhaps the main interest so far has been the discovery and interpretation of the effects of coherence (McGurk et al., 1974b), which are not relevant to this review. To date, essentially all measurements have been restricted to the two states directly pumped; collisional transfer of the initial disturbance, studied by Oka and his associates, gives rise to effects which are too weak to be investigated with present time-resolved techniques. Since pressure broadening also gives access to gross rates of rotational relaxation (Townes and Schawlow, 1955), the new methods have not yet had a great impact on our understanding of rotational relaxation, though they have a considerable potential to do so.

Double resonance methods were devised first; the populations of rotational states are disturbed with a powerful pumping source (microwave or infrared) and the decay of the disturbance is monitored at a different frequency from the pump frequency. However, it has recently been demonstrated that the relaxation rates can also be measured simply by observing the effects of changing the power at a single microwave transition. The double resonance methods are considered first.

Unland and Flygare (1966) described the first fully time-resolved technique for the measurement of rotational relaxation rates, and applied the method to the OCS molecule. Pulses of microwave power were generated using a PIN diode modulator ($<10^{-8}$ sec switch time) and molecular absorption was detected with a balance bridge spectrometer with super-heterodyne detection (conventional Stark modulation obviously cannot be used in such an experiment). With the $J = 0 \rightarrow 1$ transition pumped, transient effects were detected on the $J = 1 \rightarrow 2$ transition. In these early experiments, however, the effects of coherence were not fully analyzed or understood. Brown (1974) refined the Unland–Flygare experiment, replacing the bridge with a signal averager (which integrates over a large number of pulses into many storage elements). Brown also refined the interpretation, sorting out effects of coherence and the relaxation of polarization and state population. The rate coefficient for collisional relaxation of the $J = 1$ state is approximately 1.5×10^{-8} cm³ molecule^{-1} sec^{-1} (relaxation time 28 μsec mTorr), corresponding to a long-range interaction.

Several infrared–microwave, time-resolved experiments have been described. Levy et al. (1972) pumped ν_2 ^{Q}Q–(8, 7) of NH_3 with infrared radiation from an N_2O laser [P(13) at 928 cm^{-1}] and studied the time variation of the $NH_3(8, 7)$ inversion transition in the pure gas. A huge collision cross section of 400 (± 50) Å² was recorded for collisional relaxation. Jetter et al. (1973) pumped ν_3 $^{Q}R_3(4)$ of $^{13}CH_3F$ with CO_2 laser radiation [P(32) at 1035 cm^{-1}] and monitored relaxation via the $J = 3 \rightarrow 4$, $K = 3$ transition at 199,087 MHz. A relaxation time of 10.5 μsec mTorr was reported for the pure gas, corresponding to a total rate coefficient of roughly 1.5×10^{-8} cm³ molecule^{-1} sec^{-1} for collisional relaxation of the $J = 4$ state. McGurk et al. (1973) pumped ν_3 $^{R}Q_3(6)$ of $CH_3{}^{35}Cl$ with CO_2 laser radiation [P(26) at 1040 cm^{-1}] and monitored relaxation via the $J = 5 \rightarrow 6$, $K = 3$ transition at 159,478 MHz. The relaxation time was reported to be 14.6 μsec mTorr in self collisions, with a somewhat slower relaxation induced by the inert gases. In the work of Jetter *et al.* a very weak transient effect was observed on the $J = 3 \rightarrow 4$, $K = 0$ transition, not involving levels initially pumped. All these experiments are made possible by the use of signal averaging.

Collisional relaxation rates can also be measured either by suddenly switching power onto a particular transition, or by suddenly switching it off. In the first case the absorption varies with time, from which the relaxation rate of the population difference can be derived. When the power is suddenly switched off, the system emits coherent radiation and relaxation can be investigated from the decay profile (Brewer and Shoemaker, 1971; Brittain *et al.*, 1973). Switching is conveniently achieved by changing the Stark field. McGurk *et al.* (1974a) described an analysis of transient absorption and emission with the $J = 0 \rightarrow 1$ transition of OCS, recording a relaxation time of about 28 μsec mTorr for self collisions, close to the value recorded by Brown with the microwave double resonance experiment.

The general comments in this section on microwave techniques are evidence of the remarkable progress that has been achieved over the last decade.

VI. Fluorescence and the Lifetimes of Electronically Excited Molecules

A. INTRODUCTION

By subjecting gases to pulses of light or energetic electrons, the lifetimes of excited atoms and molecules can be determined from the delayed fluorescence. Once the lifetime has been measured, absolute rates of relaxation processes, including chemical reaction, can be derived from experiments with continuous irradiation. In this section some of these experiments are outlined, with special emphasis on diatomic molecules. The decay rate of a particular species in a gas at limiting zero pressure is determined by the sum of the spontaneous processes, i.e., emission of radiation, predissociation, and internal conversion due to perturbation by other states. At finite pressures, the decay rate is generally enhanced by collisional processes. Long-lived species ($>10^{-5}$ sec) may partly decay by interaction with the walls of the containing vessel. The spontaneous emission rate can be calculated from the strength of transitions in absorption, provided a full set of Franck–Condon factors is available and provided that any dependence of the electronic transition moment on the nuclear separation is known. If the molecule has insufficient energy to dissociate and the bands show no evidence of perturbation, the lifetime measured directly at limiting zero pressure must equal that calculated from the oscillator strength in absorption.

B. EXPERIMENTAL MEASUREMENT OF LIFETIMES

The methods of measuring the lifetimes of electronically excited molecules have been reviewed several times; a detailed treatment was given fairly recently by Corney (1970) and only a brief summary will be given here, with special reference to molecular rather than atomic species.

Lifetimes are measured directly in afterglows by selecting their specific radiation either with interference filters (if the wavelength region is not overlain with other emission) or a monochromator. The fluorescence decay can be observed following single pulse excitation by recording photon emission in the afterglow with a photomultiplier and oscilloscope, i.e., a single-shot method. The development of pulsed, tunable dye lasers with a duration of a few nsec is finding useful application to lifetime measurement on single shot and some results are listed in Table XII and will be discussed later. The single-shot method has the advantage of simplicity in the detection part of the apparatus. If excitation is achieved by electron impact, it appears that it is comparatively difficult to obtain adequate emission with a single pulse. (Optical excitation is usually specific to a particular quantum state.) An example of a single-shot, electron-pulse technique was described by Holzberlein (1964). An electron pulse with a cutoff time of 10^{-8} sec was produced with a thermionic triode. The pulse shape is controlled by the grid bias and, with a perforated anode, electronic excitation was observed from a field-free region. An accuracy of $\pm 10\%$ was claimed, with a time resolution of 20 nsec. To obtain adequate sensitivity of detection, the photomultiplier was "overloaded" for a short period following the exciting pulse. However, rather high energies are required for single-shot operation, with the result that many highly excited states tend to be populated; consequently it is difficult to determine the true lifetime of the species under study because in the afterglow its spontaneous decay is accompanied by continued population from higher states by radiative cascading. Very accurate time profiles are required to separate the effects of cascading.

With excitation by electron impact, repetitive pulsing devices have been more commonly and successfully used than the single-shot method. Bennett and Kindlemann (1966) have described a technique of producing narrow energy width pulses of ~1 nsec duration. The repetitive pulsing methods can be divided broadly into two categories; first what are called "delayed coincidence" methods, and second the "phase shift" method. Delayed coincidence is a technique that was first used in nuclear physics to study rates of nuclear decay, and lifetimes as short as 10^{-10} sec have been measured (Bell et al., 1952). The principle of the original technique was to devise an electronic coincidence circuit which recorded one unit on a counter only if two input pulses arrived "simultaneously." In its first application to the measurement of the lifetimes of electronically excited atoms by Heron et al. (1956), one pulse resulted from a light quantum arriving at the photomultiplyer and the other pulse was generated at the termination of the exciting electron pulse, but delayed by a chosen time interval. The thermionic triode produced approximately square 10-nsec pulses at a frequency of 10 kHz, and the decay profile in the afterglow was determined by counting over many pulses for each of several delay times. The principle of "delayed coincidence," with averaging over many events, has subsequently led to several ingenious developments. Bennett and Dalby (1959) pioneered the measurement of the lifetimes of excited molecules in gases. Their technique was to excite with repetitive electron impact (4 kHz with a decay time of 10 nsec) and the detecting photomultiplier was gated open only for a small time interval during the afterglow; by slowly changing the coincidence time with a motor-driven helipot, the decay profile of the excited molecules was displayed on a chart output. This "pulse sampling" technique is listed as "delayed coincidence" in Table XII.

Many time delays can now be recorded simultaneously with multichannel analyzers (or signal averagers), which are particularly suited to feeble emission intensities. Coincident with the termination of the electron pulse, the charging of a capacitor at constant current is initiated. Photon arrival at the photomultiplier terminates the charging and simultaneously a pulse at the accumulated voltage is delivered to a particular channel which is actuated only over a small voltage interval. Thus each channel corresponds to a particular time delay. The device is suitable only for very weak sources where on average less than one photon reaches the photomultiplier per pulse.

The phase shift method was originally used with optical excitation and an example of application in the study of $Hg(6\ ^3P_1)$ photosensitized luminescence was described in Section IV. The method was first applied by Lawrence (1965) to electron excitation. A sinusoidally varying potential was applied to the grid of a thermionic triode. Due to the finite lifetime of the species produced by electron impact, the fluorescence exhibits a phase lag, the measurement of which can yield the lifetime of the excited species.

Consider the simple case of an excitation rate $a \sin \omega t$. The rate equation for the concentration of excited species N with mean lifetime τ is

$$dN/dt + \tau^{-1}N = a \sin \omega t .$$

At the steady state, the solution is

$$N = [a/(\tau^{-2} + \omega^2)](\tau^{-1} \sin \omega t - \omega \cos \omega t) .$$

Defining $\phi = \tan^{-1}(\omega\tau)$, which is obviously constant for a given ω,

$$\tau^{-1} = (\tau^{-2} + \omega^2)^{1/2} \cos \phi \qquad \text{and} \qquad \omega = (\tau^{-2} + \omega^2)^{1/2} \sin \phi .$$

Thus

$$N = [a/(\tau^{-2} + \omega^2)^{1/2}] \sin(\omega t - \phi) .$$

Thus measurement of the phase shift ϕ yields τ.

The excitation function is not required to be precisely sinusoidal for the above equation to hold provided only light at the "fundamental frequency" is seen by the detector. This can easily be shown by substituting a Fourier series for $a \sin \omega t$ in the above differential equation. The phase shifts are normally measured at a variety of frequencies and invariance of τ with ω can be taken to be evidence for the absence of cascading, or vice versa.

It is necessary to mention the "beam foil" technique, to provide the background to all the results listed in Table XII. The method results from the discovery that when a high-energy ion beam passes through a thin film of carbon or aluminum ($\sim$300 Å thick), some ions undergo electronic excitation or neutralization into electronically excited states. Fluorescence is observed from the transmitted beam which decays with distance according to the exit velocity and lifetime. The incident beam is produced with a Van de Graaff and analyzing magnet, and energy spreads of $\sim$1% can be achieved. The exit beam is observed at a fixed point downstream with a monochromator and photomultiplier. There is a small decrease of velocity when the ions interact with the foil, and also an increase in the energy spread. The lifetime is determined by shifting the foil with respect to the point of observation.

TABLE XII

EXPERIMENTAL LIFETIMES OF SOME SMALL MOLECULES

Molecule	v'	τ (nsec)	Method[a]	Ref.
AlO B $^2\Sigma^+$	0–3	128 ($\pm$6)	Laser single shot	Johnson et al. (1972)
BaO A $^1\Sigma^+$	0	356	Laser single shot	Johnson (1972)
BBr A $^1\Pi$	0, 1	25.6 ($\pm$5.0)	Phase shift	Lutz and Hesser (1968)
BCl A $^1\Pi$	0, 1, 2	19.1 ($\pm$2.0)	Phase shift	Hesser (1968)
BeO C $^1\Sigma$	0	90 ($\pm$4)	Laser single shot	Capelle et al. (1972)
BF A $^1\Pi$	0, 1, 2	2.8 ($\pm$0.3)	Phase shift	Hesser (1968)
BH A $^1\Pi$	0	159 ($\pm$16)	Phase shift	Smith (1971)
Br$_2$ B $^3\Pi_{0_u+}$	14	<150	Laser single shot	Capelle et al. (1971)
	27	1.2×10^3	Range of v' studied	Capelle et al. (1971)
C$_2$ A $^3\Pi_g$	0–3	$\sim$650	Laser vaporised graphite	Jeunehomme and Schwenker (1965)
	Range	200 ($\pm$50)	Phase shift	Fink and Welge (1967)
	0	204 ($\pm$10)	EBDC	Erman et al. (1973)
	1	202 ($\pm$15)	EBDC	Erman et al. (1973)
CF A $^2\Sigma^+$	0	18.8 ($\pm$2.0)	Phase shift	Hesser (1968)
		19.1 ($\pm$2.0)	Phase shift	Hesser (1968)
CH A $^2\Delta$	0	540 ($\pm$40)	Phase shift	Fink and Welge (1967)
	0	560 ($\pm$60)	Delayed coincidence	Bennett and Dalby (1960b)
	0	476 ($\pm$60)	Phase shift	Smith (1971)
	0	470 ($\pm$75)	Phase shift	Hesser and Lutz (1970)
	0	480 ($\pm$40)	EBDC	Erman et al. (1973)
CH B $^2\Sigma^-$	—	1,000 ($\pm$400)	Delayed coincidence	Bennett and Dalby (1960b)
	0	345 ($\pm$50)	Phase shift	Hesser and Lutz (1970)
	0	400 ($\pm$60)	Phase shift	Fink and Welge (1967)
	0	335 ($\pm$40)	EBDC	Erman et al. (1973)
CH C $^2\Sigma^+$	0	$\sim$5 (F$_1$)	Phase shift	Hesser and Lutz (1970)
	0	$\sim$18 (F$_2$)	Phase shift	Hesser and Lutz (1970)

TABLE XII   (continued)

Molecule	v'	τ (nsec)	Method[a]	Ref.
CD C $^2\Sigma^+$	0	$\sim$20 (F$_1$)	Phase shift	Hesser and Lutz (1970)
	0	$\sim$55 (F$_2$)	Phase shift	Hesser and Lutz (1970)
CH$^+$ B $^1\Delta$	0	210 ($\pm$25)	Phase shift	Hesser and Lutz (1970)
	1	192 ($\pm$25)	Phase shift	Hesser and Lutz (1970)
	0	290 ($\pm$30)	EBDC	Brzozowski et al. (1974c)
	1	290 ($\pm$30)	EBDC	Brzozowski et al. (1974c)
CH$^+$ $^3\Sigma$	0	480 ($\pm$40)	EBDC	Brzozowski et al. (1974c)
	1	470 ($\pm$40)	EBDC	Brzozowski et al. (1974c)
	2	480 ($\pm$40)	EBDC	Brzozowski et al. (1974c)
CH$^+$ A $^1\Pi$	—	76 ($\pm$25)	Phase shift	Smith (1971)
	0	408 ($\pm$30)	EBDC	Brzozowski et al. (1974c)
	1	495 ($\pm$50)	EBDC	Brzozowski et al. (1974c)
	2	530 ($\pm$50)	EBDC	Brzozowski et al. (1974c)
	3	465 ($\pm$50)	EBDC	Brzozowski et al. (1974c)
	4	525 ($\pm$50)	EBDC	Brzozowski et al. (1974c)
ClS $^2\Pi$	—	10.2 ($\pm$2.0)	Phase shift	Smith (1969a)
CN A $^2\Pi$	1	7,300 ($\pm$200)	SSEI— range of v' studied	Jeunehomme (1965)
	9	6,500 ($\pm$300)		Jeunehomme (1965)
	—	3,500 ($\pm$400)	SSEI	Wentink et al. (1964)
CN B $^2\Sigma^+$	0–4	85 ($\pm$10)	Delayed coincidence	Bennett and Dalby (1962)
	0–2	59.3 ($\pm$6)	Phase shift	Liszt and Hesser (1970)
CO A $^1\Pi$	2	10.5 ($\pm$1)	Phase shift	Hesser (1968)
	0–5	$\sim$15	Delayed coincidence	Chervenak and Anderson (1971)
CO B $^1\Sigma^+$	0	25 ($\pm$4)	Phase shift	Hesser (1968)
	0	25 ($\pm$4)	Phase shift	Fink and Welge (1968)
	0	23 ($\pm$3)	Pulsed proton beam	Dotchin et al. (1973)

TABLE XII   (continued)

Molecule	v'	τ (nsec)	Method[a]	Ref.
CO C $^1\Sigma^+$	0	1.4 ($\pm$0.2)	Phase shift	Hesser (1968)
	0	2.2 ($\pm$0.8)	Pulsed proton beam	Dotchin et al. (1973)
CO b $^3\Sigma^+$	0	86 ($\pm$9)	Delayed coincidence	Schwenker (1965)
	0	800 ($\pm$200)	Phase shift	Fink and Welge (1968)
CO$^+$ A $^2\Pi$	1	2,600 ($\pm$100)	Phase shift—range of v' studied	Fink and Welge (1968)
	7	1,800 ($\pm$100)		Fink and Welge (1968)
	0–4	2,600 ($\pm$500)	Beam foil	Desquelles et al. (1968)
	1–5	2,300 ($\pm$350)	Delayed coincidence	Bennett and Dalby (1960a)
	1	3,490	Ion beam	Holland and Maier (1972)
	2	2,780	Ion beam	Holland and Maier (1972)
	4	2,630	Ion beam	Holland and Maier (1972)
	6	2,410	Ion beam	Holland and Maier (1972)
CO$^+$ B $^2\Sigma^+$	0–2	101 ($\pm$5)	Delayed coincidence	Schwenker (1965)
	0	53 ($\pm$5)	Phase shift	Hesser (1968)
	0	46 ($\pm$8)	Phase shift	Fink and Welge (1968)
	1	47 ($\pm$8)	Phase shift	Fink and Welge (1968)
	2	45 ($\pm$2)	Phase shift	Fink and Welge (1968)
	0–2	39 ($\pm$4)	Phase shift	Lawrence (1965)
	0	51 ($\pm$0.7)	Delayed coincidence	Fowler et al. (1969)
	1	52 ($\pm$2)	Delayed coincidence	Fowler et al. (1969)
	0	53.6 ($\pm$0.7)	Pulsed proton beam	Dotchin et al. (1973)
	1	64.1 ($\pm$0.8)	Pulsed proton beam	Dotchin et al. (1973)
CS A $^1\Pi$	0	255 ($\pm$25)	Phase shift	Smith (1969a)
	1	339 ($\pm$35)	Phase shift	Smith (1969a)
	2, 3, 4	292 ($\pm$30)	Phase shift	Smith (1969a)
	0	176 ($\pm$14)	Optical double resonance	Silvers and Chiu (1972)
	2	203 ($\pm$12)	Optical double resonance	Silvers and Chiu (1972)
H_2 C $^1\Pi_u$	0–3	0.6 ($\pm$0.2)	Phase shift	Hesser (1968)

TABLE XII   (continued)

Molecule	v'	τ (nsec)	Method[a]	Ref.
$H_2\ B\ ^1\Sigma_u{}^+$	3–7	0.8 (± 0.2)	Phase shift	Hesser (1968)
$I_2\ B\ ^3\Pi_{0_u+}$	14	~1000	Phase shift with optical excita-	Chutjian et al. (1967)
	25	~700	tion.	Chutjian et al. (1967).
	14	1,400	Laser single shot	Sakuri et al. (1971)
	25	900	Range of v' studied[b]	Sakuri et al. (1971)
$K_2\ B\ ^1\Pi_u$	6, 7, 8	12.4 (± 0.3)	Modulated laser phase shift	Tango and Zare (1970)
	6, 7, 8	9.7 (± 0.2)		Baumgartner et al. (1970)
$N_2\ B\ ^3\Pi_g$	3	3,300	Delayed coincidence	Johnson and Fowler (1970)
	8	4,000	Delayed coincidence	Johnson and Fowler (1970)
	0	8,000	Delayed coincidence	Jeunehomme (1966c)
	10	4,400	Delayed coincidence	Jeunehomme (1966c)
$N_2\ C\ ^3\Pi_u$	0	48 (± 8)	Phase shift	Hesser (1968)
	0	40 (± 16)	Beam foil	Desquelles et al. (1968)
	0	38 (± 2)	Delayed coincidence	Johnson and Fowler (1970)
	3	39 (± 3)	Delayed coincidence	Johnson and Fowler (1970)
	—	38	SSEI	Jeunehomme and Duncan (1964)
	—	44 (± 6)	Delayed coincidence	Bennett and Dalby (1959)
	0	40 (± 1.5)	Delayed coincidence	Calo and Axtmann (1971)
	1	44 (± 1.5)	Delayed coincidence	Calo and Axtmann (1971)
	—	49 (± 5)	Phase shift	Jeunehomme (1966a)
	0	27 (± 5)	Phase shift	Fink and Welge (1964)
	0	40.4 (± 0.5)	Pulsed proton beam	Dotchin et al. (1973)
	1	40.6 (± 0.5)	Pulsed proton beam	Dotchin et al. (1973)
	2	38.5 (± 0.6)	Pulsed proton beam	Dotchin et al. (1973)
	0	39 (± 2)	EBDC	Erman et al. (1973)
	1	38 (± 1.5)	EBDC	Erman et al. (1973)

TABLE XII (continued)

Molecule	v'	τ (nsec)	Method[a]	Ref.
$N_2 \, a \, ^1\Pi_g$	—	1.7 ($\pm$0.3) $\times 10^5$	Molecular beam	Lichten (1957)
$N_2 \, p' \, ^1\Sigma_u{}^+$	0	0.9 ($\pm$0.3)	Phase shift	Hesser (1968)
$N_2 \, E \, ^3\Sigma_g{}^+$	0	2.7 ($\pm$1) $\times 10^5$	Molecular beam	Freund (1969)
$N_2{}^+ \, A \, ^2\Pi_u$	2	12,280	Ion beam	Holland and Maier (1972)
	3	10,700	Ion beam	Holland and Maier (1972)
	4	10,080	Ion beam	Holland and Maier (1972)
	5	9,140	Ion beam	Holland and Maier (1972)
$N_2{}^+ \, B \, ^2\Sigma_u{}^+$	0	59 ($\pm$6)	Phase shift	Hesser (1968)
	0	66 ($\pm$1.4)	Beam foil	Desquelles et al. (1968)
	0	59.2 ($\pm$0.4)	Delayed coincidence	Johnson and Fowler (1970)
	1	58 ($\pm$4)	Delayed coincidence	Johnson and Fowler (1970)
	0	65 ($\pm$4)	Delayed coincidence	Bennett and Dalby (1959)
	0	45 ($\pm$4)	Phase shift	Fink and Welge (1964)
	0	71 ($\pm$5)	Phase shift	Jeunehomme (1966a)
	0	60.4 ($\pm$0.4)	Pulsed proton beam	Dotchin et. al. (1973)
	0	63 ($\pm$3)	EBDC	Erman et al. (1973)
$Na_2 \, B \, ^1\Pi_u$	6	6.5 ($\pm$0.2)	Modulated laser phase shift	Baumgartner et al. (1970)
$NH \, A \, ^3\Pi$	0, 1	455 ($\pm$90)	Phase shift	Smith (1969b)
	0, 1	425 ($\pm$60)	Delayed coincidence	Bennett and Dalby (1960b)
	0	460 ($\pm$80)	Phase shift	Fink and Welge (1964)
$NH \, c \, ^1\Pi$	0	430 ($\pm$40)	Phase shift	Fink and Welge (1964)
	0, 1	482 ($\pm$90)	Phase shift	Smith (1969b)
$NH \, d \, ^1\Sigma^+$	0	18 ($\pm$3)	Phase shift	Smith (1969b)
$NH^+ \, A \, ^2\Sigma^-$	0	1,090 ($\pm$100)	EBDC	Brzozowski et al. (1974b)
	1	1,080 ($\pm$100)	EBDC	Brzozowski et al. (1974b)
$NH^+ \, B \, ^2\Delta$	0	980 ($\pm$100)	EBDC	Brzozowski et al. (1974b)

TABLE XII   (continued)

Molecule	v'	τ (nsec)	Method[a]	Ref.
NH$^+$ C $^2\Sigma^+$	0	400 ($\pm$40)	EBDC	Brzozowski et al. (1974b)
	1	410 ($\pm$50)	EBDC	Brzozowski et al. (1974b)
	2	390 ($\pm$50)	EBDC	Brzozowski et al. (1974b)
NO A $^2\Sigma^+$	0	196 ($\pm$3)	Phase shift with optical excitation	Jeunehomme (1966d)
	0, 1	215 ($\pm$20)	Pulsed proton beam	Bubert and Froben (1971)
	0	108 ($\pm$6)	Delayed coincidence	Copeland (1972)
NO A $^2\Sigma^+$ (cont.)	1	106 ($\pm$7)	Delayed coincidence	Copeland (1972)
	2	95 ($\pm$8)	Delayed coincidence	Copeland (1972)
	1	178 ($\pm$19)	Optical double resonance	Weinstock et al. (1972)
	0	$\sim$150	Calculated from absorption	Callear and Pilling (1970)
	0	205 ($\pm$10)	EBDC	Brzozowski et al. (1974a)
	1	200 ($\pm$7)	EBDC	Brzozowski et al. (1974a)
	2	195 ($\pm$7)	EBDC	Brzozowski et al. (1974a)
NO D $^2\Sigma^+$	0	18.4 ($\pm$4)	Phase shift	Hesser (1968)
	1	20.7 ($\pm$4)	Phase shift	Hesser (1968)
	0	26 ($\pm$1)	EBDC	Brzozowski et al. (1974a)
	1	26.5 ($\pm$1.5)	EBDC	Brzozowski et al. (1974a)
	0	20	Calculated from absorption	Callear and Pilling (1970)
NO B $^2\Pi$	0	3,100 ($\pm$600)	SSEI	Jeunehomme and Duncan (1964)
	1	2,300 ($\pm$300)	SSEI	Jeunehomme and Duncan (1964)
	2	2,200 ($\pm$400)	SSEI	Jeunehomme and Duncan (1964)
	0	1,985 ($\pm$150)	EBDC	Brzozowski et al. (1974a)
	1	1,780 ($\pm$150)	EBDC	Brzozowski et al. (1974a)
	4	1,650 ($\pm$150)	EBDC	Brzozowski et al. (1974a)
NO B' $^2\Delta$	0	75 ($\pm$10)	EBDC	Brzozowski et al. (1974a)

TABLE XII   (continued)

Molecule	v'	τ (nsec)	Method[a]	Ref.
Migeotte 2nd	0	23.6 (± 2)	EBDC	Brzozowski et al. (1974a)
	1	25.5 (± 2)	EBDC	Brzozowski et al. (1974a)
NO^+ A $^1\Pi$	0	56 (± 6)	Phase shift	Hesser (1968)
O_2^+ A $^2\Pi_u$	0–6	660 (± 70)	Phase shift	Jeunehomme (1966b)
	—	710 (± 60)	Phase shift	Fink and Welge (1968)
O_2^+ b $^4\Sigma_g^-$	0	1,120 (± 40)	Phase shift	Jeunehomme (1966b)
	1	1,100 (± 50)	Phase shift	Jeunehomme (1966b)
	2	1,220 (± 40)	Phase shift	Jeunehomme (1966b)
	0	1,200 (± 100)	Phase shift	Fink and Welge (1968)
	1	1,240 (± 100)	Phase shift	Fink and Welge (1968)
	2	1,300 (± 120)	Phase shift	Fink and Welge (1968)
	0–2	1,130 (± 80)	EBDC	Erman et al. (1973)
OH A $^2\Sigma^+$	0	1,000	Delayed coincidence	Bennett and Dalby (1964)
	0	850 (± 130)	Phase shift	Smith (1970)
	1	730 (± 115)	Phase shift	Smith (1970)
	2	550 (± 85)	Phase shift	Smith (1970)
	0	820 (± 50)	Dye laser excitation	Becker et al. (1974a)
OH^+ A $^3\Pi$	0	900 (± 150)	EBDC	Brzozowski et al. (1974b)
	1	900 (± 150)	EBDC	Brzozowski et al. (1974b)
	3	980 (± 100)	EBDC	Brzozowski et al. (1974b)
PH A $^3\Pi$	0	440 (± 50)	Phase shift	Fink and Welge (1964)
S_2 B $^3\Sigma_u^-$	0–3	16.9 (± 3.5)	Phase shift	Smith (1969a)
SH^+ A $^3\Pi$	0	1090 (± 70)	EBDC	Brzozowski et al. (1974b)
SiH A $^2\Delta$	0, 1	700 (± 100)	Phase shift	Smith (1969b)
SO B $^3\Sigma^-$	0	17.3 (± 3.3)	Phase shift	Smith (1969a)
	1	16.6 (± 3.3)	Phase shift	Smith (1969a)
	2	16.2 (± 3.3)	Phase shift	Smith (1969a)
CH_2O $\tilde{A}$ $^1A''$	—	~ 200	SSEI	Jeunehomme and Duncan (1964)
	—	27 (± 2)	Laser optical	Sakurai et al. (1971)

TABLE XII   (continued)

Molecule	v'	τ (nsec)	Method[a]	Ref.
$C_2N_2 \, \tilde{A} \, ^1\Delta_u$	—	250 ($\pm$50)	Phase shift	Smith (1969c)
$CO_2{}^+ \, \tilde{A} \, ^2\Pi_u$	0–0	113 ($\pm$12)	Phase shift	Hesser (1968)
	—	139 ($\pm$10)	Delayed coincidence	Schwenker (1965)
	—	149 ($\pm$4)	Beam foil	Desquelles et al. (1968)
$CO_2{}^+ \, \tilde{B} \, ^2\Sigma_u{}^+$	—	118 ($\pm$12)	Phase shift	Hesser (1968)
	—	140 ($\pm$4)	Beam foil	Desquelles et al. (1968)
	—	139 ($\pm$10)	Delayed coincidence	Schwenker (1965)
$CS_2{}^+ \, \tilde{B}^2 \, ^2\Sigma_u{}^+$	—	249 ($\pm$30)	Phase shift	Smith (1969c)
$HgNH_3{}^* \, A_2$	0–0	1,860 ($\pm$100)	Phase shift	Freeman et al. (1971a)
		1,820 ($\pm$200)	Optical flash	Koskikallio et al. (1971)
$H_2O{}^+ \, ^2A_1$	Range	$\sim$800	EBDC	Erman and Brzozowski (1973)
$N_2O{}^+ \, \tilde{A} \, ^2\Sigma^+$	—	$\sim$200	Phase shift	Smith (1969c)
$N_2O{}^+ \, \tilde{B} \, ^2\Sigma^+$	0–0	232 ($\pm$20)	Phase shift	Fink and Welge (1968)
	—	260 ($\pm$20)	Delayed coincidence	Dayton et al. (1960)
$SO_2 \, \tilde{A} \, ^1B_1$	—	12.2 ($\pm$2.5)	Phase shift	Smith (1969c)
$SO_2 \, a \, ^3B_1$	—	7 ($\pm$1) $\times 10^6$	SSEI	Caton and Duncan (1968)

[a] EBDC = electron beam delayed coincidence. SSEI = single-shot electron impact.
[b] See Table XIII.

In the listing of Table XII, some measurements have been ignored where the same research group subsequently published improved data, and other measurements have been ignored where it is reasonably obvious that they are inaccurate. In Table XII it can be noted that although various experimental techniques have frequently yielded concordant results for the lifetimes of electronically excited molecules, in many cases serious disagreement still exists. The $CO^+ \, B \, ^2\Sigma^+$ and $N_2 \, C \, ^3\Pi_u$ have been studied by several groups, with quite close agreement of derived mean lifetimes. A curious disagreement occurs for $C_2 \, A \, ^3\Pi_g$, where the technique of irradiating a graphite target with a laser pulse yielded lifetimes some 3.5 times greater than that obtained by the phase shift method. It seems possible

that the laser method has yielded the time constant for the production of
C_2 A $^3\Pi_g$ rather than its radiative lifetime. Several measurements indicate
the occurrence of predissociation of the excited states. It appears that the
decreasing lifetime of OH A $^2\Sigma^+$ with vibrational quantum number is due
to predissociation. The laser experiments with Br_2 and I_2 were conducted
over a wide range of vibrational levels and the iodine results are discussed in
detail below. Both excited molecules undergo spontaneous predissociation.
The laser experiment with CH_2O was conducted at 3371 Å (N_2 laser); the
absorption oscillator strength corresponds to a radiative lifetime
of 10^4 nsec, and the laser experiment clearly indicates control of the
Ã $^1A_2$ lifetime by predissociation at this wavelength. The single-shot
measurements with electron impact were made on CH_2O (Ã $^1A_2$) in low
vibrational levels and no variation was found with vibrational quantum
number in the low levels. The results with CS A $^1\Pi$ are unusual, where the
$v' = 0, 2, 3, 4$ levels have a similar lifetime, with the $v' = 1$ state being
significantly longer lived. This state is strongly perturbed and it is tempting
to suggest that the two effects are interrelated.

The lifetime of NO A $^2\Sigma^+$ is still uncertain, especially in view of the
recent measurements of Copeland (1972). It is important in relation to the
determination of the nitric oxide concentration in the Earth's atmosphere by
the fluorescence method. Copeland claims that earlier measurements are
complicated by cascading, though in Jeunehomme's (1966d) work the
excitation was achieved optically, with the light filtered to allow population
only of NO A $^2\Sigma^+(v=0)$; it is difficult to see how his measurements can
be in error by a factor of two. Optical double resonance (Hanle effect)
yields a lifetime which is consistent with Jeunehomme's measurement. A
radiative lifetime of 215 nsec is found using Bethke's (1959) absorption
oscillator strength for the (0, 0) γ band, assuming that the electronic
transition moment is the same for all bands. However, there appears to be
considerable variation of the electronic transition moment with the nuclear
separation (Callear et al., 1966) and if this is taken into account, a lifetime of
~150 nsec is derived (Callear and Pilling, 1970). Notwithstanding Copeland's results, it is highly probable that the lifetime of NO A $^2\Sigma^+$ lies in the
range 180 ($\pm$20) nsec.

The earlier measurements of Smith (1971) on CH$^+$ A $^1\Pi$ appear to be in
error because of contamination by impurities.

The radiative lifetime of CO a $^3\Pi$ is a function of the rotational quantum
number (Johnson and Van Dyck, 1972). Its rate of collisional relaxation
has been investigated by Slanger and Black (1971).

C. Collisional Relaxation Processes of Electronically Excited
   Molecules Exemplified by the Systems of Nitric Oxide

In this subsection, methods of analysis of collisional quenching rates will
be described briefly, and also methods of comparing predissociation rates
with emission rates. These aspects will be exemplified by the systems of
nitric oxide with which the author is familiar (Callear and Smith, 1964;
Callear and Pilling, 1970).

The potential diagram of NO is shown in Fig. 32. The A $^2\Sigma^+$ state lies

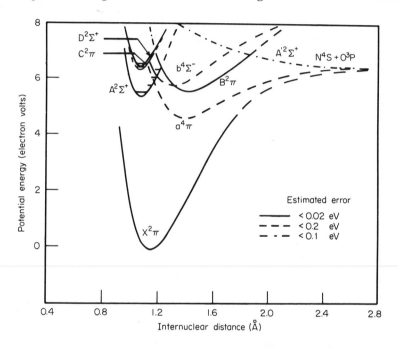

Fig. 32.   Potential diagram of nitric oxide. (Callear and Pilling, 1970).

below the dissociation limit (in vibrational levels accessible by optical
excitation from the ground state) and is conveniently excited with light
from a xenon arc. The xenon arc is a "blackbody" source with a temperature
of ∼8000°K. The advantage of using a blackbody rather than a line source
is that at low pressure the lines have a Doppler profile and the system can be
exactly defined mathematically since there is negligible variation of light
intensity over a particular band. Light from the xenon arc was focused with
a high-aperture lens system into a Wood's horn containing NO + added

gases, and the fluorescence was observed normal to the direction of excitation with a monochromator–photomultiplier combination, following probing plates to identify the various bands.

Considering first excitation only to NO A $^2\Sigma^+(v=0)$, which can easily be achieved with a light filter, rate coefficients for its relaxation in collision were measured relative to the spontaneous emission rate by the following procedure. The state is not significantly deactivated by large pressures of Ar and it was convenient to work with a large excess of the inert gas to which small partial pressures of quenching gases were added. Thereby the line shape is held constant in a series of related experiments. In the case of added CO_2, the processes are

$$\text{NO X}\,^2\Pi + h\nu \longrightarrow \text{NO A}\,^2\Sigma^+$$

$$\text{NO A}\,^2\Sigma^+ \xrightarrow{k_f} \text{NO X}\,^2\Pi + h\nu$$

$$\text{NO A}\,^2\Sigma^+ + \text{NO X}\,^2\Pi \xrightarrow{k_{NO}} \text{NO X}\,^2\Pi + \text{NO a}\,^4\Pi$$

$$\text{NO A}\,^2\Sigma^+ + CO_2 \xrightarrow{k_{CO_2}} \text{NO X}\,^2\Pi + CO_2.$$

From the stationary state equations,

$$I_0/I = 1 + k_{CO_2}[CO_2](k_f + k_{NO}[NO])^{-1},$$

where I_0 is the intensity of the fluorescence in the absence of CO_2. Thus Stern–Volmer plots of I_0/I versus $[CO_2]$ should be linear and the CO_2 "quenching half-pressure" occurs when

$$k_{CO_2}[CO_2] = k_f + k_{NO}[NO].$$

Such behavior was found experimentally and the CO_2 quenching half-pressures $(k_f + k_{NO}[NO])/k_{CO_2}$ were shown to be linearly dependent on $[NO]$, as shown in Fig. 33. The results are invariant, or very nearly so, with respect to the argon pressure. From the slope and intercept of Fig. 33, k_{CO_2}/k_f and k_{NO}/k_f were determined. From the k_f^{-1} of Table XII, the absolute rate coefficients for collisional deactivation can be derived.

When NO is excited with light from a xenon arc with no filter, the D $^2\Sigma^+(v=0)$, C $^2\Pi(v=0)$, and A $^2\Sigma^+(v=0, 1, 2, 3)$ states are populated. A detailed study of the fluorescence from the various states has revealed complex kinetic behavior, involving several collisional cascade processes. A schematic illustration of reactions which occur in $NO/Ar/N_2$ mixtures is

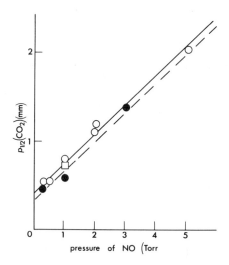

FIG. 33.   Deactivation of NO A $^2\Sigma^+(v=0)$ by NO and CO_2. A plot of the CO_2 quench-ing half-pressure versus [NO]. ○, 450 Torr Ar. ●, 100 Torr Ar. □, 450 Torr N_2. (Callear and Smith, 1964.)

shown in Fig. 34. Some of the main conclusions are briefly summarized as follows:

1. The D $^2\Sigma^+(v=0)$ state does not undergo spontaneous predissociation to any significant extent. This was established by observing the fluores-cence at very low pressures of NO and comparing the intensity of the emission with that from A $^2\Sigma^+(v=3)$ (below the dissociation limit) after division by the rates of light absorption calculated from the oscillator strengths. Furthermore, the lifetime of D $^2\Sigma^+(v=0)$ calculated from the absorption oscillator strength is 20 nsec, in good agreement with the direct lifetime measurement (Table XII). Emission from D $^2\Sigma^+(v=0)$ is quenched by low pressures (~10 Torr) of He and Ar, which is due to collisional deactivation to C $^2\Pi(v=0)$. This was established by observing emission from NO C $^2\Pi(v=0)$ without and with an ethylene filter which largely prevented population of NO D $^2\Sigma^+(v=0)$. The efficiency of the D → C deactivation was shown to be close to unity; there is negligible collisionally induced predissociation. Deactivation of NO D $^2\Sigma^+(v=0)$ by N_2 produces N_2 A $^3\Sigma_u{}^+(v=0, 1)$. The reactions associated with quenching of NO D $^2\Sigma^+(v=0)$ by NO X $^2\Pi(v=0)$ are unknown.

2. The emission from NO C $^2\Pi(v=0)$ undergoes a partial quenching in the 1 Torr of Ar pressure range; from 10 to 1000 Torr of Ar no addi-tional effect occurs. There is negligible collisionally induced predissociation.

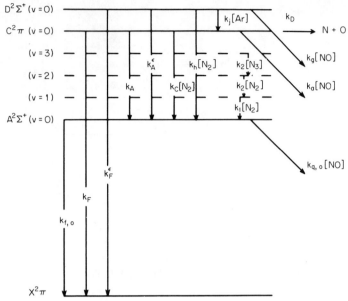

FIG. 34. Spontaneous and collisional processes in NO/Ar/N_2 mixtures (Callear and Pilling, 1970).

It appears that the partial quenching occurs because a few levels of NO C $^2\Pi(v=0)$ lie below the dissociation limit; in a high pressure of Ar, rotational equilibrium is maintained; collisions cause rotational transitions which indirectly increase the rate of predissociation. In the presence of a high pressure of Ar, NO C $^2\Pi(v=0)$ predissociates $\sim$30 times more rapidly than it radiates to NO X $^2\Pi$. This was established by three methods:

(a) Comparison with the D $^2\Sigma^+(v=0)$ and A $^2\Sigma^+$ emissions after division by the rates of light absorption calculated from the oscillator strengths.

(b) By measuring the enhancement of the C $^2\Pi(v=0)$ emission when a known rate of cascade relaxation into that state from NO D $^2\Sigma^+(v=0)$ was occurring.

(c) By observing the enhancement of the NO A $^2\Sigma^+$ emission when essentially all the NO C $^2\Pi(v=0)$ is quenched to NO A $^2\Sigma^+$ by addition of a large excess of N_2.

Deactivation of NO C $^2\Pi(v=0)$ to NO A $^2\Sigma^+$ involves the intermediacy of N_2 A $^3\Sigma_u^+(v=0, 1)$, and the roles of the two quantum states can be evaluated by the method detailed in Section IV,C. Absolute relaxation rates for NO C $^2\Pi(v=0)$ can be deduced by calculating the emission rate from the absorption oscillator strength.

3. NO A $^2\Sigma^+(v \neq 0)$ undergoes rapid vibrational relaxation in N_2 because the two species have almost exactly the same vibrational frequency. Quenching of NO A $^2\Sigma^+$ by NO X $^2\Pi$ produces NO a $^4\Pi$ though the absolute yield is not yet known.

Rate coefficients for most of these processes were listed by Callear and Pilling (1970).

Rotational relaxation of NO A $^2\Sigma^+$ was studied by Broida and Carrington (1963), by populating a single rotational level in the $v = 1$ state with the Cd line at 2144 Å. At low pressure, essentially only a single line in each branch of the bands was observed in emission. Addition of Ar or N_2 caused a spreading of the branches due to collisionally induced rotational transitions. It was shown that $\Delta J = \pm 5$ jumps occurred in single collision events. Self-quenching and quenching of NO A $^2\Sigma^+$ by O_2 have been investigated by Melton and Klemperer (1971).

D. Predissociation and Collisional Relaxation of I_2 B $^3\Pi_{0u+}$

The B $^3\Pi_{0u+}$ state of I_2, the upper level of the main system, has perhaps received more attention than any other electronically excited molecule. It has long been established that with $v' \geq 7$, the molecule undergoes collisionally induced predissociation. Many studies have also been reported of vibrational and rotational relaxation in collision. However, only quite recently has it been realized that the B $^3\Pi_{0u+}$ state also undergoes spontaneous predissociation. That this aspect remained undiscovered for so long emphasizes the difficulty of detecting and measuring the rate of a forbidden predissociation. Spontaneous predissociation of I_2 B $^3\Pi_{0u+}$ is now well established from three different types of experiment. First, Wassermann et al. (1968) used electron paramagnetic resonance spectroscopy to monitor the ground-state atom concentration produced by irradiation in the banded region of the main system. The experiments were conducted at low pressures, and the main objective appears to have been a study of magnetically induced predissociation. However, atoms were detected at very low pressures in the absence of a large field, and it was concluded that spontaneous predissociation is one of the main relaxation processes of the B $^3\Pi_{0u+}$ state.

The second piece of experimental evidence was found by Chutjian and James (1969), who made a careful study of the intensities of the lines of various bands of the B $^3\Pi_{0u+}$–X $^1\Sigma_g^+$ system in absorption, with very high dispersion. From the observed " curves of growth," oscillator strengths were measured. Using known Franck–Condon factors, the radiative lifetimes were then computed; the calculated lifetimes were found to be approximately twice those observed directly by Chutjian *et al.* (1967) by the phase shift method and optical excitation. Sakurai *et al.* (1971) have published a set of lifetime measurements obtained with a tuned dye laser pumped with an N_2 laser (2-nsec pulses). Their results are listed in Table XIII, where the emission rates have been calculated from the results of Chutjian and James (1969).

TABLE XIII

COMPARISON OF EXPERIMENTAL RECIPROCAL MEAN LIFETIMES OF THE
v' STATES OF I_2 B $^3\Pi_{0_u+}$ WITH THE CALCULATED (FROM THE f VALUES)
SPONTANEOUS EMISSION RATES[a] (Sakurai *et al.*, 1971)

v'	Observed decay rate (10^5 sec^{-1})	Calculated emission rate (10^5 sec^{-1})	Predissociation rate (10^5 sec^{-1})
0	6.7	6.3	0.4 $\pm$ 4.0
3	14.6	6.1	8.5 $\pm$ 2
4	18.9	6.0	12.9 $\pm$ 3
5	16.1	5.9	10.2 $\pm$ 3
6	11.0	5.9	5.1 $\pm$ 1
7	8.4	5.9	2.5 $\pm$ 3.5
8	9.1	5.9	3.2 $\pm$ 2
9	7.4	5.8	1.6 $\pm$ 2
10	6.8	5.8	1.0 $\pm$ 1.5
11	6.4	5.7	0.7 $\pm$ 1
12	6.6	5.6	0.95 $\pm$ 1
13	6.6	5.6	1 $\pm$ 1
14	7.0	5.5	1.5 $\pm$ 0.7
17	7.5	5.3	2.2 $\pm$ 1
20	11.1	5.1	6.0 $\pm$ 3.2
24	11.5	4.9	6.6 $\pm$ 2.1
25	10.9	4.8	6.1 $\pm$ 0.8

[a] Refinements of these data have been reported recently (Capelle and Broida, 1972, 1973; Shotton and Chapman, 1972; Chapman and Bunker, 1972).

The third piece of evidence was discovered by Busch *et al.* (1969). Laser radiation at 5310 Å (second harmonic of an Nd-glass laser) was crossed with an I_2 beam, and production of $I(5\ ^2P_{3/2})$ at the intersection was detected with a mass spectrometer:

$$I_2 + h\nu(5310\ \text{Å}) \longrightarrow 2I(5\ ^2P_{3/2}).$$

The production of two atoms in the $^2P_{3/2}$ state was demonstrated by the flight time to the detector.

Chutjian (1969) has performed some calculations of the I_2 B $^3\Pi_{0u^+}$ predissociation rate and concluded that the link over to two I (5 $^2P_{3/2}$) is a 1_u state interacting near the small r turning points. See also LeRoy (1970).

A detailed study of the vibrational and rotational relaxation of I_2 B $^3\Pi_{0u^+}(v = 15)$ (Na D lines) and $(v = 25)$ (Hg green line) was reported by Steinfeld and Klemperer (1965). It was shown that in the heavy molecule, with a high density of rotational levels, many rotational quanta are transferred in a single collision event. However, the rotational distributions were still nonstatistical after collision; in He, H_2, HD, and D_2 some persistence of the initial rotational states was observed even following $\Delta v = -1$ vibrational transitions, but not following $\Delta v = -2$ transitions, which presumably require a harder interaction. Steinfeld and Schweid (1970) have shown that as the vibrational ladder is ascended to within a few kcal of the convergence limit at 4995 Å, the quenching cross sections become abnormally large, which they attributed to the onset of collisional release, i.e., the endothermic dissociation to I(5 $^2P_{1/2}$) + I(5 $^2P_{3/2}$) discussed in Section II,C,1.

Other small molecules which have been studied in some detail by fluorescence are HD (Atkins et al., 1970), NO_2 (Schwartz and Johnston, 1969), and K_2 (Tango and Zare, 1970). Okabe (for example Okabe, 1970) has conducted an extensive survey of the formation of electronically excited molecules in vacuum-ultraviolet photolysis.

VII. Relaxation Studies of Reaction Rates Following Electrical Discharge in a Static Gas

A. Introduction

A comprehensive treatment of this large subject is beyond the scope of this review. Rather a few examples are chosen to illustrate different experimental approaches, confined almost entirely to true relaxation methods in which a static gas is subjected to a transient disturbance. In an electrical discharge most of the current is carried by the electrons. Because of their small mass compared to that of molecules, the energy of the electrons is largely converted to internal energy of the molecules, rather than to translational energy, so that at the termination of a pulsed discharge the electronically excited levels tend to be overpopulated with respect to the translational temperature, and also free radicals may be produced if fragmentation follows electronic excitation. The mechanism of vibrational excitation can be considered to result from the change of equilibrium separation associated with transient negative ion formation.

Excitation of gases by electron impact is, however, less specific than optical excitation, which leads to problems of gas heating if the electron pulse is sufficiently powerful to produce transients at a concentration suitable for spectroscopic detection. If there is a gross change of temperature, it is difficult to measure the change accurately; consequently any derived rate coefficients have little significance and certainly have no permanent value. Because of this difficulty with gas heating, relaxation measurements with pulsed electrode discharges have been largely confined to studies of the inert gases. The metastable states of the atoms are long-lived and cause detectable luminescence late in the afterglow when present at very low concentration. Also, the oscillator strengths of individual atomic lines are often large. Thus a number of fruitful experiments have been conducted with pulsed electrode discharges in He, at levels of power which were generally too small to change significantly the bulk temperature. Furthermore, homogeneous glow-type discharges can be produced at quite high pressures ($\sim$100 Torr) in the inert gases moderately easily with a two-electrode arrangement. Two techniques are available for more general application of electron impact to relaxation measurements, pulsed radiolysis and microwave-pulse flash spectroscopy. Both techniques can employ gas pressures of $\sim\frac{1}{2}$ atm and optical path lengths of the order of 1 m for absorption measurements.

B. The Helium Discharge and Afterglow

The processes which occur in the helium discharge and afterglow are complex but we shall attempt to outline as simply as possible some reactions that appear to be reasonably well established. Atomic helium has two states which are optically metastable, $He(2\,^1S_0)$ and $He(2\,^3S_1)$. The former is known to decay by two-photon emission at a rate of 50 sec^{-1} (Van Dyke et al., 1970), but in a plasma it is generally removed more rapidly by collisional processes, especially the superelastic conversion to the triplet by electrons:

$$He(2\,^1S_0) + e \longrightarrow He(2\,^3S_1) + e + \text{kinetic energy}.$$

Also with a dominant role in the discharge is He_2 a $^3\Sigma_u{}^+$.

When helium is subjected to electrical discharge, the $He(n\ ^1P_1)$ states are produced efficiently since the transitions from the ground state are allowed by the electric dipole selection rules. Atoms can also be promoted directly to the ionization continuum,

$$He(1\ ^1S_0) + e \longrightarrow He^+ + 2e.$$

At very low pressures the latter would be the main source of ionization, and the $He(n\ ^1P_1)$ would radiate to populate $He(2\ ^1S_0)$ and the ground state. At the steady state, the main ion loss process would be

$$He^+ + 2e \longrightarrow He^* + e,$$

where He^* corresponds to singlets and triplets, mainly with principle quantum numbers ≤ 10 (300°K), which radiate (Collins and Hurt, 1968). Such a consecutive process is called collisional radiative recombination (Bates and Kingston, 1964). At the steady state the $He(2\ ^3S_1)$ would reach a quasi-equilibrium concentration, balanced by formation largely in radiative processes and loss by excitation by electron impact.

At moderate pressures, >10 Torr, the chemistry of the discharge changes. The $He(n\ ^1P_1)$ with $n \geq 3$ can undergo Hornbeck–Molnar processes,

$$He^* + He \longrightarrow He_2^+ + e$$

and this must become the main source of ionization in a discharge at high pressure. DeCorpo and Lampe (1969) reported rate coefficients of $\sim$2–4 $\times 10^{-9}\ cm^3\ sec^{-1}$ for such reactions.

It appears that $He_2^+(v = 0)$ cannot undergo dissociative recombination and it may be forbidden because of the Franck–Condon principle (Mulli-kan, 1970); therefore the Hornbeck–Molnar processes must produce He_2^+ vibrationally excited. In a steady-state discharge there must exist a range of vibrational levels of the ion, though the distribution and relaxation mechanisms are totally unknown. High vibrational levels lead to neutraliza-tion by dissociative recombination while $He_2^+(v = 0)$ undergoes collisional radiative recombination to produce He_2^* which, if triplet, ultimately populates $He_2\ a\ ^3\Sigma_u^+(v = 0)$. Collisional radiative recombination of $He_2^+(v = 0)$ should cause little disturbance of the nuclear separation, to populate predominantly $He_2^*(v = 0)$. In fact collisional radiative recom-bination of $He_2^+(v = 0)$ is slow during a discharge because the electrons are hot (like most three-body processes, the reaction exhibits a negative temperature coefficient) and the molecular emission occurs largely in the early afterglow.

One of the outstanding contributions to the chemical physics of the helium afterglow can be found in the work of Phelps (1955). Helium at up to 100 Torr was repetitively pulsed with an electroded discharge, and the concentrations of $He(2\ ^1S_0)$, $He(2\ ^3S_1)$, and He_2 a $^3\Sigma_u{}^+(v=0)$ were monitored in the afterglow by kinetic absorption spectroscopy. A pulse sampling technique was employed in which a photomultiplier was gated open at particular time delays. Thereby it was possible to measure absorptions of $\sim 1\%$ to an accuracy of about 1%. The electron concentration was also determined by positioning the reaction cell inside a microwave cavity and determining the shift of the resonance frequency due to the presence of electrons. The initial concentration of $He(2\ ^3S_1)$ was $\sim 1.5 \times 10^{11}$ cm^{-3}. Phelps concluded that $He(2\ ^1S_0)$ is lost by diffusion to the walls, by electron conversion to $He(2\ ^3S_1)$ (cross section 3×10^{-14} cm^2), and in bimolecular collisions with $He(1\ ^1S_0)$ (cross section 3×10^{-20} cm^2). The nature of the latter process was not identified. $He(2\ ^3S_1)$ was shown to be lost by wall diffusion and also in the reaction

$$He(2\ ^3S_1) + 2He(1\ ^1S_0) \longrightarrow He_2\ a\ ^3\Sigma_u{}^+ + He(1\ ^1S_0)$$

(rate coefficient 2.5×10^{-34} cm^6 atom^{-2} sec^{-1} at $300°$K). A corresponding increase in the He_2 a $^3\Sigma_u{}^+(v=0)$ was observed in the early afterglow (≤ 1 msec) though at the earliest time of observation the He_2 a $^3\Sigma_u{}^+(v=0)$ was already $\sim 80\%$ of the maximum. In these experiments most of the He_2 a $^3\Sigma_u{}^+(v=0)$ is probably produced from $He_2{}^+(v=0)$ immediately at the pulse termination. Phelps showed that at low pressures the He_2 a $^3\Sigma_u{}^+$ loss was exponential in the late afterglow corresponding to wall diffusion. At 97 Torr, the decay was no longer exponential, indicating loss processes due to metastable–metastable interaction. The diffusivities of the three metastable species were measured.

Ludlum et al. (1967), with a technique similar to that of Phelps, could not detect the three-body formation of He_2 a $^3\Sigma_u{}^+(v=0)$ from $He(2\ ^3S_1)$ at $77°$K, and an activation energy of 0.067 eV was determined for the reaction. This can be identified with the height of a potential barrier between $He(2\ ^3S_1)$ and $He(1\ ^1S_0)$. They estimated a rate coefficient of 2.3×10^{-9} cm^3 sec^{-1} for loss of metastables in metastable–metastable collisions.

He_2^+ is believed to be the dominant ion in the helium discharge at moderate pressures and 300°K. The reaction

$$He^+ + 2He(1\ ^1S_0) \longrightarrow He_2^+ + He(1\ ^1S_0)$$

has been investigated several times. Smith and Copsey (1968) measured the rate by sampling ions from an afterglow at 0.3–2 Torr into a mass spectrometer. The rate coefficient was expressed as 85 ($\pm$3) Torr^{-2} sec^{-1} at 295°K. Thus with [He] = 100 Torr, the relaxation time for loss of He^+ by this reaction is $\sim 10^{-6}$ sec. At low temperatures, He_3^+ becomes the dominant ion (Ferguson et al., 1968) and even He_4^+ has been detected (de Vries and Oskam, 1969).

Collins and Hurt (1969) reported a detailed study of the processes which occur in the late afterglow of a helium discharge at 3 Torr. Intensity–time profiles following repetitive pulsing were recorded with a multichannel analyzer. The predominant active species in the late afterglow was shown to be He_2 a $^3\Sigma_u^+$ and atomic emission was attributed to

$$2He_2\ a\ ^3\Sigma_u^+ \longrightarrow He^+ + 3He(1\ ^1S_0) + e$$
$$He^+ + e + M \longrightarrow He^* + M.$$

However, most of the He^+ reformed He_2^+ by three-body attachment, resulting in molecular light emission. It seems to be clear from these experiments that He_2^+ does undergo collisional radiative recombination; otherwise it would be very difficult to understand how molecular emission could occur at low pressure and long delay times ($\sim$50 msec). There remains, however, the possibility that under these conditions the dominant ion is in fact He_3^+, which could be precursor of the bimolecular emission (Gusinow et al., 1970). The arguments against dissociative recombination of $He_2^+(v=0)$ had previously been detailed by Ferguson et al. (1965), who pointed out that the "stability" of the molecular ion is the reason why the electronic states of He_2 are so well characterized (the spectra are easily excited) whereas analogous spectra of the other inert gases are practically unknown.

Because of the accumulation of $He_2^+(v=0)$ during a helium discharge at moderate pressures, an intense spike of molecular emission is observed at the pulse termination when the electron energy falls. Huffman et al. (1965) detected molecular light emission at 810 Å with a decay constant of 4 μsec, following a pulsed discharge in helium at 45 Torr and 300°K.

The emission occurred from the $A\,^1\Sigma_u{}^+$ and $D\,^1\Sigma_u{}^+$ to the nonbonded $X\,^1\Sigma_g{}^+$ ground state. A number of investigators have found similar behavior with the triplet molecular emission. For example, Villarejo *et al.* (1965) found that the decay of the emission fell off exponentially in the early afterglow with a time constant dependent on pressure but comparable to that of Huffman *et al.* for the same pressure regime.

The formation of He_2 a $^3\Sigma_u{}^+(v = 0, 1)$ at the termination of a single-shot microwave discharge has been recorded photographically, as shown in

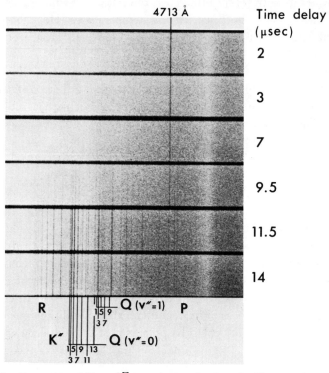

FIG. 35. Formation of He_2 a $^3\Sigma_u{}^+$ at the termination of a 10-μsec microwave pulse. 300°K and 150 Torr. Only the Q lines are marked to indicate clearly the production of the $v'' = 0$ and 1 states. (Callear and Hedges, 1970c.)

Fig. 35 (Callear and Hedges, 1970c). The spectra were obtained by microwave-pulse flash spectroscopy in which a reaction cell, length 50 cm and internal diameter 5 mm, was subjected to a single shot of microwave radiation at ~100 kW for 10 μsec. Absorption spectra were taken during and following the discharge with an electronically delayed Lyman flash. The rate coefficient for vibrational relaxation of He_2 a $^3\Sigma_u{}^+(v = 1)$ by

He($1\,^1S_0$) was recorded as $3 \times 10^{-15}\,cm^3\,sec^{-1}$ at 300°K, corresponding to about 8×10^4 collisions. A curious aspect of these experiments was the detection of rotationally hot He_2 a $^3\Sigma_u{}^+(v=0)$ in absorption with gas pressures of ~300 Torr at 300°K, as shown in Fig. 36. At the short delay

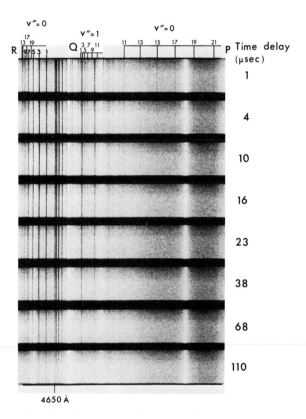

FIG. 36. Relaxation of He_2 a $^3\Sigma_u{}^+$ following a 2-μsec microwave pulse. 300°K and 300 Torr. For clarity only R and P lines of ($v=0$) are marked, and the Q lines of ($v=1$). (Callear and Hedges, 1970c.)

times, levels up to $K=23$ were detected. At long delay times, the populations tended toward a Boltzmann distribution due to the occurrence of rotational relaxation. The same experiment at 77°K showed very little rotational relaxation over the period of observation of about 200 μsec. It appears that the rotation of He_2 a $^3\Sigma_u{}^+$ is only weakly coupled to translation in collision with He, which implies that the surfaces of equipotential are very nearly spherical about the center of the diatomic molecule. A plot of

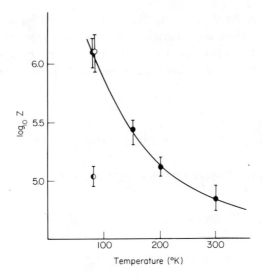

FIG. 37.   Dependence of the number of gas-kinetic collisions Z for overall rotational relaxation on the gas temperature. ●, $^4He_2$. ○, $^3He_2$. ◑, $^3He^4He$. (Callear and Hedges, 1970c.)

$\log_{10} Z$ (number of collisions for overall rotational relaxation) versus temperature is shown in Fig. 37.

Collins and Johnson (1972) reported a study of the rotational relaxation of He_2 3p $^3\Pi_g$ in $J = 8$, which was excited from the lowest triplet with a tuned dye laser. The rate coefficient for relaxation was recorded as 2×10^{-11} cm^3 molecule^{-1} sec^{-1}, very considerably faster than in the a $^3\Sigma_u^+$ state. With the outer electron in a p orbital, the potential surfaces are no longer spherically symmetric.

It is known that He(n $^1P_1$) can undergo intersystem crossing on collision with He(1 $^1S_0$):

$$He + n\,^1P \longrightarrow He + n\,^3D.$$

It was shown by Pendleton and Hughes (1965) that this involves a collisional transition to the nF states, which have mixed singlet–triplet character:

$$n\,^1P_1 + He \longrightarrow nF + He$$

$$nF + He \longrightarrow n\,^3D + He.$$

They employed a repetitively pulsed discharge with a time sampling oscilloscope, and measured directly the rate of cascading into the n ^3D states.

The reader may have concluded that the helium discharge is a complex system. The above brief outline of what appear to be established features may stimulate exploration of the subject at greater depth.

C. KINETIC PROCESSES IN THE Ne, Ar, AND Kr DISCHARGES

A definitive study of the behavior of metastable atoms in a neon discharge was reported by Phelps (1959). The first excited states have the configuration $1s^2 2s^2 2p^5 3s$, corresponding to $^1P_1$ and $^3P_{0,1,2}$ in the Russell–Saunders notation. The $^1P_1$ and $^3P_1$ states are mixed and because of its partial singlet character, the latter radiates to the ground state. Electrons with $n > 2$ are only weakly coupled to the $n = 1, 2$ core in the neon atom and the total electronic orbital angular momentum is not a constant of the motion; frequently the Paschen notation is used to designate the states: $Ne(3\ ^1P_1) \equiv 1s_2$, $Ne(3\ ^3P_0) \equiv 1s_3$, $Ne(3\ ^3P_1) \equiv 1s_4$, $Ne(3\ ^3P_2) \equiv 1s_5$.

Phelps observed the time dependence of the concentrations of the three $Ne(3\ ^3P)$ states, by reversal of atomic lines from a neon discharge with a pulse sampling technique similar to that of his earlier work on the helium discharge. At long time delays, all three species were found to decay with the same time constant, as shown in Fig. 38. This is because a quasi-equilibrium is established among the three states which are coupled by

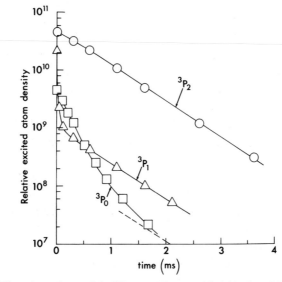

FIG. 38.   Time dependence of the ^3P states of neon with delay time following electrical discharge (Phelps, 1959; reproduced by permission of Dr. A. V. Phelps.)

collisionally induced transitions [compare with relaxation of Fe(a ^{5}D) described in Section II,G]. At high pressures the decay of the coupled set is controlled by the effective emission rate of Ne(3 ^{3}P$_1$), which was measured and found to be in agreement with that predicted from Holstein's theory. Rate coefficients for transitions between the three states were measured; for example, the rate coefficient of the process

$$Ne(3\ ^3P_1) + Ne(2\ ^1S_0) \longrightarrow Ne(3\ ^3P_2) + Ne(2\ ^1S_0)$$

was recorded as 4.2×10^{-14} cm^3 atom^{-1} sec^{-1} at 300°K. The accompanying change of internal energy is -417 cm^{-1}. The process was shown to be induced three times more rapidly with an equal concentration of He. Phelps also found evidence for wall diffusion at low pressures and termolecular removal of Ne(3 ^{3}P$_2$) (5×10^{-34} cm^6 atom^{-2} sec^{-1} at 300°K). The termolecular process presumably corresponds to Ne$_2$* formation, and showed an activation energy which was positive but smaller than that of the He(2 ^{3}S$_1$) + He(1 ^{1}S$_0$) combination, indicating a smaller potential barrier for the Ne system. Evidence for loss of metastable atoms in collision with electrons was also reported.

In a mixture of helium containing a small fraction of neon, He(2 ^{3}S$_1$) is deactivated by Ne(2 ^{1}S$_0$) to produce Ne(2s)(1s^{2}2s^{2}2p^{5}4s) because there is close energy matching. Between the 2s and 1s states are the ten 2p states (1s^{2}2s^{2}2p^{5}3p). The 2s states are longer lived with respect to emission to the 2p than are the 2p with respect to emission to the 1s. Thus it was brilliantly predicted by Javan (1959) that it should be possible to produce population inversion and to stimulate the 2s → 2p emission in a discharged He + Ne mixture. The realization of a helium–neon laser was reported later by Javan et al. (1961), who also examined carefully the relaxation processes in the early afterglow of a pulsed He–Ne mixture, to establish the mechanism. The decay of the He(2 ^{3}S$_1$) was monitored in absorption and its time profile was found to be identical to that of the Ne 2s → 2p emission. The cross section for the energy transfer process was recorded as 3.7×10^{-17} cm^2 at 300°K. It appears that a pulse sampling technique was employed.

Henderson et al. (1965) observed an emission band from He–Ne mixtures which they assigned to a transition of the HeNe molecule.

Phelps and Molnar (1953) found evidence in argon for loss of Ar(4 ^{3}P$_2$) in bimolecular and termolecular encounters with ground-state argon atoms.

The krypton discharge has been investigated in some detail by Turner (1967), by pulse sampling with a gated photomultiplier. The 1s$_4$ state was monitored via the 1236-Å resonance emission in the vacuum ultraviolet and the lifetime was shown to be consistent with Holstein's theory. The rate coefficient for the collisionally induced transition

$$1s_4 \xrightarrow{\text{Kr}} 1s_5$$

was recorded as 1.3×10^{-13} cm^3 atom^{-1} sec^{-1} (295°K), which corresponds to an internal energy change of -945 cm^{-1}; the process is faster than the analogous neon transition even though the energy change is much greater. This is presumably because the Ne(3 ^{3}P)–Ne(2 ^{1}S$_0$) interaction potential is comparatively soft because of the long-range repulsion. Turner also monitored a diffuse molecular emission from discharged krypton at $\sim$1250 Å which decayed exponentially in the afterglow, but with a time constant ten times longer than that of the $1s_4$ emission. The $1s_5$ state was shown to decay by wall diffusion, and also in two- and three-body encounters with ground-state krypton. Loss in two-body encounters was attributed to molecule formation via tunneling through a potential barrier; however, this does seem unlikely because the three-body process exhibited a negative temperature coefficient (6.9×10^{-32} cm^6 atom^{-2} sec^{-1} at 196°K and 4×10^{-32} cm^6 atom^{-2} sec^{-1} at 295°K) indicating negligible potential barrier for molecule formation. It was concluded that the molecular emission arises from both the bimolecular and termolecular loss processes of the $1s_5$ state.

Formation of atomic and diatomic ions in Ne, Ar, Kr, and Xe was reported by Kebarle et al. (1964). The gases were irradiated with α-particles from a polonium source and the ions were detected by mass spectrometry. Mullikan (1970) has reviewed the properties of the inert gas neutral molecules and ions.

In conclusion, it appears that some of the most interesting of chemical reactions occur in the "inert gases." However, even in the helium system, which has been extensively studied, many mysteries remain. What are the roles of the He$_2^+$ and He$_3^+$ ions in an actual discharge, in terms of their particular quantum states? Why is He$_2$ a $^3\Sigma_u^+(v = 0)$ formed rotationally hot at the termination of a discharge?

D. RELAXATION FOLLOWING THE PULSED RADIOLYSIS OF GASES

Relaxation measurements following pulsed radiolysis of gases are beginning to yield very interesting results and the experiment is capable of nanosecond time resolution. Most experimentalists use a reaction cell with a length of approximately 10 cm, a multiple-pass optical arrangement, and a continuous background source for kinetic absorption spectroscopy. The production of transient species is thereby monitored photoelectrically on single shot.

It appears that the first successful experiment was reported by Sauer and Dorfman (1964). The triplet state of naphthalene was observed following irradiation with a 0.4–5-μsec, 15-MeV electron pulse (linear accelerator) through a thin aluminum window. Two distinct decay rates were observed, one with a time constant of 3–6 μsec and another with a 10–20-μsec time constant. They also observed the formation of O_3 in the pulsed radiolysis of O_2. Johnson *et al.* (1969) detected the free benzyl radical (3070 Å) in absorption following the pulsed radiolysis of benzyl chloride (BzCl) in 1.3 atm of cyclohexane. Some ideas concerning the reaction mechanism were formulated, and apparently one of the main processes forming benzyl is the dissociative recombination

$$e + BzCl \longrightarrow Bz + Cl^-.$$

Inhibition of the production of Bz radicals was achieved by addition of other electron scavengers and relative rates of electron capture were measured. Johnson and Sauer (1969) studied the yield of the naphthalene triplet in the pulsed radiolysis of cyclohexane containing small concentrations of naphthalene. The triplet yields were shown to be independent of the naphthalene concentration and it was concluded that the triplet arises by neutralization of the $C_{10}H_8{}^+$ ion, formed from the cyclohexane positive ion by electron transfer. About 95% of the triplets could be eliminated by scavenging the electrons by addition of SF_6. In similar experiments with cyclohexane biphenyl mixtures, the biphenyl triplet was completely suppressed by SF_6 addition. Nishikawa and Sauer (1969) detected the naphthalene triplet in the pulsed radiolysis of 1.9 atm of benzene + naphthalene, and concluded that the triplet is produced by $C_{10}H_8{}^+$ neutralization, and also by energy transfer from C_6H_6 $^3B_{1u}$. Various rate coefficients were measured. In all these experiments, high total pressures were required to achieve adequate absorption of the electrons.

In the pulsed radiolysis of H_2/O_2 mixtures, Bishop and Dorfman (1970) recorded a rate coefficient of 1.7×10^{10} liter^2 mol^{-2} sec^{-1} for the reaction

$$H + O_2 + H_2 \longrightarrow HO_2 + H_2$$

at 300°K. The H atom decay was monitored by reversal of Lyman-α radiation. Reaction of H with CO and NO was reported by Hikida et al. (1971).

Meaburn and Perner (1966) subjected CO and CH_4, at pressures up to 500 Torr, to a 0.2-μsec pulse of 250-kV electrons; with an optical path length of 13 m, the formation and relaxation of $C(2\ ^1S)$ were recorded photographically with a Lyman flash source. The excited atoms decayed over about 2×10^{-4} sec and the half-lives were recorded under various conditions. A similar experiment can be achieved by microwave-pulse flash spectroscopy; $C(2\ ^1S)$ is remarkably stable against collisional deactivation or chemical removal.

Formation of O_3, in the pulsed radiolysis of O_2, has also been studied by Hochanadel et al. (1968) with a " Febetron " electron source. The pulse duration was 30 nsec with a peak current of 5×10^3 A at 2.3 MeV. It appears that most of the experiments were conducted with a cell 5 cm long, with multiple pass optics. A ∼1-m-long cell was also used. About 2×10^{15} molecule cm^{-3} of O_3 were produced per pulse. In these experiments it was discovered that the spectra of the newly formed O_3 exhibited a red shift, which the authors attributed to vibrational excitation. The vibrational relaxation time (if the effect is correctly interpreted) was 6 μsec in O_2 at 740 Torr at 297°K, corresponding to 5×10^5 collisions for vibrational relaxation. This is not unreasonable for O_3, the relaxation rate of which should be controlled by the lowest vibrational frequency of 705 cm^{-1}. Hochanadel et al. (1969) applied the same technique to the pulsed radiolysis of NO and observed formation of NO_2. They showed that the relaxation time of the reaction

$$NO_2 + NO \ \rightleftharpoons \ N_2O_3$$

is <1 μsec with [NO] = 1 atm. They also detected vibrationally excited NO and recorded a relaxation time of ∼1.4 μsec for decay of NO($v = 2$), presumably by the process

$$NO(v = 2) + NO(v = 0) \longrightarrow 2NO(v = 1).$$

This would correspond to V–V transfer once in 10^3 collisions. The rate of this process has also been measured by Stephenson (1974), using laser fluorescence.

With a technique similar to that of Hochanadel et al., Bullock and Cooper (1971) detected the CN radical in the pulsed radiolysis of $(CN)_2$, with an excess of Ar to avoid gas heating. A pulsed Xe arc was employed as monitoring source. Rate coefficients were measured for reaction of CN with various hydrocarbons at 300°K. The reactivity of CN was shown to be similar to that of atomic chlorine.

Formation and vibrational relaxation of N_2 A $^3\Sigma_u^+$ have been investigated by Dreyer and Perner (1973). The nitrogen triplet was monitored by optical absorption. They discovered that levels with $v \geq 4$ undergo very fast vibrational relaxation (10^4 times faster than $v = 1$). They consider that this may be due to double quantum V–V transfer to the nitrogen ground state, which is nearly resonant:

$$N_2 \text{ A } {}^3\Sigma_u^+(v = n) + N_2 \text{ X } {}^1\Sigma_g^+(v = 0)$$
$$\longrightarrow \quad N_2 \text{ A } {}^3\Sigma_u^+(v = n - 2) + N_2 \text{ X } {}^1\Sigma_g^+(v = 1).$$

However, such double quantum processes are usually very slow and it seems possible that the fast relaxation of the high levels corresponds to electronic energy transfer. In the zero points, exchange of electronic energy between N_2 A $^3\Sigma_u^+$ and N_2 X $^1\Sigma_g^+$ requires substantial changes in both nuclear separations and consequently may be slow. However, it should become more and more allowed as the initial degree of vibrational excitation is increased.

Reactions of NH and NH_2 have been investigated by Gordon *et al.* (1971).

Because of the available time resolution, the pulsed radiolysis of gases would appear to have considerable potential, especially in the field of ion molecule reactions at high pressures. The method has the disadvantage of low selectivity of excitation.

VIII. Relaxation Following Chemical Production of Excited Species

A. VIBRATIONAL RELAXATION OF CO X $^1\Sigma^+(v \leq 13)$

Hancock and Smith (1971a,b) have recently described a very fruitful relaxation experiment in which two gas streams, one of CS_2 highly diluted with Ar and the other of atomic oxygen highly diluted with Ar, were allowed to mix in a spherical, one-liter vessel at a pressure of 11.4 Torr. The relaxed products were pumped away at a rate of 1 liter sec^{-1}, to give a residence time of $\sim$1 sec. The chemical reactions are

$$CS_2 + O(2\ ^3P) \longrightarrow CS + SO$$
$$CS + O(2\ ^3P) \longrightarrow CO(v \leq 13) + S.$$

The vessel was internally gold-coated and infrared emission from the vibrationally excited CO was observed via an Infrasil window with a monochromator and PbS detector. The rates of V–V transfer from $CO^\dagger$ to $CO(v = 0)$, NO, O_2, N_2, OCS, N_2O, and CO_2 were measured over a range of vibrational states, and rate coefficients are listed in Table XIV. The treatment of the steady-state solution for each quantum state included population by the chemical reaction, and also by collisional and radiative cascade from the next highest level. Loss processes due to V–V transfer, radiation, and transport were included, though the latter was generally of minor importance. The data were finally treated as Stern–Volmer-type plots. Reduced probabilities per gas-kinetic collision for V–V transfer are plotted in Fig. 39 against the energy discrepancy. All the probabilities relate to the exothermic direction. The reduced probability is the probability derived from the rate coefficient, divided by the initial vibrational quantum number of the $CO^\dagger$. A vibrational relaxation rate depends on the product of a squared vibrational matrix element and a squared translational

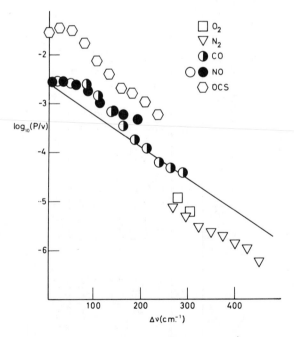

FIG. 39. Probabilities P of V–V energy transfer from $CO^\dagger$ versus the energy discrepancy $\Delta\nu$. All processes correspond to the exothermic direction. □, O_2. ▽, N_2. ◑, $CO(v = 0)$. ○, ●, NO [● for the exothermic processes with $CO(v \leq 11)$]. ○, OCS. (Hancock and Smith, 1971b; reproduced by permission of Dr. I. W. M. Smith.)

TABLE XIV

RATE COEFFICIENT (cm^3 molecule^{-1} sec^{-1}) FOR DEEXCITATION OF CO($v \leq 13$) BY He, CO($v = 0$), NO, O$_2$, N$_2$, OCS, N$_2$O, AND CO$_2$ (Hancock and Smith, 1971b)

v	He	CO	NO	O$_2$	N$_2$	OCS	N$_2$O	CO$_2$
4	—	2.0×10^{-12}	4.5×10^{-13}	—	2.4×10^{-15}	4.5×10^{-11}	5.4×10^{-13}	3.0×10^{-14}
5	—	1.3×10^{-12}	6.8×10^{-13}	—	1.7×10^{-15}	6.0×10^{-11}	2.5×10^{-13}	1.7×10^{-14}
6	—	6.3×10^{-13}	1.2×10^{-12}	—	1.1×10^{-15}	5.6×10^{-11}	1.5×10^{-13}	1.6×10^{-14}
7	—	3.4×10^{-13}	2.2×10^{-12}	—	8.5×10^{-16}	3.6×10^{-11}	9.8×10^{-14}	1.5×10^{-14}
8	—	1.8×10^{-13}	4.1×10^{-12}	—	7.2×10^{-16}	1.4×10^{-11}	8.6×10^{-14}	1.6×10^{-14}
9	1.5×10^{-16}	1.1×10^{-13}	5.9×10^{-12}	—	4.9×10^{-16}	7.1×10^{-12}	8.6×10^{-14}	2.1×10^{-14}
10	2.6×10^{-16}	6.1×10^{-14}	7.9×10^{-12}	—	4.0×10^{-16}	3.9×10^{-12}	9.9×10^{-14}	3.3×10^{-14}
11	3.4×10^{-16}	4.6×10^{-14}	8.6×10^{-12}	—	2.2×10^{-16}	3.1×10^{-12}	1.1×10^{-13}	5.3×10^{-14}
12	5.3×10^{-16}	3.4×10^{-14}	9.0×10^{-12}	2.1×10^{-14}	—	2.0×10^{-12}	1.0×10^{-13}	8.6×10^{-14}
13	6.2×10^{-16}	—	7.0×10^{-12}	4.4×10^{-14}	—	9.9×10^{-13}	9.3×10^{-14}	1.2×10^{-13}

matrix element (Callear and Lambert, 1969). It is the latter which decreases systematically with increasing energy discrepancy. However, the squared vibrational matrix element is proportional to the vibrational quantum number and it is convenient to divide the observed probabilities by the vibrational quantum number to illustrate clearly the fundamental effect of changing the energy discrepancy.

With energy discrepancies of ≤ 100 cm^{-1}, Hancock and Smith showed that the V–V probabilities agree well with values computed from Sharma's (1969) equations. Transfer to OCS is fast because its dipole derivative is much larger than those of CO and NO. With large energy discrepancies the dominant interaction in these cases is the short-range intermolecular repulsion.

Following the initial work of Hancock and Smith, several other groups have investigated the O plus CS reaction; see, for example, Powell and Kelley (1974) and references contained therein.

IX. Conclusion

In the way of general conclusions the most striking aspect of this subject is to note from the references the great volume of research that has been conducted during the last decade. Practically all the measurements were made spectroscopically, with the laser playing an increasingly important role. Parallel with the development of lasers in the ultraviolet, the increase of their application to the measurement of relaxation processes must accelerate further in the future. Also, the molecular beam experiment (beyond the scope of this review) is expected to have an increasingly important role because it gives access to the angular dependence of the relaxation process.

ACKNOWLEDGMENTS

I wish to thank Dr. P. M. Wood for reading the manuscript and suggesting some minor corrections.

826 A. B. Callear

REFERENCES

AIREY, J. R., and FRIED, S. F. (1971). *Chem. Phys. Lett.* **8**, 23.
ANDERSON, P. W. (1950). *Phys. Rev.* **80**, 511.
ASHPOLE, C. W., FORMOSINHO, S. J., and PORTER, G. (1971). *Proc. Roy. Soc. (London)* **A322**, 11.
ATKINS, D. L., FINK, E. H., and MOORE, C. B. (1970). *J. Chem. Phys.* **52**, 1604.
AZADA, T., LADENBURG, R., and TIETZE, W. (1928). *Phys. Z.* **29**, 549.
BABA, H., NAKAJIMA, A., AOI, M., and CHIHARA, K. (1971). *J. Chem. Phys.* **55**, 2433.
BAIMONTE, V. D., HARTSHORN, L. G., and BAIR, E. J. (1971). *J. Chem. Phys.* **55**, 3617.
BASCO, N., and HATHORN, F. G. M. (1971). *Chem. Phys. Lett.* **8**, 291.
BASCO, N., and NORRISH, R. G. W. (1962a). *Discuss. Faraday Soc.* **23**, 99.
BASCO, N., and NORRISH, R. G. W. (1962b). *Proc. Roy. Soc. (London)* **A268**, 291.
BASCO, N., CALLEAR, A. B., and NORRISH, R. G. W. (1961). *Proc. Roy. Soc. (London)* **A260**, 459.
BASCO, N., JAMES, D. G. L., and SUART, R. D. (1970). *Int. J. Chem. Kinet.* **2**, 215.
BATES, D. R., and KINGSTON, A. E. (1964). *Proc. Roy. Soc. (London)* **A279**, 10.
BATTAGLIA, A., GOZZINI, A., and POLACCO, E. (1959). *Nuova Cimento* **14**, 1076.
BAUER, H. J., KNESER, H. O., and SITTIG, E. (1959). *J. Chem. Phys.* **30**, 1119.
BAUMGARTNER, G., DEMTRÖDER, W., and STOCK, M. (1970). *Z. Phys.* **232**, 462.
BECKER, K. H., HAAKS, D., and TATARCZYK, T. (1974a). *Chem. Phys. Lett.* **25**, 564.
BECKER, K. H., FINK, E. H., LANGEN, P., and SCHURATH, U. (1974b). *J. Chem. Phys.* **60**, 4623.
BELL, R. E., GRAHAM, R. L., and PETCH, H. E. (1952). *Can. J. Phys.* **30**, 35.
BELLISIO, J. A., and DAVIDOVITS, P. (1970). *J. Chem. Phys.* **53**, 3474.
BENNETT, R. G., and DALBY, F. W. (1959). *J. Chem. Phys.* **31**, 434.
BENNETT, R. G., and DALBY, F. W. (1960a). *J. Chem. Phys.* **32**, 1111.
BENNETT, R. G., and DALBY, F. W. (1960b). *J. Chem. Phys.* **32**, 1716.
BENNETT, R. G., and DALBY, F. W. (1962). *J. Chem. Phys.* **36**, 399.
BENNETT, R. G., and DALBY, F. W. (1964). *J. Chem. Phys.* **40**, 1414.
BENNETT, W. R., and KINDLEMANN, P. J. (1966). *Phys. Rev.* **149**, 38.
BERRY, M. J., and PIMENTEL, G. C. (1968). *J. Chem. Phys.* **49**, 5190.
BERRY, M. J., and PIMENTEL, G. C. (1969). *J. Chem. Phys.* **51**, 2274.
BETHKE, G. W. (1959). *J. Chem. Phys.* **31**, 662.
BISHOP, W. P., and DORFMAN, L. M. (1970). *J. Chem. Phys.* **52**, 3210.
BLACK, G., and PORTER, G. (1962). *Proc. Roy. Soc. (London)* **A266**, 185.
BLACK, G., SLANGER, T. G., ST. JOHN, G. A., and YOUNG, R. A. (1969). *J. Chem. Phys.* **51**, 116.
BLACK, G., SLANGER, T. G., and WOOD, B. J., (1972). *J. Chem. Phys.* **57**, 233.
BLAK, J. A., and BURNS, G. (1971). *J. Chem. Phys.* **54**, 1481.
BONHOEFFER, K. F., and REICHHARDT, H. (1928). *Z. Phys. Chem.* **139**, 78.
BORISEVICH, N. A., and GRUZINSKII, V. V. (1967). *Sov. Phys.-Dokl.* **175**, 852.
BRADLEY, D. J., EWART, P., NICHOLAS, J. V., SHAW, J. R. D., and THOMPSON, D. G. (1973). *Phys. Rev. Lett.* **31**, 263.
BRAUN, W., McNESBY, J. R., and BASS, A. M. (1967). *J. Chem. Phys.* **46**, 2071.
BRAUN, W., BASS, A. M., DAVIES, D. D., and SIMMONS, J. D. (1969). *Proc. Roy. Soc. (London)* **A312**, 417.
BRAUN, W., BASS, A. M., and PILLING, M. J. (1970). *J. Chem. Phys.* **52**, 5131.
BRECKENRIDGE, W. H., and CALLEAR, A. B. (1971). *Trans. Faraday Soc.* **67**, 2009.
BREWER, R. G., and SHOEMAKER, R. L. (1971). *Phys. Rev. Lett.* **27**, 631.

BRITTAIN, A. H., MANER, P. J., and SCHWENDEMAN, R. H. (1973). *J. Chem. Phys.* **58**, 5735.
BROADBENT, T. W., and CALLEAR, A. B. (1972). *J. Chem. Soc. Faraday Trans. 2* **68**, 1367.
BROADBENT, T. W., CALLEAR, A. B., and LEE, H. K. (1968). *Trans. Faraday Soc.* **64**, 2320.
BROIDA, H. P., and CARRINGTON, T. (1963). *J. Chem. Phys.* **38**, 136.
BROWN, S. R. (1974). *J. Chem. Phys.* **60**, 1722.
BRZOZOWSKI, J., ELANDER, N., and ERMAN, P. (1974a). *Phys. Scripta* **9**, 99.
BRZOZOWSKI, J., ELANDER, N., ERMAN, P., and LYYRA, M. (1974b). *Phys. Scripta* **10**, 271.
BRZOZOWSKI, J., ELANDER, N., ERMAN, P., and LYYRA, M. (1974c). *Astrophys. J.* **193**, 741.
BUBERT, H., and FROBEN, F. W. (1971). *Chem. Phys. Lett.* **8**, 242.
BULLOCK, G. E., and COOPER, F. (1971). *Trans. Faraday Soc.* **67**, 3258.
BURDE, D. H., McFARLANE, R. A., and WIESENFELD, J. R. (1974). *Phys. Rev.* **A10**, 1917.
BURTON, C. S., and HUNZIKER, H. E. (1972). *J. Chem. Phys.* **57**, 339.
BUSCH, G. E., MAHONEY, R. T., MORSE, R. I., WILSON, K. R. (1969). *J. Chem. Phys.* **51**, 837.
BUSCH, G. E., RENTZEPIS, P. M., and JORTNER, J. (1972). *J. Chem. Phys.* **56**, 361.
CALLEAR, A. B. (1962). *Discuss. Faraday Soc.* **33**, 28.
CALLEAR, A. B. (1963). *Proc. Roy. Soc. (London)* **A276**, 401.
CALLEAR, A. B., and CONNOR, J. H. (1974). *J. Chem. Soc. Faraday Trans. 2*, **70**, 1667.
CALLEAR, A. B., and DICKSON, D. R. (1970). *Trans. Faraday Soc.* **66**, 1987.
CALLEAR, A. B., and HEDGES, R. E. M. (1970a). *Trans. Faraday Soc.* **66**, 605.
CALLEAR, A. B., and HEDGES, R. E. M. (1970b). *Trans. Faraday Soc.* **66**, 615.
CALLEAR, A. B., and HEDGES, R. E. M. (1970c). *Trans. Faraday Soc.* **66**, 2921.
CALLEAR, A. B., and LAMBERT, J. D. (1969). "Comprehensive Chemical Kinetics" (C. H. Bamford and C. F. H. Tipper, eds.), Vol. 3, pp. 182–269. Elsevier, Amsterdam.
CALLEAR, A. B., and LEE, H. K. (1968). *Trans. Faraday Soc.* **64**, 308.
CALLEAR, A. B., and McGURK, J. (1970a). *Chem. Phys. Lett.* **7**, 491
CALLEAR, A. B., and McGURK, J. (1970b). *Nature (London)* **266**, 844.
CALLEAR, A. B., and McGURK, J. (1972). *J. Chem. Soc. Faraday Trans. 2*, **68**, 289.
CALLEAR, A. B., and McGURK, J. (1973). *J. Chem. Soc. Faraday Trans. 2*, **69**, 917.
CALLEAR, A. B., and OLDMAN, R. J. (1967). *Trans. Faraday Soc.* **63**, 2888.
CALLEAR, A. B., and OLDMAN, R. J. (1968). *Trans. Faraday Soc.* **64**, 840.
CALLEAR, A. B., and PILLING, M. J. (1970). *Trans. Faraday Soc.* **66**, 1618.
CALLEAR, A. B., and SMITH, I. W. M. (1964). *Discuss. Faraday Soc.* **37**, 96.
CALLEAR, A. B., and TYERMAN, W. J. R. (1966a). *Trans. Faraday Soc.* **62**, 2312.
CALLEAR, A. B., and TYERMAN, W. J. R. (1966b). *Trans. Faraday Soc.* **62**, 2761.
CALLEAR, A. B., and VAN DEN BERGH, H. E. (1970). *Trans. Faraday Soc.* **66**, 2681.
CALLEAR, A. B., and VAN DEN BERGH, H. E. (1971). *Trans. Faraday Soc.* **67**, 2017.
CALLEAR, A. B., and WOOD, P. M. (1971a). *Trans. Faraday Soc.* **67**, 272.
CALLEAR, A. B., and WOOD, P. M. (1971b). *Trans. Faraday Soc.* **67**, 3399.
CALLEAR, A. B., and WOOD, P. M. (1972). *J. Chem. Soc. Faraday Trans. 2*, **68**, 302.
CALLEAR, A. B., GREEN, J. A., and WILLIAMS, G. J. (1965). *Trans. Faraday Soc.* **61**, 1831.
CALLEAR, A. B., PILLING, M. J., and SMITH, I. W. M. (1966). *Trans. Faraday Soc.* **62**, 2997.
CALO, J. M., and AXTMANN, R. M. (1971). *J. Chem. Phys.* **54**, 1332.
CAPELLE, G., and BROIDA, H. P. (1972). *J. Chem. Phys.* **57**, 5027.
CAPELLE, G., and BROIDA, H. P. (1973). *J. Chem. Phys.* **58**, 4212.
CAPELLE, G., SAKURAI, K., and BROIDA, H. P. (1971). *J. Chem. Phys.* **54**, 1728.
CAPELLE, G., JOHNSON, S. E., and BROIDA, H. P. (1972). *J. Chem. Phys.* **56**, 6264.

CATON, R. B., and DUNCAN, A. B. F. (1968). *J. Amer. Chem. Soc.* **90**, 1945.

CHANG, S. K., CLARKE, A. G., and BURNS, G. (1971). *J. Chem. Phys.* **54**, 1835.

CHAPMAN, G. D., and BUNKER, P. R. (1972). *J. Chem. Phys.* **57**, 2951.

CHEN, H. L. (1971). *J. Chem. Phys.* **55**, 5551, 5557.

CHEN, H. L., STEPHENSON, J. C., and MOORE, C. B. (1968). *Chem. Phys. Lett.* **2**, 593.

CHERVENAK, J., and ANDERSON, R. A. (1971). *J. Opt. Soc. Amer.* **61**, 952.

CHRISTIE, M. I., and PORTER, G. (1952). *Proc. Roy. Soc. (London)* **A212**, 398.

CHRISTIE, M. I., NORRISH, R. G. W., and PORTER, G. (1953). *Proc. Roy. Soc. (London)* **A216**, 152.

CHRISTIE, M. I., HARRISON, A. J., NORRISH, R. G. W., and PORTER, G. (1955). *Proc. Roy. Soc. (London)* **A231**, 446.

CHUTJIAN, A. (1969). *J. Chem. Phys.* **51**, 5414.

CHUTJIAN, A., and JAMES, T. C. (1969). *J. Chem. Phys.* **51**, 1242.

CHUTJIAN, A., LINK, J. K., and BREWER, L. (1967). *J. Chem. Phys.* **46**, 2666.

CLAESSON, S., and LINDQVIST, L. (1957). *Ark. Kemi* **60**, 535.

COLLINS, C. B., and HURT, W. B. (1968). *Phys. Rev.* **167**, 166.

COLLINS, C. B., and HURT, W. B. (1969). *Phys. Rev.* **177**, 257.

COLLINS, C. B., and JOHNSON, B. W. (1972). *J. Chem. Phys.* **57**, 5317.

COPELAND, G. E. (1972). *J. Chem. Phys.* **56**, 689.

CORNEY, A. (1970). *Advan. Electron. Electron Phys.* **29**, 116–223.

COX, A. P., FLYNN, G. W., and WILSON, E. B. (1965). *J. Chem. Phys.* **42**, 3094.

CRAIG, N. C., and MOORE, C. B. (1971). *J. Phys. Chem.* **75**, 1622.

CVETANOVIĆ, R. J. (1963). *Advan. Photochem.* **1**, 115.

CVETANOVIĆ, R. J. (1964). *Progr. Reaction Kinet.* **2**, 39.

DALY, P. W., and OKA, T. (1970). *J. Chem. Phys.* **53**, 3272.

DASHEVSKAYA, E. I., NIKITIN, E. E., and REZNIKOV, A. I. (1970). *J. Chem. Phys.* **53**, 1175.

DAVIDSON, N., MARSHALL, R., LARSH, A. E., and CARRINGTON, T. (1952). *J. Chem. Phys.* **19**, 1311.

DAYTON, I. E., BENNETT, R. G., and DALBY, F. W. (1960). *J. Chem. Phys.* **19**, 1311.

DeCORPO, J. J., and LAMPE, F. W. (1969). *J. Chem. Phys.* **51**, 943.

DeMARTINI, F., and DUCUING, J. (1966). *Phys. Rev. Lett.* **17**, 117.

DESQUELLES, J., DUFRAY, M., and POULIZAC, M. C. (1968). *Phys. Lett.* **A27**, 96.

DE VRIES, C. P., and OSKAM, H. J. (1969). *Phys. Lett.* **29**, 299.

DONOVAN, R. J., and HUSAIN, D. (1965). *Nature (London)* **206**, 171.

DONOVAN, R. J., and HUSAIN, D. (1966). *Trans. Faraday Soc.* **62**, 1050.

DONOVAN, R. J., and HUSAIN, D. (1967). *Trans. Faraday Soc.* **63**, 2879.

DONOVAN, R. J., and HUSAIN, D. (1970). *Trans. Faraday Soc.* **66**, 2148.

DONOVAN, R. J., HUSAIN, D., FAIR, R. W., STRAUSZ, O. P., and GUNNING, H. E. (1970). *Trans. Faraday Soc.* **66**, 1635.

DORGELO, H. B. (1925). *Physica*, **5**, 429.

DOTCHIN, L. W., CHUPP, E. L., and PEGG, D. J. (1973). *J. Chem. Phys.* **59**, 3960.

DREYER, J. W., and PERNER, D. (1973). *J. Chem. Phys.* **58**, 1195.

ERHARD, K. H. L., and NORRISH, R. G. W. (1956). *Proc. Roy. Soc. (London)* **A234**, 178.

ERMAN, P., and BRZOZOWSKI, J. (1973). *Phys. Lett.* **46A**, 79.

ERMAN, P., BRZOZOWSKI, J., and SIGFRIDSSON, B. (1973). *Nucl. Instrum. Methods* **110**, 471.

FABRIS, A. R., and OKA, T. (1972). *J. Chem. Phys.* **56**, 3168.

FERGUSON, E. E., FEHSENFELD, F. C., and SCHMELTEKOPF, A. L. (1965). *Phys. Rev.* **A138**, 381.

FERGUSON, E. E., DUNKIN, D. B., FEHSENFELD, F. C., and SCHMELTEKOPF, A. L. (1968). *Bull. Amer. Phys. Soc.* **13**, 212.

FILSETH, S. V., ZIA, A., and WELGE, K. H. (1970a). *J. Chem. Phys.* **52**, 5502.

FILSETH, S. V., STUHL, F., and WELGE, K. H. (1970b). *J. Chem. Phys.* **52**, 239.

FILSETH, S. V., STUHL, F., and WELGE, K. H. (1972). *J. Chem. Phys.* **57**, 4064.

FINK, E. H., and WELGE, K. H. (1964). *Z. Naturforsch.* **A19**, 1193.

FINK, E. H., and WELGE, K. H. (1967). *J. Chem. Phys.* **46**, 4315.

FINK, E. H., and WELGE, K. H. (1968). *Z. Naturforsch.* **A23**, 358.

FORMOSINHO, S. J., PORTER, G., and WEST, M. A. (1970). *Chem. Phys. Lett.* **6**, 7.

FOWLER, R. G., SKWERSKI, P. R., ANDERSON, R. A., COPELAND, G. E., and HOLZBERLEIN, T. M. (1969). *J. Chem. Phys.* **50**, 4133.

FREEMAN, C. G., McEWAN, M. J., CLARIDGE, R. F. C., and PHILLIPS, L. F. (1971a). *Chem. Phys. Lett.* **9**, 578.

FREEMAN, C. G., McEWAN, M. J., CLARIDGE, R. F. C., and PHILLIPS, L. F. (1971b). *Trans. Faraday Soc.* **67**, 2004.

FREUND, R. S. (1969). *J. Chem. Phys.* **50**, 3734.

FREUND, S. M., JOHNS, J. W. C., McKELLAR, A. R. W., and OKA, T. (1973). *J. Chem. Phys.* **59**, 3445.

GILPIN, R., SCHIFF, H. I., WELGE, K. H. (1971). *J. Chem. Phys.* **55**, 1087.

GORDON, S., MULAC, W., and NANGIA, P. (1971). *J. Phys. Chem.* **75**, 2087.

GREINER, N. R. (1970). *J. Chem. Phys.* **53**, 1074, 1284, 1285.

GUSINOW, M. A., GERBER, R. A., and GERADO, J. B. (1970). *Phys. Rev. Lett.* **25**, 1248.

HANCOCK, G., and SMITH, I. W. M. (1971a). *Chem. Phys. Lett.* **8**, 41.

HANCOCK, G., and SMITH, I. W. M. (1971b). *Appl. Opt.* **10**, 1827.

HANCOCK, J. K., and GREEN, W. H. (1972). *J. Chem. Phys.* **56**, 2474.

HENDERSON, W. R., MATSEN, F. A., and ROBERTSON, W. W. (1965). *J. Chem. Phys.* **43**, 1290.

HERON, S., McWIRTER, R. W. P., and RHODERICK, E. H. (1956). *Proc. Roy. Soc. (London)* **A234**, 565.

HERZBERG, G. (1961). *Proc. Roy. Soc. (London)* **A262**, 291.

HERZBERG, G. (1966). "Electronic Spectra of Polyatomic Molecules." Van Nostrand–Reinhold, Princeton, New Jersey.

HERZBERG, G., and RAMSAY, D. A. (1952). *J. Chem. Phys.* **20**, 347.

HERZFELD, K. F., and LITOVITZ, T. A. (1959). "Absorption and Dispersion of Ultrasonic Waves." Academic Press, New York.

HESSER, J. E. (1968). *J. Chem. Phys.* **48**, 2518.

HESSER, J. E., and LUTZ, B. L. (1970). *Astrophys. J.* **159**, 703.

HIKIDA, T., EYRE, J. A., and DORFMAN, L. M. (1971). *J. Chem. Phys.* **54**, 3422.

HOCHANADEL, C. J., and GHORMLEY, J. A. (1972). *J. Chem. Phys.* **56**, 4426.

HOCHANADEL, C. J., GHORMLEY, J. A., and BOYLE, J. W. (1968). *J. Chem. Phys.* **48**, 2416.

HOCHANADEL, C. J., GHORMLEY, J. A., and OGREN, P. J. (1969). *J. Chem. Phys.* **50**, 3075.

HOCHSTRASSER, R. M., and WESSEL, J. E. (1973). *Chem. Phys. Lett.* **19**, 156.

HOCKER, L. O., KOVACS, M. A., RHODES, C. K., FLYNN, G. W., and JAVAN, A. (1966). *Phys. Rev. Lett.* **17**, 233.

HOLLAND, R. F., and MAIER, W. B. (1972). *J. Chem. Phys.* **56**, 5229.

HOLZBERLEIN, T. M. (1964). *Rev. Sci. Instrum.* **35**, 1041.

HOPKINS, B. M., CHEN, H. L. and SHARMA, R. D. (1973). *J. Chem. Phys.* **59**, 5758.

HORNIG, D. F., and PALMER, H. B. (1957). *J. Chem. Phys.* **26**, 98.

HOUSTON, P. L., NOWAK, A. V., and STEINFELD, J. I. (1973). *J. Chem. Phys.* **58**, 3373.

HUFFMAN, R. E., LARRABEE, L. S., and TANAKA, Y. (1965). *J. Opt. Soc. Amer.* **55**, 101.

HUNZIKER, H. E. (1969). *Chem. Phys. Lett.* **3**, 504.

HUNZIKER, H. E., and WENDT, H. R. (1971). *Chem. Phys. Lett.* **12**, 181.

HUNZIKER, H. E., and WENDT, H. R. (1974). *J. Chem. Phys.* **60**, 4622.

JAVAN, A. (1959). *Phys. Rev. Lett.* **3**, 87.

JAVAN, A., BENNETT, W. R., and HERRIOTT, D. R. (1961). *Phys. Rev. Lett.* **6**, 106.

JENNINGS, D. A., BRAUN, W., and BROIDA, H. P. (1973). *J. Chem. Phys.* **59**, 4305.

JETTER, H., PEARSON, E. F., NORRIS, C. L., MCGURK, J. C., and FLYGARE, W. H. (1973). *J. Chem. Phys.*, **59**, 1796.

JEUNEHOMME, M. (1965). *J. Chem. Phys.* **42**, 4086.

JEUNEHOMME, M. (1966a). *J. Chem. Phys.* **44**, 2672.

JEUNEHOMME, M. (1966b). *J. Chem. Phys.* **44**, 4253.

JEUNEHOMME, M. (1966c). *J. Chem. Phys.* **45**, 1805.

JEUNEHOMME, M. (1966d). *J. Chem. Phys.* **45**, 4433.

JEUNEHOMME, M., and DUNCAN, A. B. F. (1964). *J. Chem. Phys.* **41**, 1692.

JEUNEHOMME, M., and SCHWENKER, R. P. (1965). *J. Chem. Phys.* **42**, 2406.

JOHNSON, A. W., and FOWLER, R. G. (1970). *J. Chem. Phys.* **53**, 65.

JOHNSON, C. E., and VAN DYKE, R. S. (1972). *J. Chem. Phys.* **56**, 1506.

JOHNSON, G. R. A., and SAUER, M. C. (1969). *J. Chem. Phys.* **51**, 496.

JOHNSON, G. R. A., SAUER, M. C., and WARMAN, J. M. (1969). *J. Chem. Phys.* **50**, 4933.

JOHNSON, S. E. (1972). *J. Chem. Phys.* **56**, 149.

JOHNSON, S. E., CAPELLE, G., and BROIDA, H. P., (1972). *J. Chem. Phys.* **56**, 663.

JOHNSTON, H. S., MORRIS, E. D., and VAN DEN BOGAERDE, J. (1969). *J. Amer. Chem. Soc.* **91**, 7712.

KALMAN, E. H., LYNN, C. K., and WILSON, K. R. (1970). *J. Chem. Phys.* **52**, 4588.

KEBARLE, P., HAYNES, R. M., and SEARLES, S. K. (1964). *J. Chem. Phys.* **47**, 1684.

KLEMM, R. B., and DAVIES, D. D. (1973). *Int. J. Chem. Kinet.* **5**, 375.

KLEMM, R. F. (1967). *Can. J. Chem.* **45**, 1693.

KLEY, D., STUHL, F., and WELGE, K. H. (1963). *Z. Naturforsch.* **18a**, 906.

KNUDTSON, J. T., and FLYNN, G. W. (1973). *J. Chem. Phys.* **58**, 1467.

KOSKIKALLIO, J., CALLEAR, A. B. and CONNOR, J. H. (1971). *Chem. Phys. Lett.* **8**, 467.

KURYLO, M. J., and HUI, R. E. (1973). *J. Chem. Phys.* **58**, 1258.

KURYLO, M. J., PETERSON, N. C., and BRAUN, W. (1970). *J. Chem. Phys.* **53**, 2776.

KURYLO, M. J., PETERSON, N. C., and BRAUN, W. (1971). *J. Chem. Phys.* **54**, 943.

LAWRENCE, G. M. (1965). *J. Quant. Spectrosc. Radiat. Trans.* **5**, 359.

LEES, R. M., and OKA, T. (1968). *J. Chem. Phys.* **49**, 4234.

LEES, R. M., and OKA, T. (1969). *J. Chem. Phys.* **51**, 3027.

LEONE, S. R., and WODARCZYK, F. J. (1974). *J. Chem. Phys.* **60**, 314.

LEROY, R. J. (1970). *J. Chem. Phys.* **52**, 2678.

LEVY, J. M., WANG, J. H. S., KUKOLICH, S. G., and STEINFELD, J. I. (1972). *Phys. Rev. Lett.* **29**, 395.

LICHTEN, W. (1957). *J. Chem. Phys.* **26**, 306.

LISZT, H. S., and HESSER, J. E. (1970). *Astrophys. J.* **159**, 1101.

LUDLUM, K. H., LARSEN, L. P., and CAFFREY, J. M. (1967). *J. Chem. Phys.* **46**, 127.

LUTZ, B. L., and HESSER, J. E. (1968). *J. Chem. Phys.* **48**, 3042.

MCGURK, J. C., NORRIS, C. L., SCHMALZ, T. G., PEARSON, E. F., and FLYGARE, W. H. (1973). *Proc. Conf. Laser Spectrosc., Boulder, Colorado.*

MCGURK, J. C., HOFMANN, R. T., and FLYGARE, W. H. (1974a). *J. Chem. Phys.* **60**, 2922.

MCGURK, J. C., SCHMALZ, T. G., and FLYGARE, W. H. (1974b). *Advan. Chem. Phys.* **25**, 1.

MAHAN, B. H. (1967). *J. Chem. Phys.* **46**, 98.

MANTEI, K. A., and BAIR, E. J. (1968). *J. Chem. Phys.* **49**, 3411.

MARCUS, R. A., and RICE, O. K. (1951). *J. Phys. Chem.* **55**, 894.

MEABURN, G. M., and PERNER, D. (1966). *Nature (London)* **212**, 1042.

MEISNER, K. W. (1925). *Phys. Z.* **26**, 687.
MELTON, L. A., and KLEMPERER, W. (1971). *J. Chem. Phys.* **55**, 1468.
MEYER, R. T. (1968). *J. Phys. Chem.* **72**, 1583.
MEYER, R. T. (1974). *J. Phys. Chem.* **78**, 878.
MILLER, D. J., and MILLIKAN, R. C. (1974). *Chem. Phys. Lett.* **27**, 10.
MITCHELL, A. C. G., and DICKENSON, R. G. (1927). *J. Amer. Chem. Soc.* **49**, 1478, 2699.
MITCHELL, R. C., and SIMONS, J. P. (1967). *Discuss. Faraday Soc.* **44**, 208.
MOORE, C. B., WOOD, R. E., HU, B. L., and YARDLEY, J. T. (1967). *J. Chem. Phys.* **46**, 4222.
MORLEY, C., and SMITH, I. W. M. (1971). *Trans. Faraday Soc.* **67**, 2575.
MULLIKAN, R. S. (1970). *J. Chem. Phys.* **52**, 5170.
NEWMAN, R. H., FREEMAN, C. G., McEWAN, M. J., CLARIDGE, R. F. C., and PHILLIPS, L. F. (1970). *Trans. Faraday Soc.* **66**, 2827.
NIKITIN, E. E. (1960). *Opt. Spectrosc.* **9**, 8.
NISHIKAWA, N., and SAUER, M. C. (1969). *J. Chem. Phys.* **51**, 1.
NORRISH, R. G. W., and OLDERSHAW, G. A. (1959). *Proc. Roy. Soc. (London)* **A249**, 498.
NORRISH, R. G. W., and PORTER, G. (1949). *Nature (London)* **164**, 658.
NOVAK, J. R., and WINDSOR, M. W. (1967). *J. Chem. Phys.* **47**, 3075.
NOVAK, J. R., and WINDSOR, M. W. (1968). *Proc. Roy. Soc. (London)* **A308**, 95.
OKA, T. (1966). *J. Chem. Phys.* **45**, 754.
OKA, T. (1967). *J. Chem. Phys.* **47**, 13.
OKA, T. (1968a). *J. Chem. Phys.* **48**, 4919.
OKA, T. (1968b). *J. Chem. Phys.* **49**, 3135.
OKABE, H. (1970). *J. Chem. Phys.* **53**, 3507.
OLDENBERG, O. (1934). *J. Chem. Phys.* **2**, 713; **3**, 266.
PARKES, D. A., PAUL, D. M., QUINN, C. P., and ROBSON, R. C. (1973). *Chem. Phys. Lett.* **23**, 425.
PAUKERT, T. T., and JOHNSTON, H. S. (1972). *J. Chem. Phys.* **56**, 2824.
PENDLETON, W. R., and HUGHES, R. H. (1965). *Phys. Rev.* **138**, A683.
PHELPS, A. V. (1955). *Phys. Rev.* **99**, 1307.
PHELPS, A. V. (1959). *Phys. Rev.* **114**, 1011.
PHELPS, A. V., and MOLNAR, J. P. (1953). *Phys. Rev.* **89**, 1202.
PIMENTEL, G. C., and CARLSO, G. A. (1966). *J. Chem. Phys.* **44**, 4053.
POLLACK, M. A. (1966). *Appl. Phys. Lett.* **9**, 94.
POOL, M. L. (1929). *Phys. Rev.* **33**, 22.
POOL, M. L. (1931). *Phys. Rev.* **38**, 955.
PORTER, G. (1950a). *Proc. Roy. Soc. (London)* **A200**, 284.
PORTER, G. (1950b). *Discuss. Faraday Soc.* **9**, 60.
PORTER, G. (1962). *Discuss. Faraday Soc.* **33**, 198.
PORTER, G., and SMITH, J. A. (1961). *Proc. Roy. Soc. (London)* **A261**, 28.
PORTER, G., and TOPP, M. R. (1970). *Proc. Roy. Soc. (London)* **A315**, 163.
PORTER, G., and WRIGHT, F. G. (1955). *Trans. Faraday Soc.* **51**, 1205.
POWELL, H. T., and KELLEY, J. D. (1974). *J. Chem. Phys.* **60**, 2191.
RAMSAY, D. A., and NELSON, L. S. (1956). *J. Chem. Phys.* **25**, 372.
REDON, M., and FOURIER, M. (1972). *Appl. Phys. Lett.* **21**, 463.
RENTZEPIS, P. M., BUSCH, G. E., and JONES, R. P. (1973). *Chem. Phys. Lett.* **18**, 178.
RIDLEY, B. A., and SMITH, I. W. M. (1971). *Chem. Phys. Lett.* **9**, 457.
RONN, A. M., and LIDE, D. R. (1967). *J. Chem. Phys.* **47**, 3669.
ROSEN, D. I., and COOL, T. A. (1973). *J. Chem. Phys.* **59**, 6097.
ROSSER, W. A., WOOD, A. D., and GERRY, E. T. (1969). *J. Chem. Phys.* **50**, 4996.

ROSSER, W. A., SHARMA, R. D., and GERRY, E. T. (1971). *J. Chem. Phys.* **54**, 1196.

SAKURI, K., CAPELLE, G., and BROIDA, H. P. (1971). *J. Chem. Phys.* **54**, 1220, 1412.

SAUER, M. C., and DORFMAN, L. M. (1964). *J. Amer. Chem. Soc.* **86**, 4218.

SCHWARTZ, S. E., and JOHNSTON, H. S. (1969). *J. Chem. Phys.* **51**, 943.

SCHWENKER, R. P. (1965). *J. Chem. Phys.* **42**, 1895, 2618.

SHARMA, R. D. (1969). *Phys. Rev.* **177**, 102.

SHARMA, R. D., and BRAU, C. A. (1969). *J. Chem. Phys.* **50**, 924.

SHIMIZU, T., and OKA, T. (1970). *J. Chem. Phys.* **53**, 2536.

SHOTTON, K. C., and CHAPMAN, G. D. (1972). *J. Chem. Phys.* **56**, 1012.

SILVERS, S. J., and CHIU, C. L. (1972). *J. Chem. Phys.* **56**, 5663.

SIMONS, J. P. (1971). "Photochemistry and Spectroscopy." Wiley (Interscience), New York.

SLANGER, J. G., and BLACK, G. (1971). *J. Chem. Phys.* **55**, 2164.

SLANGER, J. G., and BLACK, G. (1974). *J. Chem. Phys.* **60**, 468.

SLOBODSKAYA, P. V., and TKACHENKO, N. F. (1970). *Opt. Spectrosc.* **29**, 138.

SMITH, D., and COPSEY, M. J. (1968). *J. Phys. B1*, 650.

SMITH, I. W. M. (1967). *Discuss. Faraday Soc.* **44**, 194.

SMITH, I. W. M. (1968a). *Trans. Faraday Soc.* **64**, 378.

SMITH, I. W. M. (1968b). *Trans. Faraday Soc.* **64**, 3183.

SMITH, W. H. (1969a). *J. Quant. Spectrosc. Radiat. Trans.* **9**, 1191.

SMITH, W. H. (1969b). *J. Chem. Phys.* **51**, 520.

SMITH, W. H. (1969c). *J. Chem. Phys.* **51**, 3410.

SMITH, W. H. (1970). *J. Chem. Phys.* **53**, 792.

SMITH, W. H. (1971). *J. Chem. Phys.* **54**, 1384.

STEINFELD, J. I., and KLEMPERER, W. (1965). *J. Chem. Phys.* **42**, 3475.

STEINFELD, J. I., and SCHWEID, A. N. (1970). *J. Chem. Phys.* **53**, 3304.

STEINFELD, J. I., BURAK, I., SUTTON, D. G., and NOWAK, A. V. (1970). *J. Chem. Phys.* **52**, 5421.

STEPHENSON, J. C. (1973). *Appl. Phys. Lett.* **22**, 576.

STEPHENSON, J. C. (1974). *J. Chem. Phys.* **60**, 4289.

STEPHENSON, J. C., and MOORE, C. B. (1972). *J. Chem. Phys.* **56**, 1295.

STUHL, F., and NIKI, N. (1970). *Chem. Phys. Lett.* **5**, 573.

STUHL, F., and NIKI, N. (1971a). *J. Chem. Phys.* **55**, 3943.

STUHL, F., and NIKI, N. (1971b). *J. Chem. Phys.* **55**, 3954.

STUHL, F., and NIKI, N. (1972a). *J. Chem. Phys.* **57**, 3671, 3677.

STUHL, F., and NIKI, N. (1972b). *J. Chem. Phys.* **57**, 5403.

TAN, L. Y., WINER, A. M., PIMENTEL, G. C. (1972). *J. Chem. Phys.* **57**, 4028.

TANGO, W. J., and ZARE, R. N. (1970). *J. Chem. Phys.* **53**, 3094.

THOMAS, R. G. O., and THRUSH, B. A. (1975). *J. C. S. Faraday 2*, **71**, 664.

TOWNES, C. H., and SCHAWLOW, A. L. (1955). "Microwave Spectroscopy." McGraw-Hill, New York.

TURNER, R. (1967). *Phys. Rev.* **158**, 121.

UNLAND, M. L., and FLYGARE, W. H. (1966). *J. Chem. Phys.* **45**, 2421.

VAN DEN BERGH, H. E., CALLEAR, A. B., and NORSTROM, R. J. (1969). *Chem. Phys. Lett.* **4**, 101.

VAN DYKE, R. S., JOHNSON, C. E., and SHUGART, H. A. (1970). *Phys. Rev. Lett.* **25**, 1403.

VIKIS, A. C., TORRIE, G., and LE ROY, D. J. (1970). *Can. J. Chem.* **48**, 3771.

VILLAREJO, D., HERM, R. M., and INGRAM, M. G. (1965). *J. Opt. Soc. Amer.* **55**, 1504.

WASSERMANN, E. W., FALCONER, W. E., and YAGER, W. A. (1968). *Ber. Bunsenges.* **72**, 248.

WEBSTER, H., and BAIR, E. J. (1972). *J. Chem. Phys.* **57**, 3802.

WEINSTOCK, E. M., ZARE, R. N., and MELTON, L. A., (1972). *J. Chem. Phys.* **56**, 3456.

WELGE, K. H., and STUHL, F. (1967). *J. Chem. Phys.* **46**, 2440.

WENTINK, T., ISAACSON, L., and MORREAL, J. (1964). *J. Chem. Phys.* **41**, 278.

WERKHOVEN, C. J., GELDOF, P. A., POST, M. F. M., LANGELAAR, J., RETTSCHNICK, R. P. H., and VAN VOORST, J. D. W. (1971). *Chem. Phys. Lett.* **9**, 6.

WONG, Y. C., and DAVIES, D. D. (1974). *Int. J. Chem. Kinet.* **6**, 401.

WONG, Y. C., and LEE, Y. T. (1974). *J. Chem. Phys.* **60**, 4619.

YAJIMA, T., and SHIMODA, K. (1960). *J. Phys. Soc. Japan.* **15**, 1668.

YARDLEY, J. T., and MOORE, C. B. (1966). *J. Chem. Phys.* **45**, 1066.

YOUNG, P. J., GRIEG, G., and STRAUSZ, O. P. (1970). *J. Amer. Chem. Soc.* **92**, 413.

YOUNG, R. A., BLACK, G., and SLANGER, T. G. (1969). *J. Chem. Phys.* **50**, 303.

YUAN, R. C. L., and FLYNN, G. W. (1973). *J. Chem. Phys.* **58**, 649.

YUAN, R. C. L., PESES, J. M., FLYNN, G. W., and RONN, A. M. (1973). *J. Chem. Phys.* **59**, 6128.

Chapter 11

Unimolecular Reactions: Experiments and Theories

Jürgen Troe

I. General Properties of Unimolecular Processes

A. Introduction

Unimolecular reactions, in the widest sense of the term, are elementary chemical processes in which molecular species, molecules, radicals, or molecular ions undergo structural changes such as dissociation, isomerization, or electronic transition. This definition (or better, concept) suggests a general view of many different basic processes in chemical kinetics. Such processes are:

(a) thermal dissociations, isomerizations, and electronic transitions, induced by thermal collisions in inert media;

(b) photolysis, isomerizations, and electronic transitions, induced by absorption of light;

(c) radiolysis, induced by high-energy radiations;

(d) decomposition of molecular ions, induced by ionization in electron collisions, light absorption, charge exchange, etc.;

(e) secondary dissociations of excited species, formed as products of photolysis, radiolysis, molecular ion decomposition, etc.;

(f) dissociations of complexes, originating from chemical activation, association of particles, reactive or inelastic collisions;

(g) reverse processes of dissociations, i.e., recombinations and associations.

The application of one common unimolecular reaction concept to thermal as well as nonthermal kinetic systems has been stimulated mainly by the development of very detailed theories for thermal reactions. First among these theories one must mention a very powerful model for dissociation and isomerization reactions based to a large extent on the methods of equilibrium statistics, and which originates from the work of Hinshelwood, Kassel, Rice, Ramsperger, Eyring, Marcus, and others. It is used in the RRKM theory of thermal unimolecular reactions and of photochemical and chemical activation systems, in the "quasiequilibrium" theory of mass spectra, in the transition-state theory, and so on. This model can easily take into account the chemical particularities of different systems, though it describes the "statistical" limit of kinetic behavior. It is evident that a better, but more difficult, representation requires the analysis of molecular dynamics in terms of nonequilibrium statistics and quantum mechanics of nonstationary states. Much progress has been made in this direction in recent years. Dynamical theories of intramolecular motion with Monte Carlo averaging of computer-calculated classical trajectories have greatly extended the earlier work of Polanyi, Wigner, Slater, and others. Theories of radiationless transitions in photochemistry (Jortner et al., 1970) lead to explicit descriptions of quantum relaxation processes.

Parallel to this progress in the development of theories, experiments now provide very reliable and detailed information. Classical thermal unimolecular reactions, which are often completely free from heterogeneous and secondary reactions, have been studied under a very large variety of temperatures, pressures, and inert media. Primary photochemical processes, quantum yields, fluorescence and photolysis lifetimes, energy distributions in products, etc., can be investigated at well-defined excitation energies. Time-resolved mass spectra provide a direct access to dissociative lifetimes of molecular ions. Chemical activation experiments have been performed with various activation and dissociation paths.

The question arises of the extent to which one common unimolecular reaction concept applies to the different processes mentioned here. In these processes molecular species A are activated to A* in ways specific for each reaction. Different populations in phase space or at least in energies are prepared. Different electronic states may be involved. The first problem in analyzing any unimolecular reaction is, therefore, the description of the individual activation process. In this part of the analysis the kinetic systems mentioned differ from each other. The subsequent fate of the activated A* in different systems is governed by different elementary mechanisms, such as direct dissociation or isomerization after the activation, intermediate collisional deactivation, or reaction by different channels. The understanding of which elementary steps contribute to the overall reaction, therefore, is the second part of the analysis. The kinetic systems mentioned also differ from each other in this second part. Only the third and final problem, i.e., the determination of the "specific rate constants" for structural change, dissociation, isomerization, or electronic transition, is common to all unimolecular processes. If A* particles "forget" their activation path, one may expect one general expression for specific rate constants, depending only on the energy, angular momentum, and electronic state of A*. Even if A* particles do not completely "forget" their initial preparation, similar theoretical methods may be used to determine individual specific rate constants.

In the following section well-behaved experimental examples of the different unimolecular reactions mentioned shall be compared and analyzed according to our general concept. The analysis will be conducted as follows:

(a) The microscopic mechanism will be characterized.
(b) The population of states during the reaction will be determined.
(c) Specific rate constants of the unimolecular reaction will be derived.

(d) Reaction fluxes will be obtained from averages over specific rate constants and populations of states.

Since point (c) is common to all types of activation, we shall start by reviewing general theories of specific rate constants in unimolecular reactions. The points (a), (b), and (d) will be considered separately for each type of activation, after the presentation of the corresponding experimental results. For a brief introduction into the qualitative properties of the different systems, the reader may perhaps start with Sections II–VI, and come back to Section I when quantitative information on specific rate constants is required.

B. Number of States

Thermal unimolecular reactions, by collisional coupling to a thermal surrounding, involve distributions of molecular states which to a large extent are characterized by "local equilibria" in phase space. Collisional coupling to a heat reservoir, however, is not the only way to introduce equilibrium statistics into the kinetics of unimolecular processes. Isolated excited molecules, prepared in a nonequilibrium manner, often decay very fast by intramolecular coupling toward an almost equilibrium ensemble. Calculations of densities of states, numbers of states, degeneracies of levels, phase space volumes, etc., consequently form an essential part of unimolecular reaction rate theory. Theories often failed simply due to inadequate expressions of these statistical quantities.

We describe the internal state of molecules by a set of s canonically conjugate coordinates and momenta q_i and p_i. We are interested in the number of quantum states $W(E)$ in the range of energies $(0, E)$ or, alternatively, in the density of states $\rho(E)$, i.e., the number of quantum states per energy interval,

$$\rho(E) = dW(E)/dE. \qquad (1.1)$$

In classical statistics $W(E)$ is given by

$$W(E) = \int \cdots \int dq_1 \, dp_1 \cdots dq_s \, dp_s/h^s, \qquad 0 \leq H(q_i, p_i) \leq E. \qquad (1.2)$$

$H(q_i, p_i)$ is the intramolecular Hamiltonian. At small numbers of quanta per degree of freedom, $W(E)$ must be replaced by the number of combinations of internal quantum numbers which give a total energy in the range

$(0, E)$. Equation (1.2) then becomes inadequate, and the exact counting of states is necessary. This counting procedure, for a large s, even at low energies may become a very laborious problem and must be solved by computer. Therefore, semiclassical expressions have been derived which—now with excellent accuracy—extend to low energies the validity of the expressions based on Eq. (1.2). Before presenting these formulas we will give some elementary relations of statistical mechanics (see, e.g., Tolman, 1938).

For one harmonic oscillator the classical number of states according to Eq. (1.2) is given by

$$W(E) = \iint\limits_{0 \leq H(q,p) \leq E} dq \, dp/h = \int\int dE \, dT/h = E/hv = E/\varepsilon, \qquad (1.3)$$

with the vibrational period $T = 1/v$ and $\varepsilon \equiv hv$. The corresponding quantum expression may be formulated by means of delta functions of the form

$$\rho(E) = \delta(E - nhv), \qquad n = 0, 1, 2, \ldots \qquad (1.4)$$

(E is counted from the vibrational ground state). Equation (1.3) can immediately be extended to a system of s "slightly coupled harmonic" oscillators:

$$W(E) = \left[\int \cdots \int dT_1 \cdots dT_s/h^s\right]\left[\int \cdots \int dE_1 \cdots dE_s\right], \qquad 0 \leq \sum E_i \leq E. \tag{1.5}$$

This integral can be evaluated in the form

$$W(E) = \left(\prod_{i=1}^{s} \varepsilon_i\right)^{-1}\left[\int_0^E dE_1 \int_0^{E-E_1} dE_2 \cdots \int_0^{E - \sum_{i=1}^{s-1} E_i} dE_s\right] \qquad (1.6)$$

($\varepsilon_i \equiv hv_i$, E is the total energy, and E_i the energy of oscillator i). The s-fold integral corresponds to the volume of an s-dimensional sphere of radius E in the space of single oscillator energies E_i. The phrase "slightly coupled" only ensures dynamical accessibility of all the configurations. Equation (1.6) is by no means limited to strictly harmonic oscillators. It represents a first approximation for volumes in phase space of anharmonic oscillators as well (see below). After integration Eq. (1.6) gives

$$W(E) = E^s \Big/ \left[s! \prod_{i=1}^{s} \varepsilon_i\right] \qquad (1.7)$$

and

$$\rho(E) = E^{s-1} \bigg/ \bigg[(s-1)! \prod_{i=1}^{s} \varepsilon_i \bigg] \tag{1.8}$$

For $s > 1$ one observes for increasing energy a considerable increase in the density of states. The mean separation in energy between two states $\rho(E)^{-1}$ decreases and, because of the large number of possibilities of distributing a given amount of energy on several oscillators, a quasi continuum of vibrational states is formed (see below).

At low energies the number of states is underestimated by the classical statistics. This is illustrated in Fig. 1. Curve 1 gives the correct number of

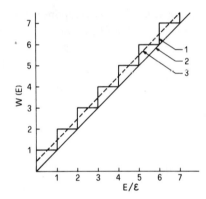

FIG. 1. Number of states in a harmonic oscillator (1, exact; 2, classical; 3, semiclassical).

states $W(E)$ for one harmonic oscillator. $W(E)$ is a step function increasing by one at each vibrational level. In the classical expression (1.3) $W(E)$ is represented by E/ε (curve 2). Obviously, curve 2 always lies below the exact step function. Therefore, a better, "smoothed," representation of curve 1 would be curve 3, given by

$$W(E) = \tfrac{1}{2} + (E/\varepsilon) = (E + \tfrac{1}{2}\varepsilon)/\varepsilon. \tag{1.9}$$

The extension of this smoothing technique to s oscillators is difficult. One might, for instance, try to use Eq. (1.6), with the upper limits of each integral replaced by the corresponding $E + \varepsilon_i/2$. With this procedure, however, the result depends on the numbering of the oscillators. Nevertheless, one may obtain by this procedure an upper limit for $W(E)$ if the upper limits of all integrals in Eq. (1.6) are replaced by $E + E_z$, where $E_z = \sum_{i=1}^{s} \varepsilon_i/2$. (Strictly, this is an upper limit at all E only if $E_z \geq \mathrm{Max}\{\varepsilon_i\}$. This is normally the case.) One obtains in this way

$$W(E) \simeq (E + E_z)^s \Big/ \Big(s! \prod_{i=1}^{s} \varepsilon_i\Big). \tag{1.10}$$

This "semiclassical" expression (Marcus and Rice, 1951) may be further modified by a correction factor $a(E)$, generally between zero and one, to be multiplied with the total zero-point energy E_z. Convenient expressions for $a(E)$ have been found empirically by Whitten and Rabinovitch (1964).

Several general expressions for the smoothed number of states are now available (among others: Thiele, 1963a; Whitten and Rabinovitch, 1963, 1964; Haarhoff, 1963; Schlag and Sandsmark, 1962; Forst et al., 1967; Tou and Lin, 1968; Lin and Eyring, 1963, 1965; Vestal et al., 1962; Forst, 1971; Hoare and Pal, 1971; Stein and Rabinovitch, 1973). As an illustration we choose the expansion of $W(E)$ into a series given by Thiele (1963a), which has been tested several times against exactly counted values (see, e.g., Tou, 1967, and Forst et. al., 1967). By the method of Laplace transformation, Thiele obtained

$$W(E) = \Big(s! \prod_{i=1}^{s} \varepsilon_i\Big)^{-1} \sum_{\substack{v=0 \\ \text{even } v \leq s}}^{s} \binom{s}{v} D_v^{(s)} (E + E_z)^{s-v}. \tag{1.11}$$

The coefficients $D_v^{(s)}$ are given in the original paper in a complete form. For small v they are

$$D_0^{(s)} = 1; \qquad D_2^{(s)} = -\tfrac{1}{3} \sum E_{zi}^2; \qquad D_4^{(s)} = \tfrac{1}{3}(\sum E_{zi}^2)^2 + (2/15) \sum E_{zi}^4 \tag{1.12}$$

$$D_6^{(s)} = -(5/9)(\sum E_{zi}^2)^3 - (2/3)(\sum E_{zi}^2)(\sum E_{zi}^4) - (16/63) \sum E_{zi}^6$$

(with $E_{zi} \equiv \tfrac{1}{2}\varepsilon_i$ and all sums from $i = 1$ to s). The first term gives the "semiclassical" equation (1.10). The second and third terms have been given by Schlag and Sandsmark (1962) in only a slightly different form. The smoothed curve $W(E)$ is given completely by Eqs. (1.11) and (1.12) for $s \leq 7$. For a larger s, the first four terms, Eq. (1.12), nevertheless give a good approximation for $E/E_z \gtrsim 0.5$. There appears no significant gap between large values of E/E_z, where a reasonable number of terms of the series (1.11) is sufficient, and small values, where counting is easily done.

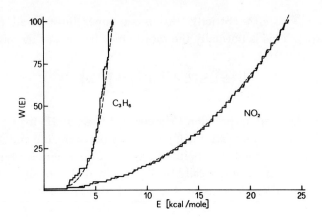

FIG. 2. Number of states in NO_2 and cyclopropane (—, exact; - - -, smoothed; C_3H_6 results from Haarhoff, 1963).

In order to illustrate the quasi continuum of vibrational states, Fig. 2 shows for NO_2 ($s = 3$) the counted (step function) and semiclassical [dashed curve, Eq. (1.10)] number of states $W(E)$ below the energy E. The rapid change from a step function to a quasi continuum is quite evident. In Fig. 2 the number of states versus energy for NO_2 is compared with the corresponding curve for cyclopropane. $W(E)$ increases much faster with energy in cyclopropane because of the larger number of oscillators (21 in C_3H_6, 3 in NO_2). A smoothed curve of $W(E)$ (from Haarhoff, 1963) is also included in Fig. 2 (dashed curve). In the energy region shown, where six hard oscillators with $\varepsilon_i \gtrsim 8$ kcal mole^{-1} are not excited, the smoothed curve lies below the counted values. A much better representation of the counted curve is obtained by the exclusion of these hard oscillators.

If dissociation is considered, the density of levels in the region of the dissociation energy is of particular interest. For small molecules like NO_2, this corresponds to the almost continuous region at $E/E_z > 1$, where the semiclassical formula (1.10) becomes sufficiently accurate. This situation changes for large polyatomic molecules. With increasing s, the total zero-point energy E_z may easily exceed a bond energy E_0, and expressions such as Eq. (1.11) or counted $W(E)$ may become necessary. Similarly, if $W(E)$ in activated complexes is used for the nondissociated and only slightly excited part of the complex, Eq. (1.10) becomes inadequate.

High degrees of excitation lead the molecule into regions of the phase space with pronounced anharmonicity of oscillators. The further use of harmonic oscillator formulas for $\rho(E)$ does not at all present a basic contradiction; only corrections for anharmonicity have to be introduced. The counting of all of the s oscillators of a molecule in formula (1.2) already implicitly introduces anharmonicity into the harmonic oscillator volumes of the phase space. Exclusion of some of the oscillators because of symmetry restrictions at high excitation energies is apparently not to be expected (see, e.g., Spicer and Rabinovitch, 1970). Estimates of anharmonicity corrections of $\rho(E)$ can be obtained in the following way. Replacing the harmonic oscillator by a Morse oscillator, the continuous density of states $\rho(E) = 1/\varepsilon$ becomes

$$\rho(E') \simeq (1/\varepsilon)[D/(D - E')]^{1/2} \tag{1.13}$$

(e.g. Thiele, 1963b). Here the dissociation energy D and the oscillator energy E' are counted, not as before from the vibrational ground state, but from the minimum of the potential curve. The calculation of $\rho(E)$ in systems containing Morse oscillators is then immediately possible using Eq. (1.13) in Eq. (1.2), e.g., by the integration technique of Eq. (1.6). As an example, we give the classical density of states of $s - 1$ harmonic oscillators coupled to one Morse oscillator at $E' < D$:

$$\rho(E') \simeq \left[(s-2)! \prod_{i=1}^{s} \varepsilon_i \right]^{-1} \int_0^{E'} \frac{(E' - E_1)^{s-2}}{(1 - E_1/D)^{1/2}} dE_1. \tag{1.14}$$

Other systems with more Morse oscillators coupled to harmonic oscillators are treated by Thiele (1963a) and Troe and Wagner (1967a). The magnitude of anharmonicity corrections can easily be estimated by these formulas. One obtains, for instance, from Eq. (1.14)

$$\rho(E') \simeq \rho_{\mathrm{har}}(s - 1)/(s - 1.5) \tag{1.15}$$

at $E' \simeq D$ and $s > 1$. The correction factor approaches one with increasing s. This corresponds to the decreasing average excitation of single oscillators. With a suitable choice of a critical surface between molecules and products, $\rho(E)$ may be extended to energies $> D$. In the extreme case of two coupled Morse oscillators of the same individual dissociation energy D, Thiele obtained $\rho(E')/\rho_{\mathrm{har}}$ values of π at $E' = D$, 4 at $E' = 1.2D$, 5.5 at $E' = 1.4D$, 6.5 at $E' = 1.6D$, and 7.8 at $E' = 1.8D$. Anharmonicity corrections in combination with appropriate smoothing techniques for $\rho(E)$

have been determined, e.g., by Schneider and Rabinovitch (1962), Schlag and Sandsmark (1962), Haarhoff (1963), Schlag *et al.* (1964), Wilde (1964) and Tou and Lin (1968). Spectroscopically determined anharmonicity coefficients have been used in some cases. In CD_4, for instance, the anharmonic density of states was found to be three times (at 100 kcal mole^{-1}), five times (at 150 kcal mole^{-1}), and six times (at 180 kcal mole^{-1}) larger than the corresponding harmonic density of states (Schlag *et al.*, 1964). Similar values were found for cyclopropane (e.g., Tou and Lin, 1968).

Additional corrections must be introduced if free or hindered internal rotations are present in a molecule or activated complex. This modifies Eq. (1.11) by replacing s by $s + \frac{1}{2}r$, where r is the number of free internal rotators, and by adding the factor $Q_{rot\ int}/(kT)^{r/2}$ with

$$Q_{rot\ int} = (8\pi^2 kT/h^2)^{r/2} \prod_i \sigma_i^{-1} I_i^{d_i/2} \Gamma(d_i/2), \qquad (1.16)$$

where for each one-dimensional rotator $d_i = 1$ and for each two-dimensional rotator $d_i = 2$; $r = \sum_i d_i$; Γ is the gamma function; I_i is the moment of inertia; and σ_i is the symmetry number of rotator i (Forst *et al.*, 1967, Forst, 1968). With hindered internal rotations numerical techniques are required (for internal rotation in H_2O_2 see Meyer *et al.*, 1969).

C. Specific Rate Constants: Statistical Theories

The central quantity in the analysis of unimolecular processes is the specific rate constant $k(E)$ for structural change. The dependence of this quantity on the internal energy E is of particular interest. $k(E)$ may be defined by the relation

$$dn(E, J, t)/dt \equiv -k(E, J, t)n(E, J, t), \qquad (1.17)$$

where $n(E, J, t)$ is the number of molecules in the region of unreacted species at energy $(E, E + dE)$ and total angular momentum J. In general $k(E)$ may depend on time and on the type of the initial preparation of reacting molecules. This can result in nonexponential decays of n. This effect is particularly well observed in dynamical and quantum relaxation theories (see Section I,D). However, under many conditions $k(E)$ may be considered independent of the initial activation. In the following section this $k(E)$ will be calculated by means of statistical theories.

Density and number of states (Section I,B) therefore play important roles. One postulates, e.g., an "activated complex," or a "critical surface" in phase space, which has the following two properties:

(a) Equilibrium between the molecules at the critical surface and all other unreacted molecules is established.

(b) The population of states beyond the critical surface is such that reaction flux only occurs from unreacted molecules toward products.

Before we explicitly derive specific rate constants according to this concept we must briefly discuss the conditions under which the "activated complexes" defined in the foregoing exist, and where they may be localized. These questions can only be answered by considering more basic theories, hopefully containing quasiequilibrium theories as their limiting case. For instance, one may start from a generalized Liouville equation in molecular phase space, including collisional coupling to a heat bath (Bergmann and Lebowitz, 1955, 1957)

$$\partial n(q, p)/\partial t + [n, H] = \Delta J. \tag{1.18}$$

Here $n(q, p)$ denotes the number of particles at (q, p); the Poisson bracket $[n, H]$ describes intramolecular fluxes due to vibrations, etc.; ΔJ are the suitable collision integrals. Under special conditions this leads to a Fokker–Planck equation which, for one dimension, has been solved in the diffusion theory in Section II,F. This solution indicates the existence in the normal high-pressure region of an "activated complex" with the required properties. It is localized at the top of high potential barriers between unreacted molecules and products. In collision-free situations, $\Delta J = 0$, the Liouville equation (1.18) may be solved by Monte Carlo averaging of explicitly calculated phase space trajectories (see Section I,D). Initial distribution of states for this solution depends, of course, on the activation process, and has to be suitably chosen. Inspection of numerical calculations of this kind confirms the intuitive guess that if an "activated complex," in the defined sense, exists, it should be placed at the "bottleneck" of reaction. This may be characterized by a minimum of the local density of states $\rho(q)$ along a reaction coordinate q, i.e.,

$$\partial \rho(q)/\partial q = 0 \qquad \text{at the critical surface}. \tag{1.19}$$

This important condition has been explicitly employed only recently (e.g. Bunker and Pattengill, 1968; Gaedtke and Troe, 1973; Quack and Troe,

1974). It focuses attention on the nonseparable coupling between the critical reaction coordinate and the other, uncritical, coordinates. From the one-dimensional solution of the Fokker–Planck equation (Section II,F) one might, for instance, expect that activated complexes in polyatomic molecules are localized at the top of centrifugal maxima of the effective potential surface for rotating molecules. This assumption has often been used. However, by applying Eq. (1.19) it has been shown inadequate. In a numerical investigation for triatomic molecules Bunker and Pattengill have found the minimum of the local density of states, i.e., the dynamical "bottleneck," at fragment distances considerably smaller than the average distances of rotation barriers. Numerical illustrations are given at the end of this section.

An alternative way of choosing the critical surface is given by the "variational theory" of reaction rates (e.g., Keck, 1967). In this theory trial critical surfaces in phase space are chosen. Then the flow of phase points through the surface from the reactant to the product side is calculated. This gives an upper limit of the reaction flow; because of the "healing" of bonds, some trajectories may cross the surface more than once. By variation of the critical surface, the surface that gives the minimum flow is chosen. It is not completely clear to what extent this method and the choice of a critical surface by condition (1.19) are equivalent.

A more general version of the statistical theory has been proposed by Quack and Troe (1974). In this model the reactant states are correlated by suitable dissociation channels with the product states. Each channel has its own effective potential curve and threshold energy. Equal statistical weight is postulated for each "open" channel, for which the available energy is larger than its threshold. With this model the notion of a localized activated complex disappears. In a certain sense each channel has its own activated complex. It can be shown that Eq. (1.19) gives a reasonable averaged activated complex for molecules of the same energy E. However, this activated complex depends on energy, and a fixed activated complex which is the same for different temperatures in general cannot be used for thermally averaged rate constants (Gaedtke and Troe, 1973; Quack and Troe, 1974).

Before we explicitly take into account these difficulties, we derive general formulas for $k(E)$ in terms of simple transition-state theory. Simple models of activated complexes are used first. One calculates the reaction flux through the critical surface from unreacted molecules toward products. Similar to the general calculation of fluxes, the reaction flux j is given by the linear density of systems dn/dq in the direction of motion multiplied by the flow velocity dq/dt. This is symbolically written

$$j = (dq/dt)(dn/dq). \tag{1.20}$$

The reaction rate constant is given by j/n, or, in a complete form, by the integral along the critical surface over linear densities along the reaction coordinate q and velocities $dq/dt = \dot{q}$ for crossing the surface in the positive direction $(\dot{q} > 0)$:

$$k(E) = \int \cdots \int_{\substack{\text{crit surf } \dot{q} > 0 \\ E \leq H \leq E + dE}} \left\{ \frac{\dot{q}[(dq_1 \, dp_1 \cdots dq_s \, dp_s/h^s)/dq]}{\int \cdots \int_{\substack{\text{uncrit conf} \\ E \leq H \leq E + dE}} dq_1 \, dp_1 \cdots dq_s \, dp_s/h^s} \right\} \tag{1.21}$$

[the coordinates are defined as in Eq. (1.2)]. For simplification, q is identified with q_1, $\dot{q}$ with p_1/μ, the critical surface with some fixed value of q_1, and dE at the critical surface with $dE = d(p_1^2/2\mu)$. This simplification, of course, is not in general correct. A suitable choice of curvilinear coordinates is required (Hofacker, 1963; Marcus, 1964). For dissociation reactions this correction nevertheless is assumed to be comparably small. At the critical surface the uncritical coordinates vary freely, provided that the condition $E \leq H \leq E + dE$ is respected. Using the definition of density and number of states at the energy E given in Eq. (1.2), $k(E)$ becomes

$$k(E) = \frac{dE \int \cdots \int_{E_0 \leq H^{\ddagger}(q_2, \ldots, p_s) \leq E} dq_2 \cdots dp_s/h^{s-1}}{h\rho(E) \, dE} = \frac{W^{\ddagger}(E - E_0)}{h\rho(E)}. \tag{1.22}$$

Here, as throughout this chapter, E_0 gives the energy threshold; $W^{\ddagger}$ $(E - E_0)$ is the number of possibilities of distributing an energy $E - E_0$ on the $2(s - 1)$ noncritical coordinates and momenta at the critical surface; $\rho(E)$ is the density of states of molecules of energy E in the phase space of unreacted states separated by the critical surface from product states. Equation (1.22) is the famous basic equation of the quasiequilibrium theory of mass spectra (Rosenstock et al., 1952). It has been derived for theories of thermal unimolecular reactions by Rice and Marcus (1951), Marcus (1952), and Giddings and Eyring (1954).

Using the classical limit of Eqs. (1.7) and (1.8), $k(E)$ can be immediately evaluated from Eq. (1.22):

$$k(E) = \frac{\prod_{i=1}^{s} \nu_i}{\prod_{i=1}^{s-1} \nu_i^{\ddagger}} \left(\frac{E - E_0}{E} \right)^{s-1}. \tag{1.23}$$

The second factor was identified by Kassel (1932) as the probability of finding an energy between E_0 and E in one of the s oscillators.

In the semiclassical approximation, Eq. (1.10), $k(E)$ from Eq. (1.22) becomes

$$k(E) = \frac{\prod_{i=1}^{s} \nu_i}{\prod_{i=0}^{s-1} \nu_i^{\ddagger}} \left(\frac{E + E_z^{\ddagger} - E_0}{E + E_z}\right)^{s-1}. \tag{1.24}$$

This introduces a minimum nonzero rate constant $k(E)$ at $E = E_0$:

$$k(E = E_0) = \frac{\prod \nu_i}{\prod \nu_i^{\ddagger}} \left(\frac{E_z^{\ddagger}}{E_0 + E_z}\right)^{s-1}, \tag{1.25}$$

whereas $k(E = E_0) = 0$ in Eq. (1.23).

Because in thermal dissociation reactions, as well as in some other systems, excitations to energies near the threshold are of central interest, the classical and also the semiclassical formulas very often become inadequate. Instead, $W^{\ddagger}(E - E_0)$ has to be counted state by state. Then the minimum rate constant is given simply by

$$k(E = E_0) = 1/h\rho(E_0). \tag{1.26}$$

This was first realized in discussions of metastable transitions in mass spectra (Wolfsberg, 1962; Vestal, 1964). Alternatively, at energies slightly higher than E_0 the smoothed number of states from Eqs. (1.11) and (1.12) can be used in the numerator of Eq. (1.22). If degeneracies of states have to be accounted for, suitable degeneracy factors appear in Eq. (1.26) (see below).

The role of rotations of the molecule has to be discussed separately. As far as internal, free or hindered, rotations are concerned, one may use the modifications of the density of states discussed in Section I,B [see Eq. (1.16)]. Rotations of the molecule as a whole are considered as "adiabatic" in the sense that the angular momentum has to be conserved or that the reaction takes place at the effective potential surface of the rotating molecule. The occurrence of centrifugal maxima in the effective potential modifies the amount of vibrational energy necessary to overcome the effective dissociation energy. This is illustrated by Fig. 3 (see Marcus, 1965). The dashed curves correspond to uncritical coordinates and their zero-point levels, and the solid curves correspond to the reaction coordinate with quantum numbers $J = 0$ and $J > 0$ for rotation (axis perpendicular

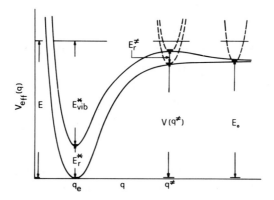

Fɪɢ. 3.   Effective potential curves of rotating molecules (upper solid curve, $J > 0$; lower solid curve, $J = 0$).

to the reaction coordinate). The rotational energy $E_r^\ddagger$ of the activated complex (here localized at the centrifugal barrier) is smaller than in the equilibrium configuration by

$$E_r^\ddagger = E_r^* I^* / I^\ddagger \tag{1.27}$$

[I is the moment of inertia around the axis perpendicular to q, $I^*/I^\ddagger \simeq (q_e/q^\ddagger)^2$]. Thus, the effective barrier of the reaction at $J > 0$ is lowered. The vibrational energy required to overcome the reaction barrier is

$$V(q^\ddagger(J)) + E_r^\ddagger(J) - E_r^*(J). \tag{1.28}$$

Thus, the specific rate constants for fixed rotational quantum numbers J and vibrational energies E_{vib}^* (in the equilibrium configuration) are given by Eq. (1.22) in the form

$$k(E, J) = \frac{\sigma}{\sigma^\ddagger} \frac{W^\ddagger(E_{vib}^* + E_r^* - E_r^\ddagger - V(q^\ddagger))}{h\rho(E_{vib}^*)}. \tag{1.29}$$

Multiplication by a suitable ratio of symmetry numbers $\sigma/\sigma^\ddagger$ is required in symmetric molecules (see Schlag and Haller, 1965; Quack and Troe, 1974). In addition, if nonequivalent reaction paths toward different products are accessible at energy E, one has to calculate the individual $k(E, J)$. The rotational contributions to $k(E)$, as given in Eq. (1.29), have been calculated explicitly by Forst (1968) and Waage and Rabinovitch (1970).

As indicated previously, these rotational contributions have to be modified if the localization of the activated complex is considered more carefully. First, $W^{\ddagger}(E - E_0, J)$ no longer has to be calculated for the centrifugal maxima but for the minimum of the local density of states, Eq. (1.19). Second, it is difficult to take into account properly the conservation of total angular momentum (Klots, 1971). The rotational motion around the axis parallel to the reaction coordinate cannot be separated from the vibrational motions. Therefore, the effective number of coordinates contributing to $W^{\ddagger}$ and ρ in Eq. (1.22) increases. A considerable change of the threshold rate constants for rotating molecules is observed.

In order to illustrate the expressions of $k(E)$ derived at the different stages of approximation, we show calculations for the dissociation of propane ions in the mass spectrum of propane in Fig. 4 and calculations for the dissociation of NO_2 molecules in thermal dissociation and thermal recombination and photolysis of NO_2 in Fig. 5. For the propane ion the competing primary processes

$$C_3H_8^+ \longrightarrow s\text{-}C_3H_7^+ + H \tag{1.30}$$

$$C_3H_8^+ \longrightarrow CH_2CH_2^+ + CH_4 \tag{1.31}$$

$$C_3H_8^+ \longrightarrow C_3H_6^+ + H_2 \tag{1.32}$$

$$C_3H_8^+ \longrightarrow C_2H_5^+ + CH_3 \tag{1.33}$$

are considered. $k(E)$ shown in Fig. 4 was calculated by Vestal (1965) using the smoothed density of states from Vestal et al. (1962). The bond energies E_0 used were 0.52 eV (1.30), 0.58 eV (1.31), 0.60 eV (1.32), and 0.77 eV (1.33). Even using smoothed densities down to the dissociation threshold, an apparent discontinuity of $k(E)$ near the threshold is observed. This corresponds to approaching the minimum rate constants for E_0, which should be between (in sec^{-1}) 2.5×10^8 and 3.0×10^5 (1.30), 1.1×10^8 and 1.0×10^5 (1.31), 8.9×10^7 and 7.3×10^4 (1.32), and 1.2×10^7 and 5.1×10^3 (1.33) [the first numbers were calculated with the frequencies of the ion, the second numbers with the frequencies of the activated complex of (1.30)]. To obtain exact values of $k(E = E_0)$, better knowledge of the molecular properties of $C_3H_8^+$ is required.

Figure 5 shows $k(E)$ calculated for NO_2. Here dissociation of both O atoms is equivalent, and $\sigma/\sigma^{\ddagger} = 2$. Curve 1 represents the classical approximation (1.23), curve 2 the semiclassical approximation (1.24), and curve 3 the smoothed approximation using Eq. (1.11), and curve 4 is calculated

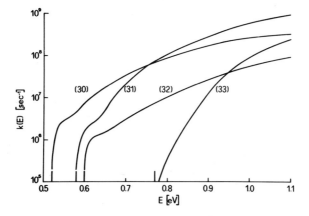

FIG. 4. Dissociation of propane ions [reactions (1.30)–(1.33); from Vestal, 1965].

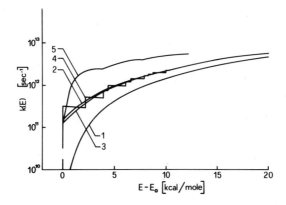

FIG. 5. Dissociation of NO_2 (1, classical; 2, semiclassical; 3, smoothed; 4, exact harmonic; 5, exact anharmonic; $J = 0$).

with exactly counted states. Curves 1–4 all use harmonic oscillator models with a frequency factor of 5×10^{13} sec^{-1}, $E_z = 5.4$ kcal mole^{-1}, $E_z^{\ddagger} = 3$ kcal mole^{-1}, and $\sigma/\sigma^{\ddagger} = 2$. It is quite evident that the classical approxima- tion is inadequate at energies near the dissociation threshold. Deviations between experimental and calculated quantities based on the classical approximation were often corrected by assuming a number of "effective oscillators," $s_{eff} < s$. This generally has nothing to do with a restricted internal coupling or an incomplete energy equilibration, but with the inadequacy of formula (1.23). Compared to propane (27 oscillators), NO_2

(three oscillators) has much higher values of $k(E)$ at the threshold. This corresponds to the smaller volume of the phase space accessible to non-critical oscillators.

The simplicity of triatomic molecules allows an explicit test of the activated complex localization of Eq. (1.19). Coupling between noncritical and critical coordinates at the activated complex, as well as rotational contributions, may be taken into account with relative ease. One may, for instance, approximately describe the decay of the bending force constant k_δ with increasing length of the reaction coordinate q, by the bond-energy bond-order method (Johnston, 1966). One obtains for NO_2, with q equal to the length of one ON—O bond, (q_e = equilibrium length),

$$k_\delta(q) \simeq k_\delta(q_e) \exp[-(4.2 \text{ Å}^{-1})(q - q_e)]. \tag{1.34}$$

At fixed q, with this force constant and the force constant of the uncritical bond, one has to solve the secular equation and obtain the "quanta" $\varepsilon_2(q)$ and $\varepsilon_3(q)$ of the uncritical coordinates (Jungen and Troe, 1970). Because $\varepsilon_2(q)$ decays approximately in proportion to $[k_\delta(q)]^{1/2}$ one obtains a considerable increase in the density of states in the bending vibration as the reaction coordinate q increases.

The coupling between bending and reaction coordinate has significant consequences on the localization of the activated complex. To show this, we consider the local density of states along the reaction coordinate $\rho(q)$, which is defined as the number of states in the range $(E, E + dE)$ and $(q, q + dq)$. This density of states can be calculated in the classical or semiclassical approximation analogous to Eqs. (1.2) and (1.6). The translational density of states

$$\rho_{\text{tr}}(E, q) = \frac{1}{h} \left[\frac{2\mu}{E - V(q)} \right]^{1/2} \tag{1.35}$$

in the calculation is combined with the vibrational density of states of the noncritical oscillators. In the semiclassical approximation one obtains, e.g., for a nonrotating, bent, triatomic molecule

$$\rho(q) = \frac{4(2\mu)^{1/2}}{h\varepsilon_2(q)\varepsilon_3(q)} \left\{ \frac{[E - V(q)]^{1.5}}{1.5} + \frac{[\varepsilon_2(q) + \varepsilon_3(q)][E - V(q)]^{0.5}}{2} \right\} \tag{1.36}$$

(Bunker and Pattengill, 1968, Gaedtke and Troe, 1973). $V(q)$ denotes the potential energy along the reaction coordinate. $E - V(q)$ decreases with increasing q. This decrease in Eq. (1.36) is compensated for by the decrease of $\varepsilon_2(q)$, which corresponds to a weakening of the bending vibration [see Eq. (1.34)], before it is transformed into an internal rotation of the fragments relative to each other. As a consequence of both effects, minima of the local density of states appear. This is illustrated in Fig. 6. At $E_0 \leq E \leq 1.4E_0$ one finds minima of $\rho(q)$ at interfragment distances of the order of 1.5–3.5 Å. The position of these minima depends strongly on the energy.

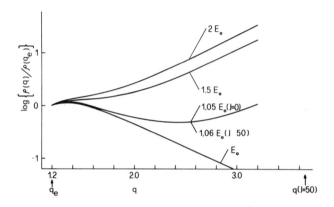

FIG. 6. Densities of states along $q(O-NO)[Å](J = 0$ except for $E = 1.06E_0$, where $J = 50$, linear model).

Molecules with different energy therefore have different activated complexes. If one uses a simplified model of rotation, replacing $V(q)$ in Eq. (1.36) by the effective potential of a rotating linear molecule, the minima of the local density of states do not at all coincide with the centrifugal maxima. In the example of Fig. 6, the centrifugal maximum for $J = 50$ is found at 3.6 Å, the minimum of the density of states for $E = 1.06E_0$ at 2.6 Å.

The strong energy dependence of the position of the activated complex and the marked changes of the quantum $\varepsilon_2(q)$ of the bending vibration lead to a particular shape of the $k(E)$ curve. This is shown in curve 5 of Fig. 5. Compared to RRKM calculations, a much steeper increase and a different curvature of the $k(E)$ curve is found. By changing of the activated complex frequencies, an RRKM calculation of $k(E)$ can be fitted to curve 5 for one energy. However, it is not possible to obtain agreement for larger energy ranges.

Whenever the semiclassical approximation becomes inadequate, a minimum local number of states criterion

$$\partial W^{(s-1)}(E,\, q)/\partial q = 0 \qquad (1.37)$$

has to be used instead of Eq. (1.19) (Quack and Troe, 1974). Here $W^{(s-1)}(E,\, q)$ denotes the number of states of the $s-1$ noncritical coordinates. $W^{(s-1)}$ can be obtained most conveniently from the individual reaction channels correlating reactant and product states; for these channel states conservation of angular momentum can be strictly fulfilled.

D. SPECIFIC RATE CONSTANTS: DYNAMICAL AND QUANTUM RELAXATION THEORIES

In dynamical theories the "occurrence of reaction" has to be defined. As long as the average lifetime is longer than about one vibrational period, the results do not markedly depend on the choice of a critical distance q_c along the reaction coordinate, provided that it is sufficiently large (e.g., $q_c \geq 2.5$–3 Å in N_2O and O_3, Bunker, 1962). With this choice of q_c the time necessary to reach q_c from a given starting point is calculated for a molecule by solving the classical equations of motion. This approach, from simple linear chain models (Polanyi and Wigner, 1928) via systems of harmonic oscillators (Slater, 1959), has now been extended to numerical calculations of trajectories at general potential surfaces, e.g., of the Morse type (Bunker, 1962, 1964, 1968; Wilson et al., 1964; Wilson and Hung, 1963; Wilson and Thiele, 1961, 1964). The latter treatments have shown that harmonic oscillator models, which imply serious restrictions to energy exchange between oscillators, are hardly applicable.

In dynamical theories, given an initial distribution of starting points, distributions $P(t)$ of lifetimes t are determined. The relation between $P(E,\, t)$ of molecules at the energy hypersurface E and specific rate constants is then given in the following way: The number of molecules $dn(E,\, t)$ reacting in the time $(t,\, t + dt)$ is given by

$$dn(E,\, t) = -n(E,\, 0)P(t)\, dt. \qquad (1.38)$$

Taking the definition of specific rate constants, Eq. (1.17), this leads to

$$k(E,\, t) = P(t)\Big/ \int_t^\infty P(t)\, dt. \qquad (1.39)$$

The "random lifetime assumption" postulates a $P(t)$ of the form

$$P(t) = k(E) \exp[-k(E)t], \qquad (1.40)$$

which identifies $k(E, t)$ with the decay constant and the intercept of $P(t)$ at $t = 0$. Equation (1.40) is the necessary condition for the time independence of $k(E, t)$.

In thermal unimolecular reactions an initial distribution of starting points which is random in phase space at the energy hypersurface E appears reasonable. For this case the Monte Carlo-averaged lifetime calculations of Bunker (1964) in the majority of models led to expressions such as Eq. (1.40). However, some nonrandom lifetime distributions have also been found (see Fig. 7). Then, intramolecular energy transfer has to be taken into

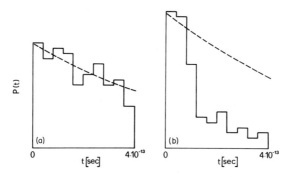

FIG. 7. Monte Carlo-averaged lifetimes: (a) random, (b) nonrandom (from Bunker, 1966).

account explicitly. Nonrandom lifetimes correspond to situations where the rate constants of intramolecular energy transfer are smaller than $k(E)$. Since time constants for intramolecular energy exchange in triatomic molecules with $E \simeq E_0$ have been found in the range 10^{-11}–10^{-13} sec (e.g., Bunker, 1964), nonrandom lifetime effects in thermal unimolecular reactions normally will be unimportant. With photochemical activation, in the classical theory, Franck–Condon distributions have to be used as starting points for trajectory calculations. In spite of this nonrandom initial distribution of phase points, random distributions of lifetimes are possibly approached if the lifetime is sufficiently long (see below).

At conditions where intramolecular energy equilibration is complete and random lifetime distributions are found, dynamical and quasi-equilibrium calculations of $k(E)$ are equivalent, provided that an adequate localization of the "activated complexes" is chosen for the quasiequilibrium theory. Excellent agreement between Monte Carlo calculations of $k(E)$ and the quasiequilibrium theory under these conditions was found (Bunker and Pattengill, 1968). Also, rate constants of thermal unimolecular reactions as calculated by the theories of Kassel, Giddings and Eyring, and Slater are equivalent to the corresponding dynamical theories, formulated by Slater's "new approach," if equivalent assumptions in phase space are applied (Thiele, 1962). Therefore, it is often most economical to take purely "statistical" theories and refine them as far as possible, instead of taking dynamical theories and losing a large part of the calculated details during the final averaging.

At very short lifetimes and for incomplete intramolecular equilibration of energy, quantum relaxation theories have to be used instead of the classical dynamical theories. Many quantum formulations of the theory of unimolecular processes are now available (e.g., Wilson and Thiele, 1964; Mies, 1969; Mies and Krauss, 1966; Levine, 1966). A very general approach is provided by theories of radiationless transitions in photochemistry (see, e.g., Jortner et al., 1969; Henry and Kasha, 1968). In this work internal mixing among (a) the electronic state excited by light absorption, (b) a manifold of vibrational states from the vibrational quasicontinuum of another electronic state, and (c) the translational continuum of dissociation products is considered. This distinction between states forces attention to the coupling of the primary excited state with the different modes of vibrational motion of the molecule. As soon as the vibrational levels of states (a) and (b) overlap, and the matrix elements of coupling are sufficiently large, the Born–Oppenheimer approximation breaks down. Then, internal mixing leads to a spreading of the nonstationary wave packet from the initial state (a), via the dense manifold of vibrational states (b), toward fragmentation (c). It is obvious that this model, at large coupling among (a), (b), and (c), remains applicable in many unimolecular processes, and that its representation of excited states of dissociating molecules as resonance scattering states is more generally valid than the quasi-bound-state picture of other theories.

The wave function ψ is composed of the zeroth-order Born–Oppenheimer wave functions for the single state (a), the manifold of states (b), and the continuum (c) at energy E:

$$\psi(E) = a(E)\varphi_a + \sum_n b_n(E)\varphi_{bn} + \int C_{E'}(E)\varphi_{cE'} \, dE'. \qquad (1.41)$$

The expansion coefficients $a(E)$, $b_n(E)$, and $C_{E'}(E)$ are expressed in terms of the coupling matrix elements:

$$\langle \varphi_a | H | \varphi_{bn} \rangle = v_1, \qquad \langle \varphi_{bn} | H | \varphi_c \rangle = v_2 \qquad (1.42)$$

(H is the complete Hamiltonian). Direct coupling between (a) and (c) is neglected. As described by Jortner $et\ al.$ (1969) and Mies and Krauss (1966), $a(E)$, $b_n(E)$, and $C(E)$ can be derived, and the probability of dissociation at time t after light absorption is calculated. Explicit solutions are difficult to obtain. However, a number of predictions were formulated by Jortner $et\ al.$ (1969): there should appear two lifetimes proportional to v_1^2 and v_2^2, respectively, similar to those derived from Fermi's golden rule; the rate of decay of excited molecules should depend on $\rho_1 v_1^2$ and $\rho_2 v_2^2$, where ρ_1 is the density of vibrational states in state (b) and ρ_2 is the density of states in the translational continuum (c). For equal orders of magnitude of $\rho_1 v_1^2$ and $\rho_2 v_2^2$ a nonstationary wave packet spreads out at about the same velocity from (a) into (b) and from (b) into (c). If $\rho_1 v_1^2 \gg \rho_2 v_2^2$, the excited state will have a long lifetime and dissociate like a vibrationally excited molecule from states (a) and (b) into the translational continuum (c). It dissociates as fast as the wave packet can spread out from state (b) into state (c). The specific rate constant of dissociation in one channel, in the simplest treatment, becomes approximately

$$k_{ch}(E) \simeq \rho_2 v_2^2 / h. \qquad (1.43)$$

Upon monochromatic light absorption, a Lorentzian distribution in state (a) is excited around energy E_a. Because of the coupling between (a) and (b), the states in (b) will be correspondingly populated and $k(E)$ in this case has to be averaged over the Lorentzian distribution. If, on the other hand, $\rho_1 v_1^2 \ll \rho_2 v_2^2$, the molecule dissociates as fast as the initial wave packet can spread out from state (a) into state (b). If, different from the model of Jortner $et\ al.$, the initial state reached by excitation is coupled directly to the translational continuum, the approach of Mies and Krauss (1966) and Mies (1969) appears preferable. Here, configurations of the molecule at energy E are regarded as resonance scattering states imbedded in the translational continuum of dissociating products. If the overlapping widths of these states are larger than their average spacing, particular quantum effects such as nonexponential decay are observed. One obtains as specific rate constants $k(E)$ [at $t \to 0$ in definition (1.17)] for dissociation in one particular dissociation channel

$$k_{ch}(E) \simeq \gamma / h\rho(E), \qquad (1.44)$$

with $\gamma = 4\pi\Gamma/D(1 + \pi\Gamma D)^2$, where D is the mean spacing of states and Γ is the width of states equal to $\pi|\langle\varphi_b|H - E|\varphi_c\rangle|^2$. After long reaction times, $k_{ch}(E)$ may decay below the value of Eq. (1.44).

An interpretation of Eq. (1.44) has been given in the compound nucleus model of nuclear physics (Blatt and Weisskopf, 1952). $h\rho(E)$ is the mean recurrence time of a particular configuration in a quantum system, and γ is a transmission coefficient for the wave outgoing from this configuration. By means of the dissociation channels correlating reactant and product states and their individual channel potential curves, a simplified estimate of γ can be tried: $\gamma \simeq 1$ is chosen at energies above the channel threshold and $\gamma \simeq 0$ below. With the statistical postulate, i.e., equal statistical weight for all open channels, the total specific rate constant takes the form of Eq. (1.22). $W^{\ddagger}$ no longer corresponds to a particular fixed activated complex, but represents the total number of open reaction channels (Quack and Troe, 1974). The statistical postulate of a quasiequilibrium theory in this way is replaced by a more general statistical assumption.

E. Distribution of Energy in Reaction Products

Absolute values of specific rate constants $k(E)$ are of importance in experiments which allow a direct access to lifetimes of excited molecules. Ratios of specific rate constants for different reaction channels are necessary to understand relative yields of chemically different reaction products. Relative yields of chemically identical but physically different reaction products are derived from experiments with energy resolution of the products.

Statistical calculations of energy distributions require knowledge of the range of interfragment distances where energy equilibration still happens. One might limit this by the "activated complexes" of Section I,C. The yield ϕ for a specific reaction channel l, with an energy E_l in one product, is then given by the ratio of the specific rate constants

$$\phi(E, E_l) = \frac{k(E, E_l)}{\sum_l k(E, E_l)} = \frac{k(E, E_l)}{k(E)} = \frac{W^{\ddagger}(E - E_0, E_l)}{W^{\ddagger}(E - E_0)}. \tag{1.45}$$

Here $W^{\ddagger}(E - E_0, E_l)$ denotes the number of quantum states in the activated complex in which the part E_l of the energy $E - E_0$ is located (and later hopefully remains) in that part of the molecule that later becomes the product of interest. $W^{\ddagger}$ is calculated as in Sections I,B and I,C. If, for instance, the distribution of energy between two parts of the molecule is of interest, the probability of finding an energy $(E_1, E_1 + dE_1)$ in part 1 is given by

$$\phi(E, E_1)\, dE_1 = \frac{\rho_1^{\ddagger}(E_1)\rho_2^{\ddagger}(E - E_0 - E_1)\, dE_1}{\int_0^{E - E_0}\rho_1^{\ddagger}(E_1)\rho_2^{\ddagger}(E - E_0 - E_1)\, dE_1} \tag{1.46}$$

(with densities ρ from Section I,B; part 2 is the rest of the complex). This expression has been used in calculating energy distributions in primary dissociations of ions which form unstable products dissociating in secondary unimolecular reactions. The distribution originating from the primary reactions gives here the activation characteristics for the secondary reaction (e.g. Vestal, 1965) (see Section VI).

The activated complex may be very loose, i.e., with bending vibrations already transformed into rotations of the fragments. Then the distribution of energy over the relative translation and relative rotation has to be explicitly included. For this case densities of vibrational states from Section I,B, densities of translational states from Eq. (1.35), and densities of rotational states given classically by

$$\rho_{\text{rot}}(E) = 2(I_A I_B)^{1/2}/\hbar^2\sigma \tag{1.47}$$

for a two-dimensional rotator, or

$$\rho_{\text{rot}}(E) = [(32 I_A I_B I_C)^{1/2}/\hbar^3\sigma]\sqrt{E} \tag{1.48}$$

for three rotational degrees of freedom, must be combined in Eq. (1.46). As an illustration Fig. 8 shows the distribution of $E - E_0 = 101$ kcal mole^{-1} on the vibrations of excited cyclopropane formed during photolysis of cyclobutanone (Campbell and Schlag, 1967):

$$\underset{s=27}{\bigtriangleup\!\!\!\!\raisebox{0.6em}{$\scriptstyle O$}} + h\nu \longrightarrow \underset{s=21}{\bigtriangledown^*} + \underset{s=1}{CO} + E_{\text{tr}} + E_{\text{rot}}. \tag{1.49}$$

Analysis of translational energies of fragments in ion decomposition (Franklin and Haney, 1968, 1969; LeRoy, 1970, 1971) or translational spectroscopy of photolysis fragments from molecular beams (Busch, et al., 1969; Busch and Wilson, 1972; Diesen et al., 1969) calls for distributions of

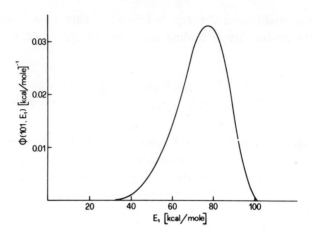

FIG. 8.   Statistical distribution of energy in cyclopropane from cyclobutanone photolysis at 2537 Å (from Campbell and Schlag, 1967).

translational energies. A statistical calculation analogous to Eq. (1.46) would use

$$\phi(E, E_{tr}) = \frac{\rho_{tr}(E_{tr})\rho_{vib, rot}(E - E_{tr})}{\int_0^E \rho_{tr}(E_{tr})\rho_{vib, rot}(E - E_{tr})\, dE_{tr}}. \qquad (1.50)$$

In a statistical channel model $W^{\ddagger}(E - E_0, E_l)$ in Eq. (1.45) is identified with the number of open channels leading to products of energy E_l. Since in this case all dissociation channels are followed from the reactant to the product side, energy distributions are accessible conveniently. Nevertheless, an assumption on the extent of vibrational adiabaticity of the channel is required (Quack and Troe, 1974). Where statistical calculations of energy distribution become inadequate, dynamical theories or quantum relaxation theories again have to be used. At very short lifetimes of dissociating triatomic molecules, nonrandom distributions of vibrational energy in the diatomic product were observed parallel to the nonrandom lifetime distributions in the Monte Carlo-averaged trajectory calculations of Bunker (1964) (see Fig. 9). The exact shape of the potential surfaces is clearly of central importance. Photolysis of triatomic molecules at nonbonding potential surfaces of excited states was shown to give preferentially vibrational excitation if vertical Franck–Condon excitation during light absorption from the ground state leads to points on the slopes of the outgoing potential valley of the excited state, and preferentially translational excitation is

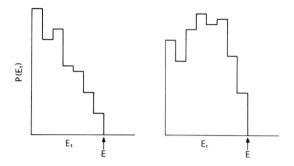

FIG. 9.   Energy distribution in the diatomic product of a dissociating triatomic molecule: (a) random, (b) nonrandom (Monte Carlo calculations from Bunker, 1964).

obtained if vertical excitation leads to the bottom of the upper potential valley (Mitchell and Simons, 1967).

II. Thermal Unimolecular Reactions

A. THREE-STEP MECHANISM FOR DISSOCIATION AND RECOMBINATION

In the following experimental results for thermally induced unimolecular reactions are presented together with the theoretical descriptions. In these reactions activation takes place by collisions of reacting particles A with the molecules or atoms M of a heat bath. The vibrational and rotational energy necessary for the reaction is transferred to A in collisions between A and M. The kinetic properties of reactions of this type may be qualitatively understood in terms of the rough three-step mechanism initially proposed by Lindemann (1922). We consider this model first, for it easily allows a classification of experimental results.

The series of competing intermolecular collisional activations and deactivations is described by two steps:

$$A + M \xrightarrow{k_{ac}} A^* + M \tag{2.1}$$

$$A^* + M \xrightarrow{k_{deac}} A + M. \tag{2.2}$$

The intramolecular rearrangement leading to structural change of A^*, dissociation, isomerization, or electronic transition, is represented by

$$A^* \xrightarrow{k_{intra}} products. \tag{2.3}$$

Here k_{intra} corresponds to a suitably averaged value of the specific rate constant $k(E)$ determined in Sections I,C and I,D. The rate equations for this system of elementary steps can easily be integrated without simplifications (e.g., Johnston, 1966). Assuming $k_{ac}[M] \ll (k_{deac}[M] + k_{intra})$, one obtains a short initial period of $(k_{deac}[M] + k_{intra})^{-1}$ during which a steady state is established. After this short period the decay of the concentration of A is given by a first-order time law

$$-\frac{1}{[A]}\frac{d[A]}{dt} = k = k_{ac}[M]\frac{k_{intra}}{k_{intra} + k_{deac}[M]}. \tag{2.4}$$

This expression can also be immediately obtained by applying directly the "steady-state assumption" $d[A^*]/dt \simeq 0$. The apparent first-order rate constant k defined by Eq. (2.54), may be understood simply as the first-order rate constant of activation $k_{ac}[M]$ multiplied by the fraction of A^* that after activation completes reaction and is not deactivated. This fraction, as given by the fraction on the right in Eq. (2.4), equals one at $k_{deac}[M] \ll k_{intra}$, i.e., in gases at sufficiently low pressures, and, consequently, long intervals between collisions. The fraction decreases with increasing [M], increasing importance of deactivations, and decreasing times between collisions, approaching $k_{intra}/k_{deac}[M]$. The reaction thus shows two different regimes, one low-pressure range with rate-determining collisional activation and one high-pressure range with rate-determining intramolecular structural change.

A limiting second-order rate law is obtained at sufficiently low pressures (for $k_{deac}[M] \ll k_{intra}$)

$$k \to k_0 = k_{ac}[M] \tag{2.5}$$

and a limiting first-order rate law at sufficiently high pressures (for $k_{deac}[M] \gg k_{intra}$)

$$k \to k_\infty = (k_{ac}/k_{deac})k_{intra}. \tag{2.6}$$

The transition between the low-pressure and the high-pressure limit occurs around concentrations of the carrier gas of

$$[M]_{1/2} = k_{intra}/k_{deac}. \tag{2.7}$$

If deactivation is assumed to occur in times of the same order as those between gas-kinetic collisions, this time may be used as a "clock" for measuring an average lifetime of A*, defined by k_{intra}^{-1}. Correspondingly, the time between gas-kinetic collisions at a concentration of collision partners $[M]_{1/2}$ may be used as a rough estimate of this lifetime. At constant temperature the dependence of k on pressure or $[M]$, as described by Eq. (2.4), is now commonly represented by a $\log k$ vs. $\log[M]$ plot and called a "falloff curve" of the rate constant. It shows the falloff of the first-order rate constants at low pressures. This representation has mostly replaced the $1/k$ vs. $[M]$ plot.

The close relationship between thermal dissociation and the reverse process, recombination, is easily illustrated by treating the recombination by the same model. Including the association of particles B and C as the initial step of recombination,

$$ B + C \xrightarrow{\ k_{\text{ass}}\ } A*, \tag{2.8} $$

one immediately obtains, under steady-state conditions,

$$ -\frac{1}{[B][C]}\frac{d[B]}{dt} \equiv k_{\text{rec}} = k_{\text{ass}}\frac{k_{\text{deac}}[M]}{k_{\text{intra}} + k_{\text{deac}}[M]}. \tag{2.9} $$

Here again the fraction on the right describes the fraction of A* that after formation by association of B and C completes the reaction by collisional stabilization before redissociating. At the low-pressure limit one obtains the third-order rate law:

$$ k_{\text{rec}} \rightarrow k_{\text{rec}\,0} = (k_{\text{ass}}/k_{\text{intra}})k_{\text{deac}}[M] \tag{2.10} $$

and at the high-pressure limit the second-order rate law:

$$ k_{\text{rec}} \rightarrow k_{\text{rec}\,\infty} = k_{\text{ass}}. \tag{2.11} $$

The transition between the third- and the second-order range occurs again at approximately $[M]_{1/2}$ given by Eq. (2.7).

According to Eqs. (2.4) and (2.9), the ratio k/k_{rec} is independent of pressure:

$$ k/k_{\text{rec}} = (k_{\text{ac}}/k_{\text{deac}})(k_{\text{intra}}/k_{\text{ass}}). \tag{2.12} $$

Therefore, the pressure dependence of recombination rate constants is given by the same type of curve as in dissociation. As long as $k_{\text{ac}}/k_{\text{deac}}$ and

$k_{\text{intra}}/k_{\text{ass}}$ may be taken equal to the equilibrium values of $[A^*]/[A]$ and $[B][C]/[A^*]$, respectively, the rate constants of dissociation and recombination are related to the equilibrium constant. This is not necessarily true, particularly with rate "constants" in the pre-steady-state period of the reaction. However, under most experimental conditions a conversion of k into k_{rec} and vice versa by means of equilibrium constants has been found to be valid (see below).

A second mechanism, in addition to the "energy-transfer mechanism" just discussed, contributes to the overall reaction of recombinations at low temperatures (possibly also to dissociations under special conditions). This "complex mechanism" involves the formation of intermediate complexes between M and reacting particles in reaction steps of the type

$$\begin{align} B + M &\;\rightleftharpoons\; BM \\ C + BM &\;\rightleftharpoons\; A + M. \end{align} \tag{2.13}$$

The importance of this type of mechanism depends, of course, on the type of interaction between B and M. For a discussion of this mechanism see, e.g., Porter (1962).

The rough model described in the foregoing provides an adequate primary classification of experimental results of thermal unimolecular reactions. A more detailed theoretical description will be presented after giving some experimental examples.

B. EXPERIMENTAL RESULTS

1. *Dissociation of Diatomic Molecules*

A large number of experimental studies have been devoted to thermal dissociations of diatomic molecules such as H_2, O_2, N_2, NO, CO, halogens, alkali halides, etc. All these studies had to be performed in shock waves, because high temperatures, short times for establishing reaction conditions, and exclusion of wall reactions were necessary. A summary of experimental results was recently given by Troe and Wagner (1973), so that the characteristic properties of these reactions will be only briefly summarized here.

Under "normal" conditions the rate "constants" of these reactions—at constant pressure and gas composition—have been found constant throughout the reaction and independent of time (at least as long as reverse recombinations of atoms are negligible). Only in a few studies on O_2, N_2, etc., at extremely high temperatures with $E_0/RT \leq 5$, were "incubation times" with initially time-dependent first-order rate "constants" observed, corresponding to the pre-steady-state period mentioned previously (Wray, 1962). This is due to the coupling of the vibrational relaxation of low levels and the collisional excitation of high levels, and will be analyzed in Section II,D.

Under most of the conditions applied, dissociation of diatomic molecules has been found to follow an overall second-order rate law, corresponding to the low-pressure limit of thermal unimolecular reactions, Eq. (2.5). In some cases this has been shown to hold up to pressures of 100 atm. This is in agreement with estimates based on the value of $[M]_{1/2}$ calculated from Eq. (2.7). If k_{intra}^{-1} is assumed to be of the order of a vibrational period and k_{deac} of the order of the gas-kinetic collision number, considerable pressures are to be expected to attain the transition region of the reaction order. A transition such as observed in the dissociation of I_2 at $T \simeq 1000$ K and pressures as low as 50 atm (Troe and Wagner, 1967b) may be explained by the very slow vibration of highly vibrationally excited iodine molecules, perhaps leading to an early transition into a diffusion-limited dissociation as described in Section II,F.

The nature of the carrier gas M has some influence on k_0; the variation of "collision efficiencies" normally is found to be within a factor of ten at most. Atoms produced in the reaction as collision partners are sometimes responsible for peculiar behavior such as large efficiencies and unusual temperature coefficients. Particularly pronounced effects were found for $H_2 + H \rightarrow H + H + H$, where exchange reactions analogous to mechanism (2.13) are assumed (Hurle *et al.*, 1968). In oxygen dissociation with oxygen atoms present as M, chemical interaction in O_3 complexes may lead to peculiar energy transfer properties, as is also observed in vibrational relaxation of O_2 with O present (Kiefer and Lutz, 1967).

Examples of rate constants and their temperature coefficients are given in Fig. 10. The rate constants are expressed in the form

$$k_0 = [M]A(T) \exp(-E_0/RT) \tag{2.14}$$

with $E_0 = \Delta H_0^\circ$ is the dissociation energy at 0 K. (The dissociation energies for the molecules used are: H_2 103.3, O_2 118.0, N_2 225, F_2 36.8, Cl_2 57.0, Br_2 45.5, I_2 35.6 kcal mole^{-1}.) M = Ar has been chosen for all the experiments. As far as possible, $k_0 = k_{\text{rec}} K_{\text{eq}}$, i.e., the converted values from recombination studies, have been included for low temperatures. Low-temperature values from recombination and high-temperature values obtained directly now generally fit together nicely. In particular, in cases where measurements in both directions of the reaction were made, $k = k_{rec} K_{eq}$ could often be verified (for difficulties see Ip and Burns, 1967). The values of the preexponential factor $A(T)$ in general exceed the values of gas-kinetic collision numbers by several orders of magnitude at low temperatures, whereas lower values are obtained at high temperatures. Individual temperature dependences of $A(T)$ vary between $T^{-0.5}$ and T^{-3}; a mean value of $A(T) \propto T^{-1}$ is found. Much of the scatter is still due to experimental uncertainties, and significant differences between different systems are difficult to establish. The general agreement of the different experimental values is such as to allow an empirical representation of the rate constants of the type

$$k_0 \simeq [Ar] \times 10^{15.3 \pm 0.5} (T/1000)^{-1 \pm 0.5} \exp(-E_0/RT) \text{ cm}^3 \text{ mole}^{-1} \text{ sec}^{-1}.$$

$$(2.15)$$

This might be of use in predictions for "normal" dissociation and recombination rates.

A more complex dissociation mechanism applies to the decomposition of gaseous alkali halides (Hartig et al., 1968; Luther et al., 1972; Berry et al., 1968; Ewing et al., 1970). Here, internal mixing between heteropolar and homopolar potential curves introduces a competition between collisional activation processes, electronic transitions, and dissociation into two possible channels, ions or atoms. Consequently, anomalous behaviour is observed, which has attracted much interest.

2. Recombination of Atoms

As shown in Fig. 10, dissociation and recombination rates related to equilibrium constants generally fit together reasonably well. An empirical representation for $M = Ar$ gives

$$k_{rec\ 0} \simeq [Ar] \times 10^{14.6 \pm 0.5} (T/1000 \text{ K})^{-1} \text{ cm}^6 \text{ mole}^{-2} \text{ sec}^{-1} \quad (2.16)$$

as an average for many experimental systems.

From the data in Fig. 10 one does not immediately see to what extent energy transfer mechanisms (2.1–2.3) or complex mechanisms (2.13) contribute to the overall dissociation or recombination rates at different temperatures. Some information is provided by the collision efficiencies of

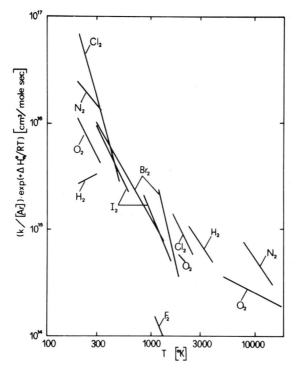

FIG. 10. Dissociation of diatomic molecules (high T, direct; low T, from recombination; from Troe and Wagner, 1973).

different carrier gases. Whereas in high-temperature dissociations collision efficiencies differ within a factor of about five, in low-temperature recombinations larger effects have been found. For instance, a great number of carrier gases have been studied in the recombination of iodine atoms, giving a variation of k_{rec} by more than two orders of magnitude. A good correlation between k_{rec} and boiling point of M exists at room temperature (Russell and Simons, 1953). This points to significant contributions of the complex mechanism at low temperatures. For M = NO, the rather stable complex INO could be directly visualized (Porter et al., 1962), although in this case a more complicated mechanism has been observed than that given by Eq. (2.13) (van den Bergh and Troe, 1975). Also, different pressure dependences of both recombination mechanisms are to be expected.

Investigation of the pressure dependence of iodine recombination has been performed in different gases up to 1000 atm (Hippler et al., 1973). Peculiar pressure dependences have been found which may be attributed to different behavior of the energy transfer and the complex components of the rate constant and to complete fixing of iodine atoms in complexes IM.

3. Spin-Allowed Dissociations of Triatomic Molecules

Thermal unimolecular dissociations of molecules such as NO_2, O_3, SO_2, H_2O, CF_2, NF_2, NOCl, and F_2O have been found to take place at the potential surface of the electronic ground state according to the mechanism of Eqs. (2.1)–(2.3). Dissociations and the reverse recombinations at $[M] \leq 10^{-4}$ mole cm^{-3} have been found in the low-pressure region [see Eqs. (2.5) and (2.10)]. Transition into the high-pressure region [Eqs. (2.6) and (2.11)] was detected only at pressures of the order of 100 atm in the dissociation of NO_2 and the recombinations $Cl + NO \rightarrow ClNO$, $I + NO \rightarrow INO$, $O + NO \rightarrow NO_2$, and $O + O_2 \rightarrow O_3$. Temperature dependences of k_0 are illustrated in the Arrhenius plots of Fig. 11. The apparent activation energies

$$E_a \equiv -R \frac{\partial \ln(k/[M])}{\partial(1/T)}, \qquad (2.17)$$

which in diatomic molecules were found to be between $E_0 - 0.5RT$ and $E_0 - 3RT$ in Eq. (2.15), could be best represented by the empirical relation

$$E_a \simeq E_0 + R \frac{\partial \ln Q_{vib}}{\partial(1/T)} - (0.5 \pm 0.5)RT, \qquad (2.18)$$

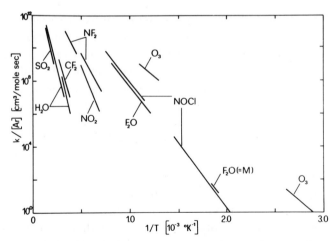

Fig. 11.   Spin-allowed dissociations of triatomic molecules (from Troe and Wagner, 1973).

where $Q_{vib}(T)$ denotes the vibrational partition function

$$Q_{vib} = \prod_{i=1}^{s} [1 - \exp(-h\nu_i/kT)]^{-1}. \qquad (2.19)$$

At extremely high temperatures ($T \gg h\nu_i/k$ for all oscillators)

$$E_a \simeq E_0 - (s + 0.5)RT \qquad (2.20a)$$

may become considerably smaller than E_0. At normal temperatures some oscillators are often not excited enough to contribute to Q_{vib}. Then, the lowering of E_a becomes less pronounced. "Effective oscillators" $s_{eff} < s$ determined from Eq. (2.20a) again have nothing to do with a restricted intramolecular coupling, but reflect the quantum form of Q_{vib}. From Eqs. (2.18) and (2.20a) one may define an s_{eff} by

$$s_{eff} = -\frac{1}{T}\frac{\partial \ln Q_{vib}}{\partial(1/T)} = \frac{U_{vib}}{RT}. \qquad (2.20b)$$

For relatively unstable molecules such as O_3, F_2O, and ClNO, experiments can be performed at low temperatures in static or flow systems and at high temperatures in shock waves. More stable molecules such as SO_2, NO_2, or H_2O have only been studied in shock waves. As in diatomic molecules, low-temperature recombination results can be reconciled nicely. This is illustrated by the results in Fig. 12 for NO_2, expressed in terms of recombination rate constants $k_{rec\,0}$. Collision efficiencies of different carrier gases M, where studied, varied only slightly (Schippert et al., 1974). Pronounced effects were found only for M $= H_2O$—probably due to the large dipole moment—in H_2O dissociation and recombination $H + OH \rightleftharpoons H_2O$ [$k(M = H_2O) \simeq 20k(M = Ar)$; Homer and Hurle, 1970)].

Whereas in the low-pressure range the reaction is activation determined [Eq. (2.1)], the structural change [Eq. (2.3)] becomes rate determining in the high-pressure range. Because of the high pressures necessary to obtain this region in triatomic molecules, only few data, for ClNO, INO, NO_2, and O_3, are available. Figure 13 shows transition curves from second to first order in NO_2 dissociation and from third to second order in the recombination $O + NO \rightarrow NO_2$ (Troe, 1969a,b). The change of order occurs at pressures around 100 atm. The high-pressure rate constants obtained are $10^{14.3}\exp(-E_0/RT)$ sec^{-1} at 1500 K and $10^{14.6}\exp(-E_0/RT)$ sec^{-1} at 300 K for NO_2 and $10^{13.4}\exp(-E_0/RT)$ sec^{-1} at 300 K for O_3

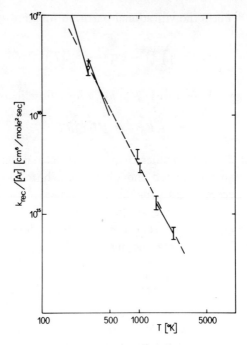

Fig. 12. Low-pressure range of recombination $O + NO + Ar \to NO_2 + Ar$ (low T, direct; high T, from dissociation, dashed curve, $\propto T^{-1.92}$; from Troe, 1969a).

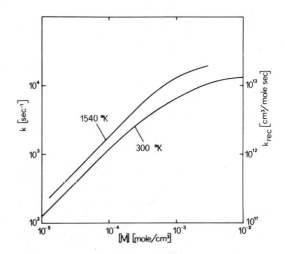

Fig. 13. Falloff curves of dissociation (1540 K) and recombination (300 K) of NO_2 (from Troe, 1969a,b).

(Hippler and Troe, 1971) when expressed as dissociation rates. Alternatively, recombination rate constants of $10^{12.4}$ (1500 K) and $10^{13.1}$ (300 K) for NO_2 and $10^{12.0}$ cm^3 mole^{-1} sec^{-1} (300 K) for O_3 are obtained.

An interesting relation between the high-pressure range for recombination and isotope exchange should be mentioned. In both processes the primary association, e.g., $O + NO \rightarrow NO_2^*$ and $O + O_2 \rightarrow O_3^*$, is rate determining. Then, in high-pressure recombination the complexes are stabilized; in isotope exchange only the subsequent dissociation of the isotopically different O atom of NO or O_2 from the complex gives a reaction. Since all complexes react in recombination, but only part of the complexes succeed in isotope exchange, $k_{iso}/k_{rec \infty}$ should be <1. This has been found with $k_{iso}/k_{rec \infty} \simeq 0.6$ for O_3, 0.3 for NO_3, and 0.1 for NO_2. These data, as soon as they are accurate enough, should provide insight into the extent of energy equilibration in the NO_2^* and O_3^* complexes.

4. Spin-Forbidden Dissociations of Triatomic Molecules

The dissociations of N_2O, CO_2, CS_2, and COS follow a different mechanism, with thermally induced electronic singlet–triplet transitions. This is illustrated by a section of the potential surface of N_2O shown in Fig. 14. Collisional activation takes place in the vibrational states of the singlet electronic ground state up to the range where singlet surface and triplet surface cross. Because electronic ground states of oxygen and sulfur atoms are ^3P and $^1\Sigma$ for N_2, CO, and CS, electronically unexcited products in

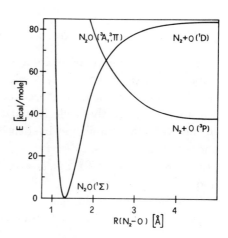

FIG. 14.   Potential curves of N_2O.

these cases correlate with the lowest triplet states of the molecules. Therefore, a singlet–triplet transition follows collisional excitation. The final dissociation out of the triplet state is fast and not rate determining. The energy threshold E_0 for N_2O is considerably higher than the heat of dissociation ΔH_0°. For CO_2, COS, and CS_2, $E_0 \gtrsim \Delta H_0^\circ$ is derived from the dissociation results.

Dissociations in the low-pressure region behave in a manner similar to spin-allowed dissociations of triatomic molecules. In the analysis one has only to take into account that the energy threshold is located in a potential region where anharmonicity and rotational contributions are much smaller than in spin-allowed dissociations. High-pressure rate constants of $10^{11.1} \exp(-59,500/RT)$ sec^{-1} for N_2O ($E_0 \simeq 63$ kcal mole^{-1}), $10^{11.3}$ $\exp(-110,000/RT)$ sec^{-1} for CO_2 ($E_0 \simeq 130$ kcal mole^{-1}), $10^{12.9}$ $\exp(-89,000/RT)$ sec^{-1} for CS_2 ($E_0 \simeq 93$ kcal mole^{-1}), and $10^{11.6}$ $\exp(-68,300/RT)$ sec^{-1} for COS ($E_0 \simeq 71$ kcal mole^{-1}) have been found (Olschewski et al., 1966a,b; Schecker and Wagner, 1969). The low preexponential factors reflect the small probability of the spin-forbidden reactions. Rough estimates for the singlet–triplet transition probabilities give 10^{-3}–10^{-2} for O atoms and 10^{-2}–10^{-1} for S atoms. These values are in good agreement with the order of magnitude of spin–orbit coupling in O and S atoms, which is larger for S than for O. The analysis of the high-pressure results requires detailed knowledge of the intersection of the potential surfaces, which give an unusual critical surface for the reaction. Also, to find flow velocities through the critical surface requires knowledge of singlet–triplet transition probabilities as a function of the position at the critical surface (see Section II,C).

5. Thermal Unimolecular Reactions of Polyatomic Molecules

A large amount of experimental work has been concerned with thermal unimolecular reactions of polyatomic molecules. It is impossible to discuss here the different chemical aspects of the individual systems. The reader will find an exhaustive collection of limiting high-pressure rate constants in the NSRDS compilation by Benson and O'Neal (1970). Other recent and excellent reviews are given, e.g., by Maccoll (1969), Frey and Walsh (1969), Kaufman (1969), Spicer and Rabinovitch (1970), and Rabinovitch and Setser (1964).

With increasing molecular complexity, the "middle" of the transition region between low- and high-pressure regions, $[M]_{1/2}$ of Eq. (2.7), shifts to lower pressures. The high-pressure limit becomes more and more the typical range of reaction. Generally, in this range apparent activation energies of the Arrhenius plot

$$k_\infty = A_\infty \exp(-E_{a\infty}/RT) \tag{2.21}$$

are found to be close to threshold energies of reaction (as far as known). The preexponential factors A_∞ show large variations depending on the properties of the activated complexes and the extent of structural change. Large values, 10^{14}–10^{18} sec^{-1}, are often found in simple bond fission reactions. Dissociation of CH_4 gives $\log A_\infty = 15.1$; for C_2H_6, $\log A_\infty = 16.8$; for $n\text{-}C_4H_{10}$, $\log A_\infty = 17.3$; and for $\phi\text{-}CH_3$, $\log A_\infty = 15.5$. Preexponential factors for molecular elimination reactions are often lower (O'Neal and Benson, 1967, 1970). These reactions may be classified as n-center reactions. There are few examples of three-center activated complexes. The reaction

$$CF_2HCl \;\rightleftharpoons\; \begin{matrix} F \\ \\ F \end{matrix}\!\!\diagdown\!\!\begin{matrix} H \\ C \\ Cl \end{matrix} \;\longrightarrow\; CF_2 + HCl$$

gives $A_\infty = 10^{13.8}$ sec^{-1}. Many alkyl halide decompositions are four-center reactions, e.g.,

$$C_2H_5Cl \;\rightleftharpoons\; \begin{matrix} H & H \\ | & | \\ H-C-\!\!-C-H \\ \diagdown / \\ H\text{---}Cl \end{matrix} \;\longrightarrow\; C_2H_4 + HCl$$

with $\log A_\infty = 13.6$. Other four-center reactions involve the elimination of simple fragments such as H_2O, CO_2, NH_3, etc.

Six-center eliminations are general. Eliminations from alcohols, organic acids, esters, etc. are in this group, e.g., the elimination of C_2H_4 from ethyl acetate

$$CH_3-C\!\!\begin{matrix} \diagup O \\ \diagdown O-CH_2 \end{matrix}\!\!\begin{matrix} \\ \diagdown CH_3 \end{matrix} \;\rightleftharpoons\; CH_3-C\!\!\begin{matrix} \diagup O\text{---}H \\ \diagdown O\text{---}CH_2 \end{matrix}\!\!CH_2 \;\longrightarrow\; CH_3COOH + C_2H_4$$

with $\log A_\infty = 12.6$. Small ring compound decompositions probably involve biradicals as intermediates, as in the isomerization of cyclopropane

$$\triangle \;\rightleftharpoons\; \text{·}\diagup\diagdown\text{·} \;\longrightarrow\; \diagup\!\!\diagdown\!\!\diagup$$

In deuterated cyclopropane, Schlag and Rabinovitch (1960) showed D migration, $\log A_\infty = 16.1$, to be ten times faster than isomerization, $\log A_\infty = 15.1$. Estimates of the activated complex structure is possible in many cases (O'Neal and Benson, 1968, 1970). As an example of a poly-cyclic compound reaction, we give the isomerization of 1,3-dimethyl-bicyclo-(1,1,0) butane

$$\bowtie \rightleftharpoons \triangle\!\!\!\!\diagdown \longrightarrow \bowtie\!\!=$$

with $\log A_\infty = 14.4$. In the group of cis–trans isomerizations such as cis-but-2-ene → trans with $\log A_\infty = 13.8$, Cope rearrangements such as

$$d_2 \diagdown\!\!\diagup d_2 \longrightarrow {}_{d_2}\diagdown\!\!\diagup{}_{d_2}$$

with $\log A_\infty = 11.1$, and isocyanide isomerizations such as $CH_3NC \rightarrow CH_3CN$ with $\log A_\infty = 13.6$, preexponential factors of 10^9–10^{14} sec^{-1} are found.

As mentioned, the pressure $p_{1/2}$ where a falloff of k to $\frac{1}{2}k_\infty$ is observed decays with increasing complexity. Table I shows rough values of $p_{1/2}$ for

TABLE I

FALLOFF PRESSURES OF THERMAL UNIMOLECULAR REACTIONS

	NO_2	NO_2Cl	CH_4	N_2H_4	CH_3NC	C_2H_6	c-C_3H_6	c-C_4H_8	cis-Butene
T (K)	1540	420	2200	1400	500	980	760	700	740
$P_{1/2}$ (Torr)	10^5	10^4	10^5	10^4	10^2	10^1	10^1	10^0	10^{-2}

representative systems. In general, the value of $p_{1/2}$ depends on temperature. This is shown in Fig. 15 for the dissociation of hydrazine. Besides the shift of $p_{1/2}$, the transition region between the low- and high-pressure limits also tends to broaden with increasing complexity of the molecules. Detailed investigations of the falloff curves for methyl-isocyanide isomerization, $CH_3NC \rightarrow CH_3CN$, showed different isotope effects: In the high-pressure limit $k(CH_3NC) : k(CH_2DNC) : k(CD_3NC) = 1 : 1 : 1.07$, while in the low-pressure region the ratios are $1 : 0.7 : 0.28$. Also, the width of the transition region was found to be different ("s_{eff}" = $3.6 : 3.9$ for

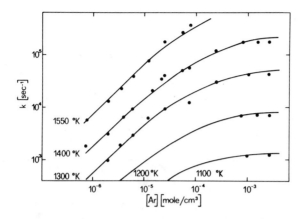

FIG. 15. Falloff curves of dissociation of hydrazine (from Meyer *et al.*, 1968).

CH$_3$NC : CD$_3$NC; Schneider and Rabinovitch, 1962, 1963 and later work cited in Spicer and Rabinovitch, 1970).

Low-pressure limiting rates have been obtained only for moderately complex molecules. They could often be estimated only by extrapolation. Extensive studies are available for a number of isomerizations. In general, low-pressure activation energies follow Eq. (2.18) nicely. Low-pressure preexponential factors may become very large with increasing complexity. If k_0 is expressed as $k_0 = [M] A_0 \exp(-\Delta H_0°/RT)$, with a T-dependent A_0, values such as those given in Table II are found, which show a considerable increase of A_0 with increasing number of oscillators.

By far the most extensive study on collision efficiencies of different M in the low-pressure region has been performed by Chan *et al.* (1970) for

TABLE II

Low-Pressure Preexponential Factors for Thermal Unimolecular Reactions[a]

	NO$_2$	NO$_2$Cl	CH$_4$	N$_2$H$_4$	CH$_3$NC	C$_2$H$_6$	c-C$_3$H$_6$	c-C$_4$H$_8$	cis-Butene
M	Ar	N$_2$	Ar	Ar	Ar	Ar	Ar	Ar	Ar
T (K)	2000	420	2200	1500	500	980	760	700	740
log A_0	16.7	16.8	18.7	17.6	18.0	24	24	25	25

[a] Representation $k_0 = [M]A_0 \exp(-\Delta H_0°/RT)$, A_0 in cm^3 mole^{-1} sec^{-1}.

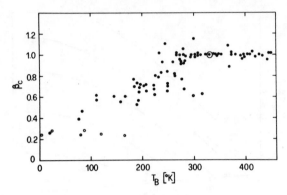

Fɪɢ. 16.   Collision efficiencies β_c of different M (boiling temperatures T_B) in the low-pressure isomerization of methyl isocyanide (○, M = rare gas; ●, M = diatomic or linear triatomic; ⊙, M = CH₃NC = reference; β_c relative to β_c(CH₃NC), using gas-kinetic collision number; from Chan *et al.*, 1970).

methyl isocyanide (=A) isomerization with 102 different carrier gases. Figure 16 shows collision efficiencies β_c of these M on a collision-for-collision basis,

$$\beta_c = [k_0(M)/k_0(A)](\sigma_{AA}/\sigma_{AM})^2(\mu_{AM}/\mu_{AA})^{1/2}$$

with σ the collision diameter and μ the reduced mass. Different inter-related correlations between the collision efficiencies β_c and parameters of M can be established: for monatomic, diatomic, and triatomic M a β_c versus boiling temperature, polarizability, or Lennard-Jones ε correlation exists. From simple to polyatomic M, a β_c versus polarizability or number of atoms in M correlation is observed. Other factors like collisional force or dipole moment are only of little importance.

A number of studies with isotopically substituted molecules have been designed to decide whether statistical equilibration takes place in activated molecules, or whether symmetry or orthogonality restrictions have to be taken into account. In most cases evidence is clearly against significant symmetry restrictions in activated molecules (Spicer and Rabinovitch, 1970).

C. Theories of the High-Pressure Limit

The simple three-step model of Section II,A already shows that at $k_{\text{deac}}[M] \gg k_{\text{intra}}$ collisional activations (2.1) and collisional deactivations (2.2) equilibrate. This results in a Boltzmann distribution of states of all unreacted molecules. The fraction of A in the energy interval $(E, E + dE)$ at equilibrium is given by

$$f(E)\, dE = \rho(E)[\exp(-E/kT)]\, dE/Q. \tag{2.22}$$

Generalization of Eq. (2.6) to include all different states above the energy threshold E_0 gives k_∞ as the thermally averaged specific rate constant of the unimolecular reaction,

$$k_\infty = \int_{E_0}^{\infty} k(E)f(E)\, dE. \tag{2.23}$$

Therefore, with densities of states $\rho(E)$ from Section I,B and specific rate constants from Sections I,C and I,D the limiting high-pressure rate constant can be obtained by integration. Since $f(E) \propto \rho(E)$ and $k(E) \propto \rho^{-1}(E)$, $\rho(E)$ cancels out. k_∞ is thus given, with Eq. (1.32), by

$$k_\infty = \frac{\int_{E_0}^{\infty} W^{\ddagger}(E - E_0)\exp(-E/kT)\, dE}{hQ} = \frac{kT}{h}\frac{Q^{\ddagger}}{Q}\exp-\frac{E_0}{kT}, \tag{2.24}$$

where Q is the partition function of unexcited molecules A and $Q^{\ddagger}$ is the partition function of activated complexes, defined by

$$Q^{\ddagger} = \int_{E_0}^{\infty} W^{\ddagger}(E - E_0)\exp\left(-\frac{E - E_0}{kT}\right)\frac{dE}{kT}. \tag{2.25}$$

One should remember the different possibilities of interpreting $W^{\ddagger}(E - E_0)$, i.e., as "number of states of the activated complex" or as "number of open reaction channels" (see Sections I,C and I,D). In the latter case $Q^{\ddagger}$ may also be written as

$$Q^{\ddagger} = \sum_{\alpha} \exp[-(V_{\alpha\,\text{max}} - E_0)/kT] \tag{2.26}$$

where the sum counts all open dissociation channels, and $V_{\alpha\,\text{max}}$ denotes the threshold energy of each individual channel (see Quack and Troe, 1974). Equation (2.24), the fundamental relation from transition-state theory, is the basis of "thermochemical" treatments of rate constants k_∞. In the form

$$k_\infty = (kT/h)\exp(\Delta S^{\ddagger}/R)\exp(-\Delta H^{\ddagger}/RT) \tag{2.27}$$

it is commonly interpreted in terms of the equilibrium between A and A‡; it contains the entropy $\Delta S^{\ddagger}$ and enthalpy $\Delta H^{\ddagger}$ of activation, i.e., of transforming the molecule A into activated complexes A‡. The technique of estimating thermodynamic data for activated complexes such as shown in Section II,B,5 has now been developed in great detail (see, e.g., O'Neal and Benson, 1967, 1968, 1970; Wieder and Marcus, 1962; Lin and Laidler, 1968). It allows predictions of k_{∞} in complex chemical systems with good accuracy. In the simplest case, with only harmonic oscillators involved, Eq. (2.24) takes the form

$$k_{\infty} = \frac{kT}{h} \frac{\prod_{i=1}^{s-1}[1 - \exp(-h\nu_i^{\ddagger}/kT)]^{-1}}{\prod_{i=1}^{s}[1 - \exp(-h\nu_i/kT)]^{-1}} \exp -\frac{E_0}{kT}, \qquad (2.28)$$

which in the high-temperature, classical limit $(T \gg \{h\nu_i^{\ddagger}/k, \ h\nu_i/k\})$ approaches

$$k_{\infty} \simeq \frac{\prod_{i=1}^{s}\nu_i}{\prod_{i=1}^{s-1}\nu_i^{\ddagger}} \exp -\frac{E_0}{kT} \equiv \bar{\nu} \exp -\frac{E_0}{kT}. \qquad (2.29)$$

In the simplest harmonic oscillator model, formulations from transition-state theory and from dynamical theories of k_{∞} coincide (see Thiele, 1962). With the proper choice of activated complexes this remains true in general situations (Bunker and Pattengill, 1968; this chapter, Sections I,C and I,D).

The simple thermochemical techniques are adequate as long as the positions of the activated complexes may be fixed independent of energy E, rotational quantum numbers, etc., and as long as no particular quantum effects such as complicated transmission coefficients for radiationless transitions, tunneling, etc., become important. As shown in Section I,C, bond fission reactions, with increase of distance between both fragments at the activated complex, require a more detailed description. Those oscillators whose energy eigenvalues are nearly constant from the reactant to the product side contribute the factors

$$Q_i = [1 - \exp(-h\nu_i/kT)]^{-1} \qquad (2.30)$$

to the partition function $Q^{\ddagger}$. However, torsional and deformation vibrations, which during the reaction are transformed into free rotations of the fragments relative to each other, have to be described in a different manner. Their energy eigenvalues depend strongly on the interfragment distance.

Furthermore, these motions cannot be separated from the overall rotation of the molecule. Therefore, except for the factors (2.30), no factorization of $Q^{\ddagger}$ is possible and Eq. (2.26) has to be evaluated by considering all individual channel states.

If the molecule or the products have some symmetry, this has to be taken into account in determining Q, $\rho(E)$, $W^{\ddagger}$, and $Q^{\ddagger}$. Only those states or channels may be counted that really occur. This procedure often is fairly cumbersome. Therefore a simplified method is useful, which applies to situations where larger energy intervals and not single channels or states are considered. If one denotes by the index m the quantities determined without symmetry considerations, on the average $\rho(E)$ and Q have to be divided by the symmetry number of the molecule σ; $W^{\ddagger}$ and $Q^{\ddagger}$ are divided by the product of the symmetry numbers of the fragments (e.g., σ_1 and σ_2). Then,

$$k_{\infty} \simeq \frac{kT}{h} \frac{\sigma}{\sigma_1 \sigma_2} \frac{Q_m{}^{\ddagger}}{Q_m} \exp - \frac{E_0}{kT}. \qquad (2.31)$$

Two important limiting cases of Eqs. (2.24)–(2.31) are often discussed, the "rigid" and the "loose" activated complex. In the rigid case the activated complexes (in the sense defined in Section I,C) are considered as being similar to the initial reactants; in the loose case they are considered as being similar to the separated fragments. In the language of Eq. (2.26), the pattern of the threshold energies of the individual reaction channels corresponds either to that of the reactant molecule or to that of the separated fragments. In these limits an approximate factorization of $Q_m{}^{\ddagger}$ becomes possible. For rigid complexes (with $\sigma/\sigma^{\ddagger}$)

$$Q_m{}^{\ddagger} \simeq Q_{\text{rot-}m}^{\ddagger} Q_{\text{vib}}^{\ddagger}; \qquad (2.32)$$

for loose complexes (e.g., with the fragments 1 and 2),

$$Q_m{}^{\ddagger} \simeq Q_{\text{rot, }m}^{p} Q_{\text{vib 1}} Q_{\text{vib 2}} Q_{\text{rot 1}} Q_{\text{rot 2}}. \qquad (2.33)$$

$Q_{\text{vib}}^{\ddagger}$ corresponds to vibrational states of the activated complex that are near those of the reactant molecule. In fact, Eqs. (2.28) and (2.29) imply this assumption of a rigid activated complex. The rotational partition function $Q_{\text{rot, }m}$ (index m for neglect of symmetry effects, as before) applies to only slightly changed rotational constants of the activated complex. $Q_{\text{vib 1}}$ and $Q_{\text{vib 2}}$ correspond to the vibrational states of the separated fragments 1 and 2. For a loose complex, $Q_{\text{rot, }m}^{p}$ does not account for the individual rotations of both fragments but their orbital motions relative to each other. In this limit the channel thresholds $V_{\alpha\,\mathrm{max}}$ of Eq. (2.26) are given by the centrifugal maxima. With a long-range interfragment potential $V(q) = -C/q^6$, after thermal averaging this leads to

$$Q^p_{\mathrm{rot},\,m}/Q^{\ddagger}_{\mathrm{rot},\,m} \simeq \ll {}^{\ddagger}q^2 \gg /q_e{}^2 \qquad (2.34)$$

where q_e is the interfragment distance in the equilibrium configuration, and $\ll q^{\ddagger 2} \gg$ is given by the averaged value

$$\ll q^{\ddagger 2} \gg = \Gamma(2/3)(2C/kT)^{1/3} = 1.354(2C/kT)^{1/3} \qquad (2.35)$$

(Waage and Rabinovitch, 1970; Eyring et al., 1936; for van der Waals constants C see Tschuikow-Roux, 1968). For different long-range potentials (e.g., for dissociating molecular ions), different $\ll q^{\ddagger 2} \gg$ are available. Unfortunately, the reality will often be found between the rigid and loose limiting cases. Then, bending vibrations of fragments relative to each other and rotational motion cannot be separated (see Quack and Troe, 1974).

Thermal unimolecular reactions involving radiationless transitions in the high-pressure limit require a special treatment. First, the region of "intersection of potential surfaces" (potential surfaces from the Born–Oppenheimer approximation taken as zeroth-order approximation) must be known. This, in general, will give a quite complex shape for the "critical surface" of the reaction. Second, in the flow rate through the critical surface, Eqs. (1.20) and (1.21), transition probabilities depending on energy and on properties of the intersection of potential surfaces such as slopes, etc., have to be included. Consequently, k_{∞} will be obtained after averaging over structural factors, i.e., the number of configurations "touching" the critical surface of the reaction, and transition probabilities depending on the position at the critical surface. Under the conditions where time-dependent perturbation theory is applicable and small widths Γ_i of the initial states occur, the decay rate constant out of an initial state i into final states f is given by Fermi's golden rule

$$k_i \simeq \Gamma_i/h \simeq (2\pi/\hbar)|\langle H_{\mathrm{el}}\rangle|^2 \sum_f \int dq\, \chi_i(q)\chi_f(q)\, \delta(E_i - E_f), \qquad (2.36)$$

With the average electronic matrix element $\langle H_{\mathrm{el}}\rangle$ of the coupling and the Franck–Condon vibrational overlap factors $\int dq\, \chi_i(q)\chi_f(q)$ (see, e.g.,

Gebelein and Jortner, 1972). For small transition probabilities the evaluation of this formula by Landau, Zener, and Nikitin (Landau and Lifshitz, 1965; Nikitin, 1966, 1968) for nonadiabatic transitions is adequate. It gives, in the one-dimensional linear model at weak adiabatic coupling, the probability P for transition within one vibrational period as

$$P = \pi^2 b^{4/3} [\text{Ai}(-\varepsilon b^{2/3})]^2, \tag{2.37}$$

where $b = (\Delta E_p F / \varepsilon_0 \Delta F)^{3/2}$, $\varepsilon_0 = [\hbar^2 F^4 / 2\mu \Delta F^2]^{3/2}$, $\varepsilon = \Delta F E / F \Delta E_p$, E is the energy minus the energy of the crossing point, $\Delta E_p = 2H_{12}$ is the full splitting of the potential curves at the zeroth-order crossing point, H_{ik} are the matrix elements of the total Hamiltonian, $F_i = -\partial H_{ii}/\partial q$, $F = |F_1 F_2|^{1/2}$, $\Delta F = F_1 - F_2$ at the crossing point, and $\text{Ai}(x)$ is the Airy function. At $E < 0$ an exponential decay due to tunneling is found. Since the slopes F of the effective potential curves depend on the rotational quantum number, thermal averaging over crossing energies, rotational quantum numbers, and critical configurations have to be performed [see Olschewski *et al.* (1966a) and Gebelein and Jortner (1972) for dissociation of N_2O, and Luther *et al.* (1972) for dissociation of alkali halides].

D. Theories of the Low-Pressure Limit

In the low-pressure limit of thermal unimolecular reactions collisional activations (2.1) are rate determining. The rates of subsequent structural changes, (2.3), with the specific rate constants $k(E)$, do not explicitly enter into the overall rate constants. In thermal systems collisional activations (2.1) do not occur in one step, but via a sequence of competing activations and deactivations

$$\text{A}_i + \text{M} \underset{k_{ij}}{\overset{k_{ji}}{\rightleftharpoons}} \text{A}_j + \text{M}. \tag{2.38}$$

At sufficiently low pressures and long periods between collisions all molecules that have gained sufficient energy for dissociation $E > E_0$ decompose before the next collision. Therefore, a quasi-random walk up the energy ladder, with a totally absorbing barrier at $E_0(J)$, is considered. A master equation

$$\frac{d[\text{A}_i]}{dt} = -\sum_j k_{ji}[\text{M}][\text{A}_i] + \sum_j k_{ij}[\text{M}][\text{A}_j] \tag{2.39}$$

for the numbers of molecules $[A_i]$ in states i, with the corresponding boundary condition at $E = E_0$, must be solved. If the temperature is constant and is undisturbed by the dissociation reaction, the second-order rate constants for collisional energy transfer k_{ji} are obtained from the cross sections for energy transfer $\sigma_e(j/i; v)$ by thermal averaging (Ross *et al.*, 1969):

$$k_{ji} = \left\langle \iint \sigma_e(j/i; v) f_A(\mathbf{v}_A) f_M(\mathbf{v}_M) |\mathbf{v}_A - \mathbf{v}_M| \, d\mathbf{v}_A \, d\mathbf{v}_M \right\rangle_{\text{ph or M int}}. \quad (2.40)$$

$\mathbf{v}_A$ and $\mathbf{v}_M$ are the velocities of A and M, f_A and f_M denote their Maxwell–Boltzmann distributions, $\langle \ \rangle_{\text{ph or M int}}$ symbolizes averaging over the initial phases of the oscillators of A before collision, collisional orientations, and distributions of internal degrees of freedom in polyatomic M.

Because of the thermal equilibrium of velocity distributions and internal distributions of M, the rate constants k_{ji} obey detailed balancing

$$k_{ij}/k_{ji} = (G_i/G_j) \exp[-(E_i - E_j)/kT] \quad (2.41)$$

with degeneracies G_i and energies E_i for vibrational levels i. By the thermal averaging according to Eqs. (2.40) and (2.41), the temperature T of the heat bath enters into the kinetic properties of the reacting molecules.

As is well known, the system of coupled first-order differential equations (2.39) is solved by a series of exponential functions of time which decay with different time constants τ. For a model set of harmonic oscillator transition rates k_{ji} the system (2.39) has been solved by McElwain and Pritchard (1969) for dissociating H_2 in He at 2000 K and 5.8×10^{-5} mole cm^{-3}. During a fast transient period of $\tau_{\text{inc}} \approx 5 \times 10^{-9}$ sec, i.e., after about 200 collisions, the population of all vibrational states achieves a steady state

$$\left(\sum_i{}^* [A_i] \right)^{-1} d[A_i]/dt \approx 0 \quad (2.42)$$

($\sum^*$ denotes the summation only over states with $E_i < E_0$). The time constant for dissociation is found to be about 70 sec, i.e., about 10^{10} times larger than τ_{inc}; the relaxation time for approaching final equilibrium by recombination is about 0.3 sec. At extremely high temperatures, with $E_0/kT \leq 5$, dissociation times approach incubation times. Experimentally, this region has recently become accessible (see Section II,B,1). As long as the gas-kinetic collision number is more than about 10^3 times larger than the dissociation rate constant, however, the assumption of a steady state (2.42) remains a very good approximation, valid under almost all experimental conditions.

Steady-state populations of vibrational states $g_i = [A_i]/\sum_i {}^*[A_i]$ in low-pressure dissociation differ in general from equilibrium populations $f_i = ([A_i]/\sum_i {}^*[A_i])_{eq}$. To obtain g_i, Eq. (2.39) has to be solved for all i at steady state. For this case Eq. (2.39) becomes:

$$\sum_j k_{ji} g_i \simeq \sum_j k_{ij} g_j . \qquad (2.43)$$

Solutions have been given by Nikitin (1966), Keck and Carrier (1965), as well as others. Since a quasi continuum of vibrational states is involved in polyatomic molecules (Section I,B), and non-next-neighbor transitions in diatomic molecules near threshold energies are very important as well, Eq. (2.43) can also be replaced by one integral equation

$$g(E_i) \int_0^\infty k(E_j, E_i) \, dE_j \simeq \int_0^{E0} k(E_i, E_j) g(E_j) \, dE_j \qquad (2.44)$$

(Keck and Carrier, 1965; Troe and Wagner, 1967). The upper limit of the integral at the rhs of Eq. (2.44) reflects the fact that at low pressure $g(E_j) \simeq 0$ at $E_j > 0$. A general solution has been given by Keck and Carrier, and Nikitin for the diffusion limit of random walk with mean energies $|\langle \Delta E \rangle|$ transferred per collision which are very small compared to kT:

$$g(E_i) \simeq f(E_i) \left\{ 1 - \frac{\int_0^{E_i} [dE_j / f(E_j) D(E_j)]}{\int_0^{E0} [dE_j / f(E_j) D(E_j)] + [1/4D^*(E_0)]} \right\} \qquad (2.45)$$

with

$$D(E_j) \simeq \int_0^\infty k(E_l, E_j)(E_l - E_j)^2 \, dE_l \qquad (2.46)$$

and

$$D^*(E_0) \simeq \int_{E0}^\infty \left[\int_0^{E0} k(E_m, E_l) f(E_l) \, dE_l \right] dE_m . \qquad (2.47)$$

This solution clearly shows the increasing "depopulation" of states at $E_i \rightarrow E_0$.

At more efficient energy transfer, $|\langle \Delta E \rangle| \gtrsim kT$, different solutions are required. Troe and Wagner (1967) used the following exponential model of collisional energy transfer, which was experimentally verified for diatomic molecules and simple collision partners (Kurzel and Steinfeld, 1970):

$$k(E_j, E_i) = Z(E_i) \frac{1 + \dfrac{\alpha}{kT}}{2 + \dfrac{\alpha}{kT}}$$

$$\times \frac{\exp - \dfrac{|E_i - E_j|}{\alpha}}{\alpha} \left\{ \begin{matrix} 1 & \text{at} & E_j < E_i \\ \exp - \dfrac{|E_i - E_j|}{kT} & \text{at} & E_j > E_i \end{matrix} \right\} \tag{2.48}$$

with

$$Z(E_i) \simeq \int_0^\infty k(E_j, E_i)\, dE_j. \tag{2.49}$$

This model accounts for the decreasing probabilities of translational–vibrational energy transfer with increasing $|E_i - E_j|$. It obeys detailed balancing (2.41) in the form

$$k(E_j, E_i) f(E_i) \simeq k(E_i, E_j) f(E_j), \tag{2.50}$$

as long as $\rho(E_i) \simeq \rho(E_j)$ and $Z(E_i) \simeq Z(E_j)$. Differentiation of Eq. (2.44) with respect to E_i and the use of Eq. (2.50) gives the boundary condition at $E_i \simeq E_0$

$$\frac{\partial [g(E_i)/f(E_i)]}{\partial E_i} \bigg|_{E_i = E_0} = -\alpha \frac{g(E_0)}{f(E_0)}. \tag{2.51}$$

This condition is the immediate consequence of the presence of the absorbing barrier, i.e., $g(E_j) \simeq 0$ at $E_j \geq E_0$ in Eq. (2.44). Twofold differentiation of Eq. (2.44) then leads to the differential equation of a damped vibration, which is easily solved. Alternatively, the method of Fourier integrals may be used. Integration constants are fixed by the boundary conditions $\lim[g(E_i)/f(E_i)] \simeq 1$ at $E_i \to 0$ and Eq. (2.51). The final solution of Eq. (2.44) is

$$g(E_i) \simeq f(E_i) \left(1 - \frac{1}{1 + \alpha/kT} \exp - \frac{E_0 - E_i}{kT} \right). \tag{2.52}$$

After determining steady-state populations during the reaction, Eqs. (2.45) and (2.52), the rate constant k_0 immediately follows by calculating the upward flux, i.e.,

$$k_0 = [M] \int_{E_0}^{\infty} \left[\int_0^{E_0} k(E_j, E_i) g(E_i) \, dE_i \right] dE_j. \tag{2.53}$$

With Eqs. (2.48), (2.49), and (2.52), and assuming $\rho(E) \simeq \rho(E_0)$ in the integration, this gives

$$k_0 \simeq [M] Z(E_0) \frac{\rho(E_0) kT}{Q} \left(\exp - \frac{E_0}{kT} \right) \left(\frac{\alpha}{\alpha + kT} \right)^2. \tag{2.54}$$

In the diffusion limit (Keck and Carrier, 1965; Nikitin, 1966)

$$k_0 \simeq [M] Z(E_0) \frac{\rho(E_0) kT}{Q} \left(\exp - \frac{E_0}{kT} \right) \frac{\langle \Delta E^2 \rangle}{2(kT)^2} \tag{2.54a}$$

is obtained (as long as

$$\int_0^{E_0} [f(E_j) D(E_j)]^{-1} \, dE_j \gg [4 D^*(E_0)]^{-1},$$

i.e., at large depopulation of states at $E \lesssim E_0$, as found in the weak collision limit). Therefore, the diffusion limit (2.54a), which is valid for arbitrary transition rates $k(E_j, E_i)$, and Eq. (2.54) are equivalent in the weak collision case $\langle \Delta E^2 \rangle = 2\alpha^2 \ll (kT)^2$.

For the "strong collision" case, $\alpha > kT$, Eq. (2.54a) is not applicable. In this case Eq. (2.54) remains valid with the last parenthesis approaching one; depopulation at states $E_i < E_0$ disappears, i.e., $g_i \simeq f_i$ in Eq. (2.52).

Near the strong collision limit the simplification $\rho(E) \simeq \rho(E_0)$ used in Eq. (2.54) for large polyatomic molecules has to be abandoned. Equation (2.53) then leads to

$$k_0 \simeq [M] Z(E_0) \frac{\rho(E_0) kT}{Q} \left(\exp - \frac{E_0}{kT} \right) \frac{\alpha}{\alpha + kT}$$

$$\times \int_{E_0}^{\infty} \frac{\rho(E)}{\rho(E_0)} \exp \left(- \frac{E - E_0}{kT} \frac{\alpha + kT}{\alpha} \right) \frac{dE}{kT}. \tag{2.55}$$

Using the semiclassical approximation for $\rho(E)$, Eq. (2.55) may be evaluated. Defining a collision efficiency β_c by the equation

$$k_0 = \beta_c k_0^{sc} = [M]\beta_c \int_{E_0}^{\infty} f(E)Z(E)\,dE, \qquad (2.56)$$

one obtains

$$\beta_c \simeq \left(\frac{\alpha}{\alpha+kT}\right)^2 \frac{\displaystyle\sum_{v=0}^{s-1} \binom{s-1}{v} v! \left(\frac{E_0+E_z}{E_0}\right)^{s-1-v}\left(\frac{kT}{E_0}\right)^v \left(\frac{\alpha}{\alpha+kT}\right)^v}{\displaystyle\sum_{v=0}^{s-1}\binom{s-1}{v} v! \left(\frac{E_0+E_z}{E_0}\right)^{s-1-v}\left(\frac{kT}{E_0}\right)^v}. \qquad (2.57)$$

Instead of the exponential model (2.48), transition probabilities with a maximum at $E_j < E_i$ can be expected for efficient colliders. An exponential model with a maximum at $E_j < E_i$ has been employed for this situation by Troe (1973). It could be shown that very similar collision efficiencies β_c are obtained with both exponential models if results with the same average energy $\langle \Delta E \rangle$ transferred per collision are compared. For the model (2.48), $\langle \Delta E \rangle$ is equal to $-\alpha^2/(\alpha+kT)$. Therefore, experimental determinations of β_c may be used to obtain $\langle \Delta E \rangle$, whereas the shape of the transition probability $k(E_j, E_i)$ is averaged out.

Explicit calculations for $k(E_j, E_i)$ near $E_i \simeq E_0$ have been possible for dissociation reactions of diatomic molecules. By numerical trajectory calculations, energy transfer rates were obtained by the variational theory (Section I,C) (Keck and Carrier, 1965). Good agreement with a number of experimental systems was found (Shui et al., 1970, 1971). For polyatomic molecules an extremely large number of individual $k(E_j, E_i)$ are required. Because almost all details of the individual $k(E_j, E_i)$ are lost during thermal averaging, only the total cross section for energy transfer $\sigma_{tot}(E_0)$ and the mean energy $\langle \Delta E \rangle$ transferred per collision in molecules at $E \simeq E_0$ remain important. For these basic quantities in polyatomic molecules appropriate theories are still lacking. Theories for energy transfer between low-lying single vibrational states (Stevens, 1967; Stretton, 1969) are apparently insufficient. The statistical theory (Keck and Kalelkar, 1969) treats redissociation of the collision complex between A and M as a unimolecular dissociation and determines the energy distribution in the products by the methods of Section I,E. Since it always gives $|\langle \Delta E \rangle| \gg kT$, it overestimates the efficiency of energy transfer in many cases.

Experimental data on k_0, if properly analyzed in terms of Eq. (2.57), only allow for a determination of the product $\beta_c Z(E_0)$. The experimental results for CH_3NC isomerization from Fig. 16 for efficient collision partners (with boiling temperatures $T_B \gtrsim 300$ K) give $\beta_c \simeq$ const. This strongly suggests a limit of $\beta_c \to 1$, and $Z(E_0) \simeq Z_0$, where Z_0 is the gas-kinetic collision number. For less efficient collision partners the product $\beta_c Z(E_0)$ decays. This corresponds most probably to a decay of β_c. The smallest values observed, $\beta_c \simeq 0.2$, corresponds to $|\langle \Delta E \rangle|/kT \simeq 0.5$. The $\langle \Delta E \rangle$ values derived are in very good agreement with data from optical and chemical activation experiments (see below). The analysis of these data indicates that even for the most efficient colliders the strong collision limit is approached only up to $\beta_c \simeq 0.9$ (Troe, 1973).

The strong collision postulate has been used in most of the earlier theories of k_0. Weak collision effects have only recently been taken into account. If the strong collision assumption is applicable, Eq. (2.55) contains the formulations of Hinshelwood (at the high-temperature limit $T \gg h\nu_i/k$), of Kassel for identical oscillators, of Rice and Marcus for arbitrary oscillators. Rotational contributions may be accounted for by using centrifugal barriers $E_0(J)$ and averaging over an equilibrium rotational distribution (as described in Section II,C) (Waage and Rabinovitch, 1969). The coupling of vibration and rotation may be accounted for, to a first approximation, by deriving $E_0(J)$ for a quasilinear model and by including the rotation around the linear reaction coordinate in the density of states $\rho(E, J)$ (see Quack and Troe, 1974). Translational–rotational energy transfer well may contribute to $\langle \Delta E \rangle$ and play an important role in the final stage of dissociation or the early stage of recombination (Benson, 1969).

E. Transition between the Low- and the High-Pressure Limit

A complete description of k in the transition range between the low- and high-pressure limits is much more difficult than at either of the limits. Particular collision effects such as nonequilibrium populations and problems of intramolecular coupling, assignment of activated complexes, and rotational averaging have to be taken into account simultaneously. Nevertheless, after k has been calculated in the limiting cases reduced interpolation formulas between both limits may be easily given with sufficient accuracy for most practical needs.

In the strong collision limit the simple three-step treatment of the rate constant k, Eq. (2.4), by distinguishing states according to their energy E may be generalized to

$$k = \int_{E_0}^{\infty} \frac{k(E)f(E)k_{\text{deac}}[M]}{k(E) + k_{\text{deac}}[M]}\, dE, \qquad (2.58)$$

where $k(E) \simeq k_{\text{intra}}$ and $k_{\text{ac}}/k_{\text{deac}}$ by detailed balancing is approximately equal to $f(E)$. This is the form of k generally used in the RRKM theory (see Marcus, 1965; Spicer and Rabinovitch, 1970).

In the classical limit, Eqs. (1.8) and (1.23), this leads to the "Kassel integral"

$$\frac{k}{k_{\infty}} = I\left(s, b, \frac{k_0}{k_{\infty}}\right) = \frac{1}{(s-1)!} \int_0^{\infty} \frac{x^{s-1} \exp(-x)\, dx}{1 + (k_{\infty}/k_0)I_0(s, b)[x/(b+x)]^{s-1}} \qquad (2.59)$$

with the low-pressure rate constant $k_0 = k_{\text{deac}}[M] \int_{E_0}^{\infty} f(E)\, dE$, $b = E_0/kT$, and

$$I_0(s, b) = [1/(s-1)!] \int_0^{\infty} (y+b)^{s-1} \exp(-y)\, dy.$$

k_0/k_{∞} is proportional to [M], and can be used as a dimensionless pressure scale. Equation (2.59) interpolates k/k_{∞} between the low-pressure value k_0/k_{∞} and the high-pressure value one, using k_0/k_{∞} as reduced pressure scale. Equation (2.59) can often be fitted to experimental data only if a smaller "effective number of oscillators" is used instead of s. This is certainly not due to restricted internal energy flow, but to the inadequacy of the classical approximations in Eq. (2.59). The quantization of the oscillators can be accounted for by replacing s by

$$S_{\text{K}} \simeq \frac{U_{\text{vib}} + E_{a\infty} - E_0}{kT} = -\frac{1}{T}\frac{\partial \ln Q_{\text{vib}}}{\partial(1/T)} + \frac{E_{a\infty} - E_0}{kT} \qquad (2.60)$$

(U_{vib} is the internal vibrational energy, $E_{a\infty}$ is the high-pressure activation energy); and by replacing b by B_{K} according to the relation

$$[\Gamma(S_{\text{K}})/B_{\text{K}}^{S_{\text{K}}-1}]I_0(S_{\text{K}}, B_{\text{K}}) \simeq [\Gamma(s)/b^{s-1}]I_0(s, b). \qquad (2.61)$$

This procedure leads to excellent agreement between the time-consuming RRKM calculations and the simple Kassel integrals [Troe, 1974; for earlier proposals, see Troe and Wagner (1967a), Benson (1968), Golden et al. (1971)]. Tabulations of Kassel integrals are available from Emanuel (1972). Restricted intramolecular energy flow (Wilson, 1960) or weak collision effects (Buff and Wilson, 1962; Troe, 1974) have been shown to influence S_K by only 0–2 units. Examples for reduced falloff curves, Eq. (2.59), are given in Fig. 17.

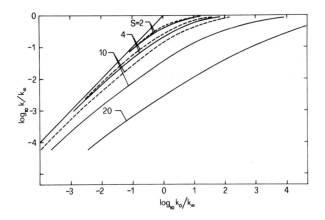

FIG. 17.   Reduced falloff curves of thermal unimolecular reactions [—, $B_K = 50$; - - -, $B_K = 10$; s defined by Eq. (2.60)].

F. Dissociation at Ultrahigh Pressures

The simple model of thermal unimolecular reactions described in Section II,A cannot be applicable at ultrahigh pressures of carrier gases and in condensed media. Here, dissociations and recombinations become quasi-diffusion controlled; cage phenomena and also pronounced reactant–solvent interactions will occur. A possible description of gas-phase unimole-cular reactions in this transition range between "normal" and ultrahigh pressures originates from the theory of Brownian motion (Kramers, 1940; Chandrasekhar, 1943). The escape of particles A over a potential barrier to a surrounding medium with a coefficient of dynamical friction β is considered. The effect of collisions on the distribution of intramolecular velocities v during time Δt is described by the Langevin equation with a systematic part $-\beta v\,\Delta t$ and a fluctuating part $B(\Delta t)$ of velocity changes:

$$(\Delta v)_{\text{coll}} = -\beta v\,\Delta t + B(\Delta t). \tag{2.62}$$

The reaction is regarded as a Markov process and a generalized Liouville equation in the phase space, of the Fokker–Planck form, is derived. In one dimension this is written as

$$\frac{\partial n}{\partial t} + v\frac{\partial n}{\partial q} + \frac{K}{\mu}\frac{\partial n}{\partial v} = \beta v\frac{\partial n}{\partial v} + \beta n + \beta\frac{kT}{\mu}\frac{\partial^2 n}{\partial v^2}. \tag{2.63}$$

n denotes the number of molecules in the intramolecular phase space at positions $(q, q + dq)$ and with velocities $(v, v + dv)$, and $K = -\partial V(q)/\partial q$ is the force of the intramolecular potential $V(q)$.

For a solution of Eq. (2.63), $V(q)$ is assumed to be of the form

$$V(q) \simeq \tfrac{1}{2}\mu(2\pi v_A)^2(q - q_A)^2 \tag{2.64}$$

in the vicinity of the potential minimum of molecules A, and of the form

$$V(q) \simeq E_0 - \tfrac{1}{2}\mu\omega_B^2(q - q_B)^2 \tag{2.65}$$

in the vicinity of the potential barrier dividing molecules A from reaction products. A stationary solution may then be expressed by

$$n = CF(q, v)\exp\{-[\tfrac{1}{2}\mu v^2 + V(q)]/kT\}. \tag{2.66}$$

Suitable boundary conditions for F at q_A and $q \gg q_B$ must be chosen. Restricting attention to the forward reaction, $F \simeq 0$ should be fulfilled at $q \gg q_B$. In Kramers' original solution $F \simeq 1$ was chosen at $q \simeq q_A$. This, however, excludes the normal low-pressure region of unimolecular reaction, where effective depopulation of states $E > E_0$ is observed at $q \simeq q_A$. We choose, instead,

$$F(q, v) \simeq k_{\text{deac}}[M]/(v_A{}^* + k_{\text{deac}}[M]) \tag{2.67}$$

at $q \simeq q_A$ and $E \geq E_0$ and $F(q, v) \simeq 1$ at $E < E_0$, corresponding to the strong collision model of collisional deactivation (see Section II,A). $v_A{}^*$ is the "mean frequency of dissociation of excited molecules."

Following the method of Kramers, the Fokker–Planck equation is solved and the distribution n in phase space is calculated. One obtains at $E \geq E_0$ and $q \simeq q_B$ [with $a = (\frac{1}{4}\beta^2 + \omega_B{}^2)^{1/2} + \frac{1}{2}\beta$]

$$n(q, v) = [A] \frac{\mu v_A}{kT} \left(\frac{k_{deac}[M]}{v_A{}^* + k_{deac}[M]} \right) \left(\exp - \frac{E_0}{kT} \right)$$

$$\times \left\{ \exp - \frac{\frac{1}{2}\mu v^2 + \frac{1}{2}\mu \omega_B{}^2(q - q_B)^2}{kT} \right\}$$

$$\times \left[\frac{(a - \beta)\mu}{2\pi\beta kT} \right]^{1/2} \int_{-\infty}^{v - a(q - q_B)} \exp - \frac{\mu(a - \beta)\zeta^2}{2\pi\beta kT} \, d\zeta. \qquad (2.68)$$

With this distribution the rate of barrier crossing of molecules A is given by

$$d[A]/dt = - \int_{-\infty}^{\infty} n(q \simeq q_B, v)v \, dv = -k[A] \qquad (2.69)$$

and the rate constant is given by

$$k = \left\{ \frac{v_A k_{deac}[M]}{v_A{}^* + k_{deac}[M]} \left(\exp - \frac{E_0}{kT} \right) \right\} \left[\frac{(\frac{1}{4}\beta^2 + \omega_B{}^2)^{1/2} - \frac{1}{2}\beta}{(\frac{1}{4}\beta^2 + \omega_B{}^2)^{1/2} + \frac{1}{2}\beta} \right]^{1/2}. \qquad (2.70)$$

The first factor in Eq. (2.70) corresponds to the simple model of the low- and high-pressure region of unimolecular reactions discussed in Section II,A. A low-pressure limit

$$k_0 \simeq \frac{v_A}{v_A{}^*} k_{deac}[M] \exp - \frac{E_0}{kT} \simeq [M]k_{deac} \frac{Q^{\ddagger}_{vib}}{Q_{vib}} \exp - \frac{E_0}{kT} \qquad (2.71)$$

and a normal high-pressure limit

$$k_{\infty} \simeq v_A \exp(-E_0/kT) \qquad (2.72)$$

are found. The second factor is approximately one, as long as $\beta \ll 2\omega_B$. With increasing density and friction of the medium, β increases and k approaches

$$k_{ultra} \simeq v_A(\omega_B/\beta) \exp(-E_0/kT). \qquad (2.73)$$

The transition curves in the falloff representation at different values of the

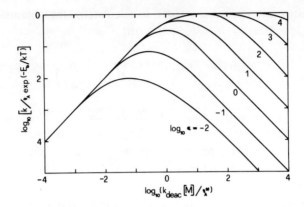

FIG. 18. Thermal dissociation at ultrahigh pressures (for model and parameters see text).

parameter $\alpha = k_{deac}[M]\omega_B/\beta v_A^*$ are shown in Fig. 18. At $\alpha \gg 1$ normal low-pressure and ultrahigh-pressure regions are separated by a broad, intermediate, normal high-pressure region. However, at $\alpha \ll 1$ the normal high-pressure region is suppressed. Possibly, dissociations of diatomic molecules in carrier gases of several hundred atmospheres, as in the dissociation of iodine (Troe and Wagner, 1967b), fall into this category.

Numerical estimates of the imaginary frequency ω_B can be obtained for dissociation reactions by identifying the barriers with maxima of centrifugal potentials. With a van der Waals long-range interaction between the fragments of A, $V(q) \simeq E_0 - C/q^6$, and a rotational constant B_A of A,

$$q_B \simeq \left[\frac{3C}{J(J+1)B_A q_A{}^2}\right]^{1/4} \quad \text{and} \quad \omega_B \simeq \frac{2J(J+1)B_A q_A{}^2}{(3\mu C/2)^{1/2}} \quad (2.74)$$

are obtained. The coefficient of dynamical friction has been calculated for hard-sphere collisions by Bak and Lebowitz (1963) and Nielsen and Bak (1964). In carrier gases with light atoms (mass m_M) and large values of the effective molecular mass μ, β is given by ($\gamma = m_M/\mu$)

$$\beta \simeq [M]\sigma^2(8\pi kT\gamma/\mu)^{1/2}. \quad (2.75)$$

This is of the order of magnitude of $k_{deac}[M]$. With the molecular constants of I_2, α is estimated by these formulas to be of the order of magnitude

0.1–1. According to Fig. 18, therefore, in this case the normal high-pressure region should be suppressed, deviations from the second-order low-pressure region should become important at $k_{deac}[M] \simeq 0.1 \nu_A{}^*$, and the intermediate maximum of k should be of the order of magnitude of $0.1 \nu_A$ $\exp(-E_0/kT)$. These estimates are in good agreement with the experiments for the dissociation of I_2 at 1000 K and at several hundred atmospheres.

The observation that the rate of NO_2Cl dissociation in a liquid medium is about ten times slower than that in the gas phase at high pressures (Beggs *et al.*, 1964) may correspond to the increase of β with increasing density. The decrease of the rate of dissociation with increasing pressure which is sometimes found in unimolecular dissociations in liquids (see Le Noble, 1967) will also be due to an increase of β with pressure. This, however, may be changed when strong interactions between molecule and solvent are present. Also, the pronounced solvent effects on the rates of unimolecular reactions in liquids (e.g., dissociation of N_2O_5, see Moelwyn-Hughes, 1947) suggest contributions from different β's. However, explicit calculation of β in liquids meets with the usual complications of theories of kinetic phenomena in liquids. In particular, the attractive interactions between the reactants and the medium, which are of primary importance in most atom recombinations at low temperatures, are difficult to incorporate at high densities.

III. Photochemical Unimolecular Reactions

The specific advantages of photochemical activation in unimolecular reactions was recognized long ago. By absorption of monochromatic light, electronically excited states can be specifically populated. In contrast to thermal activation, the excitation energy can often be varied within broad ranges by variation of the wavelength. Energies much higher than thresholds of unimolecular reactions can be obtained. Energy resolution of the excitation is limited in most cases by the initial energy distribution of unexcited molecules, which can be kept narrow by using low temperatures; sometimes single transitions can be selected. In spite of the great advantages of photochemical excitations, quantitative use of the unimolecular reaction concept in photochemistry has been made only recently. The reasons are obvious. The properties of the excited electronic states reached by the absorption of light are generally less well known than the properties of the ground states. Also, photochemical mechanisms are generally complex. Because of the high excitation energies, many channels of the reaction are often accessible; reemission of radiation such as by fluorescence or phosphorescence may occur; collisional processes, such as vibrational deactivation or activation, may be involved; radiationless transitions between different electronic states may play a central role. As a consequence, most of the photochemical literature has been concerned with the identification of photochemical mechanisms (see, e.g., Calvert and Pitts, 1966). However, recently a number of experimental systems have been studied in such detail that applications of unimolecular reaction rate theory become meaningful, and theories may be tested directly. In the following, some of these investigations will be described. Systems leading to conclusions concerning specific rate constants $k(E)$ of photolysis or photoisomerization in competition with collisional processes are discussed first (Section III,A). Distributions of different reaction products or of energy on products are briefly described in Section III,B. Secondary unimolecular reactions of excited products of primary photolysis are discussed separately in Section V.

A. Rate of Photolysis

With sufficiently fast excitation flashes and fast detection of excited species, specific rate constants $k(E)$ of photolysis can be measured directly. Although rather involved experimental techniques are necessary, experiments of this kind are feasible. Some indirect methods for deriving $k(E)$ are described in the following.

The crossing of a molecular beam and a laser flash and the monitoring of arrival times of photolysis products is used in photofragment spectroscopy. $k(E)$ can be estimated from the angular distributions of products: photolysis lifetimes longer than one average rotational period (order of magnitude 10^{-12} sec) result in symmetric distributions, shorter lifetimes give asymmetries (Busch and Wilson, 1972). Rotational periods also can be used as a clock for timing $k(E)$ in the photodissociation mapping technique (Solomon, 1967) where, after excitation with polarized light, the angular dependence of depositable photolysis products is investigated.

The determination of $k(E)$ from the pressure dependence of quantum yields is much more generally used. Here the competition between collisional stabilization of excited products and photolysis or photoisomerization results in the decrease of quantum yields with increasing pressure. This effect may be attributed to the following mechanism:

$$A + h\nu \longrightarrow A_i^* \tag{3.1}$$

$$A_i^* \xrightarrow{k(E_i)} products \tag{3.2}$$

$$A_i^* + M \longrightarrow A_j^* + M \tag{3.3}$$

$$A_j^* \xrightarrow{k(E_j)} products$$

$$\vdots$$

$$A_i^* + M \longrightarrow A + M. \tag{3.4}$$

Light absorption (3.1) is followed, for example, by photolysis (3.2) or multistep collisional deactivation (3.3). If the result of stepwise deactivation is summarized by one reaction equation with the effective rate constant k_{deac}, and photolysis by one equation with the effective rate constant k_{intra}, the mechanism corresponds directly to the three-step mechanism of thermal unimolecular reactions (Section II,A). The quantum yield ϕ of photolysis, i.e., the fraction of molecules that complete reaction (3.2) after activation (3.1), is then given by

$$\phi = k_{intra}/(k_{intra} + k_{deac}[M]). \tag{3.5}$$

A "Stern–Volmer" plot of ϕ^{-1} against pressure or [M] is, in this simple model, linear with a slope k_{deac}/k_{intra}.

Experiments on the pressure dependence of ϕ, corresponding to Eq. (3.5), can be evaluated in two ways: Either the effective rate constant of stabilization k_{deac} is assumed to be known and k_{intra} is derived; or k_{intra} is calculated from theories of unimolecular reactions and the effective rate of collisional stabilization is derived. Interpretations of this type are obviously not unique. Fortunately, in photochemical activation this difficulty may be removed by comparison with closely related experimental systems. In some cases the effective rate of collisional stabilization can be determined by studying the pressure dependence of quantum yields for fluorescence in the same molecule. For this process a mechanism analogous to photolysis is applicable, except that photolysis (3.2) is replaced by reemission of radiation. Analogous expressions for quantum yields, Stern–Volmer plots, and descriptions of the multistep deactivation are obtained. However, in contrast to the often faster photolysis, the rate of fluorescence at low pressures can be measured relatively easily, for example, by phase fluorimetry. Therefore, for fluorescence the effective rate of collisional energy transfer is directly accessible. If the states involved in fluorescence and photolysis are closely related, the fluorescence results on "k_{deac}" should also be useful for fixing "k_{deac}" in photolysis. An experimental example of this type of conclusion is given by fluorescence and photolysis of NO_2 as discussed later. In other situations radiative processes may occur simultaneously with photolysis and can be used to monitor populations of excited states during the reaction. Comparison of pyrolysis of a molecule and photolysis, if the latter process takes place from the electronic ground state after radiationless transition, also proves useful in removing uncertainties of $k(E)$.

A number of representative experimental examples are given in the following. Photolysis of NO_2 to $NO + O$ is observed at wavelengths below about 4000 Å (absorption lines become diffuse at 3979 Å); fluorescence is observed with excitation wavelengths above about 4000 Å. At 4047 Å photolysis corresponds to rotationally hot molecules, which carry their thermal rotational energy into the electronically excited states and use this energy to overcome the dissociation energy (Pitts et al., 1964). Fluorescence may be induced at the same wavelength. This is probably mainly due to rotationally cold molecules, which do not photodissociate. Stern–Volmer plots of fluorescence (Schwartz and Johnston, 1969; Keyser et al., 1971) and of photolysis [after separation from consecutive reactions, Troe (1969), Gaedtke et al. (1972), Gaedtke and Troe (1975)] have been obtained. Stern–Volmer plots of fluorescence show marked deviations from linearity, and slopes which, at constant excitation energy, depend on the wavelength of the emitted radiation. This is shown in Fig. 19, corresponding to excitation at 4360 Å and emitted light of 4700, 5460, and 7000 Å (Keyser et al., 1971). The shapes of the curves in Fig. 19 clearly show that collisional deactivation is not adequately described by a one-step, "strong collision" mechanism. Instead, multistep deactivation occurs. At 4047 Å excitation, mean energies removed per collision of about 1.4 kcal mole^{-1} have been derived for NO_2 as collision partner (Keyser et al., 1971). Total collision numbers of energy transfer have been found to be close to the gas-kinetic collision number. Calibration of the effective k_{deac} in these experiments was performed by using directly measured fluorescence lifetimes. Since these are unusually long (about 50 μsec), collisional processes compete effectively with fluorescence down to pressures as low as 10^{-2} Torr and Stern–Volmer curves of fluorescence are studied in this pressure range. Photolysis lifetimes are found to be of the order 10^{-12} sec.

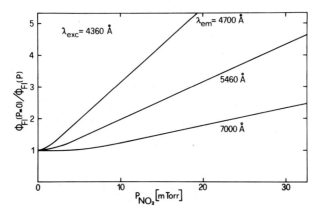

FIG. 19.   Stern–Volmer plots of NO_2 fluorescence (from Keyser *et al.*, 1971).

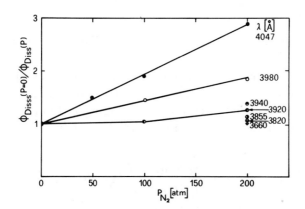

FIG. 20.   Stern–Volmer plots of NO_2 photolysis (Gaedtke and Troe, 1975).

Stern–Volmer plots of photolysis of NO_2 may therefore be studied at completely different carrier gas pressures, of the order 100 atm (Fig. 20). With increasing excess energy of the photolyzing molecules collisional stabilization requires more collisions and dissociative lifetimes become shorter. Therefore, increasing slopes of the Stern–Volmer plots are observed at decreasing excitation wavelengths. Absolute values of the specific rate constants of photolysis $k(E)$ at different energies can be estimated by using the fluorescence results for "k_{deac}" and assuming that the rate of collisional deactivation between 10^{-2} Torr and 100 atm remains proportional to pressure. Because excess energies at 3660 Å are still rather small ($\sim$7 kcal mole^{-1}), a few collisions will bring a molecule below the dissociation threshold and the treatment of multistep deactivation is simple. At greater excess energies the analysis proposed by Porter and Connelly (1960), Strachan et al. (1964), or Gandini et al. (1968) should be applied. A "many-shot" expansion may also be used, which repetitively convolutes the distribution of collisional rates, as Eq. (2.48), with the distribution obtained from the activation process (Serauskas and Schlag, 1965). One may also use an integrodifferential equation, analogous to Eq. (2.44), of the type

$$\frac{dn(E_i)}{dt} = +\mathrm{Ac}(E_i) - k(E_i)n(E_i) - \int_0^\infty [\mathrm{M}]k(E_j, E_i)n(E_i)\, dE_j$$

$$+ \int_0^\infty [\mathrm{M}]k(E_i, E_j)n(E_j)\, dE_j, \tag{3.6}$$

where $\mathrm{Ac}(E_i)$ denotes the rate of activation by light absorption to energies E_i.

The initial thermal energy content of the absorbing molecules limits the energy resolution of $k(E)$ determinations (see above). In the three-step model this is taken into account by averaging ϕ from Eq. (3.5) over the initial distribution $g(E)$ of initial thermal energy plus light energy

$$\phi \simeq \int_{E_0}^\infty \frac{k(E)g(E)}{k(E) + k_{\mathrm{deac}}[\mathrm{M}]}\, dE. \tag{3.7}$$

In NO_2 centrifugal barriers for dissociation are small. Because of the averaging (3.7), $k(E)$ cannot be determined closer to the dissociation threshold than about kT.

By analyzing Stern–Volmer plots of the photolysis of NO_2 in the way described and by calibrating the rate of collisional deactivation via fluorescence experiments, the specific rate constants for the photolysis of NO_2 in Fig. 21 are obtained. An estimate from photofragment spectroscopy (see above) with a laser wavelength of 3472 Å fits nicely to the observed data. A comparison of measured specific rate constants of photolysis $k(E)$ and calculations by theories such as those given in Section I,C requires knowledge of the excited states involved. The assignment of states, important in light absorption in the visible, has been possible recently by extensive CI calculations (Gangi and Burnelle, 1971). In these calculations

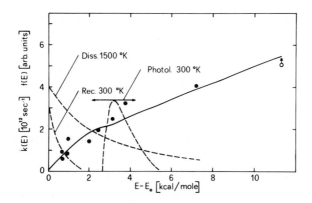

Fig. 21. Dissociation of NO_2 [—, calculated $k(E)$; ●, photolysis experiments; (Gaedtke *et al.*, 1972); ○, photofragment spectroscopy (Bush and Wilson, 1972); - - -, populations of excited states; see text].

the Born–Oppenheimer approximation is applied. It has been suggested, however, that in NO_2, SO_2, and CS_2 internal mixing between excited electronic states and the ground state is very efficient (see, e.g., Jortner *et al.*, 1969). Therefore, light absorption and fluorescence near 4000 Å well may involve the "electronically excited" Born–Oppenheimer components of the mixed state which carry an optical transition moment. Dynamical behavior of excited molecules, however, would be governed mainly by the larger volume in phase space of the ground-state component. It is possible, therefore, that thermal decomposition, thermal recombination and photolysis (in non-collision-free situations) may be governed by one common curve of specific rate constants $k(E)$. This is supported by the good agreement with calculations of $k(E)$ by the statistical theory given in Section I,C (curve 5 in Fig. 5). The agreement for the large values of $k(E)$ obtained is still surprisingly good. The common $k(E)$ curve in the three kinetic systems is multiplied by different populations of excited states, as shown in Fig. 21. It should be emphasized that in spite of the consistency of the results, the given interpretation of the experimental $k(E)$ curves is not the only one possible, and that photolysis without the contribution of the ground state may not be excluded yet.

Photoisomerization and photolysis of cycloheptatriene (CHT) have been investigated in detail by Atkinson and Thrush (1970) and by Luu and Troe (1973, 1974). It has been again suggested that internal mixing of states is strong and that the reaction involves highly vibrationally excited electronic ground-state molecules. Linear Stern–Volmer plots of photoisomerization have been observed with different carrier gases M. Half-quenching pressures for M = CHT have been found to decrease from 34 Torr at 2288 Å to 0.185 Torr at 3130 Å. Interpretation of the results shows that deactivation occurs by a multistep process. By estimating specific rate constants $k(E)$ from statistical theories of unimolecular reactions, properties of collisional deactivation are derived, i.e., "k_{deac}" of the model given above. In this case $k(E)$ values have been estimated by comparison with experiments on thermal isomerization of CHT and of deuterated CHT. The latter additional experiments considerably improve the conclusions drawn from Stern–Volmer plots. Nevertheless, uncertainties of $k(E)$ by about a factor of three still have not yet been eliminated. Average energies removed per collision from excited CHT of about 2–7 (M = CHT), 3–12 (M = hexane), 0.9–2 (M = SF_6), 0.9–2.1 (M = CO_2), and 0.1–0.3 kcal mole^{-1} (M = He) are derived in this way. The indicated uncertainties of these values are due to the mentioned uncertainties in the specific rate constants $k(E)$. These values correspond nicely to those obtained for thermal dissociations and isomerizations (Section II).

Photolysis of azoethane (e.g., Worsham and Rice, 1967; Bowers, 1970), of ketene (e.g., Bowers, 1967), of hexafluoroacetone (e.g., Strachan et al., 1964; Porter and Connelly, 1960; Bowers, 1968; Halpern and Ware, 1970), of acetone (e.g. O'Neal and Larson, 1969), and of other molecules have been studied in a similar way. Statistical theories of unimolecular processes have been used to interpret Stern–Volmer plots. The main problems are the same as those mentioned in the foregoing: The assumption of one-step collisional deactivation, which is often used even at large excess energies $E - E_0$, has to be replaced by a more detailed collision model; theoretical calculations of specific rate constants may have to be modified as shown for NO_2 in Section I,C; internal mixing between the electronic ground state and excited electronic states may be strong (Jortner et al., 1969) as is often assumed and photolysis governed by the properties of the electronic ground state; detailed mechanisms are often complicated.

As an example of a direct determination of energy-resolved specific rate constants $k(E)$ for a radiationless transition following light absorption, the phase fluorimeter study of singlet–triplet conversion in β-naphthylamine by Schlag and von Weyssenhoff (1969, 1973) are mentioned. Theories for $k(E)$ for this type of "structural change" may be analogous to theories of spin-forbidden dissociations of triatomic molecules (see Section II,C).

B. Distribution of Products and Distribution of Energy in Products

With absorbed radiation of sufficiently high energy several competitive photolysis processes may be initiated. At a fixed energy the fragment pattern is determined by the ratios of specific rate constants for the reaction channels i, $k_i(E)/\sum_i k(E_i)$ or, more precisely, if the time dependence of $k_i(E)$ has to be taken into account, by the corresponding integrals $\int_0^\infty k_i(E, t)\, dt/\sum_i \int_0^\infty k_i(E, t)\, dt$. Few experimental studies are detailed enough to allow for an analysis by theories of unimolecular reactions. This analysis would be comparable to the analysis of mass spectra (see Section IV). As an example, the energy dependence of the fragment pattern in photolysis of ethane at photon energies between 8.4 and 11.8 eV is shown in Fig. 22 (Lias *et al.*, 1970). Five major processes can be established and their quantum yields measured.

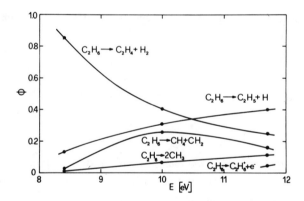

Fig. 22. Fragment yields in ethane photolysis (from Lias *et al.*, 1970).

The distributions of energy in photolysis products can be measured experimentally by direct analysis of the primary products. Alternatively, they can be observed by the properties of subsequent reactions of the excited primary products. Photolysis of small molecules from nonbonding, electronically excited states in many cases gives a marked nonequilibrium distribution of energy. Flash photolysis of nitrosyl halides produces high vibrational excitation in NO; CN from cyanogen halides, on the contrary, is formed almost vibrationally cold. H_2S photolysis gives high translational energies of the products. Energy distributions in these cases are governed by the individual shapes of the potential surface in the upper states

(Mitchell and Simons, 1967). Since photolysis is very rapid, there is no time for an equilibration of energy. Dynamical or quantum relaxation theories of dissociation are required. An example of this is the quasi-diatomic model calculation by Holdy *et al.* (1970) which has been used to predict energy partitioning in ICN photolysis.

The photolysis of cyclobutanone (Campbell and Schlag, 1967)

$$\text{[cyclobutanone]} + h\nu \longrightarrow \triangledown^* + \text{CO} \tag{3.8}$$

or the photolysis of pyrazolines (Cadman *et al.*, 1969; Dorer, 1969; Dorer *et al.*, 1971)

$$\text{[pyrazoline structure]} R + h\nu \longrightarrow \triangleright^* - R + N_2 \tag{3.9}$$

results in highly vibrationally excited cyclopropanes which, afterward, may be collisionally stabilized

$$\triangledown^* + M \longrightarrow \triangledown + M \tag{3.10}$$

or isomerized

$$\triangledown^* \longrightarrow \text{[propylene]} \ . \tag{3.11}$$

The relative yields of stabilized cyclopropane and propylene depend on the partitioning of excess energy between the products of the primary photolysis. By varying the photolysis wavelength and chemical source, different energies, different energy distributions, and, possibly, different localizations of excitation in a particle may be produced. The energy partitioning in the primary photolysis determines the activation properties of the secondary unimolecular process, which will be discussed in Section V. As long as only relative yields of products in the secondary reaction are observed, a conclusion concerning the initial energy partitioning is difficult.

IV. Unimolecular Dissociation of Molecular Ions

Molecular ions undergoing unimolecular fragmentation can be produced by a great variety of "activation methods." Among these are the impact of electrons, vacuum-uv photons, and ions, and charge exchange, field ionization, chemical ionization, and high-energy radiations in radiolysis. With sufficiently high energies of the activating process, fragmentation becomes possible in addition to the primary ionization. Charged fragments are detected directly in mass spectrometers; the observation of neutral fragments can be performed by secondary ionization. Part of the fragmentation may occur directly in the activating process [for field-induced dissociations see Beckey and Knöppel (1966)]. However, from the observation of "metastable" ions which decompose "late" after ionization it may be concluded that at least a considerable part of the fragmentations are separated in time from activation, and may be regarded as "normal" unimolecular dissociation.

The quantity observed experimentally is in most cases the fragment mass spectrum, i.e., the distribution of fragment ions at a detector far away from the ion source. Dependence on the type and the energy of the ionizing process, on initial temperature, and on chemical effects such as isotopic substitution, etc. are investigated. Since in a conventional mass spectrometer the time between ionization and detection of the ions is of the order of 10^{-5} sec, normal mass spectra are observed at reaction times when a large part of the reaction is finished. In order to obtain more information on the fragmentation history, time-resolved mass spectra have been recorded by varying the time between ionization and fragment detection. Shorter times than in a normal mass spectrometer have been resolved in electron-impact (Osberghaus and Ottinger, 1965; Hertel and Ottinger, 1967; Knewstubb and Reid, 1970), photon-impact (Knewstubb and Reid, 1970), charge-exchange (Andlauer and Ottinger, 1971), and field-ionization (Beckey et al., 1969) studies. Decomposing ions have also been stored for longer times before detection, by Tatarczyk and von Zahn (1965); and Tatarczyk, (1969).

The different activation processes mentioned in the foregoing result in different distributions of internal energies in the decomposing ions. In electron or photon impact the energy of the colliding particles is distributed between the internal energy of the ions formed and the kinetic energy of relative motion between ions and ejected electrons. In general, on impact of monoenergetic electrons or photons broad distributions of internal energies in the ions are formed. Also, with different ionization processes different average energies are transferred to the activated ions [e.g., about 0.5 eV with 10-kV field ionization (Tenschert, 1969) and more than 6 eV with 70-eV electron impact in n-heptane (Ehrhardt and Linder, 1967)]. In contrast to this, charge exchange, being a resonance process, produces parent ions with only narrow energy spreads (e.g., Lindholm, 1966; Andlauer and Ottinger, 1971). Initial distributions of energy for secondary fragmentations are determined by the properties of the primary dissociation (see Section V). As in all unimolecular processes, the populations of excited states have to be determined in order to analyze mass spectra in detail.

In the following, examples of "normal," time-integrated mass spectra and also of time-resolved mass spectra for different activation processes are presented. They are compared with calculations by the theories discussed in Section I. More detailed discussions are given, e.g., by Rosenstock and Krauss (1963) and Rosenstock (1968).

A. BREAKDOWN CURVES

Experimentally observed fragment mass spectra and theoretical calculations can conveniently be compared by means of "breakdown curves." These curves give fractional yields of fragment ions, detected about 10^{-5} sec after ionization, as a function of internal energy of the parent ions. Breakdown curves are, to a first approximation, constructed either from the second derivatives of ion yields as a function of electron energy with electron-impact ionization, or from the first derivatives as a function of photon energy with photoionization, or, with charge exchange ionization, directly from the ion yields as a function of the recombination energies of the ions used for charge exchange.

As an example, Fig. 23 shows the normalized second derivative ionization efficiencies for the electron-impact mass spectrum of propane (Chupka and Kaminsky, 1961). In these curves the ionization potential of propane is taken as energy zero. Apparent fragmentation at energies below zero is due to the broad effective energy spread of the impact electrons ($T \simeq 2500$ K) and the initial thermal energy of propane molecules ($T \simeq 250$ C). These breakdown curves have been constructed by dividing the second derivatives of intensities of fragment ions by the second derivatives of total ion intensities as functions of energy. For this calculation a linear threshold law between the ionization cross section and the difference between the energy of impact electrons and the total internal energy transferred to the ion is assumed (Morrison, 1955; Geltman, 1956). Also, under the same conditions, from the second derivatives of total ion intensities the internal energy distributions in the parent ions can be obtained. A characteristic, almost triangular distribution is found with a maximum at about 1 eV above the ionization threshold and a "width" of a few eV at

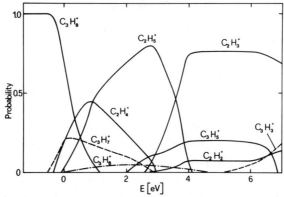

FIG. 23. Breakdown curves of propane on electron impact (from Chupka and Kaminsky, 1961).

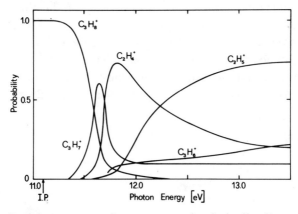

FIG. 24. Breakdown curves of propane on photoionization (from Chupka and Berkowitz, 1967).

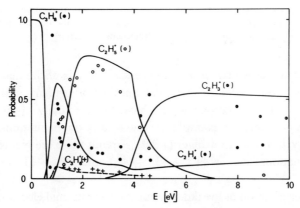

FIG. 25. Breakdown curves of propane in charge exchange experiments (—, calculations by Vestal, 1965; points, experiments by Petteson and Lindholm, 1963; only some of the fragments are shown).

50 eV electron-impact energy. The electron-impact breakdown pattern of Fig. 23 may be compared with the corresponding diagram obtained from the appropriate first derivatives of ion yields in photoionization (see Fig. 24) (Chupka and Berkowitz, 1967). Assuming a step threshold law, the internal energy distribution of the ions again can be obtained from the first derivative of total ion yields. By comparison with direct measurements of this energy distribution from photoelectron spectroscopy the validity of the threshold law in the range of a few eV above the threshold could be verified (Ehrhardt et al., 1968). Finally, Fig. 25 shows the relative ion yields for charge exchange ionization of propane (P) with different ions (A$^+$) in reactions of the type $P + A^+ \rightarrow P^{+*} + A$, $P^{+*} \rightarrow$ fragments (Petterson and Lindholm, 1963). Comparison of the three breakdown curves shows good agreement in most details. Some peculiarities are found, however. For example, the properties of the $C_3H_7^+$ curve in charge exchange may be influenced by ion molecule reactions.

Decomposition mechanisms can be constructed from the variety of fragment ions and their appearance potentials. Figure 26 gives the major

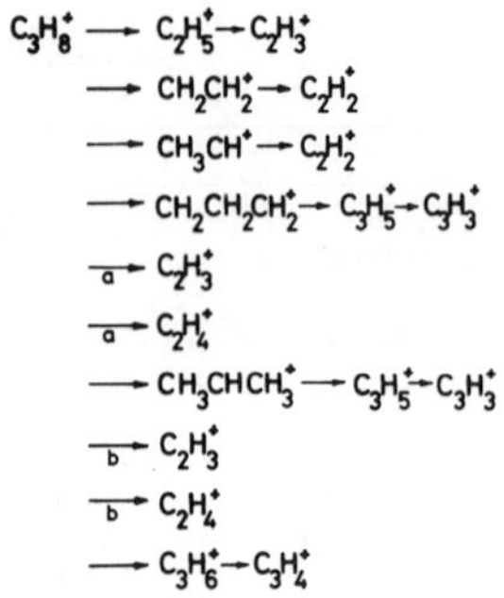

$$C_3H_8^+ \longrightarrow C_2H_5^+ - C_2H_3^+$$
$$\longrightarrow CH_2CH_2^+ \rightarrow C_2H_2^+$$
$$\longrightarrow CH_3CH^+ \rightarrow C_2H_2^+$$
$$\longrightarrow CH_2CH_2CH_2^+ \rightarrow C_3H_5^+ - C_3H_3^+$$
$$\xrightarrow{a} C_3H_3^+$$
$$\xrightarrow{a} C_2H_4^+$$
$$\longrightarrow CH_3CHCH_3^+ \rightarrow C_3H_5^+ - C_3H_3^+$$
$$\xrightarrow{b} C_2H_3^+$$
$$\xrightarrow{b} C_2H_4^+$$
$$\longrightarrow C_3H_6^+ - C_3H_4^+$$

FIG. 26. Fragmentation of propane ions (only the charged fragments are given).

decomposition paths used in the theoretical analysis of the mass spectrum of propane (Vestal, 1965). The total number of primary and secondary unimolecular fragmentations which have been actually observed is still larger. For propane, for example, 30 metastable fragmentations have been analyzed by Löhle and Ottinger (1969). Among these are metastable, two-step dissociations such as $44^+ \rightarrow 43^+ \rightarrow 41^+$ and $44^+ \rightarrow 43^+ \rightarrow 27^+$ (mass numbers).

The determination of breakdown curves from normal electron-impact or photoionization studies is always somewhat problematic because of the assumption of simple threshold laws. In charge exchange experiments and, in particular, by using photoelectron spectroscopy in photoionization, these uncertainties can be removed. A study by Brehm and von Puttkamer (1968) particularly should be mentioned. In this work the energy of electrons ejected in photoionization with the He 584-Å line was measured in coincidence with the mass-selected ions. This directly correlates the masses of a fragment ion with the internal energy of the parent ion and therefore immediately gives the breakdown curves without the assumption of a particular threshold law for photoionization. Figure 27 shows the

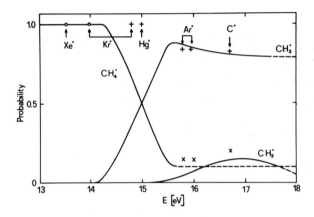

FIG. 27. Breakdown curves of methane (—, from photoionization with photoelectron spectroscopy, Brehm and von Puttkamer, 1968; points, from charge exchange, von Koch, 1964).

fragment yields obtained by these experiments for methane compared to charge exchange results by von Koch (1964). The ions used for charge exchange are given. Except for $A^+ = Kr^+$ and Hg^+, where more than one state is involved or ion–molecule reactions may be important, agreement is very good.

B. Time-Resolved Mass Spectra

Diffuse peaks in electron-impact mass spectra were first attributed to ions decomposing during transit from the ion source to the detector (Hipple and Condon, 1945; Hipple, 1947). In these experiments decomposition times of ions between 1.5 and 6 μsec could be resolved. Since these early studies of "metastable" ions the accessible time scale has been considerably extended. Today a much more direct access to unimolecular dissociations of ions may be obtained from time-resolved mass spectra, than from the breakdown curves described in Section IV,A. In electron-impact experiments by Osberghaus and Ottinger (1965), Hertel and Ottinger (1967), and Ottinger (1967) times between ionization and detection were brought down to 3×10^{-9} sec by ionizing the parent molecules in a narrow beam (10–100 μm) along one equipotential surface of the acceleration field. By ion storage in a flight tube of 2 m length observation times could also be extended to times as long as 0.5×10^{-3} sec (Tatarczyk and von Zahn, 1965; Tatarczyk 1969). In field ionization (see Beckey 1971) reaction times down to 10^{-12} sec could be resolved from the peak shapes of fast metastable ions.

In electron impact (EI) and field ionization (FI) broad distributions of internal energies in the parent ions are produced. Correspondingly, the concentrations of parent ions do not decay in these experiments according to an exponential time law $dc/dt = -kc_0 \exp(-kt)$ with a time-independent k. Instead, a continuous variation of average rate constants $\bar{k} \equiv -c^{-1} \, dc/dt$ during the reaction is observed. This is shown in Fig. 28 for the decom-

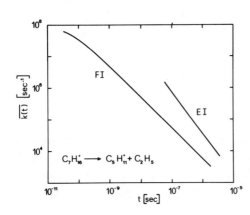

FIG. 28. Time-resolved mass spectra of n-heptane (FI, field ionization, from Beckey et al., 1969; EI, electron impact, from Hertel and Ottinger, 1967).

position $C_7H_{16}^+ \rightarrow C_5H_{11}^+ + C_2H_5$ in the mass spectrum of n-heptane. In spite of some difficulties in correlating EI and FI results because of different normalizations (Ottinger, 1970), the EI values are generally slightly higher than the FI results. This could be due to the higher internal excitation in EI experiments.

In order to derive values of the specific rate constants $k(E)$ from average rate constants $\overline{k(t)}$, the distributions of internal energies produced in ionization must be known. Then one may try to go back to $k(E)$ from the integral $\overline{k(t)}$. The conclusion $\overline{k(t)} \rightarrow k(E)$ is, of course, difficult and not completely unique. The situation is not much better than in thermal unimolecular reactions, where conclusions on $k(E)$ from limiting high-pressure rate constants $k_\infty(T)$ are difficult. A more direct access to $k(E)$ is therefore obtained if simpler distributions of internal energies are used. Studies of this kind recently were performed by Andlauer and Ottinger (1971, 1972) by measuring time-resolved mass spectra after charge exchange ionization. The decomposition reactions $C_6H_5CN^+ \rightarrow C_6H_4^+ + HCN$, $C_6H_6^+ \rightarrow C_6H_5^+ + H$, and $C_6H_6^+ \rightarrow C_4H_4^+ + C_2H_2$ have been studied in great detail. In these experiments purely exponential decay laws have been observed for nearly monoenergetic parent ions. No evidence for nonexponential decay, as discussed in Section I,D was found. Specific rate constants $k(E)$, obtained at different energies with different ions for charge exchange, are shown in Figs. 29 and 30. $k(E)$ increases monotonically with energy, as predicted by the calculations given in Section I. Agreement with values for $k(E)$ obtained from electron impact is quite satisfactory for benzonitrile (Fig. 29) in spite of the problems in analyzing $k(E)$ from electron-impact studies. In $C_6H_6^+$ decomposition two primary fragmentations could be observed (Fig. 30). The energy dependence of $k(E)$ is very different for both processes. In addition, it could be shown that both processes are not simply competing. If this were the case, the fast $C_4H_4^+$ formation would have completely suppressed the slow $C_6H_5^+$ formation. Instead, C—C bond breakage and splitting of the H atom are apparently

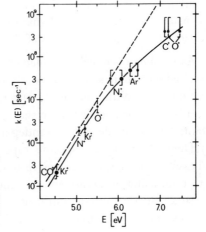

FIG. 29. Time-resolved mass spectrum of benzonitrile (—, charge exchange with given ions, Andlauer and Ottinger, 1971; - - -, electron impact, Hertel and Ottinger, 1967).

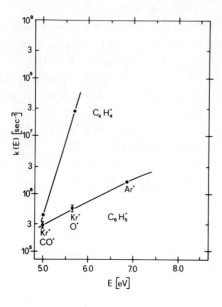

FIG. 30. Time-resolved fragmentations $C_6H_6^+ \to C_6H_5^+ + H$ and $C_6H_6^+ \to C_4H_4^+ + C_2H_2$ (from Andlauer and Ottinger, 1971).

independent and do not involve the same excited state of the parent ion. For the both noncompeting processes radiationless transitions between the initial states apparently are inefficient in the 10^{-6} sec available for fragmentation.

C. Calculation of Fragmentation Rates

Calculation of fragment patterns in normal mass spectra and of specific rate constants in time-resolved mass spectra requires knowledge of the properties of the electronic states of decomposing parent ions:

(a) As in photochemical unimolecular reactions it has to be known how fast excited electronic states can decay into the electronic ground state of the parent ions. With sufficiently fast transitions $k(E)$ can be calculated practically only for one electronic state. With slow transitions specific rate constants have to be determined independently for each state.

(b) Depending on the specific type of activation during ionization, initial excitations may be localized in some part of the parent ion. This may lead to fragmentation before energy randomization becomes complete. In this case a statistical quasiequilibrium calculation of $k(E)$ may be invalid and nonexponential decay laws may be observed.

(c) In order to calculate $k(E)$ explicitly, vibration frequencies, etc., of the parent ions, as well as of activated complexes of decomposing parent ions, are required. Energy thresholds and the type of the different reaction paths are almost always derived from the observed mass spectra.

In the following the simplest type of quasiequilibrium calculation on mass spectra is briefly described. The simplifying assumptions are: (a) after ionization, conversion to the electronic ground state is rapid and the larger volume of phase space of the ground state determines the time evolution of the system, (b) in the ground state energy randomization is complete. For further simplification the vibration frequencies, bond distances, etc. for the electronic ground state of the ion and for the activated complexes are approximated by properties of the corresponding neutral molecules. Calculation of $k(E)$ can then be performed by the methods of Section I. As an example, calculations for some primary fragmentations of propane ions by Vestal (1965) were shown in Fig. 4. A comparison with experimental $k(E)$ curves was given for heptane (Hertel and Ottinger, 1967) and good agreement was found. Breakdown curves can immediately be constructed by means of the specific rate constants: If only primary fragmentations occur, the fractional yield of a fragment i out of the total spectrum of fragments j at times long after ionization is given by

$$\phi_i(E) \simeq k_i(E)/\sum_j k_j(E). \tag{4.1}$$

If secondary fragmentations are possible, the consumption of fragment ions i has to be taken into account. If the time dependence of fragmentation may be resolved, a solution of the kinetic equations for consecutive processes is necessary. However, in breakdown curves for long times after decomposition the fractional yield of primary ions i is simply given by the ratio (4.1) multiplied by the fraction $F_i(E)$ of primary dissociations that leave the ion i with insufficient energy for subsequent fragmentation:

$$\phi_i(E) \simeq k_i(E)F_i(E)/\sum_j k_j(E). \tag{4.2}$$

The fractional yield of ions l from secondary fragmentation correspondingly follows as

$$\phi_l(E) \simeq k_i(E)[1 - F_i(E)]/\sum_j k_j(E). \tag{4.3}$$

The fraction $F_i(E)$ is calculated directly from the energy distribution curve on the products of dissociation, which has been discussed in Section I,E. Comparison of experimental charge exchange breakdown curves of some fragments of propane and calculations by Vestal (1965) is shown in Fig. 25. Similar comparisons for ethane and deuterated ethane are given by Prášil and Forst (1967). In these examples agreement between simple theory and experiment is good and can be improved by slight adjustments of the ionic parameters. Numerous improvements in the theoretical calculations of $k(E)$ for mass spectra and for unimolecular reactions in general have been proposed (e.g., Klots, 1971; Knewstubb, 1971; Mies, 1969).

V. Secondary Unimolecular Reactions

Second-generation fragments in mass spectra result from highly excited first-generation fragments undergoing secondary dissociations. A number of examples are included in the propane ion fragmentation shown in Fig. 26. The activation step for these secondary unimolecular reactions is the primary fragmentation. Populations of states for the secondary reaction are therefore governed by the distribution of energy on products in the primary reactions, as discussed in Section I,E. Processes of this type are also often observed in photochemical systems. The formation of vibrationally excited cyclopropane during the photolysis of cyclobutanone [see Eq. (1.49) and Fig. 8] may again serve as example. Here, the primary reaction (1.49) is followed by collisional stabilization (5.1) or isomerization (5.2) of cyclopropane:

$$\triangle^* + M \longrightarrow \triangle + M \tag{5.1}$$

$$\triangle^* \longrightarrow \diagdown\!\diagup \,. \tag{5.2}$$

The yield of propylene P relative to that of cyclopropane $\triangle$ may be described by an effective rate constant k_a, which is defined by

$$k_a \equiv Z[\mathrm{M}]P/\triangle \,. \tag{5.3}$$

For cyclopropane excited to only one energy E above the threshold E_0 and for strong collision, one-step collisional deactivation with collision number $Z[\mathrm{M}]$, $P/\triangle$ is given by $k(E)/Z[\mathrm{M}]$ and k_a is equal to the specific rate constant $k(E)$ for isomerization. Since the primary photolysis leads to broad distributions of energy (Fig. 8), and since collisional stabilization to energies below the threshold $E_0 \simeq 63$ kcal mole^{-1} at excitation energies of

100 kcal mole^{-1} will require more than one collision, a more difficult behavior is observed: k_a becomes a function of pressure. Keeping the assumption of a one-step stabilization, k_a is given by

$$k_a = Z[\text{M}] \left(\int \frac{f(E)k(E)}{k(E) + Z[\text{M}]} \, dE \bigg/ \int \frac{f(E)Z[\text{M}]}{k(E) + Z[\text{M}]} \, dE \right). \qquad (5.4)$$

Multistep deactivation decreases the effective Z and has to be treated by solving transport equations such as Eq. (3.6). Experimentally, k_a may be observed with different distributions $f(E)$ by varying the wavelength of the photolyzing light. A comparison of the results (at a fixed pressure) of Campbell and Schlag (1967) with statistical calculations using Fig. 8 for $f(E)$, Eq. (5.4), and quasiequilibrium calculations of $k(E)$ is shown in Fig. 31. If all the excess energy of photolysis were left in cyclopropane, k_a would be given by $k(E)$. Thus, the calculated $k(E)$ curve in Fig. 31 gives an

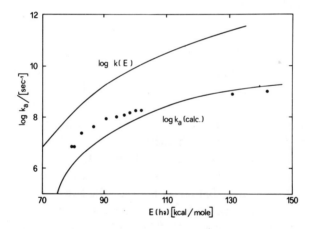

FIG. 31.   Average rate constant k_a of secondary isomerization of cyclopropane in the photolysis of cyclobutanone (●, experiments, from Campbell and Schlag, 1967).

upper limit to k_a. Disagreement between experiments and the statistical theory of k_a was claimed to constitute evidence against the statistical distribution of energy in photolysis products. This conclusion, however, may not necessarily be true, because of uncertainties concerning the efficiency of deactivation and the molecular parameters.

Other photochemical systems initiating secondary unimolecular reactions have been mentioned in Section III. Secondary unimolecular isomerization of methylisocyanide in competition with collisional stabilization was studied in the recoil tritium substitution

$$T^* + CH_3NC \longrightarrow CH_2TNC^* + H \qquad (5.5)$$

by Ting and Rowland (1968). In our nomenclature this represents a secondary unimolecular reaction following a primary unimolecular reaction with chemical activation, or following a primary bimolecular reaction.

VI. Unimolecular Reactions with Chemical Activation

The initiation of unimolecular reactions by association of atoms, radicals, molecules, and/or ions

$$B + C \longrightarrow A^* \qquad (6.1)$$

shall be termed, quite generally, "chemical activation." The intermediate A^* may then decompose unimolecularly, possibly by several reaction channels, isomerize, or be collisionally stabilized. In the given scheme a bimolecular reaction may be understood as unimolecular dissociation of an intermediate A^* initiated by an association (6.1) which is again simply the reverse of a unimolecular dissociation. Indeed, there often exists a direct correspondence between the theories of unimolecular and of bimolecular reactions, and no definite boundary between the two can be given. In the following we will discuss only those chemical activations that involve "long-lived" intermediates A^*. "Direct" processes with immediate transition from the activating association to the redissociation are excluded. As examples one may consider: (a) reactive scattering with collision complexes lasting longer than one average rotational period; (b) inelastic scattering with effective transfer of vibrational and translational energy in "sticky collisions"; (c) "usual" chemical activations with association of radicals (or atoms) and molecules, and subsequent collisional stabilization or dissociation of A^*; many secondary reactions of excited particles formed in hot atom chemistry, for example, in tritium recoil substitutions, are included in this group; and (d) thermal recombinations together with the reverse thermal dissociations as discussed in Section II.

A. Long-Lived Collision Complexes in Reactive and Inelastic Scattering

The average rotational period of collision complexes (10^{-12}–10^{-13} sec) may serve as a "clock" for measuring the lifetimes of intermediate complexes in beam scattering experiments. Longer lifetimes lead to isotropic distributions of products in the center-of-mass system; shorter lifetimes may result in anisotropies. One experiment of this type, with optical activation by the crossing of a light beam and a molecular beam in photofragment spectroscopy, was mentioned in Section III. A large number of ion–molecule reactions have been studied with chemical activation (see e.g., Henglein, 1972). By varying the impact energy of scattered particles, the transition between "complex" and "direct" mechanisms of reaction can be observed. At the transition point, $1/k(E)$ for dissociation of the complex and the rotational period are matched. This is shown in Fig. 32 for the ion–molecule reactions

$$C_2H_4 + C_2H_4{}^+ \longrightarrow C_4H_8^{+*} \longrightarrow C_3H_5{}^+ + CH_3 \tag{6.2}$$

$$\longrightarrow C_3H_3{}^+ + CH_3 + H_2 \tag{6.3}$$

(Herman et al., 1969). For reaction (6.2) the transition may be located at a collision energy $1.43 \leq E \leq 3.25$ eV; at lower energies complex lifetimes are longer, and at higher energies they are shorter, than the rotational period. In the given energy range no transition is observed for reaction

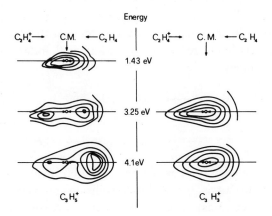

Fig. 32. Angular distribution of products in the ion–molecule reaction $C_2H_4{}^+$ + C_2H_4 (center-of-mass system; from Herman et al., 1969).

(6.3). The similarity of fragment mass spectra of butenes and cyclobutane to product distributions observed in the ion–molecule reaction

$$C_2H_4 + C_2H_4{}^+$$

clearly supports the occurrence of statistical redistributions in the collision complex of reaction (6.2) at low energies. The decrease of $k(E)$ with increasing complexity of a particle A* (see Section I,C) nicely finds its analog in the dependence of the transition energies between complex and stripping mechanism in ion–molecule reactions (see Henglein, 1972): For small complexes, such as in the reactions of D_2 with Ar^+, CO^+, or $N_2{}^+$ these energies are of the order 0.01 eV; for reactions of CD_4 with Ar^+ and $N_2{}^+$ energies of 0.3–0.5 eV are found; for $CD_4 + CD_4{}^+$ and CH_3OH^+, as well as for reaction (6.2), these energies are equal to a few eV. The rotational period is not the only "clock" in beam scattering experiments. In several cases, as in the reactions $C_2H_5Br^+ + C_2H_5Br \rightarrow C_4H_{10}Br_2{}^+$ or $C_2N_2{}^+ + C_2N_2 \rightarrow C_4N_4{}^+$, "sticky" collision complexes have been observed, i.e., complexes which after flight times of 10^{-6} sec were still not redissociated. This effect should be favored by increasing complexity of collision partners. However, a sticky collision complex was detected even for $Cl^+ + HCl \rightarrow HCl_2{}^+$, possibly due to electronic transitions that trap these complexes.

Long-lived collision complexes in the sense discussed ($\tau > 10^{-12}$ sec) have also been recently detected in beam studies of neutral molecules (Ham and Kinsey, 1968; Miller et al., 1968). In crossed beam experiments by Parson et al. (1973) unimolecular decompositions of long-lived collision complexes from the reaction of halogen atoms with olefins have been investigated in detail. The reaction F + cis-butene-2, for example, proceeds by the three channels

$$F + cis\text{-butene-2} \longrightarrow HF + C_4H_7 \tag{6.4}$$
$$\longrightarrow C_4H_8F^* \longrightarrow C_4H_7F + H \tag{6.5}$$
$$\longrightarrow C_4H_8F^* \longrightarrow C_3H_5F + CH_3. \tag{6.6}$$

The hydrogen transfer (6.4) is a direct reaction involving a short-lived intermediate; in reactions (6.5) and (6.6) collision complexes with lifetimes longer than one rotational period were observed. A similar, simultaneous occurrence of direct and complex mechanisms could be detected in the secondary reactions of the photolysis of NO_2. Here the reaction

$O + NO_2 \to NO + O_2$ could not be suppressed by collisional stabilization of the intermediate complex, even at carrier pressures of 1000 atm, whereas the competing channel $O + NO_2 \to NO_3$ attained its high-pressure limit at much lower pressures (Troe, 1969). Stereospecifity probably characterizes the reaction $F + C_2D_4$ studied in cross beams: If F approaches C_2D_4 in the molecular plane, D transfer with the formation of highly vibrationally excited DF ($v \simeq 4$) is a direct reaction; if F approaches the molecule perpendicular to the plane, a long-lived complex is formed, which then dissociates into C_2D_3F and D. The formation of long-lived complexes may also be the reason for the effective inelastic transfer of translational and vibrational energy in collisions of many polyatomic molecules. All intermediate cases between a statistical redistribution of energy among the degrees of freedom of the complex and the inefficient energy transfer in atomic–diatomic molecule collisions may be observed. For the statistical limit of redistribution the methods of Section I,E, i.e., statistical calculations of energy distributions on products of unimolecular dissociations, may be applied to collision complexes.

B. Competition between Collisional Stabilization and Dissociation of Complexes

A great amount of basic information on unimolecular reactions has been obtained from "normal" chemical activation systems. In order to illustrate unimolecular reactions with this type of activation, we consider the formation of sec-butyl radicals by the addition of H atoms to cis-butene-2 (Kohlmaier and Rabinovitch, 1963):

$$H + cis\text{-}C_4H_8 \longrightarrow C_4H_9{}^* \tag{6.7}$$

$$C_4H_9{}^* + M \longrightarrow C_4H_9 + M \tag{6.8}$$

$$C_4H_9{}^* \longrightarrow CH_3 + C_3H_6. \tag{6.9}$$

Redissociation to H atoms and cis-C_4H_8, unimolecular dissociation by the exothermic reaction (6.9), and collisional stabilization of the intermediate sec-butyl radicals $C_4H_9{}^*$ are competing processes. By analysis of the final products, the fractions of $C_4H_9{}^*$ dissociated (D) via reaction (6.9) or stabilized (S) via reaction (6.8) can be distinguished. Interpretation of these results, similar to the pressure dependence of quantum yields in photochemical unimolecular reactions, requires, in addition to the initial distribution of butyl radicals at different energies from activation (6.7), two

unknown quantities: the "effective" rate constants of collisional stabilization, and the "effective" rate constants of unimolecular dissociation (6.9)
of $C_4H_9{}^*$. The problem of separating both unknown rate constants arises
as in Section III. If the formation of monoenergetic $C_4H_9{}^*$, and strong-
collision, one-step stabilization is assumed, one obtains

$$S = \frac{Z[M]}{Z[M] + k(E)} \quad \text{and} \quad D = \frac{k(E)}{Z[M] + k(E)} \qquad (6.10)$$

for the fractions of stabilized S and dissociated D butyl radicals.

The definition of a "total rate constant" $k_a \equiv \langle k(E) \rangle$ of dissociation

$$k_a \equiv \langle k(E) \rangle \equiv Z[M]D/S \qquad (6.11)$$

similar to the case for secondary unimolecular reactions, Eq. (5.3), identifies
k_a with $k(E)$. If the energy spread from the activation reaction (6.7) is taken
into account, k_a is given by Eq. (5.4). If, on the other hand, a multistep
deactivation is considered, Eq. (6.10) is simply replaced by

$$S = \prod_{i=1}^{T} \frac{Z[M]}{Z[M] + k(E_i)} ; \quad D = 1 - S . \qquad (6.12)$$

Here T collisions are required to bring the radical down to energies below
threshold of reaction (6.9). The specific rate constant for dissociation
before each step is given by $k(E_i)$. With Eq. (6.12)

$$k_a = Z[M] \prod_{i=1}^{T} \{1 + [k(E_i)/Z[M]]\} - 1 , \qquad (6.13)$$

and

$$k_a([M] \to 0) \equiv k_{a0} = \prod_{i=1}^{T} k(E_i)/(Z[M])^{T-1} \qquad (6.14)$$

$$k_a([M] \to \infty) \equiv k_{a\infty} = \sum_{i=1}^{T} k(E_i) , \qquad (6.15)$$

k_a becomes a function of pressure. This is shown in Fig. 33, where the pressure of the carrier gas H_2 is varied within a very broad range. It is obvious that, particularly at the low-pressure limit, the given model must be too simple. It predicts an increase of k_{a0} with decreasing pressure $\propto [M]^{1-T}$. In reality, the distribution of energies removed per collision is quasicontinuous, as discussed in Section II,D [cf. e.g., Eq. (2.48)]. The deactivation (6.8) will therefore always have a "strong collision component" (i.e., the fraction of collisions that deactivate in one collision), which leads to a pressure-independent intercept of k_{a0} at $[M] \to 0$. In order to account for this, the transport equation (3.6) has to be solved.

The average step size of deactivating collisions depends on the nature of the carrier gas M. This is demonstrated in Fig. 34. A representation $k_a = f(S/D)$ is chosen: the more effective the collision partner, the lower is k_a (the effective dissociation rate constant $\langle k(E) \rangle$) at a given S/D. By fitting curves of this type for different M to the foregoing models average step sizes of deactivating collisions have been obtained. Since several, not too well-known quantities enter into the analysis, the results are again not completely unique.

Relatively independent of uncertainties in deactivating process (6.8), a number of basic properties of the specific rate constants $k(E)$ can be studied directly with $k_a \equiv \langle k(E) \rangle$ obtained from chemical activation. In several investigations by Rabinovitch and co-workers (see the summary in Spicer and Rabinovitch, 1970), k_a was determined for radicals of different complexities and isotopic substitutions and compared with calculations of $k(E)$ by the statistical theory in the RRKM version.

In the butyl system many different degrees of excitation (with average excess energies $\langle E \rangle$ varying between 8 and 14 kcal mole^{-1}) can be produced by using H or D and *cis*-butene-2, *trans*-butene-2, or butene-1 as reactants at different temperatures and pressures. The increase of k_a as a function of $\langle E \rangle$ is nicely shown in Fig. 35 and found to be in excellent agreement with theoretical predictions. Also, for the homologous series of chemically activated radicals from ethyl to octyl with virtually unchanged reaction coordinate, total energy, and threshold energy (for butyl-2 up to octyl-2), k_a decreases at a given pressure corresponding to the predicted behavior of $k(E)$ (Rabinovitch and Pearson, 1964, 1965). This decrease obviously corresponds to the increasing number of quantum states entering into Eq. (1.22).

A direct test of the randomization postulate used as the basis of statistical calculations of $k(E)$ has been possible in the following way: Chemically

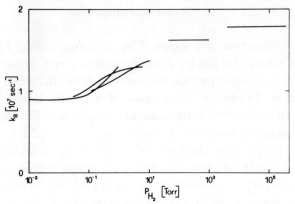

FIG. 33. Dissociation of chemically activated *sec*-butyl radicals (different sets of experiments, from Oref *et al.*, 1971).

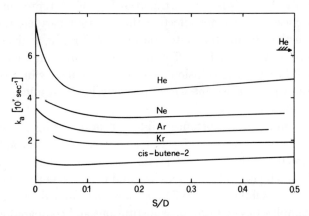

FIG. 34. Dissociation of chemically activated *sec*-butyl radicals in different carrier gases (from Kohlmaier and Rabinovitch, 1963).

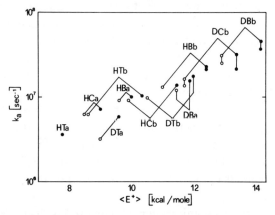

FIG. 35. Dissociation of chemically activated butyl radicals. $\bigcirc$; $p \rightarrow 0$, $\bullet$, $p \rightarrow \infty$; (H, D) + [*cis*-butene-2 (C); *trans*-butene-2 (T); butene-1 (B)] at 195 K (a) or 300 K (b) (from Rabinovitch *et al.*, 1963).

activated methylcyclopropane may be produced by the addition of methylene either to propylene or to cyclopropane

$$CH_2 + CH_3 \diagdown_H C = CH_2 \longrightarrow CH_3 \diagdown_H \overset{\overset{\displaystyle CH_2}{\diagup\diagdown}}{C - CH_2}{}^* \tag{6.16}$$

$$CH_2 + \overset{\displaystyle CH_2}{\underset{\displaystyle CH_2 - CH_2}{\diagup\diagdown}} \longrightarrow \overset{\displaystyle CH_2}{\underset{H}{\diagdown}} \overset{\displaystyle CH_2}{\underset{\underset{\displaystyle H}{C - CH_2}}{}^*} \tag{6.17}$$

(Butler and Kistiakowsky, 1960). In spite of the different initial preparation of the activated methylcyclopropanes, subsequent unimolecular reactions of $C_4H_8{}^*$ showed no influence of the special activation mode, except for the small difference of excitation energies $\langle E \rangle$. The same behavior is also shown in Fig. 35 for butyl radicals. Also, randomization is still apparently complete at the time scale of 10^{-13} sec obtained at the highest pressures in Fig. 33. This is in agreement with the observations of NO_2 photolysis described in Section III, where, up to the same range of lifetimes, evidence for agreement between experimental and statistically calculated $k(E)$ values was found.

The tests of randomization given are not very sensitive and nonrandom effects may have been too small to be detected. This is suggested by recent investigations of isotope effects in chemical activation systems. Here the more accurate product ratios are used as indicators of randomization instead of absolute values of k_a. Chemically activated hexafluorobicyclopropyl was formed by the two reactions

$$CD_2 + CF_2 \diagdown_{CH_2}{}^{\diagup} CF - CF = CF_2$$
$$\searrow$$
$$CF_2 - CF - CF - CF_2 \tag{6.18}$$
$$\diagdown_{CD_2}{}^{\diagup} \diagdown_{CH_2}{}^{\diagup}$$
$$\nearrow$$
$$CH_2 + CF_2 \diagdown_{CD_2}{}^{\diagup} CF - CF = CF_2$$

(Rynbrandt and Rabinovitch, 1971). Reaction (6.18) is followed by the elimination of CF_2, either at the deuterated or at the hydrogenated side of the activated molecule. The resulting isomers could be distinguished by their fragment mass spectra.

The mass ratio 95/97, shown in Fig. 36, is a measure of the yields of both reaction paths. A difference between these ratios for the two activation paths is observed which increases with increasing pressure. The ratio of nonrandom decomposition to total decomposition was found to be about 3.5% at low pressures, increasing to about 25% at the highest pressures where the decomposition of the randomized molecules is specifically inhibited by collisional stabilization. This behavior could be accounted for by assuming a rate constant of intramolecular energy relaxation of about 10^{12} sec^{-1} (solid lines in Fig. 36). This study shows that nonrandom effects can be observed if sufficiently sensitive detectors are used. Nonrandom energy distributions of products (see Section I,E and LeRoy, 1970, 1971) have been found at similar reaction times.

Very high excitation energies in chemical activation can be produced in hot atom substitution reactions such as

$$T^* + c\text{-}C_4H_8 \longrightarrow c\text{-}C_4H_7T^* + H \qquad (6.19)$$

$$c\text{-}C_4H_7T^* + M \longrightarrow c\text{-}C_4H_7T + M \qquad (6.20)$$

$$c\text{-}C_4H_7T^* \longrightarrow CH_2{=}CHT + C_2H_4. \qquad (6.21)$$

With increasing pressure the yield of stabilized $c\text{-}C_4H_7T$ increases (Lee and Rowland, 1963). However, even in the liquid phase some decomposition of $c\text{-}C_4H_7T^*$ is observed. If, on the other hand, excited CH_3T^* is formed by substitution of the H in methane by recoil tritium, only a slight pressure dependence is found. An interpretation of these properties can be given using Fig. 37 (Tang and Rowland, 1968). Quasi-equilibrium calculations of specific rate constants are given as a function of total energies of activated molecules. The range of reaction times and excitation energies that may contribute to the observed pressure dependences is indicated. Distributions of excitation energies as estimated from the observed pressure dependences are also shown. A much broader part of the distribution curve contributes to the observed pressure dependence in $c\text{-}C_4H_7T^*$ than in CH_3T^*, corresponding to the different slopes of the $k(E)$ curves. An extra block at the high-energy end in $c\text{-}C_4H_7T^*$ must be responsible for liquid-phase decomposition.

Compared to ordinary chemical activation systems, hot atom substitutions give much broader distributions of excited states with ranges extending up to very high energies. Therefore, the randomization postulate can be

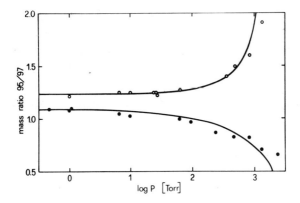

FIG. 36. Nonrandom dissociation of chemically activated hexafluorobicyclopropyl (○, formation from HVC + CD$_2$; ●, formation from HVC-d_2 + CH$_2$; from Rynbrandt and Rabinovitch, 1971).

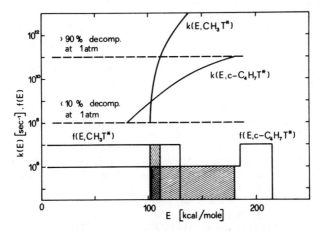

FIG. 37. Decomposition of activated CH$_3$T* and cyclo-C$_4$H$_7$T* from recoil tritium substitution (from Tang and Rowland, 1968).

tested at very short reaction times. This has been done with tritium recoil substitution in isopropyl chloride, where the two competing eliminations of HCl

$$CHT-CH-CH_2* \nearrow CHT=CH-CH_3 + HCl$$
$$\underset{H \quad Cl \quad H}{} \searrow CH_2TCH=CH_2 + HCl$$

(6.22)

can be distinguished (Tang and Rowland, 1968). Only slight differences in the relative yields in the gas phase, at 50 Torr, and in the liquid phase were observed. This indicates predominant randomization on the 10^{-12}-sec time scale. Nevertheless, a small difference between gas- and liquid-phase could be detected, which, analogous to reaction (6.18), may correspond to a minor contribution of the decomposition occurring before randomization of energy is complete.

REFERENCES

ANDLAUER, B., and OTTINGER, CH. (1971). *J. Chem. Phys.* **55**, 1471.
ANDLAUER, B., and OTTINGER, CH. (1972). *Z. Naturforsch.* **27a**, 293.
ATKINSON, R., and THRUSH, B. A. (1970). *Proc. Roy. Soc. (London)* **A316**, 123.
BAK, T. A., and LEBOWITZ, J. L. (1963). *Phys. Rev.* **131**, 1138.
BECKEY, H. D. (1971). " Field Ionization Mass Spectrometry." Pergamon, Oxford.
BECKEY, H. D., and KNÖPPEL, H. (1966). *Z. Naturforsch.* **21a**, 1920.
BECKEY, H. D., HEY, H., LEVSEN, K., and TENSCHERT, G. (1969). *Int. J. Mass Spectrom. Ion Phys.* **2**, 101.
BEGGS, D., BLOCK, C., and WILSON, D. J. (1964). *J. Phys. Chem.* **68**, 1494.
BENSON, S. W. (1968). "Thermochemical Kinetics." Wiley, New York.
BENSON, S. W. (1969). *J. Amer. Chem. Soc.* **91**, 2152.
BENSON, S. W., and O'NEAL, H. E. (1970). Kinetic Data on Gas Phase Unimolecular Reactions. NSRDS—NBS 21, Nat. Bur. Std., Washington, D.C.
BERGMANN, P. G., and LEBOWITZ, J. L. (1955). *Phys. Rev.* **99**, 578.
BERGMANN, P. G., and LEBOWITZ, J. L. (1957). *Ann. Phys. N.Y.* **1**, 1.
BERRY, R. S., CERNOCH, T., COPLAN, M., and EWING, J. J. (1968). *J. Chem. Phys.* **49**, 127.
BLATT, J., and WEISSKOPF, V. (1952). "Theoretical Nuclear Physics." Wiley, New York.
BOWERS, P. G. (1967). *J. Chem. Soc. (A)* 466.
BOWERS, P. G. (1968). *Can. J. Chem.* **46**, 307.
BOWERS, P. G. (1970). *J. Phys. Chem.* **74**, 952.
BREHM, B., and VON PUTTKAMER, E. (1967). *Z. Naturforsch.* **22a**, 8.
BUFF, F. P., and WILSON, D. J. (1962). *J. Amer. Chem. Soc.* **84**, 4063.
BUNKER, D. L. (1962). *J. Chem. Phys.* **37**, 393.
BUNKER, D. L. (1964). *J. Chem. Phys.* **40**, 1946.
BUNKER, D. L. (1966). "Theory of Elementary Gas Reactions." Pergamon, Oxford.
BUNKER, D. L., and PATTENGILL, M. (1968). *J. Chem. Phys.* **48**, 772.
BURNS, G., LEROY, R. J., MORRISS, O. J., and BLAKE, J. A. (1970). *Proc. Roy. Soc. (London)* **A316**, 81.
BUSCH, G. E., and WILSON, K. R. (1972). *J. Chem. Phys.* **56**, 3626, 3638.
BUSCH, G. E., MAHONEY, R. T., MORSE, R. I., and WILSON, K. R. (1969). *J. Chem. Phys.* **51**, 449.
BUTLER, J. N., and KISTIAKOWSKY, G. B. (1960). *J. Amer. Chem. Soc.* **82**, 759.
CADMAN, P., MEUNIER, H. M., and TROTMAN-DICKENSON, A. F. (1969). *J. Amer. Chem. Soc.* **91**, 7640.
CALVERT, J. G., and PITTS, J. N. (1966). "Photochemistry." Wiley, New York.
CAMPBELL, R. J., and SCHLAG, E. W. (1967). *J. Amer. Chem. Soc.* **89**, 5103.

CHAN, S. C., RABINOVITCH, B. S., BRYANT, J. T., SPICER, L. D., FUJIMOTO, T., LIN, Y. N., and PAVLOU, S. P. (1970). *J. Phys. Chem.* **74**, 3160.
CHANDRASEKHAR, S. (1943). *Rev. Mod. Phys.* **15**, 1.
CHRISTIE, M. I., HARRISON, A. J., NORRISH, R. G. W., and PORTER, G. (1955). *Proc. Roy. Soc. (London)* **A231**, 446.
CHUPKA, W. A., and BERKOWITZ, J. (1967). *J. Chem. Phys.* **47**, 2921.
CHUPKA, W. A., and KAMINSKY, M. (1961). *J. Chem. Phys.* **35**, 1991.
DIESEN, R. W., WAHR, J. C., and ADLER, S. E. (1969). *J. Chem. Phys.* **50**, 3635.
DORER, F. H. (1969). *J. Phys. Chem.* **73**, 3109.
DORER, F. H., BROWN, E., DO, J., and REES, R. (1971). *J. Phys. Chem.* **75**, 1640.
EHRHARDT, H., and LINDER, F. (1967). *Z. Naturforsch.* **22a**, 444.
EHRHARDT, H., LINDER, F., and TEKAAT, T. (1968). *Advan. Mass Spectrom.* **4**, 705.
EMANUEL, G. (1972). *Int. J. Chem. Kinet.* **4**, 591.
EWING, J. J., MILSTEIN, R., BERRY, R. S. (1971). *J. Chem. Phys.* **54**, 1752.
EYRING, H., HIRSCHFELDER, J. O., and TAYLOR, H. S. (1936). *J. Chem. Phys.* **4**, 479.
FORST, W. (1968). *J. Chem. Phys.* **48**, 3665.
FORST, W. (1971). *Chem. Rev.* **71**, 339.
FORST, W., PRÁŠIL, Z., and LAURENT, P. ST. (1967). *J. Chem. Phys.* **46**, 3736.
FRANKLIN, J. L., and HANEY, M. A. (1968). *J. Chem. Phys.* **48**, 4093.
FRANKLIN, J. L., and HANEY, M. A. (1969). *J. Phys. Chem.* **73**, 2857.
FREY, H. M., and WALSH, R. (1969). *Chem. Rev.* **69**, 103.
GAEDTKE, H., and TROE, J. (1973). *Ber. Bunsenges. Phys. Chem.* **77**, 24.
GAEDTKE, H., HIPPLER, H., and TROE, J. (1972). *Chem. Phys. Lett.* **16**, 177.
GAEDTKE, H., and TROE, J. (1975). *Ber. Bunsenges. Phys. Chem.* **79**, 184.
GANDINI, A., WHYTOCK, D. A., and KUTSCHKE, K. O. (1968). *Proc. Roy. Soc. (London)* **A306**, 541.
GANGI, R. A., and BURNELLE, L. (1971). *J. Chem. Phys.* **55**, 843, 851.
GEBELEIN, H., and JORTNER, J. (1972). *Theor. Chim. Acta* **25**, 143.
GELTMAN, S. (1956). *Phys. Rev.* **102**, 171.
GIDDINGS, J. C., and EYRING, H. (1954). *J. Chem. Phys.* **22**, 538.
GOLDEN, D. M., SOLLY, R. K., and BENSON, S. W. (1971). *J. Phys. Chem.* **75**, 1333.
HAARHOFF, P. C. (1963). *Mol. Phys.* **6**, 337; **7**, 101.
HALPERN, A. M., and WARE, W. R. (1970). *J. Chem. Phys.* **53**, 1969.
HAM, D. O., and KINSEY, J. L. (1968). *J. Amer. Chem. Soc.* **48**, 939.
HARTIG, R., OLSCHEWSKI, H. A., TROE, J., and WAGNER, H. GG. (1968). *Ber. Bunsenges. Phys. Chem.* **72**, 1016.
HENGLEIN, A. (1970). *In* "Molecular Beams and Reaction Kinetics" (Ch. Schlier, ed.), p. 139. Academic Press, New York.
HENRY, B. R., and KASHA, M. (1968). *Ann. Rev. Phys. Chem.* **19**, 161.
HERMAN, Z., LEE, A., and WOLFGANG, R. (1969). *J. Chem. Phys.* **51**, 452.
HERTEL, I., and OTTINGER, CH. (1967). *Z. Naturforsch.* **22a**, 1141.
HIPPLE, J. A. (1947). *Phys. Rev.* **71**, 544.
HIPPLE, J. A., and CONDON, E. U. (1945). *Phys. Rev.* **68**, 54.
HIPPLER, H., and TROE, J. (1971). *Ber. Bunsenges. Physik. Chem.* **75**, 27.
HIPPLER, H., LUTHER, K., and TROE, J. (1973). *Ber. Bunsenges. Phys. Chem.* **77**, 1104.
HOARE, M. R., and PAL, P. (1971). *Mol. Phys.* **20**, 695.
HOFACKER, L. (1963). *Z. Naturforsch.* **18a**, 607.
HOLDY, K. E., KLOTZ, L. C., and WILSON, K. R. (1970). *J. Chem. Phys.* **52**, 4588.
HOMER, J. B., and HURLE, I. R. (1970). *Proc. Roy. Soc. (London)* **A314**, 585.
HURLE, I. R., MACKEY, P., and ROSENFELD, J. L. J. (1968). *Ber. Bunsenges. Phys. Chem.* **72**, 991.

IP, J. K. K., and BURNS, G. (1967). *Discuss. Faraday Soc.* **44**, 241.

JOHNSTON, H. S. (1966). "Gas Phase Reaction Rate Theory." Ronald Press, New York.

JORTNER, J., RICE, S. A., and HOCHSTRASSER, R. M. (1969). *Advan. Photochem.* **7**, 149.

JUNGEN, M., and TROE, J. (1970). *Ber. Bunsenges. Phys. Chem.* **74**, 276.

KASSEL, L. S. (1932). "Kinetics of Homogeneous Gas Phase Reactions." Chemical Catalog Co., New York.

KAUFMAN, F. (1969). *Ann. Rev. Phys. Chem.* **20**, 45.

KECK, J. C. (1967). *Advan. Chem. Phys.* **13**, 85.

KECK, J. C., and CARRIER, G. (1965). *J. Chem. Phys.* **43**, 2284.

KECK, J. C., and KALELKAR, A. (1968). *J. Chem. Phys.* **49**, 2658.

KEYSER, L. F., LEVINE, S. Z., and KAUFMAN, F. (1971). *J. Chem. Phys.* **54**, 355.

KIEFER, J. H., and LUTZ, R. W. (1967). *Int. Symp. Combust.*, 11*th* p. 67. Combust. Inst., Pittsburgh, Pennsylvania.

KLOTS, C. E. (1971). *J. Phys. Chem.* **75**, 1526.

KNEWSTUBB, P. F. (1971). *Int. J. Mass Spectrom. Ion Phys.* **6**, 217.

KNEWSTUBB, P. F., and REID, N. W. (1970). *Int. J. Mass Spectrom. Ion Phys.* **5**, 361.

KOHLMAIER, G. H., and RABINOVITCH, B. S. (1963). *J. Chem. Phys.* **38**, 1692, 1709; **39**, 490.

KRAMERS, H. A. (1940). *Physica,* **7**, 284.

KURZEL, R. B., and STEINFELD, J. I. (1970). *J. Chem. Phys.* **53**, 3293.

LANDAU, L. D., and LIFSHITZ, E. M. (1965). "Quantum Mechanics," 2nd ed. Pergamon, Oxford.

LEE, E. K. C., and ROWLAND, F. S. (1963). *J. Amer. Chem. Soc.* **85**, 897.

LE NOBLE, W. J. (1967). *Progr. Phys. Org. Chem.* **5**, 207.

LEROY, R. L. (1970). *J. Chem. Phys.* **53**, 846.

LEROY, R. L. (1971). *J. Chem. Phys.* **55**, 1476.

LEVINE, R. D. (1966). *J. Chem. Phys.* **44**, 1567, 2029, 2035, 2046.

LIAS, S. G., COLLIN, G. J., REBBERT, R. E., and AUSLOOS, P. (1970). *J. Chem. Phys.* **52**, 1841.

LIN, S. H., and EYRING, H. (1963). *J. Chem. Phys.* **39**, 1577.

LIN, S. H., and EYRING, H. (1965). *J. Chem. Phys.* **43**, 2153.

LIN, M. C., and LAIDLER, K. J. (1968). *Trans. Faraday. Soc.* **64**, 79, 94.

LINDEMANN, F. A. (1922). *Trans. Faraday Soc.* **17**, 599.

LINDHOLM, E. (1966). *In* "Ion-Molecule Reactions in the Gas Phase" (P. J. Ausloos, ed.), p. 1. Advan. Chem. Ser. 58. Ann. Chem. Soc. Publ., Washington, D.C.

LÖHLE, U., and OTTINGER, CH. (1969). *J. Chem. Phys.* **51**, 3097.

LUTHER, K., TROE, J., and WAGNER, H. GG. (1972). *Ber. Bunsenges. Phys. Chem.* **76**, 53.

LUU, S. H., and TROE, J. (1973). *Ber. Bunsenges. Phys. Chem.* **77**, 325.

LUU, S. H., and TROE, J. (1974). *Ber. Bunsenges. Phys. Chem.* **78**, 766.

MACCOLL, A. (1969). *Chem. Rev.* **69**, 33.

McELWAIN, D. L. S., and PRITCHARD, H. O. (1969). *J. Amer. Chem. Soc.* **91**, 7693.

MARCUS, R. A. (1952). *J. Chem. Phys.* **20**, 355, 359, 364.

MARCUS, R. A. (1964). *J. Chem. Phys.* **41**, 2614.

MARCUS, R. A. (1965). *J. Chem. Phys.* **43**, 2658.

MARCUS, R. A., and RICE, O. K. (1951). *J. Phys. Colloid Chem.* **55**, 894.

MEYER, E., OLSCHEWSKI, H. A., TROE, J., and WAGNER, H. GG. (1968). *Int. Symp. Combust.* 12*th* p. 345. Combust. Inst., Pittsburgh.

MIES, F. H. (1969). *J. Chem. Phys.* **51**, 787, 798.

MIES, F. H., and KRAUSS, M. A. (1966). *J. Chem. Phys.* **45**, 4455.

MILLER, W. B., SAFRON, S. A., and HERSCHBACH, D. R. (1968). *Discuss Faraday Soc.* **44**, 108.

MITCHELL, R. C., and SIMONS, J. P. (1967). *Discuss. Faraday. Soc.* **44**, 208.

MOELWYN-HUGHES, E. A. (1947). "The Kinetics of Reactions in Solution," 2nd ed. Oxford Univ. Press, London and New York.

MORRISON, J. D. (1955). *Rev. Pure Appl. Chem.* **5**, 22.

MUKAMEL, S., and JORTNER, J. (1974). *J. Chem. Phys.* **60**, 4760.

NIELSEN, S. E., and BAK, T. A. (1964). *J. Chem. Phys.* **41**, 665.

NIKITIN, E. E. (1966). "Theory of Thermally Induced Gas Phase Reactions." Indiana Univ. Press, Bloomington, Indiana.

NIKITIN, E. E. (1968). *In* "Chemische Elementarprozesse" (H. Hartmann, ed.), p. 43. Springer-Verlag, Berlin and New York.

OLSCHEWSKI, H. A., TROE, J., and WAGNER, H. GG. (1966a). *Ber. Bunsenges. Phys. Chem.* **70**, 450.

OLSCHEWSKI, H. A., TROE, J., and WAGNER, H. GG. (1966b). *Ber. Bunsenges. Phys. Chem.* **70**, 1060.

O'NEAL, H. E., and BENSON, S. W. (1967). *J. Phys. Chem.* **71**, 2903.

O'NEAL, H. E., and BENSON, S. W. (1968). *J. Phys. Chem.* **72**, 1866.

O'NEAL, H. E., and LARSON, C. W. (1969). *J. Phys. Chem.* **73**, 1011.

OREF, I., SCHUETZLE, D., and RABINOVITCH, B. S. (1971). *J. Phys. Chem.* **75**, 2164.

OSBERGHAUS, O., and OTTINGER, CH. (1965). *Phys. Lett.* **16**, 121.

OTTINGER, CH. (1967). *Z. Naturforsch.* **22a**, 20, 40.

OTTINGER, CH. (1970). Bericht 107, Max-Planck-Inst. Strömungsforsch. Göttingen.

PARSON, J. M., SHOBOTAKE, K., LEE, Y. T., and RICE, S. A. (1973). *J. Chem. Phys.* **59**, 1402, 1416, 1427, 1435.

PETTERSON, E., and LINDHOLM, E. (1963). *Ark. Fys.* **24**, 49.

PITTS, J. N., SHARP, J. H., and CHAN, S. I. (1964). *J. Chem. Phys.* **42**, 3655.

POLANYI, M., and WIGNER, E. (1928). *Z. Phys. Chem.* **A139**, 439.

PORTER, G. (1962). *Discuss Faraday Soc.* **33**, 198.

PORTER, G. B., and CONNELLY, B. T. (1960). *J. Chem. Phys.* **33**, 81.

PORTER, G., SZABO, Z. G., and TOWNSEND, M. G. (1962). *Proc. Roy. Soc. (London)* **A270**, 493.

PRÁŠIL, Z., and FORST, W. (1967). *J. Phys. Chem.* **71**, 3166.

QUACK, M., and TROE, J. (1974). *Ber. Bunsenges. Phys. Chem.* **78**, 240.

RABINOVITCH, B. S., and PEARSON, M. J. (1964). *J. Chem. Phys.* **41**, 28.

RABINOVITCH, B. S., and PEARSON, M. J. (1965). *J. Chem. Phys.* **42**, 2470.

RABINOVITCH, B. S., and SETSER, D. W. (1964). *Advan. Photochem.* **3**, 1.

RABINOVITCH, B. S., and STEIN, S. S. (1973). *J. Chem. Phys.* **58**, 2438.

RABINOVITCH, B. S., KUBIN, R. F., and HARRINGTON, R. E. (1963). *J. Chem. Phys.* **38**, 405.

ROSENSTOCK, H. M. (1968). *Advan. Mass Spectrom.* **4**, 523.

ROSENSTOCK, H. M., and KRAUSS, M. (1963). *Advan. Mass Spectrom.* **2**, 251.

ROSENSTOCK, H. M., WALLENSTEIN, M. B., WAHRHAFTIG, A. L., and EYRING, H. (1952). *Proc. Nat. Acad. Sci. U.S.* **38**, 667.

ROSS, J., LIGHT, J. C., and SHULER, K. E. (1969). *In* "Kinetic Processes in Gases and Plasmas" (A. R. Hochstim, ed.), p. 281. Academic Press, New York.

RUSSEL, K. E., and SIMONS, J. (1953). *Proc. Roy. Soc. (London)* **A217**, 271.

RYNBRANDT, J. D., and RABINOVITCH, B. S. (1971). *J. Phys. Chem.* **75**, 2164.

SCHECKER, H. G., and WAGNER, H. GG. (1969). *Int. J. Chem. Kinet.* **1**, 541.

SCHIPPERT, C., HIPPLER, H., and TROE, J. (1975). *Int. J. Chem. Kinet.* in press.

SCHLAG, E. W., and HALLER, G. L. (1965). *J. Chem. Phys.* **42**, 584.

SCHLAG, E. W., and RABINOVITCH, B. S. (1960). *J. Amer. Chem. Soc.* **82**, 5996.

SCHLAG, E. W., and SANDSMARK, R. A. (1962). *J. Chem. Phys.* **37**, 168.

SCHLAG, E. W., and VON WEYSSENHOFF, H. (1969). *J. Chem. Phys.* **51**, 2508.

SCHLAG, E. W., and VON WEYSSENHOFF, H. (1973). *J. Chem. Phys.* **59**, 729.

SCHLAG, E. W., SANDSMARK, R. A., and VALANCE, W. G. (1964). *J. Chem. Phys.* **40**, 1461.

SCHNEIDER, F. W., and RABINOVITCH, B. S. (1962). *J. Amer. Chem. Soc.* **84**, 4215.

SCHNEIDER, F. W., and RABINOVITCH, B. S. (1963). *J. Amer. Chem. Soc.* **85**, 2365.

SCHWARTZ, S. E., and JOHNSTON, H. S. (1969). *J. Chem. Phys.* **51**, 1286.

SERAUSKAS, R. V., and SCHLAG, E. W. (1965). *J. Chem. Phys.* **43**, 898.

SHUI, H., APPLETON, J. P., and KECK, J. C. (1970). *J. Chem. Phys.* **53**, 2547.

SHUI, H., APPLETON, J. P., and KECK, J. C. (1971). *Int. Symp. Combust.*, 13th p. 21. Combust. Inst., Pittsburgh, Pennsylvania.

SLATER, N. B. (1959). "Theory of Unimolecular Reactions." Methuen, London.

SOLOMON, J. (1967). *J. Chem. Phys.* **47**, 889.

SPICER, L. D., and RABINOVITCH, B. S. (1970). *Ann. Rev. Phys. Chem.* **21**, 349.

STEVENS, B. (1967). "Collisional Activation in Gases." Pergamon, Oxford.

STRACHAN, A. N., BOYD, R. K., and KUTSCHKE, K. O. (1964). *Can. J. Chem.* **42**, 1345.

STRETTON, J. L. (1969). *In* "Transfer and Storage of Energy by Molecules" (G. M. Burnett and A. M. North, eds.), Vol. II, p. 58. Wiley, New York.

TANG, Y. N., and ROWLAND, F. S. (1968). *J. Phys. Chem.* **72**, 707.

TATARCZYK, J. (1969). Thesis, Bonn.

TATARCZYK, J., and VON ZAHN, U. (1965). *Z. Naturforsch.* **20a**, 1708.

TENSCHERT, G. (1969). Thesis, Bonn.

THIELE, E. (1962). *J. Chem. Phys.* **36**, 1466.

THIELE, E. (1963a). *J. Chem. Phys.* **39**, 3258.

THIELE, E. (1963b). *J. Chem. Phys.* **38**, 1959.

TING, C. T., and ROWLAND, F. S. (1968). *J. Amer. Chem. Soc.* **72**, 763.

TOLMAN, R. C. (1938). "The Principles of Statistical Mechanics." Oxford Univ. Press, London and New York.

TOU, J. C. (1967). *J. Phys. Chem.* **71**, 2721.

TOU, J. C., and LIN, S. H. (1968). *J. Chem. Phys.* **49**, 4187.

TROE, J. (1969a). *Ber. Bunsenges. Phys. Chem.* **73**, 144.

TROE, J. (1969b). *Ber. Bunsenges. Phys. Chem.* **73**, 906.

TROE, J. (1973). *Ber. Bunsenges. Phys. Chem.* **77**, 665.

TROE, J. (1974). *Ber. Bunsenges. Phys. Chem.* **78**, 478.

TROE, J., and WAGNER, H. GG. (1967a). *Ber. Bunsenges. Phys. Chem.* **71**, 937.

TROE, J., and WAGNER, H. GG. (1967b). *Z. Phys. Chem. NF* **55**, 326.

TROE, J., and WAGNER, H. GG. (1973). *In* "Physical Chemistry of Fast Reactions" (B. P. Levitt, ed.), Plenum Press, New York.

TSCHUIKOW-ROUX, E. (1968). *J. Phys. Chem.* **72**, 1009.

VAN DEN BERGH, H., and TROE, J. (1975). *Chem. Phys. Lett.* **31**, 351.

VESTAL, M., WAHRHAFTIG, A. L., and JOHNSTON, W. H. (1962). *J. Chem. Phys.* **37**, 1276.

VESTAL, M. L. (1964). *J. Chem. Phys.* **41**, 3997.

VESTAL, M. L. (1965). *J. Chem. Phys.* **43**, 1356.

VON KOCH, H. (1964). *Ark. Fys.* **28**, 529.

WAAGE, E. V., and RABINOVITCH, B. S. (1970). *Chem. Rev.* **70**, 377.

WHITTEN, G. Z., and RABINOVITCH, B. S. (1963). *J. Chem. Phys.* **38**, 2466.

WHITTEN, G. Z., and RABINOVITCH, B. S. (1964). *J. Chem. Phys.* **41**, 1883.

WIEDER, G. M., and MARCUS, R. A. (1962). *J. Chem. Phys.* **37**, 1835.

WILDE, K. A. (1964). *J. Chem. Phys.* **41**, 448.

WILSON, D. J. (1960). *J. Phys. Chem.* **64**, 323.

WILSON, D. J., and HUNG, N. C. (1963). *J. Chem. Phys.* **38**, 828.

WILSON, D. J., and THIELE, E. (1961). *J. Chem. Phys.* **35**, 1256.

WILSON, D. J., and THIELE, E. (1964). *J. Chem. Phys.* **40**, 3425.

WILSON, D. J., HARTER, R. J., and ALTERMAN, E. B. (1964). *J. Chem. Phys.* **40**, 2137.

WOLFSBERG, M. (1962). *J. Chem. Phys.* **36**, 1072.

WORSHAM, W. C., and RICE, O. K. (1967). *J. Chem. Phys.* **46**, 2021.

WRAY, K. L. (1965). *Int. Symp. Combust.* 10*th* p. 523. Combust. Inst., Pittsburgh, Pennsylvania.

Chapter 12

Interactions of Chemical Reactions, Transport Processes, and Flow

K. H. HOYERMANN

I. Introduction

Chemical reactions in the gas phase are normally coupled to flow and transport phenomena such as diffusion, heat conduction, and thermal diffusion. Some of the obvious fields where the three areas—chemistry, flow, and transport—interact to some extent are in considerations of detonations as systems described by chemistry and supersonic flow, of flames as systems of flow and chemical reactions coupled with transport

931

processes, of reactive nozzle flow, and of reactive flow in general. Nature subsists on the coupling of reaction, flow, and transport processes, and the experimentalist trying to determine exact figures for these phenomena is faced by their unavoidable interplay.

The general picture of a reacting system is one of conversion of oxidizer and/or fuel to products going through the main reaction zone. This zone may be fixed in space or may travel into the unburnt gas with low or high velocity. The main question is thus how the initial and final states are coupled together by chemistry, flow, and transport of heat and particles. In order to enable details to be given of some real situations, the scope of this chapter has been necessarily limited. This requires the specification of the conditions for some reacting flows where flow patterns influence chemical reactions and where chemical reactions are partly obscured by flow phenomena. The selection of topics in this chapter is somewhat arbitrary.

(1) A brief survey of the derivation of conservation laws for mass, species, momentum, and energy with reference to interesting cases is thought to be necessary for the assumptions made in the description of realistic systems.

(2) Supersonic flow driven by chemical reactions may occasion detonations, and supersonic flow, as realized in shock waves, allows the study of such chemistry as unimolecular decomposition, pyrolysis of hydrocarbons, etc., under defined temperature and pressure conditions.

(3) Flames are governed by the interplay of flow, chemical reactions, and transport processes: The slowest process determines the propagation rate; inhibitor action is understood with the knowledge of the basic mechanism of propagation of the normal flame. Flames, as high-temperature flow systems without walls, can be used for the study of elementary chemical reactions under extreme conditions.

(4) Measurements on chemical reactions in isothermal flow systems allow the deduction of very accurate rate data. Full advantage of this technique is taken when specifying flow pattern and transport explicitly.

This introduction to the field of the interaction of chemical reaction and flow neglects all structural effects, such as spin in detonation, cellular structure in flames, and stationary state structure in nearly isothermal systems. Thus this chapter is not intended to be exhaustive, but to be illustrative of the basic principles of different phenomena and to give the reference to some key papers—not chronologically ordered—from which the interested reader may start out in search of solutions to special problems.

II. Basic Relations

A chemical reaction taking place in a given volume element can influence its surroundings by causing transfer of mass, momentum, and energy. Thus, the interpretation of quantities measured in such a system in terms of chemical kinetics has to take account of the various kinds of possible transport processes and of flow phenomena. They are of vital importance, too, for the modeling of any kind of reacting system, such as flames, detonations, isothermal flow systems, and other chemical reactors.

For a description of such a system the equations of conservation of mass, conservation of momentum, and conservation of energy are required in an appropriate form. For a detailed derivation of the conservation laws the reader is referred to the standard literature (Hirschfelder *et al.*, 1954; Chapman and Cowling, 1970; Williams, 1964; Mazo, 1967). We will only briefly summarize the basic lines of derivation of the equations and the quantities normally used.

For a survey of kinetic theory see Chapter 2 by Curtiss.

A. DEFINITION OF VARIABLES

We introduce some quantities that will be useful for the treatment of multicomponent systems.

For a mixture of N components and n particles the number of molecules of chemical species i in a volume v around a position $(\mathbf{r}, t)$ at a time t is denoted as n_i (number density). The molar concentration is

$$c_i = n_i/A \qquad A = \text{Avogadro's number}. \tag{2.1}$$

The density of species i is

$$\rho_i = n_i m_i = M_i c_i, \tag{2.2}$$

where m_i is the mass of species i and M_i is its molecular weight.

The total density ρ in the volume v is then

$$\rho = \sum_{i=1}^{N} \rho_i = \sum_{i=1}^{N} n_i m_i. \tag{2.3}$$

The mole fraction of species i is

$$x_i = n_i / \sum n_i = c_i/c \tag{2.4}$$

and the mass fraction is

$$y_i = \rho_i / \sum \rho_i = \rho_i / \rho. \qquad (2.5)$$

Using the mass fraction notation, the normal flow velocity $\mathbf{v}_0$ can be expressed as

$$\mathbf{v}_0 = (1/\rho) \sum \rho_i \bar{\mathbf{v}}_i = \sum y_i \bar{\mathbf{v}}_i = (1/\rho) \sum n_i m_i \bar{\mathbf{v}}_i. \qquad (2.6)$$

Here $\bar{\mathbf{v}}_i$ is the mean velocity of species i.

It is convenient to split the average velocity $\bar{\mathbf{v}}_i$ of species i into two parts

$$\bar{\mathbf{v}}_i = \mathbf{v}_0 + \bar{\mathbf{V}}_i(\mathbf{r}, t). \qquad (2.7)$$

The quantity $\bar{\mathbf{V}}_i$ is descriptively called the diffusion velocity. From this definition of $\mathbf{V}_i$ it is evident that $\sum n_i m_i \bar{\mathbf{V}}_i$ or $\sum y_i \bar{\mathbf{V}}_i$ equals zero:

$$\sum_{i=1}^{N} n_i m_i \bar{\mathbf{V}}_i = 0. \qquad (2.8)$$

B. Conservation Laws for Multicomponent Systems

We shall give now the basic ideas for the derivation of the conservation laws for reacting mixtures in the microscopic picture. Here we will follow Hirschfelder et al. (1954) and Williams (1964).

Statistical mechanics states that particles of species i can be described in phase space according to position $\mathbf{r}$ and velocity $\mathbf{v}$ at time t. Grouping all molecules of species i lying in $d^3\mathbf{r}$ around $\mathbf{r}$ and $d^3\mathbf{v}$ around $\mathbf{v}$, the distribution function can then be chosen such that

$$f_i(\mathbf{r}, \mathbf{v}, t) \, d^3\mathbf{r} \, d^3\mathbf{v} \qquad (2.9)$$

gives all molecules of kind i in the phase space volume $d^3\mathbf{r} \, d^3\mathbf{v}$.

The total number n_i at a position $\mathbf{r}$ at time t in a particular spatial volume is given by

$$n_i(\mathbf{r}, t) = \int f_i(\mathbf{r}, \mathbf{v}, t) \, d^3\mathbf{v}. \qquad (2.10)$$

An average value for any quantity G_i, $\bar{G}_i(\mathbf{r}, t)$, associated with n_i is obtained from

$$\bar{G}_i(\mathbf{r}, t) = \frac{\int G_i(\mathbf{r}, \mathbf{v}, t) f_i(\mathbf{r}, \mathbf{v}, t) \, d^3\mathbf{v}}{\int f_i(\mathbf{r}, \mathbf{v}, t) \, d^3\mathbf{v}}, \qquad i = 1, \ldots, N$$

$$= \frac{1}{n_i} \int G_i(\mathbf{r}, \mathbf{v}, t) f_i(\mathbf{r}, \mathbf{v}, t) \, d^3\mathbf{v}. \tag{2.11}$$

The question as to how the quantities such as mass, momentum, and energy will develop with time in the phase space volume can be answered in a quite general form by using the Boltzmann equation.

The change of the distribution function with time, neglecting external forces, may be expressed by

$$\frac{\partial f_i}{\partial t} + \mathbf{v} \cdot \frac{\partial}{\partial \mathbf{r}} f_i = \frac{\delta f_i}{\delta t}. \tag{2.12}$$

Here $\delta f_i / \delta t$ gives the overall net rate of change of f_i with time caused by molecular processes such as collisions and chemical production or destruction of species i.

Consider the derivation of a quantity ψ_i associated with the particle number n_i (such as mass, momentum, energy, or the number n_i itself) for a position $\mathbf{r}$ in the spatial volume $d^3\mathbf{r}$ at time t. The procedure to obtain an average value from the Boltzmann equation (2.12) is as follows: Multiply Eq. (2.12) by ψ_i and then integrate over all velocities $\mathbf{v}$. This leads to

$$\int \psi_i \left(\frac{\partial f_i}{\partial t} + \mathbf{v} \cdot \frac{\partial f_i}{\partial \mathbf{r}} \right) d^3\mathbf{v}_i = \int \psi_i \frac{\delta f_i}{\delta t} \, d^3\mathbf{v}_i. \tag{2.13}$$

Using the definition of average value [Eq. (2.11)] and applying some mathematical manipulation, we derive the general equation of change for particles of kind i $(i = 1, \ldots, N)$

$$\frac{\partial}{\partial t} (n_i \bar{\psi}_i) + \frac{\partial}{\partial \mathbf{r}} \cdot [n_i \overline{(\psi_i \mathbf{v}_i)_i}] = \int \psi_i \frac{\delta f_i}{\delta t} \, d^3\mathbf{v}_i. \tag{2.14}$$

First we derive the conservation of species i from Eq. (2.14). Species conservation is obtained from the general equation of change setting

$\psi_i = 1$, which means that we are interested in the change of n_i itself. From Eq. (2.14) we get

$$\frac{\partial n_i}{\partial t} + \frac{\partial}{\partial \mathbf{r}} \cdot (n_i \bar{\mathbf{v}}_i) = \int \frac{\delta f_i}{\delta t} d^3 \mathbf{v}_i . \tag{2.15}$$

As is shown in the standard literature, the contribution of collisions to the integral on the right-hand side of Eq. (2.15) is zero. Thus, this integral gives just the number of particles produced or destroyed by chemical reactions.

The net rate of production of chemical species i (particles in a spatial volume per unit time) is denoted as

$$K_i = \int (\delta f_i / \delta t) \, d^3 \mathbf{v}_i . \tag{2.16}$$

Since $m_i K_i$ gives the mass production rate of species i, and since mass as a whole is neither created nor destroyed, the net rate of total mass production is zero:

$$\sum_{i=1}^{N} m_i K_i = 0 . \tag{2.17}$$

The conservation of the particular species i is expressed as

$$\frac{\partial n_i}{\partial t} + \frac{\partial}{\partial \mathbf{r}} \cdot (n_i \bar{\mathbf{v}}_i) = K_i . \tag{2.18}$$

The physical meaning of this equation becomes more obvious on recalling the definition of the average velocity $\bar{\mathbf{v}}_i$ with respect to the diffusion velocity [Eq. (2.7)] and the total change in n_i, as defined in the Euler derivative

$$\frac{Dn_i}{Dt} = \frac{\partial n_i}{\partial t} + \bar{\mathbf{v}}_i \cdot \frac{\partial}{\partial \mathbf{r}} n_i = -n_i \frac{\partial}{\partial \mathbf{r}} \cdot \mathbf{v}_0 - \frac{\partial}{\partial \mathbf{r}} \cdot n_i \mathbf{V}_i + K_i . \tag{2.19}$$

The right-hand side then presents in three terms the change of the number of the species i due to flow, due to transport processes, and due to chemical reactions.

The conservation of mass as a whole (continuity equation) is obtained by summation over the mass of all kinds of species i via Eq. (2.18), or, formally, by setting $\psi_i = m_i$ in Eq. (2.14). Using Eq. (2.17), this leads to

$$\sum_{i=1}^{N} [(\partial/\partial t)(n_i m_i) + (\partial/\partial \mathbf{r}) \cdot (n_i m_i \bar{\mathbf{v}}_i)] = \sum m_i K_i = 0, \qquad (2.20)$$

which is equivalent to

$$(\partial \rho/\partial t) + (\partial/\partial \mathbf{r}) \cdot (\rho \mathbf{v}_0) = 0 \qquad (2.21)$$

using Eqs. (3), (5), and (6).

In the derivation of the global continuity equation it is recognized that m_i is a summational invariant, conserved through microscopic processes:

$$\sum_{i=1}^{N} \int \psi_i(\delta f_i/\delta t) \, d^3\mathbf{v}_i = 0. \qquad (2.22)$$

Other summational invariants in our system are momentum and energy.

The conservation of total momentum is given by the general equation of change (2.14) by setting $\psi_i = m_i \mathbf{v}_i$:

$$\sum_{i=1}^{N} \{(\partial/\partial t)(n_i m_i \bar{\mathbf{v}}_i) + (\partial/\partial \mathbf{r}) \cdot [n_i \overline{(m_i \bar{\mathbf{v}}_i)\mathbf{v}_i}]\} = 0. \qquad (2.23)$$

Here the summational invariant relation (2.22) is used in the form

$$\sum \int m_i \mathbf{v}_i(\partial f_i/\partial t) \, d^3\mathbf{v} = 0.$$

Defining the pressure tensor $\mathbf{P}_i$ for species i as

$$\mathbf{P}_i = n_i m_i \overline{(\mathbf{VV})}_i = \int m_i \overline{(VV)}_i f_i \, d^3\mathbf{v} \qquad (2.24)$$

and the total pressure tensor $\mathbf{P}$ as

$$\mathbf{P} = \sum \mathbf{P}_i, \qquad (2.25)$$

then by use of the mass conservation law we get

$$\frac{\partial \mathbf{v}_0}{\partial t} + \mathbf{v}_0 \cdot \frac{\partial}{\partial \mathbf{r}} \mathbf{v}_0 = -\frac{1}{\rho}\left(\frac{\partial}{\partial \mathbf{r}} \cdot \mathbf{P}\right). \qquad (2.26)$$

This, converted into the Euler notation, gives the usual form of momentum conservation, known from fluid dynamics

$$D\mathbf{v}_0/Dt = -(1/\rho)[(\partial/\partial\mathbf{r}) \cdot \mathbf{P}]. \tag{2.27}$$

The total change in $\mathbf{v}_0$ is then interpreted as the change in pressure tensor (pressure and viscous effects).

In a very similar way the equation for the conservation of energy is obtained by setting $\psi_i = \frac{1}{2}m_i v_i^2 + U_i^+$, where U_i^+ denotes the energy contributions from all internal degrees of freedom of interest for molecules of type i at a position $(\mathbf{r}, \mathbf{v})$ in phase space at time t. The total internal energy $U_i(\mathbf{r}, \mathbf{v}, t)$ in phase space for a particle of kind i moving with velocity $\mathbf{v}_i$ is

$$U_i(\mathbf{r}, \mathbf{v}, t) = \frac{1}{2}m_i v_i^2 + U_i^+. \tag{2.28}$$

By definition of average values in the spatial volume $d^3\mathbf{r}$ at position $(\mathbf{r}, t)$, the average internal energy $\bar{U}_i$ is given by

$$\bar{U}_i = \int U_i f_i \, d^3\mathbf{v}/n_i = \hat{U}_i m_i = \tfrac{3}{2}kT + \bar{U}_i^+ \tag{2.29}$$

($\hat{U}_i$ is the specific internal energy per unit mass). The average specific internal energy of the mixture, known from thermodynamics, is

$$\hat{U} = \sum y_i \hat{U}_i. \tag{2.30}$$

The conservation of total internal energy in this notation follows from the general equation of change by setting $\psi_i = \frac{1}{2}m_i v_i^2 + U_i^+$, forming the average values for ψ_i, $(\overline{\psi_i \mathbf{v}_i})_i$ and $(\partial\psi_i/\partial\mathbf{v})_i$, and subsequent summing over all types of particles i. This leads to

$$(\partial/\partial t)(\tfrac{1}{2}\rho v_0^2 + \rho\hat{U}) + (\partial/\partial\mathbf{r}) \cdot (\tfrac{1}{2}\rho v_0^2 \cdot \mathbf{v}_0 + \rho\hat{U}\mathbf{v}_0 + \mathbf{v}_0 \cdot \mathbf{P} + \mathbf{q}) = 0 \tag{2.31}$$

where the heat flux $\mathbf{q}$ of all species i gives the net total energy carried by molecules of all types i across a boundary moving with velocity $\mathbf{v}_0$

$$\mathbf{q}_i \equiv n_i\overline{(U_i\mathbf{V})_i} = \int U_i \mathbf{V}_i f_i \, d^3\mathbf{v} \tag{2.32}$$

and the total heat flux vector is defined as

$$\mathbf{q} = \sum_{i=1}^{N} \mathbf{q}_i .$$ (2.33)

Equation (2.33) is transformed to

$$\rho \frac{\partial \hat{U}}{\partial t} + \rho \mathbf{v}_0 \cdot \frac{\partial}{\partial \mathbf{r}} \hat{U} = -\frac{\partial}{\partial \mathbf{r}} \cdot \mathbf{q} - \mathbf{P} : \left(\frac{\partial}{\partial \mathbf{r}} \mathbf{v}_0 \right).$$ (2.34)

Here the colon (:) indicates that the expression is equal to the sum of the products of the corresponding components of $\mathbf{P}$ and $(\partial \mathbf{v}_0 / \partial \mathbf{r})$.

The total change of internal energy in the barycentric system when using Euler derivatives is

$$\frac{D\hat{U}}{Dt} = \frac{\partial \hat{U}}{\partial t} + \mathbf{v}_0 \cdot \frac{\partial}{\partial \mathbf{r}} \hat{U} = -\frac{1}{\rho} \left(\frac{\partial}{\partial \mathbf{r}} \cdot \mathbf{q} \right) - \frac{1}{\rho} \left(\mathbf{P} : \frac{\partial}{\partial \mathbf{r}} \mathbf{v}_0 \right).$$ (2.35)

Physically speaking, the first term on the right side gives the change due to heat flux, including radiation losses; the second term gives the change due to viscous effects and pV work.

The macroscopic conservation equations for chemical species, total mass, momentum, and energy govern in principle the development of a flowing reactive system.

A derivation of the quantities $\bar{\mathbf{V}}_i$, $\mathbf{P}$, and $\mathbf{q}$ from the pertubation solutions of the Boltzmann equations are outside the scope of this chapter. Thus, we will restrict the next section to a summary of the associated flux of each of these quantities in terms of macroscopic variables such as pressure and temperature and the appropriate transport coefficients for dilute gases.

The full description of transport processes in terms of microscopic variables will be found in Sections III and IV of Chapter 2.

C. The Quantities K_i, V_i, $\mathbf{P}$, and $\mathbf{q}$

1. Explicit Form of K_i

The net rate of production of species i (in particles per unit time) is given by Eq. (2.16)

$$K_i = \int (\delta f_i / \delta t) \, d^3 \mathbf{v} .$$

An explicit expression in terms of chemical kinetics can be given when the reaction mechanism is known. A scheme of the following form is assumed:

$$\alpha_{A_1}A + \alpha_{B_1}B + \cdots \xrightarrow{k_{10}} \beta_{A_1}A + \beta_{B_1}B + \cdots$$

$$\alpha_{A_2}A + \alpha_{B_2}B + \cdots \xrightarrow{k_{20}} \beta_{A_2}A + \cdots$$

where the α_{A_j} and β_{A_j} are the normal stoichiometric coefficients. The reverse reactions should be listed separately, in order to avoid errors.

The production of species A according to reaction $j = 1$ is given by

$$K_A^{(1)} = k_{10}(\beta_{A1} - \alpha_{A1})n_A^{\alpha_{A1}} n_B^{\alpha_{B1}}.$$

Thus, the net production of species A for the whole scheme is

$$K_A = \sum_j (\beta_{Aj} - \alpha_{Aj})k_{j0}\, n_A^{\alpha_{Aj}} n_B^{\alpha_{Bj}} \tag{2.36}$$

where summation is over all listed chemical reactions j. All K_i ($i = 1, \ldots, N$) are found in the same way as $K_A = K_1$. It must be kept in mind that not all K_i can be independent, since Eq. (2.17) must hold for the total mass production.

2. Explicit Form of V_i

The mass flux vector $\mathbf{j}_i$ for species i can be shown to be

$$\mathbf{j}_i = n_i m_i \bar{\mathbf{V}}_i = \frac{n^2}{\rho} \sum_{j=1}^{N} m_i n_i D_{ij}^* \mathbf{d}_j - D_i^{T*} \frac{\partial \ln T}{\partial \mathbf{r}} \tag{2.37}$$

where $\mathbf{d}_j$ denotes the gradients of mole fractions and gradients of pressure

$$\mathbf{d}_j = \frac{\partial}{\partial \mathbf{r}}\left(\frac{n_j}{n}\right) + \left(\frac{n_j}{n} - \frac{n_j m_j}{\rho}\right)\frac{\partial \ln p}{\partial \mathbf{r}}. \tag{2.38}$$

The D_{ij}^* and D_i^{T*} are the multicomponent diffusion and thermal diffusion coefficients for dilute mixtures. The D_{ij}^* can be related to the normal binary diffusion coefficients D_{ij}.

3. Explicit Form of the Pressure Tensor $\mathbf{P}$

The physical significance of the pressure tensor is twofold, relating both to the hydrostatic pressure p and to viscous effects in the system,

$$\mathbf{P} = p\mathbf{U} + \mathbf{p} \tag{2.39}$$

(**U** denotes the unit tensor). **p** is of the form

$$\mathbf{p} = -\eta \left[\frac{\partial}{\partial \mathbf{r}} \mathbf{v}_0 + \left(\frac{\partial}{\partial \mathbf{r}} \mathbf{v}_0 \right)^t \right] + \left(\frac{2}{3} \eta - \kappa \right) \left(\frac{\partial}{\partial \mathbf{r}} \cdot \mathbf{v}_0 \right) \mathbf{U} . \tag{2.40}$$

Here the coefficient η gives the shear viscosity of the gas moving with different velocities, and the coefficient κ gives the bulk viscosity due to pure expansion of the gas. The bulk viscosity coefficient is negligibly small in the cases to be considered and will therefore be omitted. The superscript t denotes the transposed tensor.

4. *Explicit Form of the Energy Flux Vector*

We will concentrate in the following sections on systems in which the macroscopic variables pressure p and temperature T afford the best description. The specific enthalpy $\hat{H}$ is then given by the thermodynamic identity

$$\hat{U} = \sum y_i \hat{H}_i - p/\rho . \tag{2.41}$$

The energy flux vector is given by the expression

$$\mathbf{q} = -\lambda \frac{\partial T}{\partial \mathbf{r}} + \sum_{i=1}^{N} n_i \bar{\mathbf{V}}_i \hat{H}_i + \frac{RT}{n} \sum \frac{n_j D_i^{T*}}{m_i D_{ij}^*} (\bar{\mathbf{V}}_i - \bar{\mathbf{V}}_j) . \tag{2.42}$$

The physical interpretation is obvious: The first term gives the energy flux due to heat conduction (λ is the thermal conductivity coefficient), the second term gives the transport of enthalpy due to the diffusion of particles relative to the center of mass, which is itself moving at the flow velocity, and the third term gives the contribution due to diffusion thermoeffect.

In the expression for the energy flux vector the contributions of losses due to radiation are omitted, since they are normally small compared to the other effects in systems under consideration.

D. One-Dimensional Flow

The differential equations governing strictly one-dimensional flow in the z direction can be derived from the general equations (2.19), (2.21), (2.26), and (2.35). This is accomplished by neglecting all contributions of flow and transport processes coming from x and y components ($\partial/\partial x, \partial/\partial y$). This means that all properties at a position z are uniform over a fixed reference area of unit size in the (x, y) plane.

1. Mass Conservation

The overall continuity equation for the total mass, Eq. (2.21), becomes for the z direction

$$(\partial\rho/\partial t) + (d/dz)(\rho v_0) = 0. \tag{2.43}$$

For systems where a steady state is achieved Eq. (2.43) reduces to

$$(d/dz)(\rho v_0) = 0 \tag{2.44}$$

which means that the total mass flux ρv_0 is constant.

2. Species Conservation

The conservation of a particular chemical species i is derived from Eq. (2.19):

$$(\partial n_i/\partial t) + (d/dz)(n_i \bar{v}_i) = K_i. \tag{2.45}$$

On multiplying Eq. (2.45) by m_i, the continuity equation in mass fraction notation follows from (2.2) and (2.5) as

$$(\partial/\partial t)(\rho y_i) + (d/dz)[\rho y_i(v_0 + \bar{V}_i)] = m_i K_i. \tag{2.46}$$

On making use of the overall continuity equation (2.8), this is converted into

$$\frac{\partial y_i}{\partial t} + v_0\frac{dy_i}{dt} = \frac{m_i K_i}{\rho} - \frac{1}{\rho}\left[\frac{d}{dz}(\rho y_i V_i)\right]. \tag{2.47}$$

Sometimes it is more convenient to consider the mass flux fraction G_i of species i than the mass fraction itself; G_i is defined as

$$G_i = n_i m_i(v_0 + \bar{V}_i)/\rho v_0 \tag{2.48}$$

from which follows, for the sum of all G_i, using (2.3) and (2.8),

$$\sum G_i = 1. \tag{2.49}$$

The conservation of chemical species i for the steady state is derived in the notation of mass flux fraction from Eqs. (2.46) (2.46), and (2.48) as

$$\rho v_0 \, dG_i/dz = m_i K_i .$$ (2.50)

For practical purposes it is useful to consider chemical element conservation besides the species conservation. Let v_i^E denote the number of atoms of chemical element E in the chemical species i. Equation (2.50) is multiplied by v_i^E and arranged to give

$$(\rho v_0/m_i)v_i^E \, dG_i/dz = v_i^E K_i .$$ (2.51)

Since element conservation must hold, the relation

$$\sum v_i^E K_i = 0$$ (2.52)

is obvious for each element E. Thus, Eq. (2.51) reads

$$\frac{d}{dz} \left(\sum_{i=1}^{N} \frac{v_i^E G_i}{m_i} \right) = 0$$ (2.53)

for every chemical element.

3. Conservation of Momentum

The general equation of conservation of momentum is given by Eq. (2.26):

$$\frac{\partial \mathbf{v}_0}{\partial t} + \mathbf{v}_0 \cdot \frac{\partial}{\partial \mathbf{r}} \mathbf{v}_0 = -\frac{1}{\rho} \left(\frac{\partial}{\partial \mathbf{r}} \cdot \mathbf{P} \right)$$ (2.54)

In order to derive an explicit form of Eq. (2.54), we have to consider first the pressure tensor $\mathbf{p}$.

Equation (2.40) gives the part of the pressure tensor due to viscous effects

$$\mathbf{p} = -\eta \left[\frac{\partial}{\partial \mathbf{r}} \mathbf{v}_0 + \left(\frac{\partial}{\partial \mathbf{r}} \mathbf{v}_0 \right)^t \right] + \frac{2}{3} \eta \left(\frac{\partial}{\partial \mathbf{r}} \cdot \mathbf{v}_0 \right) \mathbf{U} .$$

Here, the bulk viscosity κ is neglected. Equating the components of $\mathbf{p}$

and combining these results with Eq. (2.39), the total pressure tensor reduces for flow in z-direction to

$$\mathbf{p} = \begin{pmatrix} p + \dfrac{2}{3}\eta\,\dfrac{\partial v_z}{\partial z} & 0 & 0 \\[2ex] 0 & p + \dfrac{2}{3}\eta\,\dfrac{\partial v_z}{\partial z} & 0 \\[2ex] 0 & 0 & p - \dfrac{4}{3}\eta\,\dfrac{dv_z}{dz} \end{pmatrix}. \qquad (2.55)$$

As the z-component of $(\partial/\partial \mathbf{r} \cdot \mathbf{p})$ is given by

$$\frac{\partial}{\partial \mathbf{r}} \cdot \mathbf{p} = \frac{\partial p_{xz}}{\partial x} + \frac{\partial p_{yz}}{\partial y} + \frac{\partial p_{zz}}{\partial z} \,,$$

the general equation of motion is deduced from Eq. (2.54) giving

$$\rho\,\frac{\partial v_0}{\partial t} + \rho v_0\,\frac{dv_0}{dz} + \frac{dp}{dz} - \frac{d}{dz}\left(\frac{4}{3}\eta\,\frac{dv}{dz}\right) = 0 \qquad (2.56)$$

or for systems in a steady state

$$\rho v_0\,\frac{dv_0}{dz} + \frac{dp}{dz} - \frac{d}{dz}\left(\frac{4}{3}\eta\,\frac{dv_0}{dz}\right) = 0. \qquad (2.57)$$

4. Energy Conservation

Energy conservation is described by Eq. (2.35):

$$\frac{\partial \hat{U}}{\partial t} + \mathbf{v}_0\,\frac{\partial}{\partial \mathbf{r}}\,\hat{U} = -\frac{1}{\rho}\left(\frac{\partial}{\partial \mathbf{r}} \cdot \mathbf{q}\right) - \frac{1}{\rho}\left(\mathbf{P} : \frac{\partial}{\partial \mathbf{r}}\,\mathbf{v}_0\right).$$

This expression reduces appreciably for one-dimensional flow. Using the simplified form of the pressure tensor as given in Eq. (2.55) and writing out the velocity gradient tensor expression $(\mathbf{P} : \partial \mathbf{v}_0/\partial \mathbf{r})$ in full, the latter then becomes

$$\mathbf{P} : \frac{\partial}{\partial \mathbf{r}}\,\mathbf{v}_0 = \frac{d(pv_0)}{dz} - v_0\,\frac{dp}{dz} + v_0\,\frac{d}{dz}\left(\frac{4}{3}\eta\,\frac{dv}{dz}\right) - \frac{d}{dz}\left(v_0\,\frac{4\eta}{3}\,\frac{dv_0}{dz}\right). \qquad (2.58)$$

Making use of the momentum equation (2.56), we obtain

$$\mathbf{P}: \frac{\partial}{\partial \mathbf{r}} v_0 = \rho v_0 \frac{\partial v_0}{\partial t} + \rho v_0{}^2 \frac{dv_0}{dz} + \frac{d(pv_0)}{dz} - \frac{d}{dz}\left(v_0 \frac{4}{3}\eta \frac{dv_0}{dz}\right). \quad (2.59)$$

Thus the conservation of energy is given by

$$\rho \frac{\partial \hat{U}}{\partial t} + \rho v_0 \frac{d\hat{U}}{dz} = -\frac{dq}{dz} - \rho v_0 \frac{\partial v}{\partial t}$$

$$- \rho v_0{}^2 \frac{dv_0}{dz} - \frac{d(pv_0)}{dz} + \frac{d}{dz}\left(v_0 \frac{4\eta}{3}\frac{dv_0}{dz}\right). \quad (2.60)$$

For the case of a steady state ($\partial/\partial t = 0$) this leads to

$$\rho v_0 \frac{d\hat{U}}{dz} + \frac{dq}{dz} + \rho v_0{}^2 \frac{dv_0}{dz} + \frac{d(pv_0)}{dz} - \frac{d}{dz}\left(v_0 \frac{4}{3}\eta \frac{dv}{dz}\right) = 0. \quad (2.61)$$

In some practical cases it is desirable to describe energy conservation in terms of enthalpy. The specific enthalpy $\hat{H}$ is defined via Eq. (2.41) as

$$\hat{H} = \hat{U} + p/\rho = \sum y_i \hat{H}_i.$$

By using relation (2.41), we transform (2.61) to

$$\rho v_0 \frac{d}{dz}\left(\hat{H} + \frac{v_0{}^2}{2}\right) + \frac{dq}{dz} - \frac{d}{dz}\left(v_0 \frac{4}{3}\eta \frac{dv_0}{dz}\right) = 0. \quad (2.62)$$

The energy flux vector q is given by Eq. (2.42) and in this case can expressed as

$$q = -\lambda \frac{dT}{dz} + \sum_{i=1}^{N} n_i \bar{V}_i \hat{H}_i + \frac{RT}{n}\sum_{i,j} \frac{n_j D_i^{T*}}{m_i D_{ij}^*}(\bar{V}_i - \bar{V}_j). \quad (2.63)$$

III. Shock Waves and Chemical Reactions

A. THE RANKINE–HUGONIOT RELATIONS

Detonation, shock waves, and flames have proved to be very useful tools for the investigation of chemical reactions and energy transfer processes. Some of their essential properties can be well described, applying the

equations for strictly one-dimensional steady flow. The reaction zone may
be fixed around $z = 0$. In this coordinate system the reactants (subscript 1)
move with a velocity $u_1 = -D$ into the reaction zone. The products
(index 2) move with velocity u_2 away from the fixed front. The flow
velocity with respect to a laboratory coordinate system is v. One therefore
obtains

$$u_i = v_i - D.$$

If the reactants ahead of the reaction zone are at rest, then the reaction
zone will move with a velocity D against the z direction. The reaction zone
may be regarded as limited by two reference planes, 1 and 2. Outside of
that zone let d/dz be zero. We first restrict our considerations to steady
shock waves and detonations. In this case the conservation equations (2.44),
(2.50), (2.57), and (2.62) can be simplified by neglecting the transport
terms. Outside the shock front this is a good approximation. The conservation equations therefore read

$$\rho v - M' \qquad \text{mass conservation} \qquad (3.1)$$

$$M \, dG_i/dz = m_i K_i \qquad \text{species conservation.} \qquad (3.2)$$

Here $G_i = n_i m_i/\rho$. This equation may also be written $d(n_i v)/dz = K_i$; we
have

$$\rho v^2 + p = I' \qquad \text{momentum conservation} \qquad (3.3)$$

$$\hat{H} + \tfrac{1}{2}v^2 = E' \qquad \text{energy conservation.} \qquad (3.4)$$

In addition, the perfect gas equation is assumed to hold and hence
$p = kTn = kT \sum n_i$. The density ρ is defined as $\sum n_i m_i$ in Eq. (2.3).

In shock wave experiments the velocity of the shock wave, initial conditions, and thermodynamic properties of the gas are normally known.
Therefore the quantities M', I', and E' are fixed for a given experiment.
As long as no reaction takes place the individual values of G_i remain constant and one can fix the two reference planes ahead of (index 1) and behind
(index 2) the shock front (see Fig. 1). In a coordinate system fixed in the
shock front the conservation equations for mass (3.1), momentum (3.3),
and energy (3.4) reduce to the well-known forms

$$\rho_1 u_1 = \rho_2 u_2 = M \qquad (3.5)$$

$$p_1 + Mu_1 = p_2 + Mu_2 = I \qquad (3.6)$$

$$\hat{H}_1 + \tfrac{1}{2}u_1{}^2 = \hat{H}_2 + \tfrac{1}{2}u_2{}^2 = E. \qquad (3.7)$$

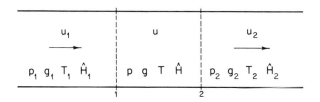

FIG. 1.   Variables describing a shock wave (index 1, initial state; index 2, final state).

Combining Eqs. (3.5) and (3.6) by eliminating the velocity leads to

$$p_2 - p_1 = -M^2[(1/\rho_2) - (1/\rho_1)]. \tag{3.8}$$

Equation (3.8) represents a fan of straight lines, the Rayleigh lines, in the p vs. $1/\rho$ plane through the point p_1, ρ_1 with the slope $-M^2$. Since M^2 must of course always be positive and give the possible range of values of p_1, ρ_1, only two quadrangles are accessible in the p vs. $1/\rho$ plane.

Case a. $p_2 > p_1$.   Pressure and density increase across the reaction zone. This case corresponds to shock waves. (In practice the thickness of a shock front equals a few mean free paths of the gas molecules. A calculation of the shock front profile can of course not be performed with the simplified equations mentioned in the foregoing.) Case (a) also corresponds to detonations.

Case b. $p_2 < p_1$.   This situation corresponds to deflagration waves. They can only occur if exothermic reaction takes place.

It should be noted that Eq. (3.8) holds irrespective of the form of the equation of state, because it is based on purely mechanical conditions.

Two other forms of Eq. (3.8) are occasionally useful. Since $M^2 = (\rho_1 u_1)(\rho_2 u_2)$, one can write (Courant and Friedrichs, 1956)

$$p_2 - p_1 = u_1 u_2 (\rho_2 - \rho_1). \tag{3.9}$$

Solving Eq. (3.8) for u_1^2 and u_2^2 and subtracting one from the other results in

$$(p_2 - p_1)[(1/\rho_2) + (1/\rho_1)] = u_1^2 - u_2^2. \tag{3.10}$$

Combining this equation with Eq. (3.7), the conservation of energy equation gives the Hugoniot equation

$$\hat{H}_2 - \hat{H}_1 = \tfrac{1}{2}(p_2 - p_1)[(1/\rho_1) + (1/\rho_2)]. \tag{3.11}$$

For further discussion it is convenient to assume a polytropic gas for which the enthalpy is $\hat{H} = [\gamma/(\gamma - 1)]p(1/\rho)$, where γ is the ratio of the specific heats c_p/c_v. This condition is very well fulfilled in most reaction kinetic investigations in shock waves. In this case Eq. (3.11) can easily be handled (see Fig. 2), becoming

$$\frac{p_2}{p_1} = \left(\frac{\gamma + 1}{\gamma - 1} - \frac{\rho_1}{\rho_2}\right) \Big/ \left(\frac{(\gamma + 1)\rho_1}{(\gamma - 1)\rho_2} - 1\right). \tag{3.12}$$

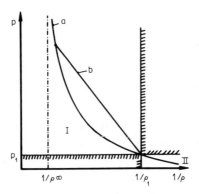

FIG. 2.   (a) Hugoniot curve and (b) Rayleigh line. The domains I, II which are accessible from $(p_1, 1/\rho_1)$ are separated by cross-hatched lines.

If the initial conditions (subscript 1) are fixed, the final states (subscript 2) in the p vs. $1/\rho$ plane form a curve which at p_1, ρ_1 coincides with the isentrope through that point. For densities $\rho > \rho_1$ it deviates from the isentrope toward higher pressures. The increase of entropy across the shock front and therefore the deviation of the Hugoniot curve from the isentrope is of third order in the difference $(1/\rho_2) - (1/\rho_1)$. Formally the pressure p_2 becomes zero at the limiting density $\rho_2 = [(\gamma - 1)/(\gamma + 1)]\rho_1$ and infinite at $\rho_2 = [(\gamma + 1)/(\gamma - 1)]\rho_1$.

The Hugoniot curve is the locus of points that can be reached behind a shock wave with initial conditions p_1, ρ_1, as long as $p_2 > p_1$. The part of the curve for which $p_2 < p_1$ is normally not accessible.

The equilibrium state behind a shock front is uniquely determined by the two equations (3.8) and (3.11) or (3.12), if the shock velocity and the initial conditions are given.

By combining (3.8) and (3.12) and by introducing the expression $c_1{}^2 = \gamma(p_1)/\rho_1$ for the velocity of sound, one easily obtains

$$\frac{p_2}{p_1} = \frac{2\gamma}{\gamma+1} M_1{}^2 - \frac{\gamma-1}{\gamma+1}. \tag{3.13}$$

Here $M_1 = |D|/c_1$ and is the Mach number of the shock wave based on the sound velocity of the gas ahead of the shock.

The corresponding expression for the reciprocal density ratio is

$$\frac{\rho_1}{\rho_2} = \frac{2}{(\gamma+1)M^2} + \frac{\gamma-1}{\gamma+1}. \tag{3.14}$$

The temperature ratio across the shock front is given by $T_2/T_1 = p_2\rho_1/p_1\rho_2$. One can see that for high Mach numbers the temperature and pressure ratios increase in a manner proportional to M^2.

These formulas are useful for estimating the conditions behind a shock front. For accurate measurements, however, the assumption of constant γ is very often not good enough and one has to use the accurate (mostly tabulated) thermodynamic properties.

As long as no chemical change takes place the calculations are comparatively simple. The initial conditions $\hat{H}_1$, T_1, p_1, and ρ_1 can be well defined in an experiment. For hand calculation it is convenient to assume T_2 and take $\hat{H}_2(T_2)$ from a table. Then the density ratio is obtained from

$$\begin{aligned}
\frac{\rho_1}{\rho_2} = \frac{1}{2}\left\{ \frac{T_2-T_1}{T_1} - \frac{2[\hat{H}_2(T_2)-\hat{H}_1(T_1)]}{R'T_1}\right\} \\
+ \frac{1}{2}\left\{ \frac{T_2-T_1}{T_1} - \frac{2[\hat{H}_2(T_2)-\hat{H}_1(T_1)]}{R'T_1} + \frac{T_2}{T_1}\right\}^{1/2}
\end{aligned} \tag{3.15}$$

where $R' = R/\bar{m}$, with $\bar{m} = \sum m_i x_1$ being the mean molecular weight.

The shock velocity is calculated from

$$D^2[1 - (\rho_1/\rho_2)^2] = 2[\hat{H}_2(T_2) - \hat{H}_1(T_1)].$$

If the calculation of the data behind a plane shock is to be started from the shock velocity directly, one can use the two expressions

$$u_2{}^2 - (I/M)u_2 + R'T_2 = 0 \quad \text{and} \quad u_2{}^2 = 2[E - \hat{H}_2(T_2)]$$

for the iterative determination of T_2 and u_2. Here M, I, and E [Eqs. (3.5)–(3.7)] are calculated using the shock velocity and the properties of the gas ahead of the shock.

B. Shock Waves with Heat Addition

The easiest way to take into account the influence of chemical reactions behind shock waves is to consider only the effect of the reaction enthalpy ΔH_R, leaving the other conditions unchanged. The progress of reaction is described by a reaction variable ε which changes from zero to one. Under these circumstances the Hugoniot curves for various ε are given by

$$\frac{p}{p_1} = \left(\frac{\gamma+1}{\gamma-1} - \frac{\rho_1}{\rho} + \frac{2\gamma\varepsilon\Delta H_R}{c_1{}^2}\right) \bigg/ \left(\frac{\gamma+1}{\gamma-1}\frac{\rho_1}{\rho} - 1\right) \qquad (3.16)$$

for an ideal gas (c_1 is the velocity of sound ahead of the shock front).

As long as the reaction time is long compared to the transition time in the shock front, the shock brings the gas into state (N) (Fig. 3).

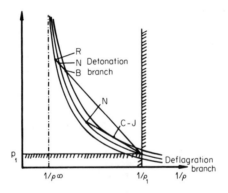

Fig. 3. Hugoniot curves for shock waves followed by exothermic thermoneutral and endothermic processes (N, von Neumann spike; B, final state for exothermic reaction; R, final state for endothermic process; C–J, Chapman–Jouguet state).

If an endothermic process such as relaxation or dissociation takes place, the state of the gas changes, tending toward higher densities, from N ($\varepsilon = 0$) toward R ($\varepsilon = 1$) along the Rayleigh line with an accompanying pressure increase and temperature drop. In the case of mixtures highly diluted with rare gas, this simple model is a very good approximation, because γ remains practically constant.

For exothermic reaction the state of the gas changes along the Rayleigh line from N toward B, where B lies on the Hugoniot curve for complete reaction ($\varepsilon = 1$). In what way and at what speed that change takes place depend in both cases on the rate and/or the mechanism of chemical reaction.

Therefore a measurement of the density profile can give kinetic information only when the mechanism of the chemical change is known and when relaxation processes in both reactants and products are sufficiently rapid.

One well-known case of shock waves followed by exothermic reaction is that of detonation (see, e.g., Jost, 1938; Lewis, von Elbe, 1961; Soloukhin, 1966).

Berthelot and Vieille, as well as Mallard and Le Chatelier, established that flames propagating in tubes can attain high velocities (1.5–3 km sec^{-1}). Berthelot and Vieille found that the final velocity of such a wave depends on the mixture composition but is independent of the length of the column of gas traversed or of the method of ignition or tube diameter, provided that a small limiting diameter is exceeded. Chapman and Jouguet stated that the velocity of a stable detonation is the minimum velocity consistent with the Hugoniot curve for the burned gas. This means that the Rayleigh line has to be a tangent to the Hugoniot curve for the reacted burnt gas (see Fig. 3). The point where both curves touch each other is called Chapman–Jouguet (CJ) point. This point has the following properties: $dS = 0$ and

$$\left(\frac{\partial p}{\partial(1/\rho)}\right)_{\text{R line}} = \left(\frac{\partial p}{\partial(1/\rho)}\right)_{\text{Hugoniot}} = \left(\frac{\partial p}{\partial(1/\rho)}\right)_{S=\text{const}}.$$

This means that at the CJ point the local velocity u_{CJ} relative to the detonation front is equal to the local sound velocity: $|u_{\text{CJ}}| = C_{\text{CJ}}$; the local Mach number is one and $D = v_{\text{CJ}} + C_{\text{CJ}}$. Seen from the CJ point, the detonation front moves with the sound velocity.

The velocity u_{CJ} has a local minimum for a CJ detonation, and both $d^2p/d(1/\rho^2)$ and $d^2S/d(1/\rho^2)$ are larger than zero at the CJ point on the Hugoniot curve; therefore at the CJ point S has a local minimum (see, e.g., Courant and Friederichs, 1956). It should be mentioned that for a CJ deflagration S_{CJ} and u_{CJ} have local maxima. In normal stationary flames, however, which are propagated via transport processes in contrast to detonations, the CJ deflagration case is not realized in practice.

This simple one-dimensional model proves very useful as far as the calculation of detonation velocities is concerned. Other properties of detonations are not as well predicted. There are various reasons for these deviations. The model applied takes into account the chemical change only as a heat source. This can easily be removed by applying Eq. (3.2). This means, however, that for the definition of the final Hugoniot curve further conditions have to be stated, e.g., chemical equilibrium, frozen equilibrium, etc. For a real system chemical reaction approaches equilibrium asymptotically. In addition, the local sound velocity is not a uniquely defined quantity, because the relaxation of the rotational and vibrational degrees of freedom and also the effect of the chemical reaction can cause dispersion of the sound wave. It is not immediately obvious which one of the various sound speeds one should use on which to base the Mach number at the CJ point, M_{CJ}, in practical cases. For many calculations it has been assumed that the composition does not change along the Hugoniot curve near the CJ point (frozen composition) and that the other relaxation processes are sufficiently fast to follow the sound wave (see, e.g., Lewis and von Elbe, 1961). A more serious problem, however, is the structure of the reaction zone in shock waves followed by exothermic reactions. If the detonation is propagated in a tube, a boundary layer is formed which influences the detonation strongly. According to Pusch (1964), under these conditions a one-dimensional CJ detonation cannot occur. In fact, experimental observations of detonations in tubes normally show a pronounced structure. If that structure is regular in form, it is called spin (see, e.g., W. Jost, 1938). The traces of such detonations on soot-covered walls clearly indicate the appearance of waves moving perpendicular to the direction of propagation of the detonation and of Mach stems (see e.g., Manson, Oppenheim, and Wagner, 1963). This far from simple structure very much complicates the investigation of chemical reactions in detonations, and it may also obscure kinetic results obtained from shock waves followed by exothermic reactions, even if ΔH_R is small.

C. LIMITATIONS FOR THE INVESTIGATION OF CHEMICAL REACTIONS IN SHOCK WAVES

Shock waves generated in normal or in chemical shock tubes have proved to be a powerful tool for the investigation of chemical reactions, of energy transfer, and of many other processes. The advantage shock waves offer for the investigation of chemical reactions is the relatively easy accessibility of a large range of pressures and temperatures as well as the very rapid compression time. Many successful applications of shock tubes are described in detail in the monographs of Greene and Toennies (1964), Gaydon and Hurle (1963) and Bradley (1962) as well as in the various Proceedings of Shock Tube Conferences.

If shock waves were to behave ideally, a shock tube would be the ideal method for the investigation of fast chemical reactions, though from a chemical point of view the observer of chemical changes in a shock wave remains relatively blind. There are, however, some effects which may cause serious deviations of testing time, temperature, and density of a real shock wave from those of an ideal one which occasionally are overlooked. These effects are briefly the following:

(1) The diaphragm which separates the driver from the low-pressure section does not burst ideally. The shock wave normally accelerates behind the diaphragm.

(2) A boundary layer is formed at the wall of the shock tube which causes a deceleration of the shock.

(3) For the evaluation of kinetic data it is convenient to measure in the reflected shock because there the gas is at rest. Here also the laboratory time is, at least for ideal behavior, equal to the reaction time, while in the incident wave the reaction time t_p is obtained from the laboratory time t_l by multiplication by ρ_2/ρ_1, the density ratio; thus $t_p = t_l\rho_2/\rho_1$; in an ideal reflected wave the laboratory time and the reaction time are equal. If the reflected wave travels against the gas flow of the incident wave, however, it interacts with the boundary layer. This may cause very complex flow patterns.

Ideal and real flow in a shock wave are shown in Figs. 4 and 5 (taken from Belford and Strehlow) in a space–time–pressure coordinate system. Regions 1 and 4 are undisturbed driven and driver gas. Region 2 is the hot gas behind the incident shock I. It is separated from region 3 by the contact surface C and from region 5 by the reflected shock R. In 5 particles are at rest for an ideal wave. Line E is the head of the rarefaction wave after reflection from the end of the driver section. The dotted line P represents the particle path.

In Figure 5 the symbol M is the region where the shock wave accelerates due to the finite opening time of the diaphragm. N is the region of rapid deceleration due to boundary layer growth. O is the late flow region, in which the shock and the contact surface move approximately with equal and almost constant speed.

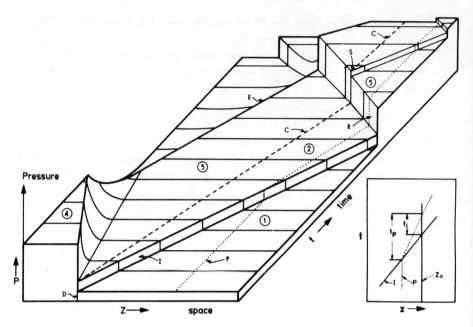

FIG. 4. Schematic distance–time–pressure diagram of ideal shock tube flow (taken from Belford and Strehlow, 1969).

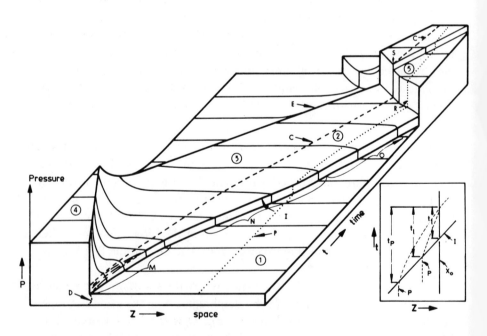

FIG. 5. Schematic distance–time–pressure diagram of real shock tube flow (taken from Belford and Strehlow, 1969).

The influence of the boundary layer growth has been treated in great detail by Mirels and others. Mirels' (1971) results for laminar boundary layer have been used by Strehlow and others to evaluate some simple formulas. These are useful for estimating the errors introduced by non-ideal shocks on kinetic data taken from shock tube measurements, and these we will briefly report here. In order to estimate the magnitude of these errors for a shock tube of given diameter d (cm), the following quantities must be measured

(1) The initial pressure (p_1, Torr).
(2) The average shock Mach number M_s.
(3) The rate of change of the shock velocity with time, the shock attenuation.

Using these data, one can calculate the hot flow transient time t_m, a fictitious characteristic time which is not applicable to late flow conditions since $t_m \approx 5.9 d^2 p_1 / M_s^{1.7} c_1$. Here d is the hydraulic radius of the shock tube ($d = 4A/L$, A is the tube area, L is the tube perimeter) and c_1 is the sound velocity of the gas ahead of the shock. The actual reaction time t_p is now obtained from the laboratory time t_l by $t_p \approx t_l \rho_2 / \rho_1 [1 + 0.7(t_l/t_m)^{1/2}]$ as long as $t_l/t_m < 0.1$.

The deviation from ideal temperature can be attributed to the deceleration of the mainstream flow and to the deceleration of the shock front. For a monatomic gas one may write the approximation

$$\Delta T/T_2 \approx 0.2(t_l/t_m)^{1/2} + 0.3 t_l[1 + 0.7(t_l/t_m)^{1/2}](dM/dt).$$

The term dM/dt can be expressed by the velocity decrement $\Delta v/(v \, \Delta x)$ as

$$\Delta M/\Delta t = c_1 M^2 \, \Delta v/(v \, \Delta x).$$

The density correction is $\Delta \rho/\rho \approx 1.5 \, \Delta T/T$. Values of the transient time t_m for a shock tube of 7.5 cm diameter and argon as test gas are given for various values of M_s and p_1 in Table I. This table shows that the conditions may become critical for low initial pressures. If the tube radius is reduced to 2.5 cm, the corresponding t_m values are smaller by a factor of nine, so that here the corrections become much more pronounced.

If the shock tube is operated at high pressures, then a transition of the boundary layer from laminar to turbulent flow may take place (see, e.g., Mirels, 1971). The critical Reynolds number lies in the range $0.5 \leq \mathrm{Re}_l \times 10^{-6} \leq 4$ for Mach numbers $1 \leq M_s \leq 9$. It is defined as $\mathrm{Re}_l = u_r(\rho_2/\rho_1 - 1)l_t/\nu$, where u_r is the free stream velocity relative to the wall in a

TABLE I

TRANSIENT TIMES FOR DIFFERENT MACH NUMBERS AND INITIAL PRESSURES p_1

		Transient time (sec)		
M_s	p_1 (Torr):	50	200	500
3		8.8×10^{-2}	3.6×10^{-1}	8.9×10^{-1}
4		5.2×10^{-2}	2.1×10^{-1}	5.2×10^{-1}
5		3.7×10^{-2}	1.5×10^{-1}	5.7×10^{-1}

coordinate system fixed at the shock front, l_t is the transition distance measured from the shock front, and v is the kinematic viscosity of the gas behind the shock.

The magnitude of the corrections can be seen in the following example for $d = 7.5$ cm, $M_s = 3$, $p_1 = 50$ Torr, and an attentuation of 1% per meter. The values to be given in parentheses hold for the same conditions but for a 2.5-cm-diameter tube. Here $t_m = 8.9 \times 10^{-2}$ and $dM/dt - 26$ sec^{-1}. For an observation at $t_l = 200$ μsec behind the shock front the correction of the reaction time amounts to 3% (10%). The temperature deviates by 1% (3%) and the density by 1.5% (4.5%). These corrections vary with the observation time. Even under the mild conditions treated here they are remarkable and show the advantage of a shock tube with large diameter. For more accurate calculations the original papers of Mirels (1971) and of other authors cited in Mirels' paper should be consulted.

The theoretical treatment of these effects for reflected shock waves, that is, those that are very convenient for kinetic investigations, becomes very complicated. There are no simple formulas yet available which allow an estimation of the influence of nonideal flow conditions. Here independent pressure and density measurements may help the investigator to judge the reliability of measurements made in reflected shock waves.

IV. Flame Structure

A. INTRODUCTION

Flames have been an important research area in chemical kinetics for many reasons. Some applications related to flame propagation include the following: explosions in mines and their prevention, the discovery of the difference between flame and detonation propagation, the use of flames as a simple source of atoms and radicals and their spectroscopic investigation, the use of industrial furnaces, the cracking of fuels to yield the raw materials for polymers, and propulsion of automobiles, aircraft, and rockets.

To illustrate the term "flame" and the processes which influence its macroscopic appearance, we give a somewhat arbitrary classification in respect to the initial state, the flow field, and the time and kinetic behavior. Since they are intercorrelated, we will find the same feature in several categories.

The combustible mixture may consist of homogeneous or heterogeneous material in the gaseous, liquid, or solid state. The state may change during combustion, i.e., melting or vaporization may be an important process for the propagation of the flame. In most practical cases, as in combustion in aircraft or rocket engines, spray or droplet combustion depends on particle size, which is influenced by the preparation of the reaction mixture, the ratio of dynamic force to surface tension force in oscillatory combustion, and the admixture of inert material. Premixed and diffusion flames can be grouped with respect to the characteristic times of reaction and diffusion of the reacting species.

Some of the simplest cases with respect to chemical kinetics are decomposition flames and gaseous premixed flames. The character of flow differs between laminar flames, which can be described to some extent by deflagration waves, and turbulent and polyhedral and cellular flames. In these cases higher and different flow speeds and selective diffusion of molecules have to be considered in detail.

Since the flame front is a surface of discontinuity, it may exhibit a stationary, periodic, or nonstationary behavior. Flame front instability may be caused by vibratory flow, interaction with shock waves, or by interaction with artificial obstacles. Examples are the development of unstable to stable combustion and the transition from a flame to a stable detonation.

Consideration of flames in terms of production of chemical compounds leads to two classes: (1) normal, i.e., high-temperature flames, where chemical equilibrium is attained, and (2) cool flames, where two-stage ignition is observed at low temperature, with partial combustion leading to products such as aldehydes, ketones, and hydrocarbon peroxides. Even slow combustion processes such as those in cool flames may be stabilized and show a definite burning rate.

To illustrate some details of flame microstructure and to deduce a reaction scheme, we will concentrate on a simple system: the stationary,

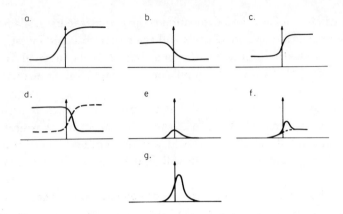

FIG. 6.   Schematic profiles of some parameters through a flame. a, temperature; b, density; c, velocity; d, fuel and product; e, intermediate; f, radicals; g, reaction rate.

premixed, gaseous, one-dimensional flame. A schematic picture of this flame, which also applies to complex, higher dimensional flames, is given in Fig. 6. The main conversion of unburnt to burnt gas takes place in a relatively small region, the reaction zone. A relatively high reaction rate is necessary to explain the disappearance of fuel and oxidizer, the increase of the final products, and the rise in temperature. The latter is accompanied by a decrease in density. Intermediates are found, including reactive radicals, whose concentrations can exceed that of chemical equilibrium by several orders of magnitude. Thus, large gradients are expected in the reaction zone.

The question debated in great detail is the dominant mechanism for transferring the reaction zone from one layer of gas to another. A formal description of the process of flame propagation is given by the flame equations, which will be treated in the following section. These equations show that both diffusion and heat conduction are essential transport processes for the propagation of a flame.

For a simplified treatment of flame propagation, in the past two limiting cases were considered and discussed which neglected either diffusion (thermal theories) or heat conduction (diffusion theories):

(i) In *thermal theories* it is assumed that heat liberated in chemical reactions is transferred into the unburnt gas by heat conduction. At a certain "ignition temperature" the unburnt mixture begins to react, either due to the higher temperatures or via local production of radicals by decomposition of some material. Up to this point only small amounts of material have reacted and the main conversion occurs in the reaction zone.

(ii) In *diffusion theories* it is postulated that radicals or atoms from the hot part of the flame diffuse into the unburnt gas, giving rise to flame propagation by reaction chains or chain-branching. Several different situations can be visualized with respect to the particle transferred to the colder parts of the flame:

(a) There may be radicals which are present in the burnt gas and whose concentrations increase monotonically to the maximum value of final chemical equilibrium (Fig. 6f).

(b) There may be an intermediate particle whose concentration is at a maximum in the main reaction zone (Fig. 6e) at concentrations far beyond equilibrium (Fig. 6f).

(c) It may be possible for unburnt gas to diffuse into the main reaction zone due to the large concentration gradient. Diffusion of burnt gas against the flow direction also requires attention since by this mechanism energy is transferred into the unreacted, unburnt combustible mixture.

B. FLAME EQUATIONS

The factors governing flame systems will now be derived from the mass, momentum, and energy balance equations outlined in Section 2. The basic assumptions are as follows: (i) one-dimensional, flat, stationary flame in the z direction; (ii) no external fields (negligible influence of gravity, no electric fields for ion acceleration). For a detailed discussion see Fristrom and Westenberg (1965).

1. *Mass Balance*

The overall continuity equation for the steady flow ($\partial/\partial t = 0$) reads [Eq. (2.21)]

$$(\partial/\partial \mathbf{r}) \cdot (\rho \mathbf{v}_0) = 0 , \tag{4.1}$$

which gives by integration over the whole surface of the streamtube walls s

$$\iint_s (\partial/\partial \mathbf{r}) \cdot (\rho \mathbf{v}_0) \, dx \, dy = (d/dz) \iint_s \rho v_z \, dx \, dy = 0 . \tag{4.2}$$

Here v_z denotes the z component of $\mathbf{v}$. If ρ and $v_z = v$ are constant over the cross-sectional area a in the x, y plane, or some average values of ρ and v are taken fulfilling (4.2), then

$$\rho v a = \text{const} . \tag{4.3}$$

For example, if the reference planes are the flame front and the burner surface (subscript 0), this becomes

$$\rho v a = \rho_0 v_0 a_0 = M a_0 .$$

This relation defines the normal burning rate $v_0 = \Lambda$:

$$\Lambda = M/\rho = \rho v a / \rho_0 a_0 \qquad (4.4)$$

as the normal component of the velocity of flame propagation. The continuity equation for species i, based on the same arguments as in the foregoing, reads [(2.50)]

$$M \, dG_i/dz = m_i K_i a , \qquad (4.5)$$

where the G_i (the mass flux fraction ratio) is as defined in Section II. In the case of strict one-dimensionality the surface ratio a is equal to one. We will neglect it therefore in the following equations.

2. Momentum

The momentum equation is unimportant for the velocity of flames and moderate pressures with which we will be concerned [Eq. (2.57)]. Under typical experimental conditions (pressure 10^{-2}–1 atm, 10^4–10^6 g cm^{-2} sec^{-1}, respectively; $\rho v = 10^{-2}$ g cm^{-2} sec^{-1}; $\Delta v = 10^2$ cm sec^{-1}; $dv/dx = 20$ sec^{-1}; $\eta = 10^{-4}$ P) the normal static pressure far exceeds the viscous contribution to the pressure tensor. This means that the flame can be considered as a system at constant pressure.

3. Energy Conservation

The conservation of energy through the flame is given by Eq. (2.60), and for stationary flames by Eq. (2.61).

4. Some General Remarks on the Solution of Flame Equations

The set of coupled differential equations (4.5)-(2.61) describes all features of the flame in principle. But analytical solutions for the concentration profiles of all species as well as for temperature, and ab initio calculation of accurate burning rates, are impractical. The reasons for these difficulties are illustrated by the following three points:

(i) The set of differential equations has to be solved subject to boundary conditions which are given by experiment. At the *cold end of the flame* ($z = -\infty$) the chemical production K_i of species i at a finite temperature is small but nonzero, as can be seen from the usual rate coefficients [$k \propto \exp(-E_a/RT)$]. Thus, in a combustible mixture the reaction rate is always described as finite by this expression. For monotonically infinite systems, that is, actual flames, this must be excluded by arbitrarily fixing the mixture composition flowing without reaction through a reference plane at finite position. Some theories introduce an ignition temperature T_i for onset of flame propagation. The other possibility is a flameholder which acts as a sink for heat and diffusing particles at the inlet of the combustible unburnt gas. At the *hot end of the flame* ($z = +\infty$) the boundary conditions are those of chemical equilibrium. But although the G_i and mass fractions are known, this is no advantage since the derivatives are both zero.

The mathematical approaches to the solution of flame equations are discussed and reviewed extensively by Evans (1952), Franze and Wagner (1955), Spalding (1956), Klein (1957), Minkoff and Tipper (1962), Hirschfelder (1963), Weinberg (1963), Dixon-Lewis and Williams (1963), and Fristrom and Westenberg (1965).

(ii) Since flames are systems where several species are present in different amounts at different temperatures, the multicomponent transport coefficients have to be known with high accuracy if accurate calculations are to be made. Even though there is an extensive literature on transport processes and a large amount of experimental data available, the evaluation of appropriate multicomponent transport coefficients is still uncertain. The reader is referred to the reviews of Hirschfelder *et al.* (1954), Waldmann (1958), Jost (1960), Fristrom and Westenberg (1965), Mason *et al.* (1966), and Dixon-Lewis (1968).

(iii) A quantitative description of the flame is based on an appropriate reaction mechanism and rate coefficients. Good rate coefficients are available for most of the reactions thought to be of importance. But the proper choice can only be proven experimentally. Experience shows that burning rates provide only a poor indication of the validity of a reaction scheme. A much better criterion of the validity of such a scheme is its success in prediction of the absolute concentrations of all chemical species present. The continued introduction of more elementary chemical reactions increases numerical calculation enormously. On the other hand, the evaluation of mechanism and rate data from flame studies is limited by the precision of concentration and temperature measurement and by the identification of unknown species in small concentrations.

The difficulties of the mathematical procedures necessary to deal with the transport processes and the chemistry have given rise to different approaches to the solution of the flame equations, dictated by different aims.

(a) Calculations of the burning velocity are in most cases performed with sufficient accuracy by assuming an overall rate, including the branching step, in the high-temperature region.

(b) It may be desired to determine final reaction products.

(c) An estimation of radical concentrations may be possible in some flames by assuming a steady-state approximation for some radicals.

(d) The microstructure of a flame may be explained by the coupling of flow, transport, and chemical reaction, making assumptions such as using a Lewis number of one.

As has been pointed out, a quantitative description of a flame in every respect is only possible where there exists a great deal of information on the chemistry of the flame and the transport coefficients. Thus we will concentrate on simple flames which show the main principles; one of these is the H_2–O_2 or H_2–O_2–N_2 flame.

C. Experimental Methods

A short review of some experimental topics is given to illustrate the phrase "experimental evidence coming from flame studies" and to shed some light on the experimental aspect of flame investigations.

Flame velocity Λ is one of the common parameters used in describing flame propagation. It is an eigenvalue of the flame equations. A number of methods have been described for measuring Λ, such as those involving the constant-pressure bomb, constant-volume bomb, flat flame (Powling-Egerton), particle-track, Bunsen burner, etc.

A survey of these experimental techniques and a critical discussion of the factors influencing the evaluation of Λ is given by Jost (1938), Franze and Wagner (1955), Lewis and von Elbe (1961), Gaydon and Wolfard (1971), and Andrews and Bradley (1972). These latter structural studies on stationary premixed flames give maximum information on the kinetics and the transport processes and allow a straightforward analysis. The reasons for this are clear as far as an experiment is concerned:

(a) In a stationary flame the observation time is not restricted; this enhances precision in temperature and concentration measurements.

(b) Since the thickness of the main reaction zone varies with pressure approximately as

$$\delta \approx \lambda/c_p \rho \Lambda \qquad (4.6)$$

low pressure is preferable. The reaction zone can be extended up to several cm at pressures around 0.01–0.1 atm.

Typical features of burner systems are a flameholder which acts as a heat sink or for the removal of radicals, a housing which can be evacuated, and the analytical tools for the measurements. Experimental approaches to the production of a strictly one-dimensional flame are the use of a spherical flame (Fig. 7) or of a flat flame. The radical removal element and/or heat sink may be in the form of a piece of metal mesh, for example, platinum mesh, or porous sintered plates with water-cooled capillaries inside. This arrangement allows a determination of heat transferred to the burner by

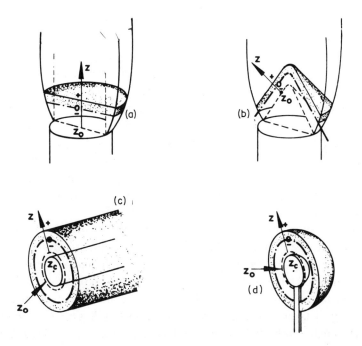

FIG. 7. Unidimensional coordinate systems for describing several flame geometries (after Fristrom, 1961). (a) Flat flame. $pVA = \text{const}$. Ideal (- -), $pV = p_0 V_0 A_0$. Experimental (—), $pVA = p_0 V_0 A_0$. (b) Bunsen flame. $pVA = \text{const} = p_0 V_0 A_0$. (c) Cylindrical flame. $pV(z - z_c) = \text{const} = p_0 V_0(z_0 - z_t)$. (d) Spherical flame. $pV(z - z_c)^2 = \text{const} = p_0 V_0(z_0 - z_0)^2$.

heat conduction, radical recombination, or radiation. The size of the burner is restricted by the available pumping speed. For the one-dimensional concept the burner diameter should be at least 3–5 times the thickness of the reaction zone. The fuel and oxidizer are commonly premixed, giving a homogeneous and constant concentration profile perpendicular to the flow. In systems where premixing is not possible (for example, H_2–F_2, N_2H_4–O_2, H_2–O_3 flames) slit or diffusion burners are used. The distance h at which homogeneous mixing is achieved can be calculated approximately by the relation

$$h \approx vr^2/2D, \tag{4.7}$$

where r is the distance between two slits, v is the flow velocity, and D is the diffusion coefficient. Burning velocity varies with pressure according to

$$\Lambda \propto 1/p^{n/2}, \tag{4.8}$$

where n is the overall reaction order. This means that the burning velocity is independent of pressure if the flame is described by a second-order rate law. Therefore, the mixing distance h, according to relation (4.7), is small for low pressures when diffusion coefficients are high.

Temperature measurements can be performed by several methods, including the use of x-ray absorption, interferometric determination, a pneumatic probe, the line reversal method, a thermocouple, rotational temperature, and line shape pyrometry. These methods differ in temperature range, resolution, and precision. A comparison of the temperature profiles as measured by different techniques is found in the review of Fristrom and Westenberg (1965).

Concentration measurements of radicals and stable products are the critical factors in flame studies. Direct measurements in situ cannot be performed for all particles of interest, since difficulties arise in probe design and detection methods. The universal method is mass spectrometry as a specific tool, either combined with microprobes or with molecular beam sampling. A typical arrangement is shown in Fig. 8. Other techniques are gas chromatography (for stable products), calorimetry (radicals, but nonspecific), tracer and isotope methods, absorption and emission spectroscopy (for radicals such as H, OH, O), and electron spin resonance spectroscopy. For the detection of ions in flames, radiofrequency absorption, conductivity measurements, the Hall effect, and mass spectrometry have been

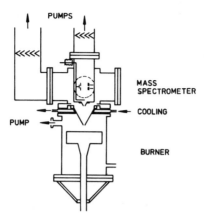

FIG. 8.   Experimental arrangement for flame investigations using a mass spectrometer with molecular beam sampling system (after Homann *et al.*, 1963).

used. An explicit description of a detection system is given in Chapter 9. For quantitative concentration measurements the combination of different detection systems is advisable to allow cross-checks. One of these experimental arrangements is shown in Fig. 9, used for the study of H_2–O_2

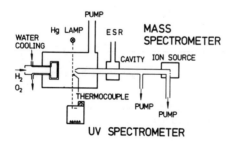

FIG. 9.   Experimental setup for flame investigations using different analytical tools (after Eberius *et al.*, 1971).

flames. Temperature measurements are performed by a thermocouple coated with quartz to reduce radical recombination at the surface. Compensatory heating of the thermocouple by ac current allows corrections for radiative losses. Samples are withdrawn from the flame by a conical sampling tube. Moving the cavity of a ESR spectrometer along the sampling line allows a determination of the oxygen and hydrogen atom concentration by extrapolation to the tip of the probe. The stable products are analyzed by a mass spectrometer with continuous intake. The

other unpaired electron species, OH, is monitored by uv absorption. The
population of the rotational levels of OH gives an independent determination of the gas temperature.

Figure 10 shows the concentration and temperature profiles of an

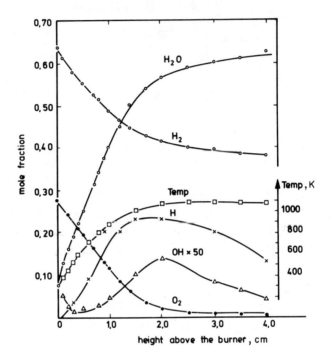

FIG. 10.   Concentration and temperature profiles measured on a 75% H_2, 25% O_2
flame burning at a pressure of 10.6 Torr ($v_0 = 178$ cm sec^{-1}) (after Eberius *et al.*, 1971).

75% H_2/25% O_2 flame with $v_0 = 178$ cm sec^{-1}. Descriptions of experimental methods used in flame research are given by Fristrom and Westenberg (1965), Gaydon and Wolfhard (1971), and Minkoff and Tipper (1962).

D. AN EXAMPLE: H_2–O_2 FLAME

1. *Some Experimental Facts*

The influence of transport processes and heat conduction on flame propagation and the evaluation of elementary kinetic data from measurements
on flames can be demonstrated explicitly with H_2–O_2 flames. Here more

data are available from measurements using other techniques, e.g., fast flow reactor and shock tube studies.

Some experimental facts may be summarized before going into detailed calculations. Early studies of combustion showed that there exists a unique burning velocity v_0 which is a function of composition, initial temperature and pressure. At atmospheric pressure this is maximal around $v_0 = 1400$ cm sec^{-1} for H_2–O_2 and around $v_0 = 310$ cm sec^{-1} for H_2–air mixtures. The pressure dependence of a 21.8% H_2–5.4% O_2–72.8% N_2 flame is given by $v_0 \propto p^{-0.27}$ in the range $90 < p < 760$ Torr (Dixon-Lewis et al., 1973). Assuming relation (4.8), this gives an overall reaction order between two and three.

One striking feature in flames is the high radical concentration, which can exceed both local and final equilibrium values. This is shown in Fig. 11 for hydrogen atom in a H_2–O_2–N_2 flame, where hydrogen atoms were measured indirectly via the reactions

$$Li + H_2O \longrightarrow LiOH + H$$
$$Na + HCl \longrightarrow NaCl + H.$$

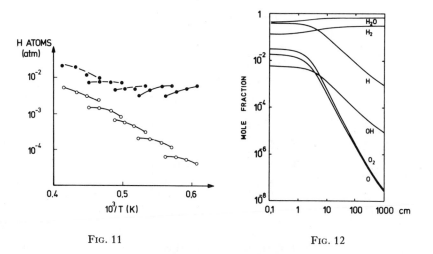

FIG. 11   FIG. 12

FIG. 11.   Hydrogen atom concentration in different H_2–O_2–N_2 flames at atmospheric pressure ($\bigcirc$, equilibrium concentrations; $\bullet$, measured concentrations) (after Bulewicz et al., 1956).

FIG. 12.   Calculated concentration profiles in the post-flame region of a 74.6% H_2/ 25.4% O_2 flame at 10.6 Torr, 1100 K, $v_0 = 178$ cm sec^{-1} (Eberius, 1968).

The supra-equilibrium concentration of H atoms is explained by the slow
equilibration even at 1 atm of the termolecular reaction (4.23)–(4.24) in the
reaction scheme proposed later. This effect becomes even more pronounced
in low-pressure flames (Fig. 10). As an example, calculations on the post-
flame region at 10.6 Torr and 1100 K are shown in Fig. 12. The concentrations are given as a function of height above the burner. The main reaction
zone ends around $z = 20$ mm. Here the concentrations match the experimental values as given in Fig. 10. This slow decrease in radical concentrations shows that even at substantial distances from the main reaction zone,
where most of the final product (H_2O) is built up, high radical concentrations can be observed. At low pressures, on the other hand, the slow
equilibration of the termolecular reactions simplifies the reaction mechanism: The main features of the chemistry of the flame can be approximated
by partial equilibria of the bimolecular steps, although third-order reactions
are an essential part of real flames.

2. Flame Modeling

Calculations of the burning velocity v_0 have to assume a reaction
mechanism. A complete set of elementary reactions from which mechanisms
can be composed is given as follows. The kinetic data for these reactions
involved in the H_2–O_2 system, can be found in the review of Baulch *et al.*,
(1972):

$$OH + H_2 \longrightarrow H_2O + H \tag{4.9}$$

$$H + O_2 \longrightarrow OH + O \tag{4.10}$$

$$O + H_2 \longrightarrow OH + H \tag{4.11}$$

$$H + O_2 + M \longrightarrow HO_2 + M \tag{4.12}$$

$$HO_2 + HO_2 \longrightarrow H_2O_2 + O_2 \tag{4.13}$$

$$HO_2 + H_2 \longrightarrow H_2O_2 + H \tag{4.14}$$

$$H + HO_2 \longrightarrow OH + OH \tag{4.15}$$

$$H_2O_2 + M \longrightarrow OH + OH + M \tag{4.16}$$

$$H + H_2O_2 \longrightarrow H_2O + OH \tag{4.17}$$

$$H + H_2O_2 \longrightarrow HO_2 + H_2 \tag{4.18}$$

$$OH + H_2O_2 \longrightarrow HO_2 + H_2O \tag{4.19}$$

$$H + HO_2 \longrightarrow H_2 + O_2 \tag{4.20}$$

$$OH + HO_2 \longrightarrow H_2O + O_2 \tag{4.21}$$

$$O + HO_2 \longrightarrow OH + O_2 \qquad (4.22)$$

$$H + H + M \longrightarrow H_2 + M \qquad (4.23)$$

$$H + OH + M \longrightarrow H_2O + M \qquad (4.24)$$

$$H + O + M \longrightarrow OH + M \qquad (4.25)$$

$$O + H_2O \longrightarrow 2OH \qquad (4.26)$$

$$H_2O_2 + M \longrightarrow 2OH. \qquad (4.27)$$

The results are now given for the burning rate v_0, assuming different underlying reactions. Dixon-Lewis (1967, 1970), using the time-dependent continuity equations (2.41), (2.47), and (2.60) for mass and energy with transport (diffusion, heat conduction), calculated v_0 under the mild approximations: $\lambda\rho$ independent of temperature, average specific heat $\bar{c}_p$, and Lewis number $D_{O_2}\rho\bar{c}_p/\lambda$) of one. The mechanisms proposed for a fuel-rich H_2–O_2–N_2 flame ($X_{H_2}^\circ = 0.1883$, $X_{O_2}^\circ = 0.0460$, $X_{N_2}^\circ = 0.7656$) were as follows:

(a) $H + O_2 + (3H_2) \xrightarrow{k_{4.10}} 2H_2O + 3H.$

This mechanism is composed of reactions (4.9)–(4.11), which would lead to a very simple reaction scheme for an atmospheric pressure flame when including reaction (4.22). Ignoring transport processes of the N_2, since this is present in large excess, the burning rate v_0 can be approximated within between 10% and 2%, depending on the diffusion coefficient of H and the rate coefficient of reaction (4.22).

(b) $H + O_2 (+ H_2) \xrightarrow{k_{4.10}} 2OH + H.$

A more complex mechanism, from (4.9), (b), (4.21), and (4.22) gives the observed equilibrium concentrations of H and OH at high temperatures in the post-flame region and the correct burning rate.

(c) Including the radical HO_2, the mechanism becomes

(a) $H + O_2 + (3H_2) \xrightarrow{k_{4.10}} 2H_2O + 3H$

together with (4.21), (4.12), and (4.15), leading to the chain propagation cycle

$$H + O_2 + M (+ 2H_2) \longrightarrow 2H_2O + M + H.$$

The burning rate v_0 ranges from 6.1 to 86.4 cm sec^{-1}.

(d) Reactions (a), (4.21), and (4.12) generate a system whereby HO_2 is now destroyed by (4.13) and H_2O_2 is attacked via (4.17). The effective chain breaking cycle is therefore

$$H + O_2 + M \left(+ \tfrac{1}{2}H + \tfrac{1}{2}H_2\right) \longrightarrow H_2O + \tfrac{1}{2}H + \tfrac{1}{2}O_2.$$

Here the burning velocity drops to zero.

(e) Wilde (1972) used a different mathematical approach (two-boundary problem with quasilinearized differential equations) and approximated the burning rate within 50% when assuming the reactions (4.9), (-4.9), (4.10)–(4.12), (4.23), (4.24), and (4.26), and within 4% when also including (4.12), (4.18), (4.27), (4.15), (4.17), and (4.19).

These examples clearly indicate that the calculations of burning rates allow one to rule out some highly unrealistic reaction mechanisms, e.g., (d). But even some very rough reaction mechanisms such as (a), including the right branching reaction (4.10), reproduce v_0 fairly well. This allows a twofold interpretation: (i) If the desired parameter is v_0, even a poor mechanism can be satisfactory; (ii) since the burning rate v_0 is so insensitive to the mechanism, v_0 alone might give only minor insight into the micro-structure of the flame.

A more sensitive proof of the correct reaction mechanism is given when the calculated and measured profiles of the stable molecules coincide throughout the flame. (The final equilibrium values do not give such a sensitive indication, as seen, for example, from Fig. 12.)

Even if H_2O formation is almost complete, the radical concentrations are far from equilibrium in other parts of the flame. The profiles of the stable molecule concentrations, as well as the final radical concentrations, in an atmospheric pressure flame can be explained by a mechanism com-bining reactions (4.9)–(4.12), (4.15), (4.20), and (4.23). It is worthy of note that this leads to the right burning rate v_0.

Thus, a more detailed understanding of flame processes is expected with this reaction scheme and the inclusion of the appropriate transport processes. In order to demonstrate the interplay of chemical reactions and the transport processes, the explicit fluxes for the main reactants H_2, O_2, H, and N_2 are given in Fig. 13. Here the fluxes are split into the funda-mental processes, as given in the different terms of the conservation laws [Eqs. (2.19) and (2.37)]: (1) the convective flow, which propagates the bulk flow of chemically reacting gas, (2) the diffusional flux, transporting

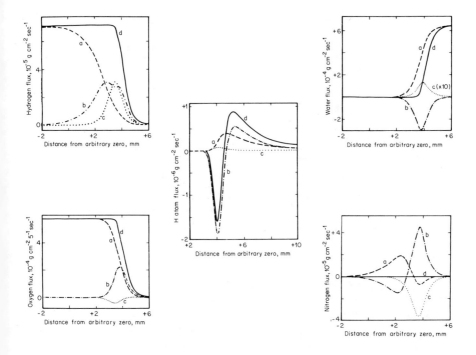

FIG. 13. Computed fluxes of H_2, O_2, H_2O, N_2, and H through a 18.83% H_2–4.6% O_2–76.56% N_2 atmospheric pressure flame (a, convective flux; b, ordinary diffusional flux; c, thermal diffusional flux; d, overall flux) (after Dixon-Lewis, 1967).

mass along the concentration gradients, and (3) the thermal diffusion flux of matter along temperature gradients, the driving force of this diffusion. Positive values signify flux of matter from the unburnt gas to the hot end of the flame, negative values denote mass transfer to the cold, unburnt gas. All fluxes together explain the observed steep drop of concentration in the main reaction zone (solid line).

It is clearly seen that hydrogen atoms are transported back into the prereaction zone as suggested by Jost (1938), since the diffusion term is larger than convective flow and thermal diffusion, resulting in the overall negative flux.

The relatively small contribution of thermal diffusion in atmospheric pressure flames can be explained by the low hydrogen atom concentration in the region of a large gradient in $\ln T$, the driving force in thermal diffusion [Eq. (2.37)]. This may be different in low-pressure flames, where H-atom concentrations are appreciably higher.

Ordinary and thermal diffusion are of equal influence on the fluxes of molecular hydrogen, whereas thermal diffusion plays only a minor role in O_2 fluxes. The sharp decrease of the overall H_2 and O_2 fluxes indicates the consumption of fuel in the main reaction zone.

Interestingly enough, N_2, a nearly inert gas in this H_2–O_2 system, takes part in the transport processes of the flame: a negative mass transfer due to thermal diffusion over the whole flame, whereas ordinary diffusion causes mass transfer in the flow direction into the main reaction zone. These calculations should be reliable since the evaluation starts with a detailed reaction mechanism, without using the steady-state approximation. Moreover, the calculated concentrations and temperature profiles match measured values fairly well. Some minor uncertainties remain due to unreliable transport coefficients for multicomponent mixtures at high temperatures.

3. *Experimental Studies on Microstructure*

A different approach to the understanding of the H_2–O_2 flame may originate from the experimental side. On measuring the concentration profiles of the main constituents H_2, O_2, H_2O, OH, and H and O atoms

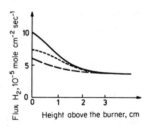

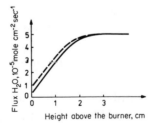

FIG. 14.   Fluxes of H_2 and H_2O as evaluated from flame (Fig. 10) (– –, neglecting diffusion; - - -, corrected for including ternary diffusion; —, corrected for including ternary and thermal diffusion) (Eberius *et al.*, 1971).

with respect to the height above the burner, (Fig. 10), these concentrations can then be transformed to fluxes. By evaluating the fluxes caused by ordinary diffusion and thermal diffusion, the fluxes due to chemical reaction alone are obtained. The result of this procedure is shown in Fig. 14 for the fluxes of H_2O and of H_2. Ternary diffusion was assumed for a mixture of H_2–O_2–H_2O, where H atoms were treated as if they were hydrogen molecules for the sake of simplicity.

The flux of H_2O, as measured (broken line), is reduced to one-third at z around zero when ternary and thermal diffusion are taken into account (solid line). A strong influence of transport processes on the flux of H_2 is found (Fig. 14); the broken line gives the fluxes neglecting diffusion, the solid line gives the fluxes considering both ternary and thermal diffusion.

Another interesting feature is the energy flux at different positions in the flame (Fig. 15). The energy flux is split into four parts corresponding to

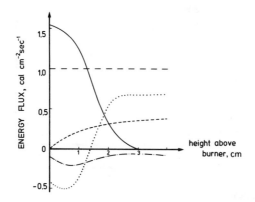

FIG. 15.   Energy fluxes in a rich H_2–O_2 flame (Fig. 10) (—, flux of unreacted gas; $\cdots$, flux associated with the production and destruction of radicals and their transport; - - -, flux due to temperature rise of the gas mixture; – · –, flux of energy via heat conduction; – –, sum. Reaction enthalpies for H_2, H_2O were taken to be zero, 115 kcal/ mole^{-1} for O_2).

different processes: (i) a negative flux of energy toward the cold boundary of the flame, due to heat conduction; (ii) energy flux associated with the formation and destruction of radicals; (iii) the energy flux of the unburnt gas; and (iv) the energy flux of the streaming gas. The flame gives energy to the burner both by heat conduction of 0.15 cal cm^{-2} sec^{-1} and by recombination reactions, 0.44 cal cm^{-2} sec^{-1}. To raise the temperature from the initial state (300 K) to the final state (1050 K), 0.63 cal cm^{-2}

sec^{-1} is needed and for the production of radicals 1.30 cal cm^{-2} sec^{-1} is required. The sum of energy consumed (corresponding to a flux of 2.52 cal cm^{-2} sec^{-1}) matches fairly well with the energy flux associated with the production of water (-2.75 cal cm^{-2} sec^{-1}). Both energy and mass fluxes in the prereaction zone are understood best when the formation of the HO_2 radical is included.

After the evaluation of the different contributions of transport to the total mass fluxes, a determination of the chemical production rate K_i on the basis of Eq. (4.5) is possible in principle. This is shown in Fig. 16 for

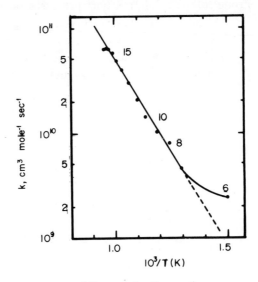

FIG. 16.   Disappearance rate of O_2 assuming the reaction

$$H + O_2 \quad \xrightarrow{k} \quad products$$

for different positions ($z = 6$–18 mm height above burner) in a H_2–O_2 flame (Fig. 10).

the destruction of O_2 by H atoms for different heights above burner, corresponding to different temperatures. As can be deduced from this Arrhenius plot, the rate coefficients can be fitted in the region $h = 17$ mm to $h = 7$ mm by

$$k = 2.25 \times 10^{14} \exp(-16,800/RT) \text{ cm}^3 \text{ mole}^{-1} \text{ sec}^{-1}.$$

This is the accepted value for the rate of reaction (4.10). Thus, the destruction of O_2 by H atoms may be assigned to reaction (4.10) in this region of the flame. At higher temperatures the deviations from the normal

Arrhenius plot can be explained when the equilibration of reaction (4.10) is included. But the errors become appreciable in this region since here the limited accuracy of concentration gradients becomes very important in the evaluation of flux changes introduced by reactions. The deviation of k in the low-temperature regime from the Arrhenius line indicates the occurrence of some other reactions. Probably this is reaction (4.12); the absolute value, $k_{4.12} = 3 \times 10^{16}$ cm^6 mole^{-2} sec^{-1}, agrees within 50% with the values derived from independent investigations (Baulch *et al.*, 1972) when specifying M (H_2, O_2, H_2O) with regard to its effectiveness as a third body.

However, it may be noted, as pointed out by Dixon-Lewis (1970), that this procedure leads to erroneous results for $k_{4.10}$ when evaluating $k_{4.10}$ from atmospheric pressure flames. Here the oxygen-producing reactions (4.20) and (4.13) have to be included explicitly in the reaction scheme [(4.9)–(4.12), (4.15), (4.23)].

The explanation of the propagation and the microstructure of the flame can be given along the lines of these theoretical and experimental studies.

For a hydrogen-rich H_2–O_2–N_2 system the main chemistry of the reaction zone is described by reactions (4.9)–(4.12), where the most important branching reaction (4.10) is the slowest step, controlling the burning rate. Hydrogen atoms react, via the HO_2 radical, to give the OH radical; OH is removed by H_2 in a reaction of low activation energy (4.9 kcal mole^{-1}). Equilibration of radical concentrations in the post-flame region occurs via termolecular recombination reactions.

More detailed discussions of the hydrogen–oxygen system may be found in the papers of Fenimore (1964), Bulewicz *et al.* (1956) Dixon-Lewis *et al.* (1973), and Fristrom and Brown (1973).

E. Some Applications of Flame Studies

The fundamentals of flame propagation and microstructure as outlined in the foregoing indicate where flame studies may give further information concerning combustion. We will group together the areas where this is so somewhat arbitrarily and will give an interpretation of their significance.

1. *Inhibition*

Flame propagation is not determined exclusively by chemical reactions but also be transport processes. The transfer of mass, mainly in the form of radicals, and the transfer of energy may initiate or extinguish chemical reactions in the initial low-temperature region. The term "inhibition" in this context means a drastic reduction of flame propagation rate by relatively small amounts of material (inhibitors). Examples are halogens, halogenated hydrocarbons, transition metal compounds (involving CO) and alkali metal carbonates, e.g., $Pb(C_2H_5)$. For a review see Creitz (1970) or Fristrom and Sawyer (1972).

For example, the addition of 1% C_2H_2 to a H_2-O_2 flame leads to 50% reduction in burning rate. Jost (1938) suggested that this inhibiting effect is due to the destruction of diffusing H atoms via the homogeneously catalyzed reaction $2H + C_2H_2 \rightarrow C_2H_2 + H_2$. This explanation has been substantiated by three recent experimental results: (i) As known from the H_2-O_2 flame, the main chain carrier is H atoms, which react mainly via reactions (4.12) and (4.15) to give two OH radicals. (ii) Studies of the $H + C_2H_2$ reaction in isothermal flow reactors (Chapter 9) show that at temperatures below 1000 K the mechanism is

$$
\begin{aligned}
H + C_2H_2 &\longrightarrow C_2H_3* \\
C_2H_3* + M &\longrightarrow C_2H_3 \qquad\qquad (4.28) \\
H + C_2H_3 &\longrightarrow C_2H_2 + H_2.
\end{aligned}
$$

The abstraction reaction, leading to $C_2H + H_2$, can be neglected. (iii) When analyzing $C_2H_2-O_2$ flames (Westenberg and Fristrom (1965), Eberius et al., (1973)) large amounts of H_2 are found in the prereaction zone, where C_2H_2 has not undergone reaction.

Therefore it is concluded that in the C_2H_2-inhibited H_2-O_2 flame the chain reaction (4.12), (4.15) competes with the fast chain breaking reaction (4.28), thus lowering the unpaired electron species concentration (H, OH) appreciably. Moreover, C_2H_2 is conserved for further cycling in H-atom removal. This will, of course, lower the burning rate. (The effect of heating of the gas by the recombination energy of H_2 may be considered minor since the C_2H_2 concentration is small.) The observation that burning rate increases when larger amounts of C_2H_2 are added does not contradict this explanation. For H_2-O_2 flames rich in H_2 the reactions of O atoms and OH radicals with C_2H_2, which have lower activation energies than reaction (4.9) or (4.11), will dominate the overall flame mechanism. These reactions then will build up higher radical concentrations in the prereaction zone.

Even though inhibitor action, in this special case, is understood best in terms of homogeneous chain breaking, this will not necessarily be the only mechanism for all inhibition in flames. For example, $Fe(CO)_5$ strongly inhibits flames without regenerating $Fe(CO)_5$ in the reaction cycle. Here, besides homogeneous reactions of Fe-containing substances, heterogeneous reactions on particles of the type Fe_xO_y need to be included. [The solid particles can act as effective recombination centers, even more effective than C_2H_2 in the previous case, since C_2H_2 and Fe_xO_y may recycle. This recycling, enabling a species to act as a chain-breaking carrier several times and not undergo reaction, seems to be an essential part of the inhibitor action (Fristrom, 1972)]. The formation of solid particles causes a change in heat conduction, surface reactions at the surface of Fe_xO_y, and heat liberation at this surface. These will shift the initial temperature of the total gas mixture just above the burner as well as the temperature gradient, two quantities which enter explicitly into the calculation of the burning rate. But the participation of homogeneous and heterogeneous reaction in the inhibited flame is not understood in any detail. For inhibitors in flames see, for example, Wilson *et al.* (1969) and Bulewicz and Padley (1971).

2. Determination of Rate Coefficients

Flames appear to be an ideal tool for the determination of rate coefficients at high temperature. Wall-free conditions can be achieved at temperatures up to several thousands of degrees, where normal materials are not available for fast flow reactors. High radical concentrations can be obtained by choosing proper initial conditions (composition, initial temperature, mass flow rate). The main problem in deducing rate coefficients from experimentally determined concentration profiles is the coupling with transport processes. Thus, rate coefficients are evaluated most easily where the influence of transport (diffusion, thermal diffusion) is unimportant. Since this region is physically small, one only obtains values over a limited temperature range. In order to extend the temperature range, the initial conditions have to be varied. This is demonstrated for the reaction $OH + H_2 \rightarrow H_2O + H$ in Fig. 17, where different flames have been used.

The results of a variety of other elementary reactions as studied in flames are given in the book by Fristrom and Westenberg (1965) and in the review of high-temperature rate data by Baulch *et al.* (1969–1972).

A somewhat different technique, using flames as a source of radicals, where coupling with transport phenomena is almost completely avoided is as follows. A low-pressure flame of H_2–O_2 yields high and nearly constant amounts of H atoms in the post-flame region (Fig. 10). When a trace of

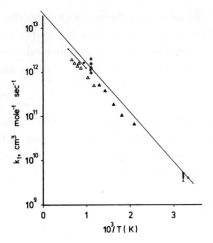

FIG. 17. The rate coefficients for the reaction $OH + H_2 \rightarrow H_2O + H$ as evaluated from different flames. $\triangle$, 48% H_2–52% O_2; $\blacktriangle$, 81% H_2–19% O_2; —, C_2H_2–O_2–H_2; $\bullet$, $\bigcirc$; H_2–O_2–N_2. Included for comparison: $+$, shock tube studies, $\times$, studies isothermal flow reactor. (Taken from Baulch et al., 1972.)

CO_2 is added to the premixed H_2–O_2, reaction does not occur until the high-temperature, high-H-atom-concentration region is reached. Since the reaction $H + CO_2$ is the reverse of $OH + CO$, this gives further information on both reactions (Eberius et al., 1971; Dixon-Lewis, 1972).

This procedure of injecting trace quantities of reactant can be extended to other systems where premixing is not possible because of the low activation energy. As used by Hart and Fristrom (1972), the reactant as a trace is injected by a probe into a mixture of known radical concentration. The decay of radical concentration, or better of the injected material concentration, the most favorable of the injected material, is then followed by a suitable analytical tool. [This procedure is comparable to the reverse technique of radical measurement (Fenimore and Jones, 1961; Bulewicz et al., 1956) and needs an interpretation corresponding to that encountered in atomic flames (Rabinovitch and Reed, 1955) as outlined in the subsection on diffusion flames.]

If reaction of other radicals as well as H atoms, e.g., O atoms or OH radicals, is to be studied, the initial concentration relation H_2/O_2 has to be changed. At low pressure, equilibrium of bimolecular reaction is the predominant step. Figure 18 shows the possible radical concentrations for low pressure and a temperature of 1200 K, assuming reactions (4.9), (4.10), (−4.10), (4.11), and (−4.11).

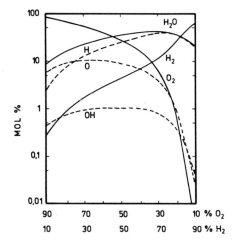

Fig. 18.   Calculated concentration in H_2–O_2 mixtures at $T = 1200$ K assuming equilibration of bimolecular reactions.

Relatively high O-atom concentrations compared to those of the H atoms are obtained in lean flames. Using the specific initial concentration ratio of H_2/O_2, the H_2–O_2 flame will be an isothermal, wall-free flow system for the study of reaction rates of the injected gas into the post-flame region. For the usefulness of flames in connection with the study of reaction rates the computer studies of Dixon-Lewis *et al.* (1973) may be mentioned.

The limitations of rate coefficient measurements from flame studies may be illustrated by reaction (4.11), $O + H_2 \rightarrow OH + H$. Here the decay of H_2 is accompanied by reaction (4.9) in the H_2–O_2 system. Thus, the decay in H_2 according to reaction (4.9), since it has an activation energy higher than reaction (4.11), does not allow the evaluation of $k_{4.11}$. The changes in H_2 flux as found from experimental studies are primarily due to reaction (4.11), the analysis of which involves a small difference between large values of H_2 concentration, making for poor accuracy.

V. Chemical Reaction in Isothermal Flow

A. Introduction

In recent years there has been a revival of interest in the Wood–Bonhoeffer flow discharge experiments. This has been resulted from improvements in available materials, the production of atoms and radicals in

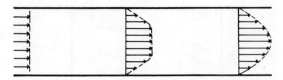

FIG. 19. Development of the velocity profile at the entrance of a circular tube from plug flow to fully developed conduit flow. (Taken from Knudsen and Katz, 1958.)

electrodeless discharges, the quantitative measurements of these labile species, and the increased availability of simple computer analysis.

Chemical reactions in isothermal flow can usually be treated more simply, both experimentally and theoretically, than flames and detonations. This results from easier experimental determination of concentration profiles and the lack of strong temperature and density gradients, which complicate sampling (cf. Chapter 9). In addition, the underlying differential equations are easier to handle since the coupling via gradients (e.g., temperature, pressure, concentration gradients) has less influence. Therefore calculations of concentration profiles for specified conditions of flow, chemistry, and transport involve fewer problems than in flame calculations.

Before going into specific detail, the general picture of an isothermal flow reactor will be given (Figs. 19 and 20). The labile particles A are generated in a large excess of inert gas. They enter the flow reactor. From this point entrance flow develops from plug to Poiseuille flow (Fig. 19). At some position a stable or unstable reactant BC is admixed, either homogeneously and rapidly over the whole cross section (Fig. 20a) or as a point source (e.g., diffusion flame) (Fig. 20b). Analysis of particle

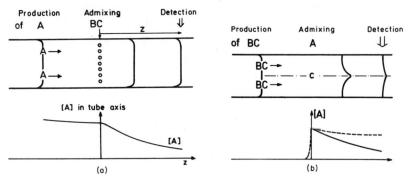

FIG. 20. (a) Chemical reactions in isothermal flow reactor. The concentration profile for a trace of species A mixed homogeneously and instantaneously with an excess of species BC. (b) The concentration profile of a trace of species A mixed via a point source into a diluted flow of species BC ("diffusion flame").

concentration at several positions z downstream then allows the description of concentration profiles in terms of the relevant reactions. Both temperature and pressure are effectively constant. The observed concentration changes can be due to flow, transport, or reaction:

Flow field The simplest flow pattern is plug flow. It can be handled as a one-dimensional problem (Fig. 19) with an average mass flow velocity $\langle v \rangle$. If an appreciable boundary layer is built up, plug flow is transformed downstream to Poiseuille flow with its characteristic velocity profile $v = 2\langle v \rangle[1 - (r/R^2)]$. Slip flow, which is observed at very low pressures, will not be treated here.

Transport processes Since pressure and temperature gradients are small compared with concentration gradients, mass transfer by diffusion, both axial and radial, is dominant.

Chemical reaction Labile species can be destroyed both by reaction at the wall (usually first order) and by homogeneous reactions, which can be first, second, and/or third order and can occur simultaneously or consecutively.

Figure 21 illustrates the ranges of these combinations of flow, diffusion,

FLOW / TRANSPORT — CHEMICAL REACTIONS	PLUG FLOW $\langle v_z \rangle = $ const		POISEUILLE FLOW $v(r,z) = 2\langle v_z \rangle[1-(\frac{r}{R})^2]$	
	DIFFUSION neglected	DIFFUSION included	DIFFUSION neglected	DIFFUSION included
no reaction	①			②
A+wall $\xrightarrow{k_w} \frac{1}{2} A_2$				
A+BC $\xrightarrow{k}$ products		⑧		⑤
A+wall $\xrightarrow{k_w} \frac{1}{2} A_2$ A+BC $\xrightarrow{k}$ products	④			⑥
A+wall $\xrightarrow{k_w} \frac{1}{2} A_2$ A+A $\xrightarrow{k}$ products				⑦
A+wall $\xrightarrow{k_w} \frac{1}{2} A_2$ A+BC $\xrightarrow{k}$ products A+A+M $\xrightarrow{k_M} A_2+M$	③			

FIG. 21. Summary of some important cases in reacting systems, specified for flow, transport, and chemistry (numbers refer to cases treated in text).

and reaction. Whereas the concentration profiles for reactions in one-dimensional flow, neglecting diffusion effects, can be derived straightforwardly, the cases in the second to fourth row need extensive calculations. Cases numbered 1–8 in Fig. 21 have been chosen for discussion since they give an insight into the problem and can easily be extended to include a number of other cases.

The organization of this section is as follows:

Section B   The mass balance equation will be set up with the following assumptions:

(1) Low Mach number, constant flow velocity.
(2) Negligible temperature and pressure gradients.
(3) Reactive species (A, BC) present only in traces.
(4) A large excess of BC over A at every point.
(5) Time independence of the system.
(6) Tubular geometry, radius R.

Section C   The concentration profiles will be outlined for cases 1–8 in Fig. 21.

Section D

(1) Conditions will be outlined for practical realization of the assumptions.
(2) Rate data will be derived from experimental results.

B. Mass Balance Equation for Chemical Reaction in Isothermal Flow

Mass conservation for species A is given by Eq. (2.18) in connection with diffusion velocity (2.7). By the same procedure as given in the one-dimensional, the mass conservation law for the time-independent case reads

$$\mathbf{v}_0 \frac{\partial}{\partial \mathbf{r}}(y_i) = \frac{m_i K_i}{\rho} - \frac{1}{\rho}\left[\frac{\partial}{\partial \mathbf{r}} \cdot (\rho y_i \mathbf{\bar{V}}_i)\right]. \tag{5.1}$$

For some cases it is convenient to use molar density N_i (number of moles per unit volume), leading to the continuity equation in the form

$$(\partial/\partial \mathbf{r}) \cdot [N_i(\mathbf{v}_0 + \mathbf{\bar{V}}_i)] = K_i. \tag{5.2}$$

Here the net rate of chemical production K_i is then taken in moles per unit volume per unit time.

The expressions for the diffusion velocities $\bar{\mathbf{V}}_i$ as given in Eqs. (2.37) and (2.38) simplify appreciably, since according to the original assumptions, $\partial(\ln p)/\partial\mathbf{r}$ and $\partial(\ln T)/\partial\mathbf{r}$ are both zero:

$$\bar{\mathbf{V}}_i = \frac{n^2}{n_i \rho} \sum_j m_j D_{ij}^* \frac{\partial}{\partial\mathbf{r}} \left(\frac{n_j}{n}\right). \tag{5.3}$$

For further discussion we introduce some simplification of the continuity equation: Since the number density of the inert carrier gas is large compared to the density of the reactive species, the total density is approximately constant.

The diffusion velocity $\bar{\mathbf{V}}_i$ for the reactive species i can be approximated by an effective diffusion coefficient D_i, defined as

$$D_i = \sum_{i \neq j} (x_j/D_{ij})^{-1} \tag{5.4}$$

where D_{ij} is the binary diffusion coefficient and x_j is the mole fraction of species j. This leads to an approximate diffusion velocity of

$$\bar{\mathbf{V}}_i = -(D_i/n_i) \, \partial n_i/\partial\mathbf{r}. \tag{5.5}$$

Thus the equation for species conservation is given for the reactive species i, in a fairly good approximation for practical purposes, as

$$(\partial/\partial\mathbf{r}) \cdot (\mathbf{v}_0 n_i) - D_i(\partial^2/\partial\mathbf{r}^2)(n_i) = K_i. \tag{5.6}$$

Conservation of momentum   Equations (2.26) and (2.40) simplify for the assumption of constant flow velocity and negligible viscous effects to the statement that the pressure is constant.

Conservation of energy   By the assumption that the temperature and pressure are constant, and since the chemical reactive species are injected only as a trace, not altering the composition of the fluid, the total enthalpy does not change [Eq. (2.35)]. Changes of energy will not be considered in further derivations of this section.

The rate of production K_i by chemical reactions in the gas phase is given explicitly in Eq. (2.36). In most of the experiments in isothermal flow reactors, however, some wall reactions have to be taken into account for a quantitative description. In the following we assume that recombination of reactive species (atoms, radicals) at the wall can be described by first-order kinetics:

$$A \xrightarrow{k_w} \tfrac{1}{2}A_2$$

As shown by kinetic theory, the macroscopic rate constant k_w can be expressed by

$$k_w = \tfrac{1}{4}\gamma \bar{v}_i S/V, \tag{5.7}$$

where γ is the fraction of collisions leading to disappearance of A, $\bar{v}_i$ is the mean velocity of particle i, and S and V are the total surface and volume of reaction vessel, respectively. For tubular reactors Eq. (5.7) becomes

$$k_w = \gamma \bar{v}_i/2R. \tag{5.8}$$

The rate constant k_w in terms of the concentration gradient at the wall $[\partial(n_i/n)/\partial \mathbf{r}]_{\text{wall}}$ is given for tubular reactors of radius R by

$$k_w = -\frac{2D_i}{R}\left(\frac{n}{n_i}\right)\left[\frac{\partial(n_i/n)}{\partial \mathbf{r}}\right]_{\text{wall}}. \tag{5.9}$$

A description of the reacting flow is only based on Eq. (5.6) in connection with (5.5), (5.9), and (2.26), and introducing

$$\psi_i = n_i/n.$$

C. QUANTITATIVE DESCRIPTION

The description of the concentration profiles in isothermal flow will now be given with respect to the conditions of flow, diffusion, and reaction as listed in Fig. 21 and the assumptions given in Section V,A.

1. *The One-Dimensional Flow: Entrance Flow**

For a survey on flow patterns in pipes the reader is referred to standard texts. Gas entering the flow system by expansion through orifices smaller than the flow tube will normally show one-dimensional plug flow, because turbulent mixing is applicable. (Cases of supersonic expansion and turbulent flow, Reynolds numbers higher than 2300, will be excluded.) For

*c.f. Knudsen and Katz, 1958; Jost, 1960.

tubular reactors the entrance length L^e, i.e., the length where the flow velocity reaches 99% of that of the fully developed laminar flow, can be predicted from the relation

$$L^e/2R \approx 0.058 \, \text{Re}, \qquad (5.10)$$

L^e is the entrance length, $2R$ the tube diameter, and Re the Reynolds number.

For a more detailed description of development of the flow across the whole cross section the extensive study of Langhaar (1942) is recommended.

A description of concentration profiles is given as a special case in the next example (see, for example, Jost and Hauffe, 1972).

2. Poiseuille Flow with Diffusion, No Reaction*

The concentration profiles in fully developed Poiseuille flow, where no reaction takes place, are calculated on the basis of the assumption that axial diffusion may be neglected in comparison with convective flow,

$$D(\partial^2\psi_A/\partial z^2) \ll v(r)(\partial\psi_A/\partial z).$$

The mass balance equation (5.6) then becomes

$$2\langle v\rangle(1 - r^{*2})\left(\frac{\partial\psi_A}{\partial z}\right) = \frac{D}{R^2 r^*}\frac{\partial}{\partial r^*}\left(\frac{\partial\psi_A}{\partial r^*}\right) = 0. \qquad (5.11)$$

This is in the form of the Graetz–Nusselt equation and solutions may be written as

$$\psi_A = \phi(z)\theta(r^*),$$

$$\theta = 0 \quad \text{for} \quad r^* = 1, \qquad \partial\theta/\partial r^* = 0 \quad \text{for} \quad r^* = 0,$$

$$\phi = \phi_0 \exp(-D\beta_n^2 z/2\langle v\rangle R).$$

The differential equation for the radial part (Sturm–Liouville type)

$$(\partial/\partial r^*)(r^* \, \partial\theta/\partial r^*) + \beta_n^2 r^*(1 - r^{*2})\theta = 0 \qquad (5.12)$$

*Cf. Jost and Hauffe, 1972, Farragher, 1970.

determines the eigenvalues β_n and leads to final solution in an infinite-series expansion

$$\psi_A(r_1{}^*z)/\psi_A(0, 0) = \sum_{n=0}^{\infty} C_n F_n(r^*) \exp(-D\beta_n{}^2z/2\langle v\rangle R^2). \quad (5.13)$$

The C_n and $F_n(r^*)$ have to be specified for different conditions:

(a) In the absence of radial velocity gradients (plug-flow conditions) Eq. (5.11) reduces to Bessel's equation. Thus the solution [Eq. (5.13)] reduces to

$$F_n(r^*) = J_0(\beta_n r^*)$$

where J_0 is the Bessel function of order zero and β_n are the roots of J_0; and

$$C_n = 2/\beta_n J_1(\beta_n)$$

where J_1 is the Bessel function order one. ($\beta_0 = 2.405$, $\beta_1 = 5.520$; $C_0 = 1.602$, $C_1 = -1.064$). For most practical cases in our context the simplest approximation of taking only the first root is legitimate.

(b) When the parabolic velocity profile is developed the solutions of Graetz–Nusselt are obtained, and these are listed in the literature ($\beta_0 = 2.704$, $\beta_1 = 6.679$; $C_0 = 1.466$, $C_1 = -0.802$). To give an idea of the types of solution, the result of the simplest approximation is given here. $F_0(r^*)$ is obtained by application of the variation principle to Eq. (5.12) and the first mode of the Graetz–Nusselt equation is then

$$\frac{\psi(r^*, z)}{\psi(0, 0)} = [0.43(1 - r^{*2}) + 0.57(1 - r^{*2})^2] \exp - \frac{7.313 Dz}{2\langle v\rangle R^2}. \quad (5.14)$$

For higher approximations, other geometric configurations, and average values of concentrations over different cross sections reference is made to the cited papers.

3. *One-Dimensional Flow, No Diffusion, First-, Second-, Third-Order Chemical Reaction**

The mass balance equation (5.6) simply reduces to

$$\langle v\rangle \, d\psi/dz = K_A = k_w \psi + k\psi\psi_{BC} + 2k_M \psi^2\psi_M,$$

*Clyne and Thrush, 1963.

expressing the normal rate of disappearance of A for the underlying reaction scheme. This differential equation of Bernoulli type is integrated with the initial condition

$$\psi = \psi^0 \qquad \text{at} \quad z = 0$$

which is equivalent to

$$\psi = \psi^0 \qquad \text{when} \quad \psi_{BC} \equiv 0,$$

to give

$$\frac{1}{\psi} = \left(\frac{1}{\psi^0} + \frac{2k_M \psi_M}{k_w + k\psi_{BC}} \right) \exp\left(k_w + \frac{k\psi_{BC} z}{\langle v \rangle} \right) - \frac{2k_M \psi_M}{k_w + k\psi_{BC}}. \tag{5.15}$$

Rearrangement then leads to

$$\ln \frac{\psi^0}{\psi} = (k_w + k\psi_{BC}) \frac{z}{\langle v \rangle} + \ln \frac{k_w + k\psi_{BC} + 2k_M \psi_M \psi^0}{k_w + k\psi_{BC} + 2k_M \psi_M \psi}. \tag{5.16}$$

4. *One-Dimensional Flow, Axial Diffusion, First-, Second-Order Chemical Reaction**

The general equation of continuity reduces to

$$(d/dz)\langle \psi v_z \rangle - D(d^2/dz^2)\langle \psi \rangle = -k\langle \psi \rangle \psi_{BC} - k_w \langle \psi \rangle$$

which can be solved for the boundary conditions

$$\psi = \psi^0 \qquad \text{for} \quad z/R = 0$$
$$\psi = 0 \qquad \text{for} \quad z/R = \pm\infty.$$

Setting

$$\psi = \psi^0 \exp(-\lambda z/R), \tag{5.17}$$

the values for λ are then given as

$$\lambda = \lambda_+ = -\frac{1}{2} \frac{\langle v \rangle R}{D} + \left[\frac{1}{4} \left(\frac{\langle v \rangle R}{D} \right)^2 + \frac{k\psi_{BC} R^2}{D} + \frac{k_w R^2}{D} \right]^{1/2}; \qquad \frac{z}{R} \geq 0 \tag{5.18}$$

*Walker, 1961.

and

$$\lambda = \lambda_- = -\frac{1}{2}\frac{\langle v\rangle R}{D} - \left[\frac{1}{4}\left(\frac{\langle v\rangle R}{D}\right)^2 + \frac{k\psi_{BC}R^2}{D} + \frac{k_w R^2}{D}\right]^{1/2}; \quad \frac{z}{R} \leq 0.$$

(5.19)

Physically speaking, the positive root gives the behavior in direction of the flow, whereas the negative root describes the behavior of the system against the flow direction.

This solution contains two limiting cases.

Case a. When diffusion effects are small compared to flow, i.e., large flow velocity, the roots λ reduce to

$$\lambda_+ \approx -k\psi_{BC}R/\langle v\rangle - k_w R/\langle v\rangle, \qquad \lambda_- \approx -\langle v\rangle R/D.$$

This is the solution as known from case 3, setting $k_M = 0$,

$$\ln(\psi^0/\psi) = (k_w + k\psi_{BC})z/\langle v\rangle.$$

(5.20)

Case b. Assuming wall reactions to be slow ($k_w \ll k\psi_{BC}$ or $\langle v\rangle^2/D$), the term λ_+,

$$\lambda_+ = -\frac{1}{2}\frac{\langle v\rangle R}{D} + \left[\frac{1}{4}\left(\frac{\langle v\rangle R}{D}\right)^2 + \frac{k\psi_{BC}R^2}{D}\right]^{1/2}$$

becomes by series expansion

$$\lambda_+ \approx \frac{k\psi_{BC}R}{\langle v\rangle} - \frac{k^2\psi_{BC}^2 RD}{\langle v\rangle^3}.$$

(5.21)

Insertion of λ_+ into the solution (5.17) gives

$$\psi = \psi_0 \exp\left(-\frac{k\psi_{BC}z}{\langle v\rangle} + \frac{k^2\psi_{BC}^2 Dz}{\langle v\rangle^3}\right),$$

(5.22)

showing that the rate of decay of the concentration of A by reaction is partially counterbalanced by diffusion. The influence of diffusion is most pronounced when the flow speed is low.

5. *Poiseuille Flow, Diffusion, Homogeneous First-Order Reaction**

In looking for the solution of $\psi(r, z)$ with respect to the initial concentration $\psi(0, 0)$ and using

$$\chi = \psi(r, z)/\psi(0, 0)$$

the mass balance equation becomes

$$2\langle v \rangle (1 - r^{*2}) \frac{\partial \chi}{\partial \sigma} - \frac{1}{r^*} \frac{\partial}{\partial r^*} \left(r^* \frac{\partial \chi}{\partial r^*} \right) + B^2 \chi = 0 \qquad (5.23)$$

with $r^* = r/R$, $\sigma = z/R\langle v \rangle$, and $B^2 = k\psi_{BC} R^2/D$. Solution of the form

$$\chi = \theta(r^*) \exp(-k_i^2 z)$$

yields for the radial part an equation

$$(\partial/\partial r^*)(r^* \, \partial\theta/\partial r^*) + [K_n^2(1 - r^{*2}) - B^2]r^*\theta = 0,$$

with

$$K_n = 2R^2 \langle v \rangle k_i^2/D \, .$$

For the lowest mode solution an approximate expression can be given as

$$K_0^2 = 7.342 + 1.258B^2 \, .$$

Assuming no distortion of the radial distribution of the flow pattern due to reaction we obtain (see case 2), we have

$$\psi(r^*, z)/\psi(0, 0) = [0.43(1 - r^{*2}) + 0.57(1 - r^{*2})^2]$$

$$\times \exp\left[-\left(\frac{7.342D}{R^2} + 1.258k\psi_{BC} \right) z/2\langle v \rangle \right]. \qquad (5.24)$$

6. *Poiseuille Flow, Diffusion, Homogeneous First Order and Wall Reaction†*

Numerical solutions of the continuity equation were given in the excellent paper of Walker. The objective of this work was to judge under what conditions the one-dimensional or the two-dimensional description is realistic and to estimate errors for various experimental regimes.

*Huggins and Cahn, 1967; Farragher, 1970; Smith *et al.*, 1960.
†Walker, 1961; Kaufman, 1961; Poirrier and Carr, 1971.

The mass balance is

$$2\langle v\rangle\left(1-\frac{r^2}{R^2}\right)\frac{\partial\psi}{\partial z}-D\left(\frac{\partial^2\psi}{\partial r^2}+\frac{1}{r}\frac{\partial\psi}{\partial r}+\frac{\partial^2\psi}{\partial z^2}\right)=k\psi\psi_{BC} \qquad (5.25)$$

with the boundary conditions

$$\psi=\psi^0 \quad \text{for} \quad z=0, \qquad \psi=0 \quad \text{for} \quad z=\infty;$$

$$\left(\frac{\partial\psi}{\partial r}\right)=-\psi\frac{k_w R}{D}=-\psi\frac{2}{\delta R} \qquad \text{at} \quad r=R; \qquad \delta=\frac{2D}{R^2 k_w}.$$

The partial differential equation is transformed to an infinite set of ordinary differential equations by the method of separation of variables. Using

$$\psi=\sum_{i=1}^{\infty} g_i(r^*)\exp(-\phi_i z^*); \qquad r^*=r/R, \quad z^*=z/R, \qquad (5.26)$$

Eq. (5.25) becomes

$$\frac{d^2 g_i}{dr^{*2}}+\frac{1}{r^*}\frac{dg_i}{dr^*}+[\phi_i^2-B^2+2u\phi_i(1-r^{*2})]g_i=0, \qquad (5.27)$$

where $u=\langle v\rangle R/D$ and $B^2=k\psi_{BC}R^2/D$. In the case of the flow term vanishing ($u=0$), or large ϕ_i, Eq. (5.27) reduces to a Bessel equation of zeroth order,

$$g_i(r^*)\propto J_0[(\phi_i^2-B^2)r^*]. \qquad (5.28)$$

The full solution, where all terms are included, can be given numerically when an infinite series is assumed for the $g_i(r^*)$

$$g_i(r^*)=\sum (C_i)_n(-1)^n\bar{r}^{2n}/(n!\,2^{2n}), \qquad \bar{r}=r^*(\phi_i+2u\phi_i-B^2)^{1/2} \quad (5.29)$$

with a recurrence relation for the $(C_i)_n$.

Assuming large values of z^*, the first term in (5.26) yields a satisfactory asymptotic solution. The concentration profile was evaluated according to

$$\psi\approx g_i(r^*)\exp(-\phi_i z^*) \qquad (5.30)$$

for different groups of the experimental parameters δ, u, and B^2. Comparison of Eq. (30) with the equivalent equation for the one-dimensional flow shows that the ratio of λ/ϕ_1 is a quantitative measure of the deviation from the one-dimensional concept. The values upstream (λ_+/ϕ_1) and downstream (λ_-/ϕ_1) are given in Tables II and III. The results clearly indicate

TABLE II

COMPUTED VALUES OF λ_+/ϕ_1 [EQS. (5.18) AND (5.26)] FOR DIFFERENT GROUPS OF PARAMETERS[a]

Parameters[b]		λ_+/ϕ_1			
B^2	u	δ: 0.1	1.0	10	100
0.01	0.01	2.055	1.127	1.012	1.001
	0.1	2.097	1.136	1.015	1.002
	1	2.563	1.244	1.036	1.004
	10	5.495	1.471	1.045	1.004
0.1	0.01	2.040	1.120	1.008	1.000
	0.1	2.083	1.130	1.011	1.001
	1	2.537	1.232	1.029	1.004
	10	5.418	1.455	1.039	1.004
1.0	0.01	1.915	1.079	1.002	1.000
	0.1	1.950	1.087	1.004	1.002
	1	2.327	1.158	1.016	1.007
	10	4.777	1.367	1.044	1.022
10	0.01	1.428	1.018	1.000	1.000
	0.1	1.441	1.021	1.001	1.000
	1	1.580	1.051	1.012	1.010
	10	2.673	1.297	1.164	1.152

[a] Walker (1961).
[b] $u = \langle v \rangle R/D$, $B^2 = k\psi_{BC} R^2/D$, $\delta = 2D/R^2 k_w$.[a]

that the description of the two-dimensional flow patterns in terms of one-dimensional parameters is valid within the limits

$$\delta \geq 5, \qquad u \leq 10\text{--}20; \qquad B^2 > 5\text{--}10 \quad \text{(not so critical)}$$

or

$$D \geq 2.5R^2 k_w; \qquad \langle v \rangle R \leq 10D, \qquad k\psi_{BC} \geq (5\text{--}10)D/R^2.$$

In other cases corrections have to be made (see case 5).

Poirrier and Carr (1971) treated the first-order reaction under the assumptions of no axial diffusion and no wall reaction ($1/\delta = 0$). Their results indicate that the usual first-order plots hold for $B^2 > 3$.

TABLE III

COMPUTED VALUES OF λ_-/ϕ_1 [EQS. (5.19) AND (5.26)] FOR DIFFERENT
GROUPS OF PARAMETERS[a]

Parameters[b]		λ_-/ϕ_1			
B^2	u	δ: 0.1	1.0	10	100
0.01	0.01	2.046	1.124	1.012	1.001
	0.1	2.004	1.114	1.009	1.000
	1.0	1.655	1.039	1.009	1.018
	10	1.283	1.564	1.741	1.761
0.1	0.01	2.031	1.118	1.008	1.000
	0.1	1.991	1.109	1.006	1.000
	1.0	1.647	1.037	1.009	1.017
	10	1.283	1.590	1.739	1.759
1.0	0.01	1.907	1.078	1.002	1.000
	0.1	1.874	1.072	1.002	1.000
	1.0	1.584	1.025	1.008	1.014
	10	1.280	1.578	1.720	1.737
10	0.01	1.425	1.018	1.000	1.000
	0.1	1.412	1.016	1.000	1.000
	1.0	1.298	1.007	1.009	1.011
	10	1.257	1.489	1.581	1.593

[a] Walker (1961).
[b] $u = \langle v \rangle R/D$, $B^2 = k\psi_{BC} R^2/D$, $\delta = 2D/R^2 k_w$.

When taking samples from the flow reactors a decision has to be made
whether the samples represent the composition of the mixture over the
whole cross section or not. Therefore the radial concentration profiles are
of special interest. In the paper by Walker the normalized concentration
profiles $\psi(r^*, z^*)/\psi(0, z^*)$ are given for different parameters (see Fig. 22).

7. Poiseuille Flow, Diffusion, First-, Second-Order Kinetics*

For this case mass balance reads

$$(1 - r^*)^2 \frac{\partial \theta}{\partial \lambda} = \alpha \frac{1}{r^*} \frac{\partial}{\partial r^*} \left(r^* \frac{\partial \theta}{\partial r^*} \right) - \theta^2,$$

*Krongelb and Strandberg, 1959; Vignes and Tambrouze, 1962; Poirrier and Carr,
1971.

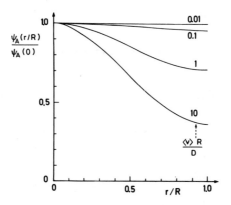

FIG. 22.   Influence of flow and diffusion on radical concentration profiles in reacting Poiseuille flow. Reactions

$$A + BC \xrightarrow{\ k\ } \text{products}, \qquad A \xrightarrow{\ k_w\ } \text{products}$$

Conditions: $k_w = D/50R^2$; $k\psi_{BC} = 10D/R^2$. (Taken from Walker, 1961.)

where

$$\theta = \psi/\psi^0, \qquad \psi^0 = \psi(r^* = 0, z^* = 0),$$

$$\lambda = k\psi^0 z/2\langle v\rangle, \qquad \alpha = D/kR^2\psi^0, \qquad \beta = k_w/k\psi^0 R.$$

The description, taking into account diffusion terms, is complex and needs numerical procedures in most cases. Due to the complex form of the radial gradient, different average concentrations will be obtained using different analytical methods.

Average concentration values were obtained for the following different experimental conditions:

(a) Optical concentration measurement, where the averaging is performed across the diameter of the reactor

$$\bar{\psi} = \int_0^1 \theta \, dr^*.$$

(b) Averaging over a volume

$$\bar{\psi} = 2 \int_0^1 \theta r^* \, dr^*.$$

(c) Averaging in cup mixing

$$\bar{\psi} = 4 \int_0^1 (1 - r^{*2})\theta r^* \, dr^* .$$

Figures 23 and 24 show the normalized concentration profile against the

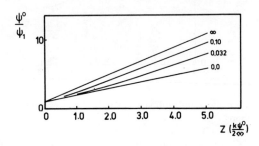

FIG. 23. Influence of diffusion on concentration profile in reacting Poiseuille flow, as calculated in the reactor axis, for different values of $D/k\psi^0 R^2$ as indicated on the curves. Reaction

$$A + A \quad \xrightarrow{\ k\ } \quad \text{products}$$

$\psi_A^0 = \psi_A(r = 0, z = 0); \psi_1 = \psi(z, r = 0)$. (Taken from Poirrier and Carr, 1971.)

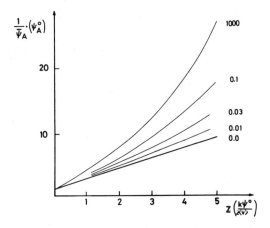

FIG. 24. Influence of axial diffusion on concentration profile in reacting Poiseuille flow for different values of $D/k\psi^0 R^2$ as indicated on the curves. Reactions

$$A + A \quad \xrightarrow{\ k\ } \quad \text{products}, \quad A \quad \xrightarrow{\ kw\ } \quad \text{products}$$

$k_w = 0.07 k \psi_A \, R. \; \psi_A^0 = \psi_A(z = 0); \; \bar{\psi}_A = \int_0^1 (\psi/\psi^0) \, d(r/R)$. (Taken from Poirrier and Carr, 1971.)

reaction time (λ proportional to reaction time) for different parameters. As is shown for this example, the usual second-order plot is valid for the range $\alpha = D/kR^2\psi^0 < 0.03$. In other cases corrections are necessary.

The behavior of the radial concentration profile with respect to the concentration along the reactor axis is shown in Fig. 23. For negligible wall reaction the parameter α should be in the region $0.5 \lesssim \alpha < \infty$ to avoid errors in calculating the reaction time, evaluated simply by $t = z/\langle v \rangle$. The simple reaction time will lead to rate constants smaller than the true value. This means in practice that the initial concentration ψ^0 should be chosen as small as sensitivity allows.

8. *Diffusion Flame Method*

In the description given so far the reactants A and BC are mixed homogeneously and instantaneously. Since mixing takes some time, the investigations are restricted to the state where a well-mixed condition obtains. Otherwise the concentration pattern introduced by mixing has to be taken into account.

The diffusion flame method is used for the study of very fast reactions and the measurement of diffusion coefficient for labile species, e.g., atoms and radicals. It takes advantage of the finite mixing time. The scheme of the experimental arrangement is given in Fig. 20b. A trace of the substance under study (atoms, molecules, inert gas) is injected into a stream of gas flowing in the z direction with constant speed at a constant pressure and temperature. The concentration of A is followed by suitable analysis in the centerline or over the whole profile, as indicated in Fig. 20b. A number of different types of flow pattern have to be considered. References are made only to some key papers.

a. Flow, Diffusion, No Reaction. (Walker and Westenberg, 1958; Jost, 1960). With the assumptions: (i) constant flow speed, (ii) averaged diffusion coefficient D, and (iii) no reaction of the trace A, with a flow rate Q, the continuity equation then reads

$$D(\partial^2/\partial \mathbf{r}^2)\psi_A - \mathbf{v} \cdot (\partial/\partial \mathbf{r})\psi_A = 0.$$

For the initial condition

$$\psi = 0 \qquad \text{at} \quad r = \infty$$

and the normalization condition

$$Q = \lim_{r \to 0} 4\pi r^2 D(\partial \psi / \partial r)$$

the solution for the axial symmetric problem is given in the coordinates z and r ($r^2 = x^2 + y^2 + z^2$) as

$$\psi = (Q/4\pi Dr) \exp[-(r - z)\langle v \rangle / 2D]. \tag{5.31}$$

Thus a plot of $\ln(\psi r)$ vs. $(r - z)$ gives the diffusion coefficient.

b. Flow, Diffusion, First-Order Reaction. (Walker, 1961; Yolles *et al.*, 1970). The solution for concentration profile may be obtained on the basis of the assumptions (i) constant flow speed, (ii) average diffusion coefficient D, (iii) first-order homogeneous reaction

$$A + BC \xrightarrow{\quad k \quad} products$$

for a trace of A ($\psi_A \ll \psi_{BC}$). The continuity equation

$$v(\partial \psi / \partial z) - D(\partial^2 / \partial \mathbf{r}^2)\psi - k\psi\psi_{BC} = 0$$

is solved by setting

$$\psi = [\exp(\alpha z)]\phi(r)$$

with $\alpha = v/2D$. The solution for ϕ is

$$\phi = (A'/r) \exp(-\beta r) + (B'/r) \exp(+\beta r)$$

where $\beta^2 = \alpha^2 + k\psi/D$. Since the boundary condition is $\psi(\infty) = 0$ and the relation $\beta \geq \alpha$ holds, it is seen from $\psi = [\exp(\alpha z)]\phi(r)$ that $B' = 0$. Thus the total solution is

$$\psi(z, r) = (A'/r) \exp(\alpha z - \beta r).$$

The concentration profile along the tube axis is then

$$\psi(z, 0) = \frac{A'}{z} \exp\left\{\frac{vz}{2D} - \left[\frac{z^2}{D}\left(k\psi_{BC} + \frac{v^2}{4D}\right)\right]^{1/2}\right\}. \tag{5.32}$$

For the determination of A' in reaction systems the reader is referred to Reed and Rabinovitch (1955) and Garvin and Kistiakowsky (1952).

c. *Flow, Diffusion, Subsequent Reaction First Order.*   The assumptions here are (i) constant flow v, (ii) average diffusion coefficient D for BC in the mixture, and (iii) a trace of A undergoing the reactions

$$A + BC \xrightarrow{\quad k_1 \quad} C + products$$

$$C + BC \xrightarrow{\quad k_2 \quad} products.$$

A concentration profile for the intermediate C is given along the z axis $(r = z)$ by the relation

$$\psi_C = \frac{Q k_1 \psi_{BC}}{4\pi D \cdot z(k_2 \psi_{BC} - k_1 \psi_{BC})} \exp\left\{\frac{vz}{2D}\left[\exp\left(-z\left(\frac{k_1 \psi_{BC}}{D} + \frac{v^2}{4D^2}\right)^{1/2}\right)\right]\right.$$
$$\left. -\exp\left[-z\left(\frac{k\psi_{BC}}{D} - \frac{v^2}{4D^2}\right)^{1/2}\right]\right\} \quad (5.33)$$

The influence of wall reactions will not be discussed here. A discussion of this problem can be found in the paper of Talroze *et al.* (1966).

D. PRACTICAL CONSIDERATIONS

1. *Realization of Assumed Conditions*

   As outlined in Section V,A and used in Section V,B, it has been assumed that temperature and pressure are uniform over the whole flow reactor.
   A well-defined *temperature* can be obtained by preheating the gas entering the chemical reactor. Turbulent flow is best employed since heat transfer coefficients for turbulent flow are much larger than for laminar flow. This allows the use of very short heating lengths. If the gas enters with a different temperature than that of the reactor wall, equilibration is accomplished after a certain length, called the thermal entrance length L^{th}, controlled by development of the boundary layer. An estimate of the upper limit for L^{th} can be obtained from Eq. (5.10) (Knudsen and Katz, 1958)

$$L^{th}/d \simeq 0.05 \text{ Re Pr}$$

where d is the tube diameter, Re is the Reynolds number, and Pr is the Prandtl number. To give an example: For a flow of He ($v_0 = 70$ m sec^{-1}, $p = 2$ Torr, $T_0 = 298$ K) in a 2.2-cm-diameter tube the gas temperature reaches the wall temperature of 660 K at a distance of $L^{th} \simeq 7$ cm. A lower value of thermal conductivity (Ar) would lead to a much larger value of $L^{th} \approx 56$ cm. Thus He would be preferable as a carrier gas when short reactors are desired.

For very high flow velocity and low thermal conductivity, radial temperature gradients can be built up. For calculations of radial temperature distributions one should consult the standard literature (Jakob, 1949; Carslaw and Jaeger, 1959; Gebhart, 1961; Bennett and Myers, 1962).

When studying highly exothermic reactions care has to be taken that the amount of heat liberated by reaction is small compared with the heat capacity of carrier gas or that there is an effective heat transfer to the wall. This means in practice that it is best to employ low initial concentrations of reactive species, limited by the sensitivity of the analytical method, coupled with high-thermal-conductivity carrier gases.

Calculation and measurement show that in most cases (v_0 up to 100 m sec^{-1}, mole fraction $<10^{-3}$, $p = 1$–100 Torr) temperature can be kept constant witin 1–5 K.

Constant *pressure* in flow reactors, as has been described, is a limiting case since a pressure gradient is necessary to accomplish mass transfer. The viscous pressure drop from p_2 to p_1 is given by the Poiseuille law

$$p_2{}^2 - p_1{}^2 = 16Fl\eta RT/\pi R^4 \qquad (5.34)$$

where F is the flow rate in mole sec^{-1}, η is the viscosity, and l and R are the length and the radius of tubular reactor, respectively.

In a typical reactor ($R = 1$ cm, $l = 20$ cm, $F = 4.1 \times 10^{-5}$ mole sec^{-1} at NTP, $v_0 = 10$ m sec^{-1}, $p_2 = 5$ Torr, $T = 298$ K) the pressure drop is of the order of 0.5%. But at lower pressures (<1 Torr) and higher linear velocities (up to 100 m sec^{-1}) the error can be appreciable. Thus short reactors of several cm in diameter are advisable and these should not be used at low pressures. For very low pressures, corrections for slip flow have to be considered (see, for example, Ferguson *et al.*, 1969).

In cases 3–7 of Section V,C it was assumed that *admixing of the reactant* BC to the main flow is achieved instantaneously and homogeneously over the whole cross section. This assumption cannot be realized completely. To improve mixing, the trace of BC can be diluted with inert gas so that it is 5% that of main flow. Under these conditions mixing times of the order of 0.5–1 msec are realized. Reactions in this turbulent regime will influence the absolute concentration profiles; but when dealing with relative concentrations as in Section V,D,2, this influence of finite mixing time on rate determination is negligible.

2. *Elementary Chemical Reactions As Studied in Isothermal Flow Reactors*

Isothermal flow reactor studies have yielded information on elementary chemical reactions. A survey of the reactions so studied can be found in Chapter 9.

The advantages of this technique are as follows. The temperature can be chosen independently of the other parameters (pressure, mixture, composition) from 70 to 1500 K. Heat transfer to the wall can be made very rapid compared to the rate of heat production by suitable choice of experimental conditions. Furthermore, reactions of the type

$$A + BC \longrightarrow AB + C, ABC, AC + B$$

can be investigated using several concentration relations (A ≪ BC, A ≫ BC). This allows elimination of subsequent reaction to some extent. By selection of different pressures, pressure-dependent reactions such as homogeneously catalyzed recombination reactions can be studied under isothermal conditions. By diluting the reactive species with a high excess of inert gas, equilibration of excited states of produced species can be established.

Good time–space resolution can be obtained and reaction time can be matched to the requirements of the analytic detection methods. Moreover, gradients can be kept small so that the influence of transport processes is negligible or such that reliable correction can be made. This enhances the accuracy of the rate measurement. The procedures for evaluating rate data are given explicitly for concentration profiles under known flow and diffusion conditions. Since we are interested in gas-phase reactions, such knowledge requires conditions where the influences of diffusion and wall reactions cancel or their net contributions are small.

The experiment is often used as an " on–off technique " where the concentration of A is measured with ("on") and without ("off") added reactant BC for a fixed distance z between reactant inlet and detection point (see Fig. 20a). Assuming that the overall flow pattern (velocity profile, mean diffusion coefficient, k_w) does not change substantially by admixing BC, the formulas derived for k are simplified. This will now be demonstrated for four cases, for the numbering of which refer to Fig. 21. The notation is as follows:

ψ^0 concentration of A at $z = 0$.

ψ_{off} concentration of A at z, no BC added.

ψ_{on} concentration of A at z, BC added.

Case 3 (Fig. 21)   One-dimensional flow without diffusion, first-order wall, first-order and second-order homogeneous reaction. From the evaluated concentration profile [Eq. (5.16)] and the foregoing notation the relation becomes

$$\ln\frac{\psi_{on}}{\psi_{off}} - \ln\left(\frac{2k_M\psi_M\psi_{on} + k_w + k\psi_{BC}}{2k_M\psi_M\psi^0 + k_w + k\psi_{BC}}\right)$$
$$\left(\frac{2k_M\psi_M\psi^0 + k_w}{2k_M\psi_M\psi_{off} + k_w}\right) = -k\psi_{BC}\frac{z}{\langle v\rangle}. \qquad (5.35)$$

When the recombination reaction is negligible ($2k_M\psi_M\psi^0 \ll k_w$) this reduces to

$$\ln(\psi_{off}/\psi_{on}) = k\psi_{BC}\, z/\langle v\rangle,$$

which means that the influence of the finite rate of wall reaction cancels in evaluating k by the "on–off technique":

$$k = (\langle v\rangle/z\psi_{BC})\ln(\psi_{off}/\psi_{on}) \qquad (5.36)$$

(this relation can also be simply derived from case 4a). Moreover, only a relative concentration measurement of A is necessary, increasing the precision of the k value.

Even for nonvanishing recombination reaction the simple formula (5.36) can be applied under some experimental conditions: since $\psi_{on}, \psi_{off} \ll \psi^0$, the second term in Eq. (5.16) is nearly zero because of cancellation of terms when small concentration of A and small decay of A are chosen in the experiment.

Case 4 (Fig. 21)   One-dimensional flow with axial diffusion, first-order homogeneous reaction, wall reaction negligible. From Eq. (5.22) it follows that

$$\ln\frac{\psi_{off}}{\psi_{on}} = \frac{k\psi_{BC}\, z}{\langle v\rangle} - \frac{k^2\psi_{BC}^2\, Dz}{\langle v\rangle^3},$$

which leads to a quadratic equation for k. Since the diffusion correction $k\psi_{BC} D/\langle v \rangle^2$ is assumed to be small compared to one, series expansion of the root leads to

$$k = \frac{\langle v \rangle}{z\psi_{BC}} \left(\ln \frac{\psi_{off}}{\psi_{on}} \right) \left(1 + \frac{D}{z\langle v \rangle} \ln \frac{\psi_{off}}{\psi_{on}} \right).$$

This means that the apparent rate constant without diffusion correction is lower than the true one. This can be understood, since mass transfer by diffusion flattens the chemically produced decay of A.

Case 5 (Fig. 21)   Poiseuille flow with axial diffusion, first-order homogeneous reaction.   From the solution of $\psi(r^*z)/\psi(0, 0)$ [Eq. (5.24)] it can be shown that

$$\ln[\psi_{off}(r^*,z)/\psi_{on}(r^*, z)] = 1.258 k\psi_{BC} z/2\langle v \rangle.$$

This result,

$$k = \frac{1}{1.258} \frac{2\langle v \rangle}{z\psi_{BC}} \ln \frac{\psi_{off}}{\psi_{on}}$$

shows that the mass transfer due to diffusion cancels, whereas the velocity profile introduces a correction of 60%. But it has to be kept in mind that in the derivation of Eq. (5.24) in Section V,C5 only the poorest approximation has been given. In this context see the paper of Wilde (1948).

Case 8 (Fig. 21)   Diffusion flame method, where reactant A is admixed from a point source (Fig. 20b).   The measured concentration ratios for on–off conditions on the reactor axis are expressed using Eq. (5.32) as

$$\ln \frac{\psi_{off}(0, z)}{\psi_{on}(0, z)} = -\frac{z\langle v \rangle}{2D} \left[1 - \left(1 + \frac{4Dk\psi}{\langle v \rangle^2} \right) \right],$$

from which the value of k is deduced as in case 5, assuming that

$$4D \ln(\psi_{off}/\psi_{on})/\langle v \rangle z \ll 1.$$

In this approximation the k value is given explicitly as

$$k = \frac{\langle v \rangle}{\psi^2} \left(\ln \frac{\psi_{off}}{\psi_{on}} \right) \left[1 + \frac{D \ln(\psi_{off}/\psi_{on})}{z\langle v \rangle} \right].$$

This result indicates that pure radial diffusion (without reaction) out of the tube axis no longer enters into the analysis by virtue of an on–off technique, only the axial decay of species A due to reaction and the diffusion along this chemically produced gradient.

Some remarks follow on the chemistry alone, neglecting flow and diffusion. In most practical cases the underlying reaction scheme is more complex than assumed in the foregoing; e.g.,

$$A + BC \xrightarrow{k} AB + C$$

$$A + AB \xrightarrow{k_2} A_2 + B.$$

When the consecutive reaction occurs at a very fast rate the measured decay of species A is twice that expected from the first reaction alone. Introducing a stoichiometric factor n such that

$$n = (d\psi_A/dt)/(d\psi_{BC}/dt),$$

then the rate coefficient for the first reaction is deduced from the overall measured decay of species A, giving k_m, by

$$k = k_m/n$$

A typical example is the study of the reaction

$$O + H_2 \longrightarrow OH + H$$

where a large excess of H_2 is applied compared with O atom concentration. Oxygen atoms also react with the product OH

$$O + OH \longrightarrow O_2 + H.$$

This gives a stoichiometric factor of two. The concentration profiles for H and O atoms are given in Fig. 10 for a typical set of experimental conditions. (See Chapter 9.)

A simple correction of measured rate data via the stoichiometric factor can lead to erroneous results if reactant BC is re-formed in subsequent reactions. For example, the stoichiometric factor n is not well defined when dealing with the homogeneous catalytic recombination of H atoms in the presence of acetylene, where the reaction scheme is

$$H + C_2H_2 \longrightarrow C_2H_3*$$
$$C_2H_3* + M \longrightarrow C_2H_3$$
$$H + C_2H_3 \longrightarrow C_2H_2 + H_2.$$

Here as in most other reacting systems careful analysis of the whole set of reactions has to be carried out. This is in spite of the ability to choose independently the concentration ratios and other parameters in fast flow reactors.

The advantages of studies in fast flow reactors for measurements of rates for a single reaction are demonstrated by the reaction $O + N_2H_4$. Instead of following the unstable species, the O atom, the pseudo-first-order decay of N_2H_4 in very low concentration is followed:

$$\psi^0_{N_2H_4} = 9.4 \times 10^{-12}, \qquad \psi^0_{O\ atom} = 1.4 \times 10^{-10}\ \text{mole cm}^{-3}$$

(see Fig. 25). Since the rate of the reaction

$$O + N_2H_4 \longrightarrow N_2H_2 + H_2O$$

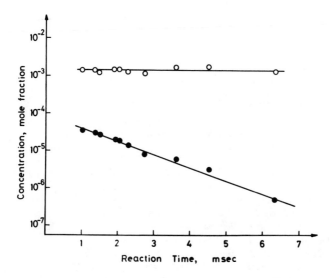

FIG. 25. Measured concentration profiles in isothermal flow reactor: $O + N_2H_4 \rightarrow N_2H_2 + H_2O$ ($T = 281$ K, $p = 1.65$ Torr). Upper, O atoms; lower N_2H_4O.

is very fast, the N_2H_4 is attacked mainly by O atoms and not by reaction products such as N_2H_2. The large excess of O atoms, practically constant throughout the reaction, removes all labile species produced. Thus the rate of the single reaction is derived directly from the decay of N_2H_4, uncomplicated by subsequent reactions. The influence of diffusion of N_2H_4 along the measured concentration gradient is estimated from the values given in the legend to Fig. 25 to be smaller than 2%.

REFERENCES

ADAMS, G. K., and COOK, G. B. (1960). *Combust. Flame* **4**, 9.

ANDREWS, G. E., and BRADLEY, D. (1972). *Combust. Flame* **18**, 133.

BELFORD, R. L., and STREHLOW, R. A. (1969). *Annu. Rev. Phys. Chem.* **20**, 247.

BENNETT, C. O., and MYERS, J. E. (1962). "Momentum, Heat and Mass Transfer." McGraw-Hill, New York.

BRADLEY, J. N. (1962). "Shock Waves in Chemistry and Physics." Wiley, New York.

BROWN, N. J., FRISTROM, R. M., SAWYER, R. F. (1974). *Comb. Flame* **23**, 269.

BULEWICZ, E. M., and PADLEY, P. J. (1971). *Int. Symp. Combust.*, 13*th* p. 73. Combust. Inst. Pittsburgh, Pennsylvania.

BULEWICZ, E. M., JAMES, C. G., and SUGDEN, T. M. (1956). *Proc. Roy. Soc. London* **A235**, 89.

CARSLAW, H. S., and JAEGER, J. C. (1959). "Conduction of Heat in Solids. "Oxford Univ. Press, London and New York.

CHAPMAN, S., and COWLING, T. G. (1970). "The Mathematical Theory of Non-Uniform Gases." Cambridge Univ. Press, London and New York.

CLYNE, M. A. A., and THRUSH, B. A. (1963). *Trans. Faraday Soc.* **275**, 544.

COURANT, R., and FRIEDRICHS, K. O. (1956). "Supersonic Flow and Shock Waves." Wiley (Interscience), New York.

CREITZ, E. C. (1970). *J. Res. Nat. Bur. Std.* U. S. **74A**, 521.

DIXON-LEWIS, G. (1967). *Proc. Roy. Soc. London* **A298**, 495.

DIXON-LEWIS, G. (1968). *Proc. Roy. Soc. London* **A307**, 111.

DIXON-LEWIS, G. (1970). *Proc. Roy. Soc. London* **A317**, 235.

DIXON-LEWIS, G., and WILLIAMS, A. (1963). *Quart. Rev.* **17**, 243.

DIXON-LEWIS, G., ISLES, G. L., and WALMSLEY, R. (1973). *Proc. Roy. Soc. London* **A331**, 571.

EBERIUS, K. H., HOYERMANN, K., and WAGNER, H. GG. (1971). *Int. Symp. Combust.*, 13*th* p. 713. Combust. Inst., Pittsburgh, Pennsylvania.

EBERIUS, K. H., HOYERMANN, K., and WAGNER, H. GG. (1973). *Int. Symp. Combust.*, 14*th* p. 147. Combust. Inst., Pittsburgh, Pennsylvania.

EVANS, M. W. (1952). *Chem. Rev.* **53**, 363.

FARRAGHER, A. L. (1970). *Trans. Faraday. Soc.* **66**, 1411.

FENIMORE, C. P. (1964). "Chemistry in Premixed Flames." Pergamon, Oxford.

FENIMORE, C. P., and JONES, G. W. (1961). *J. Phys. Chem.* **65**, 993.

FERGUSON, E. E., FEHSENFELD, F. C., and SCHMELTEKOPF, A. L. (1969). Flowing afterglow measurements of ion-neutral reactions. *Advan. At. Mol. Phys.* **5**, 1.

FRANZE, C., and WAGNER, H. GG. (1955). *Ber. Bunsenges. Phys. Chem.* **60**, 525.

FRISTROM, R. M. (1961). *In* "Experimental Methods in Combustion Research" (J. Surugue, ed.), Chapter 1.4. Pergamon, Oxford.

FRISTROM, R. M. (1972). Private communication.

FRISTROM, R. M., and SAWYER, R. F. (1972). AGARDOGRAPH 82, Flame Inhibition.

FRISTROM, R. M., and WESTENBERG, A. A. (1965). "Flame Structure." McGraw Hill, New York.

GAYDON, A. G., and HURLE, I. R. (1963). "The Shock Tube in High Temperature Chemical Physics." Van Nostrand-Reinhold, New Jersey.

GAYDON, A. G., and WOLFHARD, H. G. (1971). "Flames." Chapman and Hall, London.

GEBHART, B. (1961). "Heat Transfer." McGraw-Hill, New York.

GREENE, E. F., and TOENNIES, J. P. (1964). "Chemical Reactions in Shock Waves." Academic Press, New York.

HART, L. W., and FRISTROM, R. M. (1972). Presented Eastern State Sect. Combust. Inst., Fall Meeting.

HIRSCHFELDER, J. O. (1961). *Phys. Fluids* **4**, 253.

HIRSCHFELDER, J. O. (1963). *Symp. Int. Combust.*, *9th* p. 553. Academic Press, New York.

HIRSCHFELDER, J. O., CURTISS, C. F., and BIRD, R. B. (1954). "Molecular Theory of Gases and Liquids." Wiley, New York.

HOMANN, K. H., MOCHIZUKI, M., and WAGNER, H. GG. (1963). *Z. Phys. Chem. (Frankfurt)* **NF37**, 299.

HUGGINS, R. W., and CAHN, J. H. (1967). *J. Appl. Phys.* **38**, 180.

JOST, W. (1938). "Explosions- und Verbrennungsvorgänge in Gasen. " Springer, Berlin and New York.

JOST, W. (1960). "Diffusion in Solids, Liquids, Gases." Academic Press, New York.

JOST, W., and HAUFFE, K. (1972). "Diffusion. Methoden der Messung und Auswertung." Steinkopff, Darmstadt.

KAUFMAN, F. (1961). "Progress in Reaction Kinetics," Vol. 1. Pergamon, Oxford.

KLEIN, G. (1957). *Phil. Trans. Roy. Soc.* **A249**, 389.

KNUDSEN, J. G., and KATZ, D. L. (1958). "Fluid Dynamics and Heat Transfer." McGraw-Hill, New York.

KRONGELB, S., and STRANDBERG, M. W. P. (1959). *J. Chem. Phys.* **31**, 1196.

LANGHAAR, H. L. (1942). *Trans. ASME* **64**, A 55.

LEWIS, B., and VON ELBE, G. (1961). "Combustion, Flames and Explosions of Cases." Academic Press, New York.

MASON, E. A., MUNN, R. J., and SMITH, F. J. (1966). Thermal diffusion in gases. *Advan. At. Mol. Phys.* **2**, 33.

MAZO, R. M. (1967). "Statistical Mechanical Theories of Transport Processes." Pergamon, Oxford.

MINKOFF, G. J., and TIPPER, C. F. H. (1962). "Chemistry of Combustion Reactions." Butterworths, London and Washington, D.C.

MIRELS, H. (1971). *In* "Shock Tube Research" (J. Stallberg, A. G. Gaydon, J. H. Owen, eds.). Chapman and Hall, London.

OPPENHEIM, A. K., MANSON, N., and WAGNER, H. GG. (1963). *AIAA J.* 2243.

POIRRIER, R. V. and CARR, R. W., Jr. (1971). *J. Phys. Chem.* **75**, 1593.

PUSCH, W. (1964). Ph.D. Thesis, Univ. of Göttingen.

REED, J. F., and RABINOVITCH, B. S. (1955). *J. Phys. Chem.* **59**, 261.

REED, J. F., and RABINOVITCH, B. S. (1957). *J. Phys. Chem.* **61**, 598.

SMITH, D., GOODALL, C. V., ADAMS, N. G., and DEAN, A. G. (1960). *J. Phys. B At. Mol. Phys.* **3**, 34.

SOLOUKHIN, R. I. (1966). "Shock Waves and Detonations in Gases." Mono Book Corp., Baltimore, Maryland.

SPALDING, D. B. (1956). *Phil. Trans.* **A249**, 1.

TALROZE, V. L. and STRUNIN, V. P., DODONOV, A. F., and LAVROSKAYA, G. K. (1966). *Advan. Mass Spectrom.* **3**.

VAN TIGGELEN, A. (1968). "Oxydations et Combustions." Editions Technique., Paris.

VIGNES, J. P., and TRAMBOUZE, P. J. (1962). *Chem. Eng. Sci.* **17**, 73.

WALDMANN, L. (1958). *In* "Handbuch der Physik (S. Flügge, ed.), Vol. 12, p. 295. Springer, Berlin.

WALKER, R. E. (1961). *Phys. Fluids* **4**, 1211.

WALKER, R. E., and WESTENBERG, A. A. (1958). *J. Chem. Phys.* **29**, 1139.

WEINBERG, F. J. (1963). "Optics of Flames." Butterworths, London and Washington, D.C.

WESTENBERG, A. A., and FRISTROM, R. M. (1965). *Int. Symp. Combust.*, 10th p. 473. Combust. Inst., Pittsburgh, Pennsylvania.

WILDE, K. A. (1957). *J. Phys. Chem.* **61**, 1668.

WILDE, K. A. (1972). *Combust. Flame* **18**, 43.

WILLIAMS, F. A. (1964). "Combustion Theory." Addition Wesley, Reading, Massachusetts.

WILSON, W. E., O'DONOVAN, J. T., and FRISTROM, R. M. (1969). *Int. Symp. Combust.*, 12th p. 929. Combust. Inst., Pittsburgh, Pennsylvania.

YOLLES, R. S., McCULLEY, L., and WISE, H. (1970). *J. Chem. Phys.* **52**, 723.

Author Index

Numbers in italics refer to the pages on which the complete references are listed.

A

Aberth, W., 530, *549*
Abramowitz, M., 624, *625*
Abramson, F. P., 540, *549*
Adams, G. K., *1004*
Adams, J. T., 670, *716*
Adams, N. G., *1005*
Adler, F. T., 599, *626*
Adler, S. E., 859, *925*
Airey, J. R., 761, *826*
Albers, E. A., 678, 679, 695, 697, *710*
Albright, R. G., 680, *710*
Allison, A. C., 599, *625*
Alterman, E. B., 854, *929*
Amdur, I., 569, *625*
Anderson, P. W., 787, *826*
Anderson, R. A., 795, 796, *828, 829*
Andlauer, B., 903, 904, 909, 910, *924*
Andrews, G. E., 962, *1004*
Aoi, M., 764, *826*
Appleton, J. P., 886, *928*
Arnold, S. J., 704, *716*
Arthurs, A. M., 597, *625*
Ashkenas, H., 649, *710*
Ashpole, C. W., 751, *826*
Atkins, D. L., 809, *826*
Atkinson, R., 661, *710*, 899, *924*
Ausloos, P., 901, *926*
Axtmann, R. M., 797, *827*
Azada, T., 757, *826*

B

Baba, H., 764, *826*
Baer, M., 669, *710*
Bailey, T. L., 521, 532, *549, 550*
Baimonte, V. D., 756, *826*
Bair, E. J., 697, *711*, 738, 756, *826, 830, 833*

Bak, T. A., 892, *924, 927*
Balakhin, V. P., *710*
Baldwin, R. R., 637, *710*
Basco, N., 704, *710*, 734, 735, 739, 742, 743, 744, 748, 749, 762, *826*
Bass, A. M., 661, 686, 688, *711, 715*, 738, 753, *826*
Bates, D. R., 811, *826*
Battaglia, A., 781, *826*
Bauer, H. J., 748, *826*
Bauer, S. H., 664, *714*
Baulch, D. L., 632, 691, *710*
Baumgartner, G., 797, 798, *826*
Bayes, K. D., 651, 699, *710, 713*
Beck, D., 553, *625*
Becker, E. W., 647, 649, *710*
Becker, K. H., 642, 643, 644, 690, 691, 699, 700, *710*, 800, *826*
Becker, R., 662, *710*
Beckey, H. D., 650, *710*, 903, 908, *924*
Beggs, D., 893, *924*
Behringer, R., 653, *710*
Belford, R. L., 954, *1004*
Bell, R. E., 792, *826*
Bellisio, J. A., 751, *826*
Bender, C. F., *715*
Bennett, C. O., 998, *1004*
Bennett, R. G., 792, 794, 795, 796, 797, 798, 800, 801, *826, 828*
Bennett, W. R., 791, 818, *826, 830*
Benson, S. W., 633, 635, 677, *711*, 872, 873, 874, 878, 887, 889, *924, 925, 927*
Bergmann, P. G., 845, *924*
Berkowitz, J., 905, 906, *925*
Bernstein, R. B., 553, 558, 572, 579, 580, 584, 585, 591, 594, 599, 600, 601, 617, 618, 619, *625, 626, 627, 628*
Berry, M. J., 745, *826*

Johnston, H. S., 632, 661, 668, 674, 676, 713, 714, 756, 809, *830*, *831*, *832*, 852, 862, 896, *926*, *928*
Jones, G. W., 978, *1004*
Jones, I. T. N., 651, 699, *713*
Jones, R. P., 763, *831*
Jordan, J. E., 569, *625*
Jortner, J., 763, *827*, 856, 857, 881, 899, 900, *925*, *926*, *927*
Jost, W., 664, 680, *713*, *714*, 952, 961, 962, 971, 976, 984, 985, 995, *1005*
Jud, W., 643, 644, 690, *710*
Jungen, M., 852, *926*

K

Kalelkar, A., 886, *926*
Kalman, E. H., 742, *830*
Kaminsky, M., 904, 905, *925*
Kanofsky, J. R., 702, *714*
Kantrowitz, A., 647, *713*
Karplus, M., 599, *628*, 666, 667, 668, 669, 670, 671, *714*, *715*, *716*, 717
Kasha, M., 856, *925*
Kasper, J. V. V., 642, 679, 681, *713*, *714*
Kassel, L. S., 848, *926*
Katz, D. L., 980, 984, 997, *1005*
Kaufman, F., 641, 644, 645, 682, 693, 694, 697, *712*, *714*, 872, 896, 897, *926*, 989, *1005*
Kay, I., 570, *626*
Kebarle, P., 819, *830*
Keck, J. C., 846, 883, 885, 886, *926*, *928*
Keller, J. B., 570, *626*
Keller, R. A., 661, *715*
Kelley, J. D., 825, *831*
Kelso, J. R., 641, *714*
Kerstetter, J., 539, *550*
Kerstetter, J. D., 532, *550*
Keyser, L. F., 896, 897, *926*
Kiefer, J. H., 865, *926*
Kiefer, L. J., 652, *714*
Kim, P., 703, *716*
Kimbell, G. H., 704, *716*
Kindlmann, P. J., 792, *828*
Kingston, A. E., 811, *826*
Kinsey, J. L., 916, *925*
Kirmse, W., 701, *714*
Kirsch, L. J., *713*
Kistiakowsky, G. B., 641, 664, 691, 701, 711, *714*, 921, *924*

Klein, G., 961, *1005*
Klein, R., 701, *714*
Klemm, R. B., 639, 701, 704, *711*, 757, *830*
Klemm, R. F., 769, *830*
Klemperer, W., 807, 809, *831*, *832*
Kley, D., 643, 644, 690, 691, 700, *710*, 753, *830*
Klots, C. E., 850, 912, *926*
Klotz, L. C., 902, *925*
Kneser, H. O., 748, *826*
Knewstubb, P. F., 903, 912, *926*
Knöppel, H., 903, *924*
Knoll, B., 536, 547, *550*
Knox, J. H., 633, *712*
Knudsen, J. G., 980, 984, 997, *1005*
Knudtson, J. T., 761, *830*
Kohlmaier, G. H., 917, 920, *926*
Kompa, K., *714*
Kondratiev, V. N., 632, *710*, *714*
Koskikallio, J., 774, 801, *830*
Kouri, D. J., 599, *626*, 669, *710*
Kovacs, M. A., 759, *829*
Kramer, K. H., 617, *625*
Kramers. H. A., 889, *926*
Krause, H. F., 667, *712*
Krauss, M., 650, *712*, 904, *927*
Krauss, M. A., 856, 857, *926*
Krome, G., 703, *713*
Krongelb, S., 656, *714*, 992, *1005*
Kubach, C., 528, *550*
Kubin, R. F., 920, *927*
Kukolich, S. G., 789, *830*
Kuntz, P. J., 526, 527, 528, 537, *550*, *551*
Kuppermann, A., 670, 671, *711*, *714*, *716*
Kurylo, M. J., 660, 661, 675, 685, *711*, *714*, 757, *830*
Kurzel, R. B., 884, *926*
Kutschke, K. O., 898, 900, *925*, *928*

L

LaBudde, R. A., 572, 618, 619, *625*, *626*
Lacmann, K., 513, 532, 535, 536, 539, 540, 547, *549*, *550*
Ladenburg, R., 757, *826*
Laidler, K. J., 878, *926*
Lambert, J. D., 747, 750, 761, 825, *827*
Lampe, F. W., 510, 547, *550*, 811, *828*
Landau, L. D., 617, *626*, 881, *926*
Landman, D. A., 540, *549*

Wood, B. J., 757, *826*
Wood, H. T., *625*
Wood, P. M., 769, 771, 772, 778, 779, 780, 781, *827*
Wood, R. E., 759, *831*
Wood, R. W., 639, *717*
Worley, S. D., 682, *715*
Worsham, W. C., 900, *929*
Wray, K. L., 705, *717*, 865, *929*
Wrede, E., 645, *717*
Wright, A. N., 689, *717*
Wright, F. G., 751, *831*

Y

Yager, W. A., 807, *832*
Yajima, T., 781, *833*

Yang, C. H., 635, *712*
Yardley, J. T., 759, *831*, *833*
Yennie, D. R., 579, *627*
Yolles, R. S., 996, *1006*
Young, P. J., 778, *833*
Young, R. A., 642, *717*, 778, 781, *826*, *833*
Yuan, R. C. L., 761, *833*

Z

Zabur, G., 599, *628*
Zare, R. N., 797, 799, 809, *832*, *833*
Zeldovich, J., 705, *717*
Zellenberg, A. P., 704, *715*
Zellner, R., 686, *716*
Zia, A., 755, *829*

Subject Index

A

Acetylene, oxygen atom reaction with, 699–700

Afterglow
  in atomic reactions, 640–641
  helium discharge and, 810–817

Alkanes, oxygen reaction with, 698–699

Alkenes, oxygen reaction with, 701–703

Appearance potential, 650

Argon discharge, kinetic processes in, 818–820

Atom concentrations, measurement of, 644–645

Atom detection, by chemiluminescence, 639–644, 660, 695

Atomic iodine, from flash photolysis, 728–732

Atom–molecule rate constants, 655

Atom–radical reactions, in flash photolysis, 660–661

Atom reactions, 629–710
  abstraction of atoms in, 673–683
  afterglow in, 640–642, 810–817

Atom reactions
  carbon, 686–689
  catalytic probes in, 644–645
  chemiluminescence in, 640–643, 660, 695
  concentration measurements in, 631
  following electrical discharge, 642
  experimental techniques in, 632–634
  explosion limits in, 635–639
  flash photolysis in, 658–661
  flow methods in, 639–657
  generation of atoms in, 631
  hydrogen, 664–686
  in isothermal flow reactor, 632–633, 657–658
  mass spectrometric detection of, 645–652

nitrogen, 689–694
oxygen, 694–709
pulse methods in, 657–664
pulse radiolysis in, 662
shock waves in, 662–663
static methods in, 632–639
in static reactor, 637–638
stationary photolysis in, 638–639
Wrede–Harteck gauges in, 645

Atoms
  dissociation and recombination of, 861–868
  hot, 922–924
  metastable states of, 750–751
  recombination of, 728–735, 861–868
  resonance radiation of, 766–781

Azoethane, photolysis of, 900

B

Beam foil technique, in lifetimes measurements for electronically excited molecules, 793

BEBO (bond-energy bond-order) method, in hydrogen atom abstraction, 673–676, 696

Beer–Lambert law, 727

Bessel function, in isothermal flow, 986

Blackbody flash photolysis, 723–757
  atomic iodine in, 728–732
  Beer–Lambert law in, 727
  CH_3 radicals in, 733–735
  combustion and, 752–756
  energy distribution in, 744–745
  and energy partitioning in photochemical reactions, 739–746
  energy transfer model in, 729
  free radical detection by infrared absorption in, 756
  mass spectrometry and, 757
  and organic triplets in gas phase, 751